Fundamentals of Engineering

The Ohio State University

Dennis K. Lieu | Sheryl Sorby

D1306228

CENGAGE
Learning·

Australia • Brazil • Japan • Korea • Mexico • Singapore • Spain • United Kingdom • United States

Fundamentals of Engineering: The Ohio State University

Visualization, Modeling, and Graphics for Engineering Design, 1st Edition
Dennis K. Lieu and Sheryl Sorby

© 2009 Cengage Learning. All rights reserved.

Library of Congress Control Number: 2007942951

Senior Project Development Manager:
  Linda deStefano

Market Development Manager:
  Heather Kramer

Senior Production/Manufacturing Manager:
  Donna M. Brown

Production Editorial Manager:
  Kim Fry

Sr. Rights Acquisition Account Manager:
  Todd Osborne

ALL RIGHTS RESERVED. No part of this work covered by the copyright herein may be reproduced, transmitted, stored or used in any form or by any means graphic, electronic, or mechanical, including but not limited to photocopying, recording, scanning, digitizing, taping, Web distribution, information networks, or information storage and retrieval systems, except as permitted under Section 107 or 108 of the 1976 United States Copyright Act, without the prior written permission of the publisher.

For product information and technology assistance, contact us at
Cengage Learning Customer & Sales Support, 1-800-354-9706

For permission to use material from this text or product,
submit all requests online at **cengage.com/permissions**
Further permissions questions can be emailed to
permissionrequest@cengage.com

This book contains select works from existing Cengage Learning resources and was produced by Cengage Learning Custom Solutions for collegiate use. As such, those adopting and/or contributing to this work are responsible for editorial content accuracy, continuity and completeness.

Compilation © 2013 Cengage Learning
ISBN-13: 978-1-305-03583-6

ISBN-10: 1-305-03583-6
Cengage Learning
5191 Natorp Boulevard
Mason, Ohio 45040
USA

Cengage Learning is a leading provider of customized learning solutions with office locations around the globe, including Singapore, the United Kingdom, Australia, Mexico, Brazil, and Japan. Locate your local office at:
international.cengage.com/region.
Cengage Learning products are represented in Canada by Nelson Education, Ltd.
For your lifelong learning solutions, visit **www.cengage.com/custom.**
Visit our corporate website at **www.cengage.com.**

Printed in the United States of America

contents

sectionone
Laying the Foundation

sectiontwo
Modern Design Practice and Tools

section three
Setting Up an Engineering Drawing

sectionfour
Drawing Annotation and Design Implementation

2

Sketching

objectives

After completing this chapter, you should be able to

- Explain the importance of sketching in the engineering design process
- Make simple sketches of basic shapes such as lines, circles, and ellipses
- Use 3-D coordinate systems, particularly right-handed systems
- Draw simple isometric sketches from coded plans
- Make simple oblique pictorial sketches
- Use advanced sketching skills for complex objects

2.01
introduction

Sketching is one of the primary modes of communication in the initial stages of the design process. Sketching also is a means to creative thinking. It has been shown that your mind works more creatively when your hand is sketching as you are engaged in thinking about a problem.

This chapter focuses on one of the fundamental skills required of engineers and technologists—freehand sketching. The importance of sketching in the initial phases of the design process is presented, as are some techniques to help you create sketches that correctly convey your design ideas. The definition of 3-D coordinate systems and the way they are portrayed on a 2-D sheet of paper will be covered, along with the difference between right-handed and left-handed coordinate systems. The chapter will investigate how to create simple pictorial sketches. Finally, the advanced sketching techniques of shading and cartooning will be presented with a framework for creating sketches of complex objects. You will begin to explore these topics in this chapter and will further refine your sketching abilities as you progress through your graphics course.

2.02   Sketching in the Engineering Design Process

As you may remember from Chapter 1, engineers communicate with one another primarily through graphical means. Those graphical communications take several forms, ranging from precise, complex drawings to simple sketches on the back of an envelope. Most of this text is focused on complex drawings; however, this chapter focuses on simple sketches.

Technically speaking, a sketch is any drawing made without the use of drawing instruments such as triangles and T squares. Some computer graphics packages allow you to create sketches; however, you will probably be more creative (and thus more effective) if you stick to hand sketching, particularly in the initial stages of the design process. In fact, carefully constructed, exact drawings often serve as a hindrance to creativity when they are employed in the initial stages of the design process. Typically, all you need for sketching are a pencil, paper, an eraser, and your imagination.

Your initial sketches may be based on rough ideas. But as you refine your ideas, you will want to refine your sketches, including details that you left out of the originals. For example, suppose you were remodeling the bathroom in your house. Figure 2.01 shows two sketches that define the layout of the bathroom, with details added as ideas evolve. Once you have completed the layout to your satisfaction, you can create an official engineering drawing showing exact dimensions and features that you can give to the contractor who will perform the remodeling work for you.

When engineers sit down to brainstorm solutions to problems, before long, one of them usually takes out a sheet of paper and sketches an idea on it. The others in the

FIGURE 2.01. Sketches for a bathroom remodel.

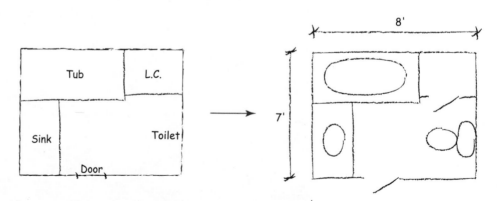

discussion may add to the original sketch, or they may create sketches of their own. The paper-and-pencil sketches then become media for the effective exchange of ideas. Although few "rules" regulate the creation of sketches, you should follow some general guidelines to ensure clarity.

2.03 **Sketching Lines**

Most of your sketches will involve basic shapes made from lines and circles. Although you are not expected to make perfect sketches, a few simple techniques will enable you to create understandable sketches.

When drawing **lines**, the key is to make them as straight as possible. If you are right-handed, you should sketch your vertical lines from top to bottom and your horizontal lines from left to right. If you are sketching an angled line, choose a direction that matches the general inclination of the line—for angled lines that are mostly vertical, sketch them from top to bottom; for angled lines that are mostly horizontal, sketch them from left to right. If you are left-handed, you should sketch your vertical lines from top to bottom, but your horizontal lines from right to left. For angled lines, left-handed people should sketch from either right to left or top to bottom, again depending on the inclination of the line. To keep your lines straight, focus on the endpoint as you sketch. The best practices for sketching straight lines are illustrated in Figure 2.02.

FIGURE 2.02. Techniques for sketching straight lines.

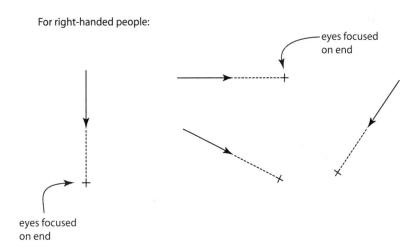

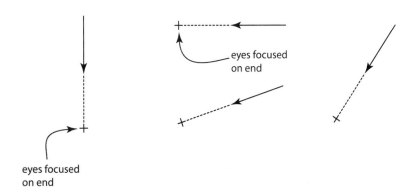

FIGURE 2.03. Rotating the paper to draw an angled line.

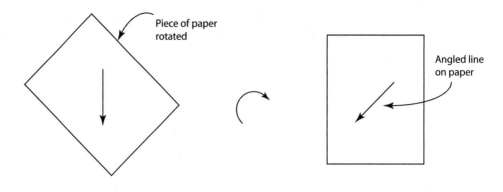

FIGURE 2.04. Sketching long lines in segments.

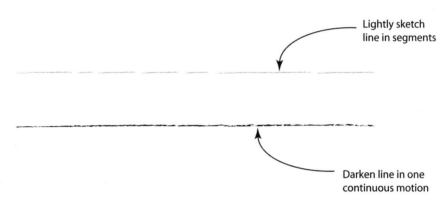

You also can try rotating the paper on the desk to suit your preferences. For example, if you find that drawing vertical lines is easiest for you and you are confronted with an angled line to sketch, rotate the paper on the desk so you can sketch a "vertical" line. Or you can rotate the paper 90 degrees to sketch a horizontal line. Figure 2.03 illustrates rotation of the paper to create an angled line.

One last point to consider when sketching lines is that you initially may have to create "long" lines as a series of connected segments. Then you can sketch over the segments in a continuous motion to make sure the line appears to be one entity and not several joined end to end. Using segments to define long lines is illustrated in Figure 2.04.

2.04 Sketching Curved Entities

Arcs and **circles** are other types of geometric entities you often will be required to sketch. When sketching arcs and circles, use lightly sketched square **bounding boxes** to define the limits of the curved entities and then construct the curved entities as tangent to the edges of the bounding box. For example, to sketch a circle, you first lightly sketch a square (with straight lines). Note that the length of the sides of the bounding box is equal to the diameter of the circle you are attempting to sketch. At the centers of each edge of the box, you can make a short **tick mark** to establish the point of tangency for the circle, then draw the four arcs that make up the circle. Initially, you may find it easier to sketch one arc at a time to complete the circle; but as you gain experience, you may be able to sketch the entire circle all at once. Figure 2.05 shows the procedure used to sketch a circle by creating a bounding box first.

One problem you may have when using a bounding box to sketch a circle occurs when the radius of the circle is relatively large. In that case, the arcs you create may be too flat or too curved, as shown in Figure 2.06. To avoid this type of error, you might try marking the radius at points halfway between the tick marks included on the bounding box. Using simple geometry, when you draw a line between the center of the circle and the corner of the bounding box, the radius is about two-thirds of the distance (technically, the radius is 0.707, but that number is close enough to two-thirds for your purposes). Then you can include some additional tick marks around the circle to guide your sketching and to improve the appearance of your circles. This technique is illustrated in Figure 2.07.

Sketching an arc follows the same general procedure as sketching a circle, except that your curved entity is only a portion of a circle. Sketching an **ellipse** follows the same general rules as sketching a circle, except that your bounding box is a rectangle and not a square. Sketching arcs and ellipses is illustrated in Figure 2.08.

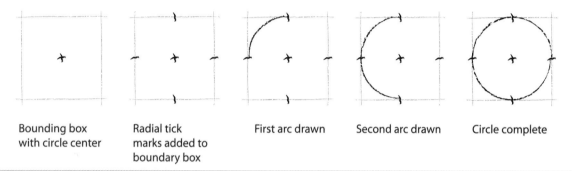

| Bounding box with circle center | Radial tick marks added to boundary box | First arc drawn | Second arc drawn | Circle complete |

FIGURE 2.05. Sketching a circle using a bounding box.

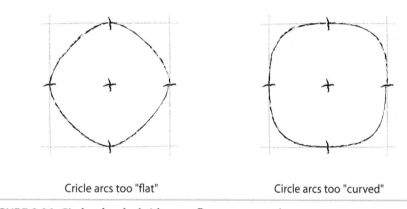

Cricle arcs too "flat"   Circle arcs too "curved"

FIGURE 2.06. Circles sketched either too flat or too curved.

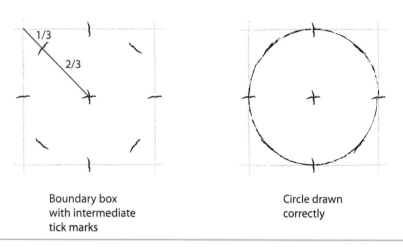

1/3
2/3

Boundary box with intermediate tick marks   Circle drawn correctly

FIGURE 2.07. Using intermediate radial tick marks for large circles.

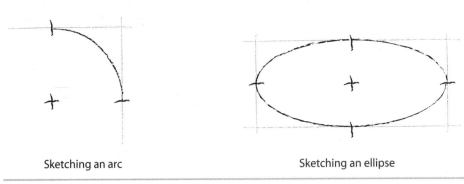

Sketching an arc   Sketching an ellipse

FIGURE 2.08. Using boundary boxes to sketch arcs and ellipses.

2.05 Construction Lines

Similar to the way you used bounding boxes to create circles and ellipses, other construction lines help with your sketching. Using construction lines, you outline the shape of the object you are trying to sketch. Then you fill in the details of the sketch using the construction lines as a guide. Figure 2.09 shows the front view of an object you need to sketch. To create the sketch, you lightly draw the construction lines that outline the main body of the object and then create the construction lines that define the prominent features of it. One rule of thumb is that construction lines should be drawn so lightly on the page that when it is held at arm's length, the lines are nearly impossible to see. The creation of the relevant construction lines is illustrated in Figure 2.10.

Using construction lines as a guide, you can fill in the details of the front view of the object until it is complete. The final result is shown in Figure 2.11.

Another way you can use construction lines is to locate the center of a square or rectangle. Recall from your geometry class that the diagonals of a box (either a rectangle or a square) intersect at its center. After you create construction lines for the edges of the box, you sketch the two diagonals that intersect at the center. Once you find the center of the box, you can use it to create a new centered box of smaller dimensions—a kind of concentric box. Locating the center of a box and creating construction lines for a newly centered box within the original box are illustrated in Figure 2.12.

Once you have created your centered box within a box, you can sketch a circle using the smaller box as a bounding box, resulting in a circle that is centered within the larger box as shown in Figure 2.13. Or you can use these techniques to create a square with four holes located in the corners of the box as illustrated in Figure 2.14.

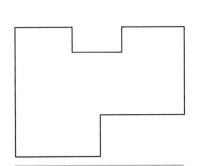

FIGURE 2.09. The front view of an object to sketch.

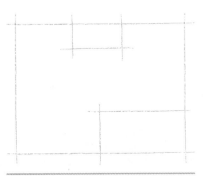

FIGURE 2.10. Construction lines used to create a sketch.

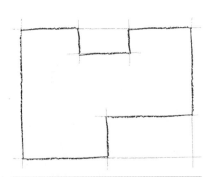

FIGURE 2.11. Completed sketch using construction lines as a guide.

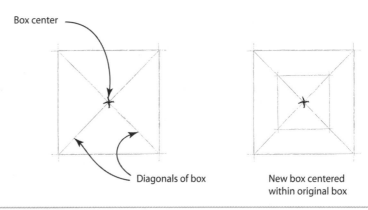

Box center

Diagonals of box

New box centered
within original box

FIGURE 2.12. Creating concentric bounding boxes.

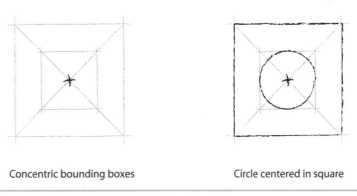

Concentric bounding boxes

Circle centered in square

FIGURE 2.13. Sketching a circle in a box.

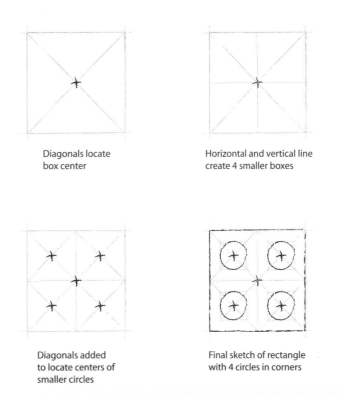

Diagonals locate
box center

Horizontal and vertical line
create 4 smaller boxes

Diagonals added
to locate centers of
smaller circles

Final sketch of rectangle
with 4 circles in corners

FIGURE 2.14. Using diagonal construction lines to locate centers.

2.06 Coordinate Systems

When sketching, you often have to portray 3-D objects on a flat 2-D sheet of paper. As is usually the case with graphical communication, a few conventions have evolved over time for representing 3-D space on a 2-D sheet of paper. One convention, called the **3-D coordinate system**, is that space can be represented by three mutually perpendicular coordinate axes, typically the x-, y-, and z-axes. To visualize those three axes, look at the bottom corner of the room. Notice the lines that are formed by the intersection of each of the two walls with the floor and the line that is formed where the two walls intersect. You can think of these lines of intersection as the x-, y-, and z-coordinate axes. You can define all locations in the room with respect to this corner, just as all points in 3-D space can be defined from an origin where the three axes intersect.

You are probably familiar with the concept of the three coordinate axes from your math classes. In Figure 2.15, a set of coordinate axes, notice the positive and negative directions for each of the axes. Typically, arrows at the ends of the axes denote the positive direction along the axes.

For engineering, the axes usually define a right-handed coordinate system. Since most engineering analysis techniques are defined by a right-handed system, you should learn what this means and how to recognize such a system when you see it. A **right-handed system** means that if you point the fingers of your right hand down the positive x-axis and curl them in the direction of the positive y-axis, your thumb will point in the direction of the positive z-axis, as illustrated in Figure 2.16. This procedure is sometimes referred to as the **right-hand rule**.

Another way to think about the right-hand rule is to point your thumb down the positive x-axis and your index finger down the positive y-axis; your middle finger will then automatically point down the positive z-axis. This technique is illustrated in Figure 2.17. Either method for illustrating the right-hand rule results in the same set of coordinate axes; choose the method that is easiest for you to use.

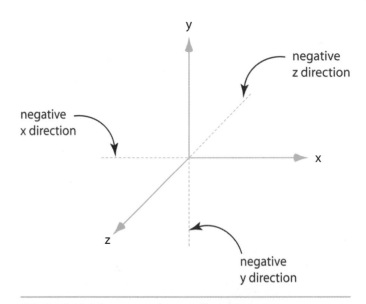

FIGURE 2.15. The x-, y-, and z- coordinate axes.

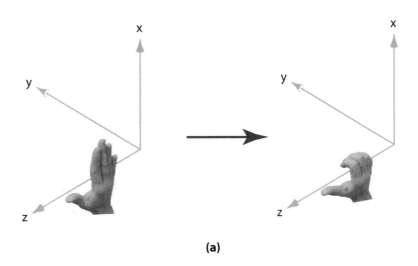

(a)

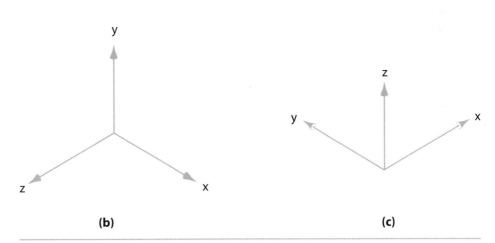

(b) **(c)**

FIGURE 2.16. Curling the fingers to check for a right-handed coordinate system in (a) and alternative presentations of right-handed coordinate systems in (b) and (c).

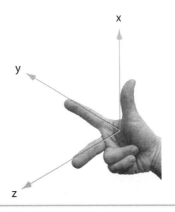

FIGURE 2.17. An alternative method to check for a right-handed coordinate system.

FIGURE 2.18. The result of using the left hand to test for a right-handed coordinate system.

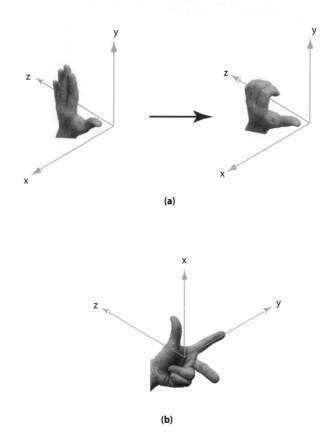

(a)

(b)

Notice that if you try either technique with your left hand, your thumb (or middle finger) will point down the negative z-axis, as illustrated in Figure 2.18.

A **left-handed system** is defined similarly to a right-handed system, except that you use your left hand to show the positive directions of the coordinate axes. Left-handed systems are typically used in engineering applications that are geologically based—positive z is defined as going down into the earth. Figure 2.19 illustrates left-handed coordinate systems. (Use the left-hand rule to verify that these are left-handed coordinate systems.)

The question remains about how to represent 3-D space on a 2-D sheet of paper when sketching. The answer is that the three coordinate axes are typically represented as oblique or isometric, depending on the preferences of the person making the sketch. You are probably most familiar with oblique representation of the coordinate axes, which seems to be the preferred method of many individuals. With this method, two axes are sketched perpendicular to each other and the third is drawn at an angle, usually 45 degrees to both axes. The angle of the inclined line does not have to be 45 degrees, but

FIGURE 2.19. Left-handed coordinate systems.

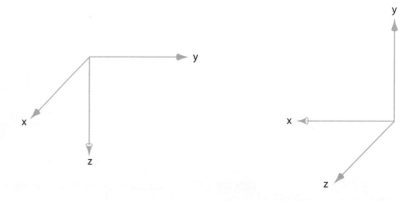

FIGURE 2.20. An oblique representation of right-handed coordinate systems.

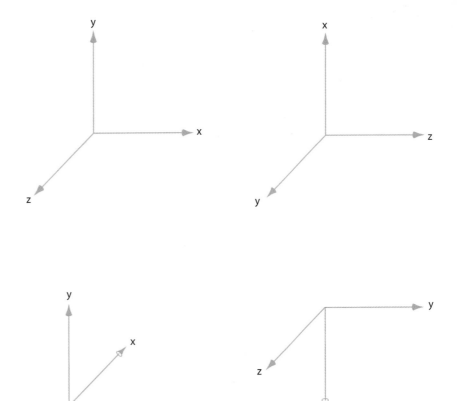

it is usually sketched that way. Your math teachers probably sketched the three coordinate axes that way in their classes. Figure 2.20 shows multiple sets of coordinate axes drawn as oblique axes. Notice that all of the coordinate systems are right-handed systems. (Verify this for yourself by using the right-hand rule.)

Another way of portraying the 3-D coordinate axes on a 2-D sheet of paper is through isometric representation. With this method, the axes are projected onto the paper as if you were looking down the diagonal of a cube. When you do this, the axes appear to be 120 degrees apart, as shown in Figure 2.21. In fact, the term *isometric* comes from the Greek *iso* (meaning "the same") and *metric* (meaning "measure"). Notice that for **isometric axes** representations, the right-hand rule still applies.

Isometric axes also can be sketched with one of the axes extending in the "opposite" direction. This results in angles other than 120 degrees, depending on the orientation of the axes with respect to the paper, as shown in Figure 2.22.

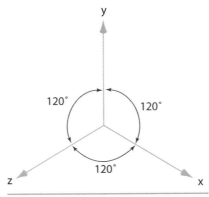

FIGURE 2.21. An isometric representation of a right-handed coordinate system.

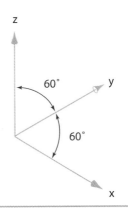

FIGURE 2.22. An isometric representation of axes with angles less than 120 degrees.

FIGURE 2.23. Isometric grid and dot paper.

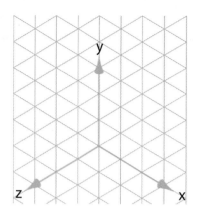 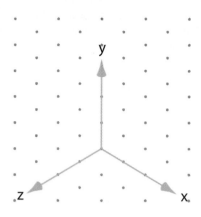

Grid or dot paper can help you make isometric sketches. With **isometric dot paper**, the dots are oriented such that when you sketch lines through the dots, you end up with standard 120 degree axes. With grid paper, the lines are already drawn at an angle of 120 degrees with respect to one another. Isometric grid paper and isometric dot paper are illustrated in Figure 2.23.

2.07   Isometric Sketches of Simple Objects

Creating isometric drawings and sketches of complex objects will be covered in more detail in a later chapter; however, this section serves as an introduction to the topic for simple objects. Mastering the techniques used to create isometric sketches of simple objects may help as you branch out to tackle increasingly complex objects. Figure 2.24 shows how **isometric grid paper** is used to sketch a 3 × 3 × 3 block. Notice that there is more than one orientation from which the block can be sketched on the same sheet of grid paper. Ultimately, the orientation you choose depends on your needs or preferences.

Coded plans can be used to define simple objects that are constructed entirely out of blocks. The numerical values in the coded plan represent the height of the stack of blocks at that location. The object then "grows" up from the plan according to the numbers specified. Figure 2.25 shows a coded plan on isometric grid paper and the object that results from it.

The object shown in Figure 2.25 clearly outlines all of the blocks used to create it. When isometric sketches of an object are made, however, standard practice dictates that lines appear only where two surfaces intersect—lines between blocks on the same surface are not shown. Figure 2.26 shows the object from Figure 2.25 after the unwanted lines have been removed. Notice that the only lines on the sketch are those formed from the intersection of two surfaces. Also notice that object edges hidden from view on the back side are not shown in the sketch. Not showing hidden edges on an **isometric pictorial** also is standard practice in technical sketching.

FIGURE 2.24. Using isometric grid paper to sketch a block.

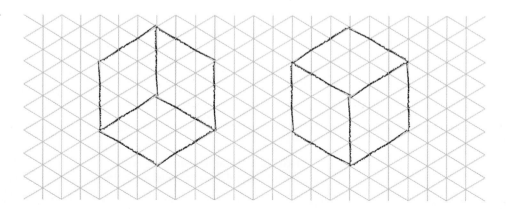

Sometimes when you are creating an isometric sketch of a simple object, part of one surface is obscured by one of the more prominent features of the object. When creating the sketch, make sure you show only the visible part of the surface in question, as illustrated in Figure 2.27.

Figure 2.28 shows several coded plans and the corresponding isometric sketches. Look at each isometric sketch carefully to verify that it matches the defining coded plan: those lines are shown only at the edges between surfaces (not to define each block), that no hidden edges are shown, and that only the visible portions of partially obscured surfaces are shown.

FIGURE 2.25. A coded plan and the resulting object.

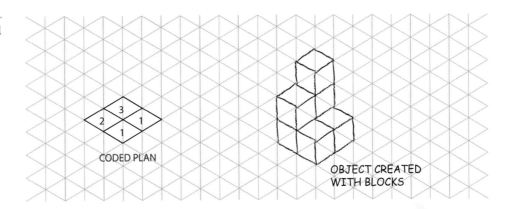

FIGURE 2.26. A properly drawn isometric sketch of the object from the coded plan.

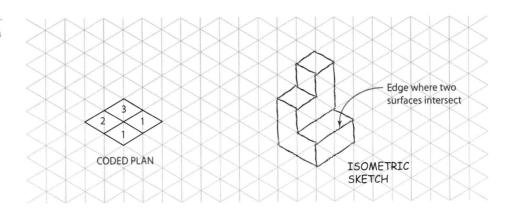

FIGURE 2.27. The partially obscured surface on an isometric sketch.

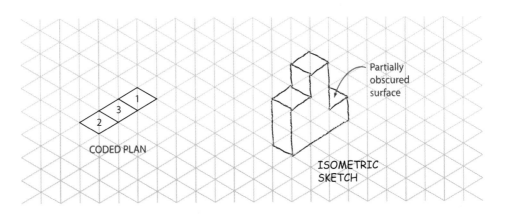

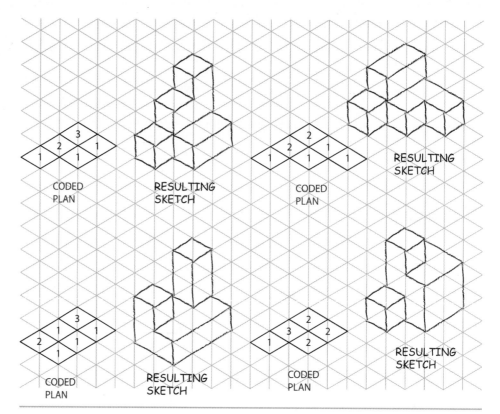

FIGURE 2.28. Four coded plans and the resulting isometric sketches.

2.07.01 Circles in Isometric Sketches

Look back at the $3 \times 3 \times 3$ block shown in Figure 2.24. In reality, you know that all of the surfaces of the block are 3×3 squares; yet in the isometric sketch, each surface is shown as a parallelogram. The distortion of planar surfaces is one disadvantage of creating isometric sketches. The isometric portrayal of circles and arcs is particularly difficult. Circles appear as ellipses in isometric sketches; however, you will not be able to create a rectangular bounding box to sketch the ellipse in isometric as described earlier in this chapter. To create an ellipse that represents a circle in an isometric sketch, you first create a square bounding box as before; however, the bounding box will appear as a parallelogram in the isometric sketch. To create your bounding box, locate the center of the circle first. From the center, locate the four radial points. The direction you move on the grid corresponds to the lines that define the surface. If you are sketching the circle on a rectangular surface, look at the sides of the rectangle as they appear in isometric and move that same direction on the grid. Figure 2.29 shows a $4 \times 4 \times 4$ cube with a circle center and four radial points located on one of the sides.

Once you have located the center of the circle and the four radial points, the next step is to create the bounding box through the radial points. The edges of the bounding box should correspond to the lines that define this particular surface. The edges will be parallel to the edges of the parallelogram that define the surface if that surface is square or rectangular. Figure 2.30 shows the cube with the circle center and the bounding box located on its side.

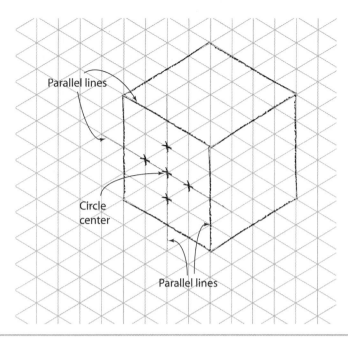

FIGURE 2.29. A cube with a circle center and radial points located.

Four arcs that go through the radial points define the ellipse, just like an ellipse drawn in a regular rectangular bounding box. The difference is that for the isometric ellipse, the arcs are of varying curvatures—two long arcs and two short arcs in this case. The arcs are tangent to the bounding box at the radial points, as before. It is usually

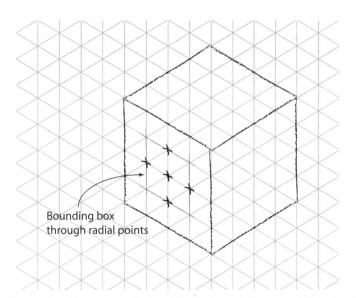

FIGURE 2.30. A cube with the circle center and bounding box on the side.

best if you start by sketching the long arcs, and then add the short arcs to complete the ellipse. Sketching the arcs that form the ellipse is illustrated in Figure 2.31.

Creating ellipses that represent circles on the other faces of the cube is accomplished in a similar manner, as illustrated in Figure 2.32 and Figure 2.33.

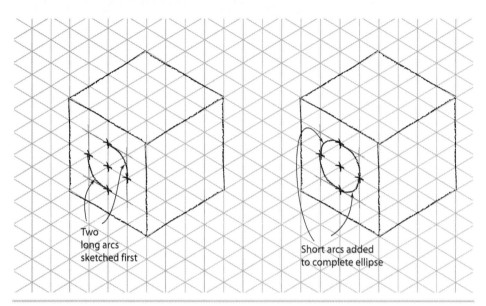

Two long arcs sketched first

Short arcs added to complete ellipse

FIGURE 2.31. Sketching arcs to form an ellipse.

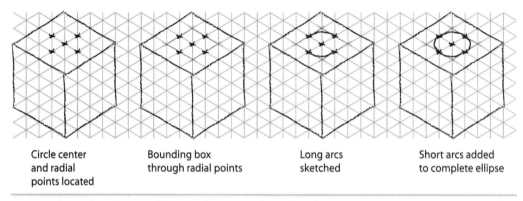

Circle center and radial points located

Bounding box through radial points

Long arcs sketched

Short arcs added to complete ellipse

FIGURE 2.32. Sketching an ellipse on the top surface of a cube.

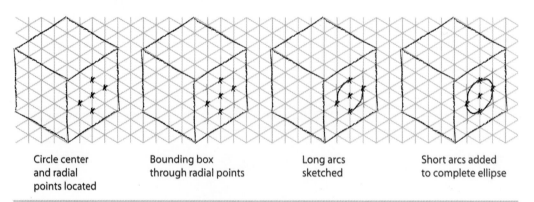

Circle center and radial points located

Bounding box through radial points

Long arcs sketched

Short arcs added to complete ellipse

FIGURE 2.33. Sketching an ellipse on the side face of a cube.

2.07.02 Circular Holes in Isometric Sketches

One of the most common occurrences that produces a circular feature in an isometric sketch is a hole in the object. You will learn more about circular holes and object features in a later chapter, but a short introduction follows here. A circular hole usually extends all the way through an object. In an isometric pictorial, a portion of the "back" edge of a circular hole is often visible through the hole and should be included in your sketch. As a rule of thumb, the back edge of a hole is partially visible when the object is relatively thin or the hole is relatively large; when the object is thick or the diameter of the hole is small, the back edge of the hole is not visible. Figure 2.34 shows two blocks with circular holes going through them. Notice in the "thin" block that you can see a portion of the back edge of the hole; in the thicker block, though, the back edge is not visible.

To determine whether a part of the back edge of a hole is visible in an isometric sketch, you first need to locate the center of the back hole. To locate the back center, start from the center of the hole on the front surface and move in a direction perpendicular to the front surface toward the back of the object a distance equal to the object's dimension in that direction. Figure 2.35 shows the location of the center of the two back circles for the objects in Figure 2.34.

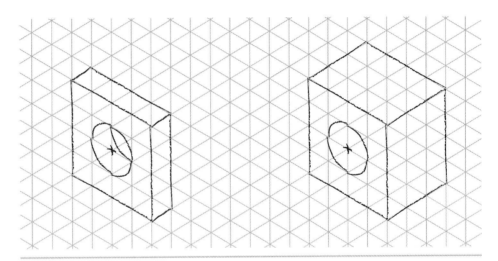

FIGURE 2.34. Blocks with circular holes in them.

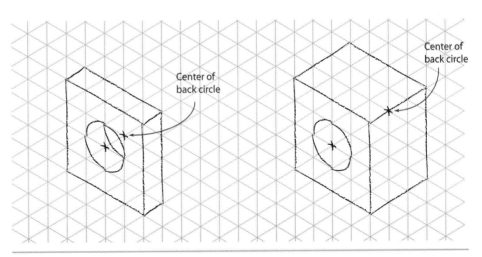

FIGURE 2.35. Centers of back circles located.

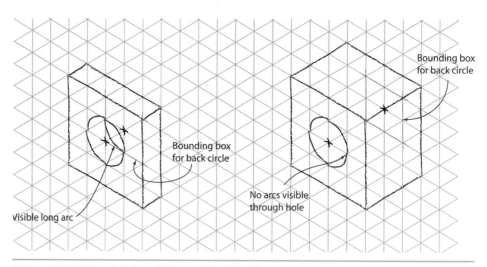

FIGURE 2.36. Determining visibility of back circles.

Starting from the back center point, lightly sketch the radial points and the bounding box for the back circle similar to the way you did for the front circle. Then add the long arc that is visible through the hole. (Note that only *one* of the long arcs is typically visible through the hole.) Add segments of the short arcs as needed to complete the visible portion of the back edge of the hole. Conversely, if after you sketch the back bounding box you notice that no portion of the ellipse will be visible on the sketch, do not include any arcs within the hole on the sketch and erase any lines associated with the bounding box. Figure 2.36 illustrates the inclusion and noninclusion of segments of the back edges of holes for the objects in Figure 2.34 and Figure 2.35.

2.08 Oblique Pictorials

Oblique pictorials are another type of sketch you can create to show a 3-D object. Oblique pictorials are usually preferred for freehand sketching because a specialized grid is not required. With oblique pictorials, as with **oblique axes**, the three dimensions of the object are shown with the height and width of the object in the plane of the paper and the third dimension (the depth) receding off at an angle from the others. Although the angle is usually 45 degrees, it can be any value.

The advantage that oblique pictorials have over isometric pictorials is that when one face of the object is placed in the plane of the paper, the object will appear in its true shape and size in that plane—it will be undistorted. This means that squares remain squares, rectangles remain rectangles, and circles remain circles. Figure 2.37 shows two pictorial representations of simple objects—one in isometric and one in

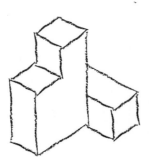

ISOMETRIC PICTORIAL

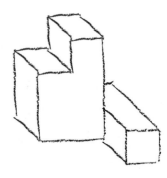

OBLIQUE PICTORIAL

FIGURE 2.37. A comparison of isometric and oblique pictorials.

oblique. Notice that the rules established for isometric pictorial sketches also hold true for oblique pictorial sketches—you do not show the hidden back edges, you show lines only where two surfaces intersect to form an edge, and you show only the visible parts of partially obstructed surfaces.

When making oblique sketches, the length of the **receding dimension** is not too important. In fact, oblique pictorials typically look better when the true length of the receding dimension is not shown. When the true length of an object's receding dimension is sketched, the object often appears distorted and unrealistic. Figure 2.38a shows the true length of a cube's receding dimension (use a ruler to make sure), and Figure 2.38b shows the same cube with the receding dimension drawn at about one-half to three-fourths its true length. Notice that the sketch in Figure 2.38a appears distorted—it does not look very much like a cube—whereas the sketch in Figure 2.38b looks like a cube.

Other conventions pertain to the way the receding dimension is portrayed in an oblique sketch; you will learn about them in a later chapter. For now, you will concentrate on trying to make a sketch that looks proportionally correct.

When creating oblique pictorials, you can choose to have the receding dimension going back and to the left or back and to the right. The direction you choose should be the one that produces the fewest obstructed surfaces in the resulting sketch. Figure 2.39 shows two possible sketches of the same object—one with the receding dimension to the left and one with the receding dimension to the right. Notice that the first sketch (Figure 2.39a) is preferable since none of the surfaces are obscured as they are with the second sketch (Figure 2.39b).

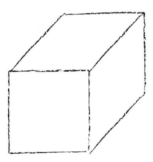 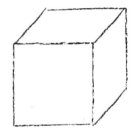

(a) Receding dimension drawn true length.

(b) Receding dimension drawn less than true length.

FIGURE 2.38. Oblique pictorials of a cube.

(a)   **(b)**

FIGURE 2.39. Two possible orientations for an oblique pictorial.

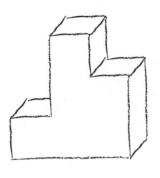
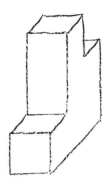

(a) Irregular surface in plane of paper.

(b) Irregular surface in receding direction.

FIGURE 2.40. Two possible orientations for an oblique pictorial.

When creating an oblique pictorial, you should put the most irregular surface in the plane of the paper. This is particularly true about any surface that has a circular feature on it. Figure 2.40 shows two different oblique pictorials of the same object. In the first sketch (Figure 2.40a), the most irregular surface is placed in the plane of the paper as it should be; in the second sketch (Figure 2.40b), the irregular surface is shown in the receding dimension. Notice that the first sketch shows the features of the object more clearly than the second sketch does.

2.08.01 Circular Holes in Oblique Pictorial Sketches

When circular holes appear in an oblique pictorial sketch, as with isometric sketches, you show the partial edges of the back circle where they are visible through the hole. Once again, partial circles are visible when the object is relatively thin or when the hole has a relatively large diameter; otherwise, partial edges are not shown. Figure 2.41 shows two oblique sketches—one in which a portion of the back edge of the hole is visible and the other in which it is not.

The procedure you use to determine whether a portion of the back circle edge is visible and, if so, which portion is visible follows the procedure outlined for isometric sketches. You start by locating the center of the back edge of the hole and marking off the four radial points. You then lightly sketch the bounding box that defines the circle. Finally, as needed, you sketch the visible portions of arcs within the circular hole. Figure 2.42 shows the procedure used to sketch the visible back edges of a circular hole in an oblique pictorial.

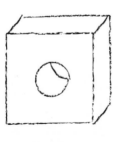
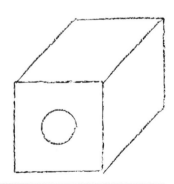

FIGURE 2.41. Oblique pictorials with circular holes in objects.

FIGURE 2.42. Determining visible back arcs in a hole.

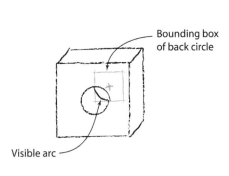

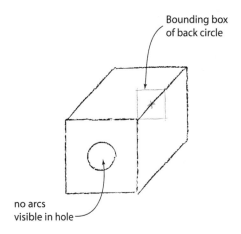

2.09 Shading and Other Special Effects

One thing you can do to improve the quality of your pictorial sketches is to include **shading** on selected surfaces to make them stand out from other surfaces or to provide clarity for the viewer. Figure 2.43 shows an isometric sketch with all of the top surfaces shaded. Notice that the shading better defines the object for the viewer. When including shading on a pictorial sketch, try not to overdo the shading. Too much shading can be confusing or irritating to the viewer—two things you should avoid in effective graphical communication.

Another common use of shading is to show curvature of a surface. For example, the visible portion of a hole's curved surface might be shaded in a pictorial sketch. A curved surface on an exterior corner also might be shaded to highlight its curvature. Figure 2.44 shows a pictorial sketch of a simple object with curved surfaces that are shaded.

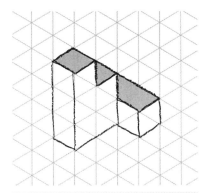

FIGURE 2.43. An object with the top surface shaded.

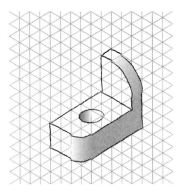

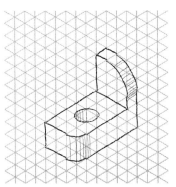

FIGURE 2.44. A simple object with two possible types of progressive shading used to emphasize the curvature of surfaces.

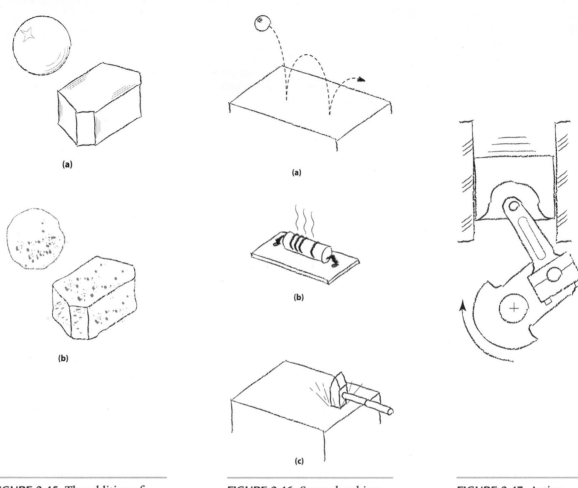

FIGURE 2.45. The addition of surface treatments to convey smooth surfaces (a) and rough surfaces (b).

FIGURE 2.46. Some sketching techniques that can be used to convey motion (a), temperature (b), and sound (c).

FIGURE 2.47. Action lines used to convey the motion of linkages.

Other sketching techniques can be used to convey features such as smooth or rough surfaces. Figure 2.45 shows different types of surface treatments that are possible for sketched objects.

You are probably familiar with techniques used in cartoons to convey ideas such as motion, temperature, and sound. Figure 2.46 shows typical cartooning lines that convey concepts not easily incorporated in a static sketch. Many of these same markings can be used in technical sketches. For example, Figure 2.47 uses action lines to convey motion for the sketch of linkages.

2.10 Sketching Complex Objects

As you refine your sketching skills, you will be able to tackle increasingly complex objects. Figures 2.48, 2.49, and 2.50 show pictorial sketches of small electronic devices. These sketches were not made to any particular scale, but were constructed so the object features appear proportionally correct with respect to one another. Notice the use of shading to enhance object appearance and to make the objects look

FIGURE 2.48. A sketch of a cell telephone.

FIGURE 2.49. A sketch of a set of headphones.

FIGURE 2.50. A sketch of a camera.

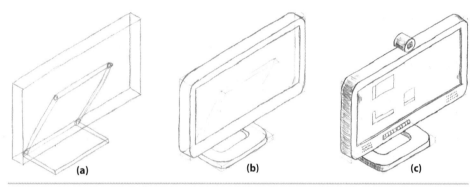

(a)   (b)   (c)

FIGURE 2.51. A sketch of a computer monitor using the method of "foundation (a), frame (b), finish (c)."

more realistic. Being able to sketch relatively complicated objects such as these will improve your ability to communicate with colleagues throughout your career. To develop this important skill, you should practice often. Do not be afraid to make mistakes—just keep trying until you get the results you want.

One way to tackle sketching a complex object is to think about it in the same way that a house is constructed—namely, "foundation, frame, finish." Using this method, you start with the "foundation" of the sketch, which usually consists of multiple guidelines and construction lines. When creating the sketch foundation, think about outlining the volume taken up by the entire object. You next "frame" the object by darkening some of the construction lines to define the basic shape of the object and its features. Once the basic frame is complete, you "finish" the sketch by adding necessary details and special features such as shading, especially on curved surfaces. Figure 2.51 shows a sketch of a flat panel computer monitor by the "foundation, frame, finish" method. Several of the exercises at the end of this chapter ask you to use this technique to develop your skills in sketching complex objects.

2.11 Strategies for Simple Pictorial Sketches

In this chapter, you learned two different ways to construct pictorial views of objects. This section outlines strategies for each type.

2.11.01 Simple Isometric Sketches

When creating an isometric pictorial from a coded plan, remember that the object "grows" up from the base according to the specified heights. You should start your sketch by drawing the visible *V* at the base of the object, as shown in Figure 2.52. You can determine the length of each side of the *V* from the coded plan. For the object defined by the coded plan in Figure 2.52, the left leg of the *V* is 2 units long and the right leg is 3 units long. The remaining bottom edges of the coded plans are hidden from view in the sketch and, therefore, are not included in the first drawing stages.

After you have created the base *V*, sketch the corner of the object at the correct height of the apex. Note that this corner will be the edge that is closest to you, the viewer. For the object shown in Figure 2.52, the height of this corner is 2 units as defined by the coded plan. The start of the isometric sketch including this corner is shown in Figure 2.53.

Starting at the "top" of this corner, move back and to the left the number of squares that are at this same height. If a change in object height is specified in the coded plan, move up or down (as shown in the coded plan) where the change occurs. When you reach the back corner, draw a vertical line back to the tip of the *V* you first sketched. This procedure is illustrated in Figure 2.54.

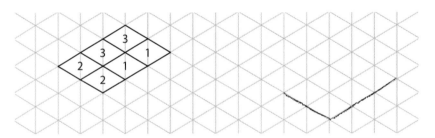

FIGURE 2.52. A coded plan with the *V* for the isometric sketch drawn.

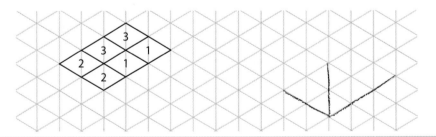

FIGURE 2.53. An isometric sketch with the nearest corner included.

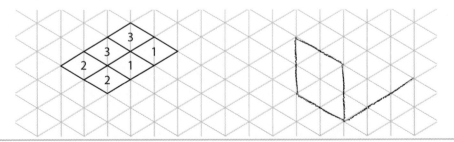

FIGURE 2.54. An isometric sketch with the first side of the surface drawn.

Follow the same procedure for the surface going off to the right from the apex of the *V*, as shown in Figure 2.55.

Complete the sketch by drawing the missing top and side surfaces of the object as shown in Figure 2.56. When adding these final features, make sure you do not include lines on surfaces—only *between* surfaces. Also, include only the visible portions of surfaces that are partially obscured.

Some of the objects you sketch may not form a simple *V* at a point nearest the viewer; instead, they will have a jagged edge along the bottom. You can use a similar procedure to sketch these objects, again starting at the bottom and outlining the shape of the object from the coded plan, as shown in Figure 2.57.

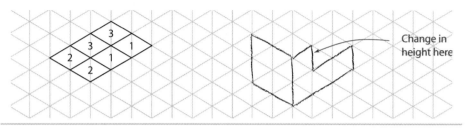

FIGURE 2.55. An isometric sketch with two side surfaces drawn.

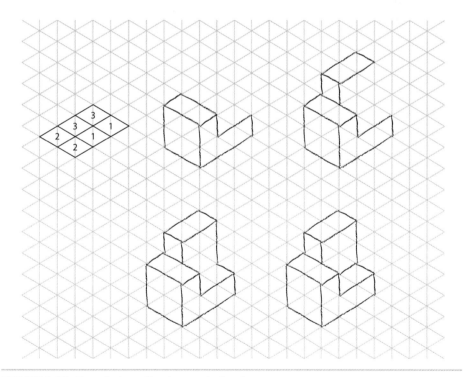

FIGURE 2.56. Completion of an isometric sketch.

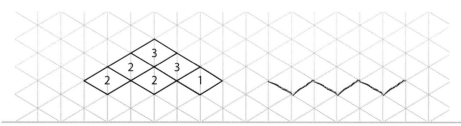

FIGURE 2.57. A jagged *V* from a coded plan.

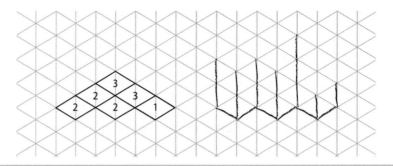

FIGURE 2.58. Heights at each corner included.

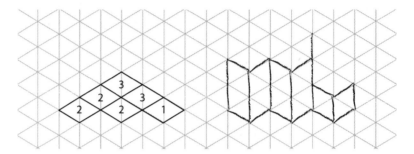

FIGURE 2.59. Side surfaces sketched.

FIGURE 2.60. A completed isometric sketch.

Then you can sketch the lines that represent the height at each corner, similar to the way you sketched the height from the apex of the single *V* (see Figure 2.58). Complete the sketch by including the side and top surfaces of the object as illustrated in Figure 2.59 and Figure 2.60. For the object shown in the example, note that the final step involves erasing a portion of one of the first lines drawn (the corner at a height of 3). You need to remove part of this line so a line does not appear on the jagged side of the object.

2.11.02 Oblique Sketches

To begin your oblique sketch, you need to determine which surface on the object is closest to the viewer. Figure 2.61 shows an isometric sketch of an object with an arrow denoting the direction of the desired oblique pictorial. For this object and viewing direction, the surface labeled *A* is the one closest to the viewer in the oblique pictorial sketch.

Sketch the closest surface (in this case, surface A) in its true shape and size and decide whether you want the third dimension on the object receding back and to the left or back and to the right. Draw the visible edges receding back from each corner of

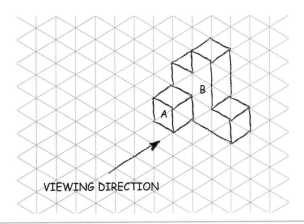

FIGURE 2.61. An isometric pictorial of an object and a viewing direction for an oblique sketch.

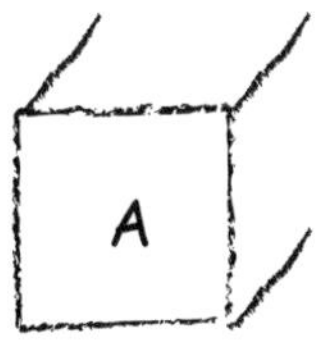

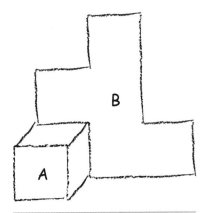

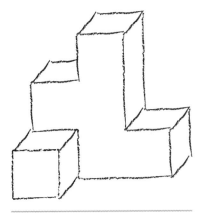

FIGURE 2.62. Surface A with receding dimensions sketched.

FIGURE 2.63. Surface B included in pictorial.

FIGURE 2.64. A completed oblique pictorial sketch.

the surface. Note that at least one corner on the surface will not have a receding line extending back from it—the receding edge will not be visible in the sketch. Figure 2.62 shows surface A with the receding edges sketched in place.

Now sketch the next surface that is parallel to the plane of the paper. For the object shown in Figure 2.63, the next closest surface is the one labeled *B*. Notice that by sketching this surface, you are connecting the endpoints of the lines drawn receding from the corners of the initial surface and, thus, are defining the side and top surfaces of the object in the pictorial. Figure 2.63 shows the result from including surface B in the oblique pictorial sketch.

Repeat these steps as often as necessary until the pictorial sketch is finished. Note that the final step is to include the back edges of the object (connecting the ends of the last set of receding lines drawn) to complete the sketch as shown in Figure 2.64.

CAUTION

When creating isometric pictorials of simple objects, remember the general rules presented earlier in this chapter—that lines are included only at the intersection between surfaces, that no hidden lines are shown, and that only the visible portion of partially obscured surfaces are sketched. One common error novices are prone to make is to include extra lines on a single surface of an object, especially when there are several changes in the object's height. Figure 2.65a shows an improper isometric pictorial sketch. Notice the extra lines included on the sketch. Figure 2.65b shows the sketch after it has been cleaned up to remove the unnecessary lines.

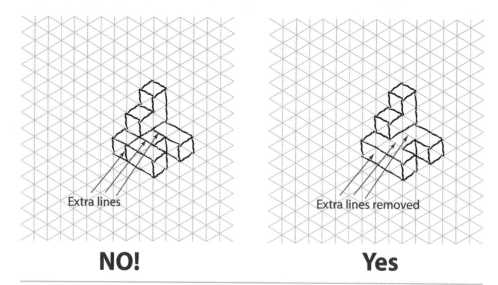

NO!   Yes

FIGURE 2.65. Isometric pictorials with and without extra lines.

Students make other common mistakes when sketching holes in isometric pictorials. One of those mistakes involves including the "back" edges of holes, even when they are not visible. Figure 2.66 shows an isometric pictorial with a hole in the object that goes all the way through. An arc representing the back edge of the hole is shown improperly in the visible part of the hole. Including the arc implies that the hole does not go all the way through the object, but stops part-way back. (Such holes are referred to as blind holes.) To avoid confusion in your isometric pictorial sketches, show only the back edge if it is visible—do not include a back edge every time you sketch an object with a hole.

Sometimes students use grid points improperly to mark off the bounding box for an isometric circular hole. Those novices fail to remember that in order to set the radial points, they need to move in the directions of the edges of the face of the object. Consider a simple box in which you want to include a circular hole emanating from the top surface. Figure 2.67a shows the four radial points incorrectly located from the center of the circle, and Figure 2.67b shows the resulting incorrect hole. Figure 2.68a shows the radial points located properly, and Figure 2.68b shows the resulting correct circular hole.

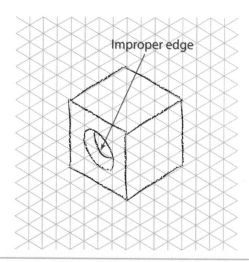

FIGURE 2.66. An isometric pictorial improperly showing the back edge of a hole.

One final error that students commonly make involves the creation of oblique pictorials. Novices sometimes forget to put the most complicated surface in the plane of the paper and show it in the receding direction instead. Figure 2.69a shows an oblique pictorial with a complex surface in the receding dimension, and Figure 2.69b shows the same object with the complex surface in the plane of the paper. Observe how the object is more understandable when you are viewing the complex surface "straight on." Also note that putting the complex surface in the plane of the paper actually makes your job easier; it is far easier to sketch the complex surface in its true size and shape than it is to sketch it as a distorted receding surface.

FIGURE 2.67. Improperly locating radial points on an isometric pictorial.

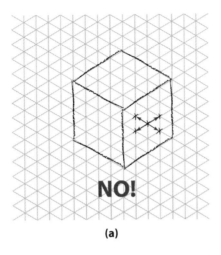

(a)

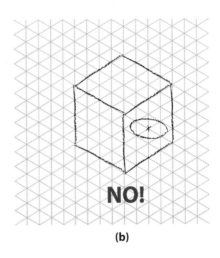

(b)

FIGURE 2.68. Properly locating radial points on an isometric pictorial.

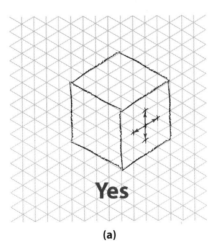

(a)

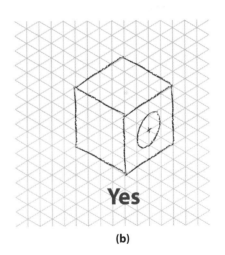

(b)

FIGURE 2.69. Oblique pictorials showing improper and proper placement of a complex surface.

NO!

Yes

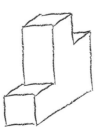

(a)

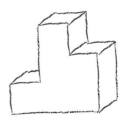

(b)

2.12 Chapter Summary

In this chapter, you learned about technical sketching and about some techniques to help you master this important form of communication. Specifically, you:

- Learned about the importance of sketching for engineering professionals and the link between creativity and freehand sketching.
- Developed techniques for successfully sketching basic shapes such as lines, arcs, circles, and ellipses.
- Learned about the right-hand rule and the way it is used to define 3-D coordinate systems in space. The axes can be portrayed on paper in either isometric or oblique format.
- Discovered how to make basic isometric sketches of objects from coded plans and about some of the rules that govern the creation of these sketches. You also learned about creating ellipses in isometric to represent circular holes in objects.
- Developed techniques for creating oblique pictorials. You also learned that for this type of pictorial, you should not show the receding dimension of the object true to size in order to avoid a distorted image.

2.13 glossary of key terms

arc: A curved entity that represents a portion of a circle.

bounding box: A square box used to sketch circles or ellipses.

circle: A closed curved figure where all points on it are equidistant from its center point.

construction line: A faint line used in sketching to align items and define shapes.

ellipse: A closed curve figure where the sum of the distance between any point on the figure and its two foci is constant.

isometric axes: A set of three coordinate axes that are portrayed on the paper at 120 degrees relative to one another.

isometric dot paper: Paper used for sketching purposes that includes dots located along lines that meet at 120 degrees.

isometric grid paper: Paper used for sketching purposes that includes grid lines at 120 degrees relative to one another.

isometric pictorial: A sketch of an object that shows its three dimensions where isometric axes were used as the basis for defining the edges of the object.

left-handed system: Any 3-D coordinate system that is defined by the left-hand rule.

line: Shortest distance between two points.

oblique axes: A set of three coordinate axes that are portrayed on the paper as two perpendicular lines, with the third axis meeting them at an angle, typically 45 degrees.

oblique pictorial: A sketch of an object that shows one face in the plane of the paper and the third dimension receding off at an angle relative to the face.

receding dimension: The portion of the object that appears to go back from the plane of the paper in an oblique pictorial.

right-hand rule: Used to define a 3-D coordinate system whereby by pointing the fingers of the right hand down the x-axis and curling them in the direction of the y-axis, the thumb will point down the z-axis.

right-handed system: Any 3-D coordinate system that is defined by the right-hand-rule.

shading: Marks added to surfaces and features of a sketch to highlight 3-D effects.

3-D coordinate system: A set of three mutually perpendicular axes used to define 3-D space.

tick mark: A short dash used in sketching to locate points on the paper.

2.14 questions for review

1. What is the role of sketching in engineering design? In creativity?

2. Describe which procedure you should use to sketch straight lines. (Are you right- or left-handed?)

3. How do circles appear on an isometric pictorial? On an oblique pictorial?

4. What is a bounding box?

5. How are construction lines used in sketching?

6. Why is it important to know the right-hand rule?

2.15 problems

1. For each of the coordinate axes shown below, indicate whether they are isometric or oblique and whether they represent right-handed or left-handed systems.

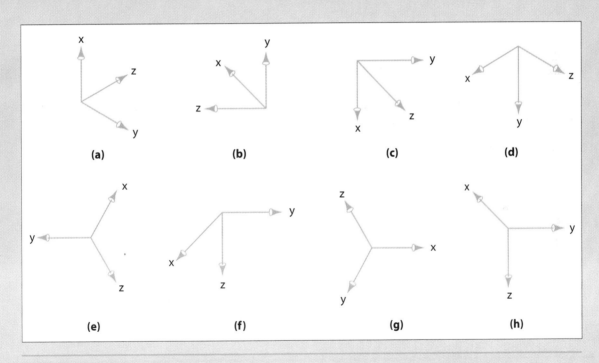

FIGURE P2.1.

2.15 problems (continued)

2. Label the third axis in each of the following figures to define a right-handed system.

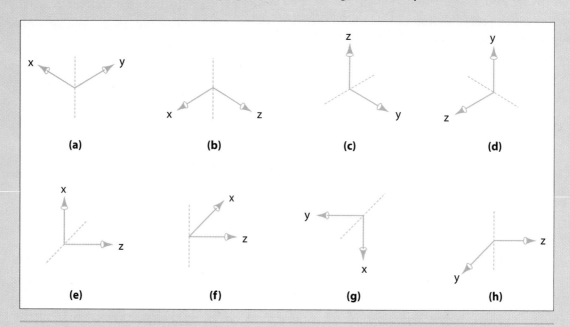

FIGURE P2.2.

2.15 problems (continued)

3. Create isometric sketches from the coded plans shown below.

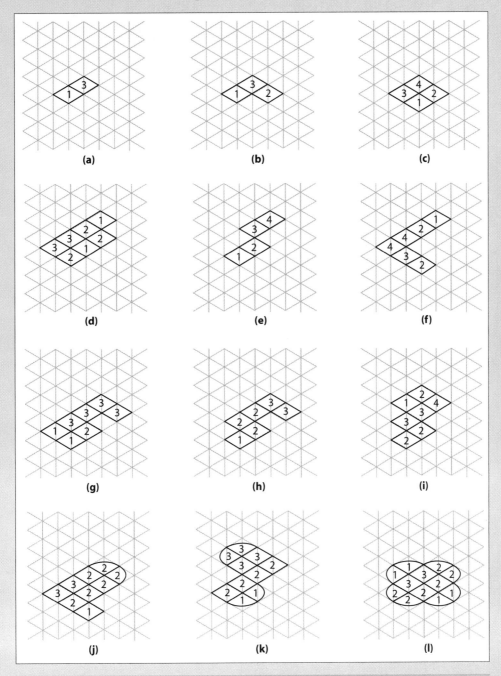

FIGURE P2.3.

4. Sketch a $6 \times 6 \times 2$ block in isometric. On the 6×6 side, sketch a hole of diameter 4, making sure you include back edges of the hole as appropriate. Also create an oblique pictorial of the block.

5. Sketch a $6 \times 6 \times 2$ block in isometric. On the 6×6 side, sketch a hole of diameter 2, making sure you include back edges of the hole as appropriate. Also create an oblique pictorial of the block.

2.15 problems (continued)

6. Sketch a 6 × 6 × 4 block in isometric. On the 6 × 6 side, sketch a hole of diameter 2, making sure you include back edges of the hole as appropriate. Also create an oblique pictorial of the block.

7. From the isometric pictorials and viewing directions defined in the following sketches, create oblique pictorial sketches that look proportionally correct.

8. Use the "foundation, frame, finish" method to create sketches of the following:

    a. stapler   c. coffee mug   e. calculator

    b. speedboat   d. bicycle   f. laptop computer

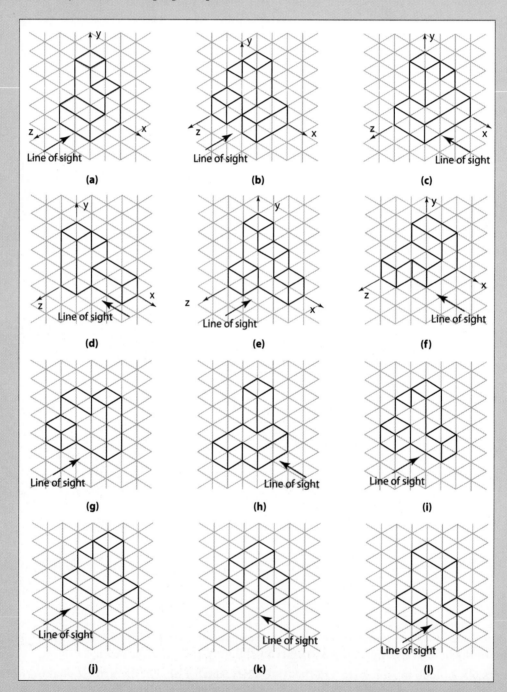

FIGURE P2.4.

3

Visualization

objectives

After completing this chapter, you should be able to

- Recognize that 3-D spatial skills are necessary for success in engineering
- Describe how a person's spatial skills develop as they age
- Examine the types of questions used to assess a person's spatial skill level
- Show how you can improve your 3-D spatial skills through techniques that include
  - Drawing different corner views of an object.
  - Rotating objects about one or more axes.
  - Sketching object reflections and making use of symmetries.
  - Considering cross sections of objects.
  - Combining two objects to form a third object through Boolean operations.

3.01 introduction

When you start your first job in the real world, an engineer or a technologist is likely to hand you a drawing and expect you to understand what is on the page. Imagine your embarrassment if you have no clue what all of the lines and symbols on the drawing mean. One of the fundamental skills you need to understand that drawing is the ability to visualize in three dimensions. The ability to visualize in three dimensions is also linked to creativity in design. People who think creatively are able to "see" things in their minds that others cannot. Their imaginations are not confined by traditional boundaries.

In this chapter, you will learn about the different types of three-dimensional (3-D) spatial skills and ways they can be developed through practice. The chapter will begin with an introduction to the background research conducted in education and to 3-D spatial skills. Then the chapter will take you through several types of visualization activities to further develop your 3-D skills through practice.

3.02 Background

Beginning in the early part of the twentieth century, IQ testing was developed to categorize a person based on his or her intelligence quotient. Anyone who took the IQ test was defined by a number that identified a level of intelligence. IQ scores over 140 identified geniuses; scores below 100 identified slow thinkers. Beginning in the 1970s, scholars began to perceive problems with this one-number categorization of a person's ability to think. One scholar in particular, Howard Gardner, theorized that there were multiple human intelligences and the one-number-fits-all theory did not accurately reflect the scope of human thought processes. Although some of his theories might be subject to scrutiny, they have gained acceptance within the scientific and educational communities. Gardner theorized that there are eight distinct human intelligences; he identified them as:

- Linguistic—the ability to use words effectively in speaking or in writing.
- Logical-Mathematical—the ability to use numbers effectively and to reason well.
- Spatial—the ability to perceive the visual-spatial world accurately and to perform transformations on those perceptions.
- Bodily-Kinesthetic—the capacity of a person to use the whole body to express ideas or feelings and the facility to use the hands to produce or transform things.
- Musical—the capacity to perceive, discriminate, transform, and express musical forms.
- Interpersonal—the ability to perceive and make distinctions in the moods, intentions, motivations, and feelings of other people.
- Intrapersonal—self-knowledge and the ability to act adaptively on the basis of that knowledge.
- Naturalist—the ability to recognize plant or animal species within the environment.

You may be acquainted with someone who has a high level of linguistic intelligence but a low level of musical intelligence. Or you might know someone who has a high level of logical-mathematical intelligence but who lacks interpersonal intelligence relationships. You may even have a friend who is generally smart but who lacks intrapersonal intelligence and attempts stunts that are beyond his or her limitations.

Most people are born with one or more of the intelligences listed. As a child, Tiger Woods was gifted with a natural ability in bodily-kinesthetic intelligence. Mozart was born with a high level of musical intelligence. However, just because a person naturally has a high level of intelligence in one area, does not mean that he or she cannot learn and improve his or her abilities in weaker areas. A person might naturally have strength in linguistics and musical intelligences, but he or she can still learn and improve in logical-mathematical endeavors. The goal of this chapter is to help those of you not born with a high level of spatial intelligence as defined by Gardner.

Learning in general and spatial skills in particular have been the subject of education research studies over the past several decades. The following are a few important questions that the research raised in the area of spatial intelligence:

- How does a person develop spatial skills?
- Why does a person need well-developed spatial skills?
- How are spatial skills measured?

The next few sections will examine researchers' answers to these questions.

3.03 Development of Spatial Skills

As a child grows, the brain develops in ways that enable the child to learn. If you think of each of the eight intelligences described by Gardner, you can understand how these skills and abilities develop as a child grows to maturity. Consider kinesthetic intelligence. Newborn infants cannot move on their own during the first few weeks of life. Within a few months, they can hold up their heads without support. By the age of four months, they can roll over; by six months, they can crawl; by one year, they can walk. Children learn to run, skip, and jump within the next year or so. Eventually, they usually develop all sorts of kinesthetic abilities that enable them to enjoy physical activities such as basketball, swimming, ballet, and bike riding. Nearly every child goes through this natural progression. However, some children develop more quickly than others; some even skip a step and go directly from rolling over to walking without ever crawling. As with most types of intelligence, some individuals—such as professional athletes—have exceptional kinesthetic skills, while others have poorly developed skills and struggle to perform the simplest tasks. However, even people who naturally have little kinesthetic ability can improve through practice and perseverance.

The remaining intelligences (mathematics, verbal, etc.) also have a natural progression; for example, to develop your mathematical intelligence, you have to learn addition before you can learn algebra. Children also acquire spatial skills through a natural progression; however, you may not be as aware of that progression of development as you are of the progressions for the other intelligences. Educational psychologists theorize that there are three distinct stages of development for spatial skills.

The first stage of development involves 2-D spatial skills. As children develop these skills, they are able to recognize 2-D shapes and eventually are able to recognize that a 2-D shape has a certain orientation in space. If you watched Sesame Street as a child, you may remember the game where four pictures of 2-D objects are shown on the TV screen—three objects are identical; the fourth is different in some way. A song urges you to pick out the object that does not belong with the other three. A child who can accomplish this task has developed some of the spatial skills at the first stage. You also may remember playing with a toy similar to a Tupperware ShapeSorter, shown in Figure 3.01. The toy is a ball that is half red and half blue with ten holes in it, each hole a different shape. A child playing this game not only has to recognize that the star-shaped piece corresponds to the star-shaped hole but also has to turn the piece to the correct orientation to fit the piece through the hole. This game challenges different 2-D skills found at the first stage of development of spatial intelligence—a child must recognize the 2-D shape of the object and then must be able to recognize its orientation in 2-D space to complete the task.

Three-dimensional spatial skills are acquired during the second stage of development. Children at this stage can imagine what a 3-D object looks like when it is rotated in space. They can imagine what an object looks like from a different point of view, or they can imagine what an object would look like when folded up from a 2-D pattern.

FIGURE 3.01. A Tupperware ShapeSorter toy.

People who are adept at solving the Rubik's Cube puzzle have well-developed 3-D spatial skills. Computer games such as 3D Tetris require well-developed 3-D spatial skills to perform the manipulations required to remain "alive." Soccer players who can imagine the trajectory that puts the ball in the goal from any angle on the playing field typically have well-developed 3-D spatial skills. Children have usually acquired 3-D spatial skills by the time they are in middle school. For some children, it may take a few more years, depending on their natural predisposition toward spatial intelligence and their childhood experiences.

People at an advanced stage of the development of spatial intelligence can combine their 3-D skills with concepts of measurement. Assume you are buying sand for a turtle-shaped sandbox. You go to the local gravel pit where an employee loads the sand in the back of your pickup using a big "scoop." How many scoopfuls will you need? If you can successfully visualize the volume of sand as it is transformed from the 3-D volume of one full scoop to the 3-D volume of the turtle-shaped sandbox, you have acquired this advanced 3-D visualization skill.

Many people never develop the advanced level in spatial intelligence, just like the many people who never achieve advanced skill levels in mathematics or kinesthetic intelligence. Not achieving advanced levels in some of the intelligence areas is not likely to hamper your ability to become a productive, well-adjusted member of society. However, just as a lack of basic development in verbal intelligence is likely to hurt your chances professionally, a lack of basic skills in spatial intelligence may limit your ability to be successful, especially in engineering or a technical field.

Schools help students develop most of the intelligence types, although schools do not usually provide formal training to develop spatial intelligence. You began learning mathematics in kindergarten and are likely continuing your education in math at the present time. If you get a graduate degree in a technical area, you will probably be developing your mathematical intelligence for many years thereafter. The focus on developing spatial skills from an early age, continuing through high school and beyond, is typically absent in the U.S. educational system. Developing spatial intelligence is largely ignored in schools for a variety of reasons; however, those reasons are not the subject of this text.

The lack of prior spatial training may not be a problem for you—you developed your spatial skills informally through everyday experiences or you naturally have a high level of ability in spatial intelligence. However, poorly developed 3-D spatial skills may hinder your success in fields such as engineering and technology. This is especially true as you embark on a journey through an engineering graphics course. Poorly developed spatial skills will leave you frustrated and possibly discouraged about engineering graphics. The good news if you do not have a natural ability in 3-D spatial skills is that you can develop them through practice and exercise.

3.04 Types of Spatial Skills

According to McGee (1979), spatial ability is "the ability to mentally manipulate, rotate, twist, or invert pictorially presented visual stimuli." McGee identifies five components of spatial skills:

- **Spatial perception**—the ability to identify horizontal and vertical directions.
- **Spatial visualization**—the ability to mentally transform (rotate, translate, or mirror) or to mentally alter (twist, fold, or invert) 2-D figures and/or 3-D objects.
- **Mental rotations**—the ability to mentally turn a 3-D object in space and then be able to mentally rotate a different 3-D object in the same way.
- **Spatial relations**—the ability to visualize the relationship between two objects in space, i.e., overlapping or nonoverlapping.
- **Spatial orientation**—the ability of a person to mentally determine his or her own location and orientation within a given environment.

A different researcher (Tartre, 1990) proposed a classification scheme for spatial skills based on the mental processes that are expected to be used in performing a given task. She believes that there are two distinct categories of 3-D spatial skills—spatial visualization and spatial orientation. Spatial visualization is mentally moving an object. Spatial orientation is mentally shifting the point from which you view the object while it remains fixed in space.

Regardless of the classification scheme you choose to believe, it is clear that more than one component skill makes up the broad category of human intelligence known as spatial visualization. Thus, you cannot do just one type of activity and expect to develop equally all of the components of spatial skills. You need to do a variety of tasks to develop your spatial intelligence, just as developing linguistic intelligence requires you to speak, read, write, and listen.

3.05 Assessing Spatial Skills

As with the seven other intelligence types, standardized tests have been developed to determine your level of achievements in spatial intelligence. There are many different tests—some are for 2-D shapes, and some are for 3-D objects. Some evaluate mental rotation skills, and others measure spatial relations skills. The standardized tests usually measure only one specific component of visualization skill. If you were to take a number of different visualization tests, you might find that you have a high level of ability in one component (perhaps paper folding) relative to a low ability in a different component, such as 3-D object rotations. That is normal. Many educators and psychologists believe there is no one-size-fits-all measure of spatial intelligence, just as a single IQ number does not give a clear indication of a person's overall intelligence.

One of the tests designed to measure your level of 2-D spatial skills is the Minnesota Paper Form Board (MPFB) test. Figure 3.02 shows a visualization problem similar to those found on the MPFB test. This problem tests a person's ability to determine which set of five 2-D shapes, A through E, is the composite of the 2-D fragments given in the upper left corner of the figure. The way to solve this test is to mentally rotate or move the three pieces to visualize how to put them together to coincide with the combined shape that contains the pieces. The test may seem easy, but you should have fully developed the 2-D spatial skills needed to solve this test when you were four or five years old. During the years since then, you should have developed more advanced 2-D visualization skills. For example, you should now be able to follow a map and determine whether to make a right or a left turn without turning the map.

FIGURE 3.02. A problem similar to that found on the Minnesota Paper Form Board Test.

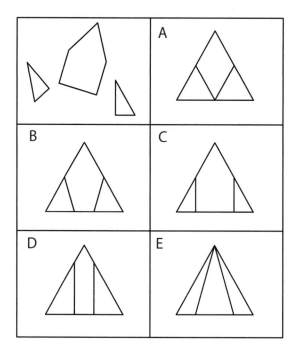

Figure 3.03 shows a visualization problem similar to what is found on the Differential Aptitude Test: Space Relations. This test is designed to measure your ability to move from the 2-D to the 3-D world. The objective is to mentally fold the 2-D pattern along the solid lines, which designate the fold lines, so the object will result in the 3-D shape. You then choose the correct 3-D object from the four possibilities shown in the figure. In your previous math classes, these 2-D patterns may have been referred to as *nets*. In engineering, the 2-D figures are called *flat patterns* or *developments*.

Mental rotations—the ability to visualize the rotation of 3-D objects—is a necessary component skill in engineering graphics and in the use of 3-D modeling software. Figure 3.4 and Figure 3.5 show problems similar to those found on two widely used 3-D spatial tests for rotations.

In the Purdue Spatial Visualization Test: Rotations, an object such as shown in Figure 3.04 is given on the top line before and after it has been rotated in 3-D space. You then have to mentally rotate a different object on the second line by the same amount and select the correct result from the choices given on the third line.

In the Mental Rotation Test, you are given an object such as shown in Figure 3.05 on the left. Of the four choices given, you pick the *two* that show correct possible rotations in space of the original object. (Note that two choices are the same object and two choices are different objects.)

FIGURE 3.03. A problem similar to that found on the Differential Aptitude Test: Space Relations.

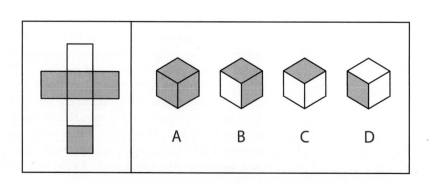

FIGURE 3.04. A problem similar to that found on the Purdue Spatial Visualization Test: Rotations.

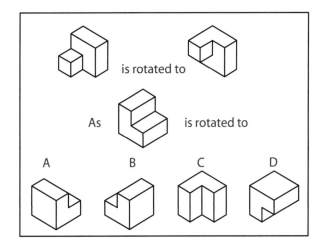

FIGURE 3.05. A problem similar to that found on the Mental Rotation Test.

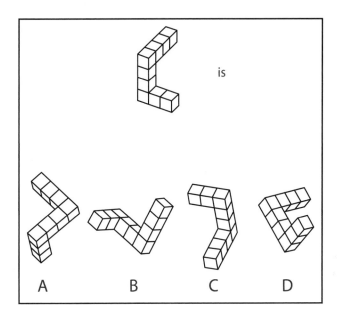

Another type of spatial skill that is often tested is the ability to visualize the **cross section** that results from "slicing" a 3-D object with a **cutting plane**. One popular test of this type is the Mental Cutting Test. Figure 3.06 shows the type of problem found on this test, which challenges you to imagine the 2-D shape that is the intersection between the cutting plane and the 3-D object.

Engineers and technologists communicate with each other largely through graphical means. They use drawings, sketches, charts, graphs, and CAD models to convey ideas. Design solutions commonly have a graphical component that is backed up by pages of calculations and analysis. Your designs will not be complete without graphics. Even chemical and electrical engineers use drawings for the processes and circuits they design.

So to communicate as an engineer, you must be able to visualize and interpret the images represented in the drawings. Besides satisfying the need for effective communication, a side benefit to having well-developed 3-D spatial skills is that your brain works better when *all* parts of it are focused on solving a problem. Sketching and visualization have been shown to improve the creative process. Well-developed spatial skills contribute to your ability to work innovatively, as well as to learn to use 3-D modeling software.

FIGURE 3.06. A problem similar to that found on the Mental Cutting Test.

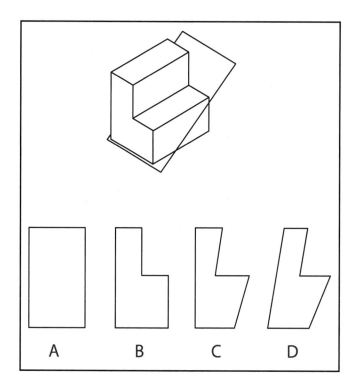

The remaining sections of this chapter will provide exercises for your brain—exercises that develop your 3-D spatial skills; exercises that help you think differently from the way you are thinking in your math and science courses; exercises that will help you improve your sketching skills.

3.06 Isometric Corner Views of Simple Objects

In Chapter 2, you learned how to create a simple isometric sketch of an object made out of blocks as specified by a coded plan. The coded plan is a 2-D portrayal of the object, using numbers to specify the height of the stack of blocks at a given location. Figure 3.07 illustrates the relationship between the coded plan, the object constructed out of blocks, and the resulting isometric sketch of the object—remember, you show edges only between surfaces on the isometric sketch.

The coded plans you viewed in Chapter 2 were constructed on isometric grid paper. The building "grew up" from the plan into the isometric grid. In the previous exercises,

FIGURE 3.07. A coded plan and its resulting isometric sketch.

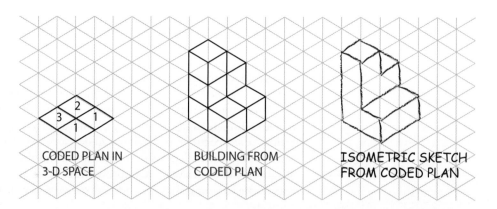

CODED PLAN IN
3-D SPACE

BUILDING FROM
CODED PLAN

ISOMETRIC SKETCH
FROM CODED PLAN

the coded plan was oriented in 3-D space on the isometric grid, which represents 3-D space. Now think about laying the coded plan flat on a 2-D sheet of paper. Figure 3.08 shows the coded plan for the object shown in Figure 3.07 laid flat in a 2-D orientation. Figure 3.9 shows the relationship between a coded plan in 2-D space, the coded plan in 3-D space, the object made of blocks, and the resulting isometric sketch.

When you orient the coded plan in 2-D space, everything you learned about these plans still applies: you "build up" from the plan. The numbers represent the height of the stack of blocks at a given location, and you show lines only where two surfaces intersect. However, now one more consideration has been introduced into the isometric sketching equation—the orientation of your "eye" with respect to the object itself. (Note that *the orientation of your eye* is often referred to as *your viewpoint*.)

Examine again the coded plans in 2-D space. Figure 3.10 shows a simple coded plan with its four corners labeled as *W*, *X*, *Y*, and *Z*. A **corner view** of the object represented by the coded plan in Figure 3.10 is the view from a given corner when the viewpoint is

FIGURE 3.08. The relationship between a coded plan in 2-D space and 3-D space.

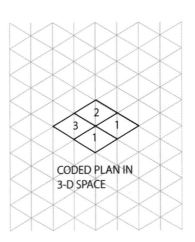

CODED PLAN IN
2-D SPACE

CODED PLAN IN
3-D SPACE

FIGURE 3.09. The relationship between coded plans, a building, and an isometric sketch.

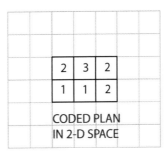

CODED PLAN
IN 2-D SPACE

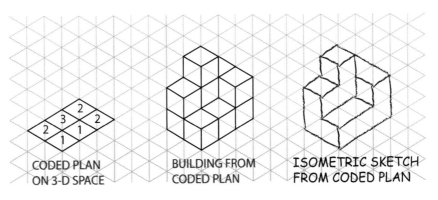

CODED PLAN
ON 3-D SPACE

BUILDING FROM
CODED PLAN

ISOMETRIC SKETCH
FROM CODED PLAN

w			z
	2	3	
	1	1	
x			y

CODED PLAN IN
2-D SPACE

FIGURE 3.10. A simple coded plan with corners labeled.

above the object in question. This view is sometimes referred to as *the bird's-eye view*, because the viewpoint is above the object. A worm's-eye view is the viewpoint from *below* the object. Figure 3.11 shows the four corner views for the coded plan from Figure 3.10.

When the four corner views of the object are created, the object does not change—just your viewpoint of the object. The importance of viewpoint in visualization is readily apparent when you think about a complex system such as an automobile. When you are looking at a car from the front, you may have an entirely different mental image of the car than if you look at it from the side or rear. What you "see" depends largely on where your eye is located relative to the object.

With more practice, you will find it easier to make corner views from coded plans. At first, you may need to turn the paper to visualize what an object will look like from a given corner. With continued practice, however, you should be able to mentally turn the paper to sketch the object from the vantage point of any corner.

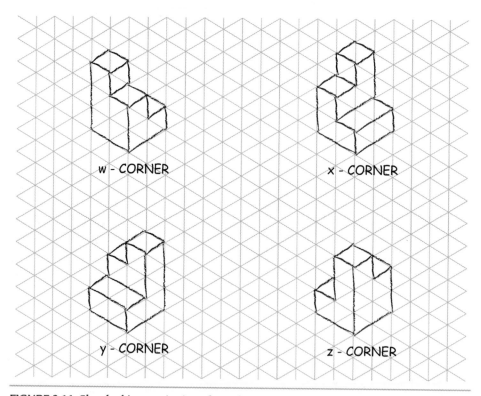

w - CORNER   x - CORNER

y - CORNER   z - CORNER

FIGURE 3.11. Sketched isometric views from the corners of the coded plan in Figure 3.10.

3.07 Object Rotations about a Single Axis

Being able to mentally visualize an object as it rotates in space is an important skill for you to acquire as an engineer or a technologist. You already have had limited exposure to the concept of rotating objects through your work with mentally rotating coded plans to obtain different corner views. In the preceding section, you started with the Y-corner view to draw the isometric. Having done that, you should be able to imagine what the object will look like from the X-corner view. If you can see in your mind what the object looks like from the X-corner view, you are mentally rotating the object in space. In this section, you will continue to work with object rotations, tackling increasingly complex objects and using increasingly complex manipulations.

You probably learned in your math classes how 2-D shapes are rotated in 2-D space about a pivot point, as illustrated in Figure 3.12. In this figure, the shape has been rotated 90 degrees counterclockwise (CCW) about the pivot point, which is the origin of the 2-D xy coordinate system. After rotation, the newly oriented shape is referred to as the "image" of the original shape. Notice that when the 2-D shape is rotated about the pivot point, each line on the shape is rotated by the same amount—in this case, 90 degrees CCW about the pivot point. Also notice that the point on the shape that was originally located at the pivot point, the origin, remains at that same location after rotation.

In Chapter 2, you learned about 3-D coordinate systems and how three axes (the x-, y-, and z-axes) can be used to describe 3-D space. When you rotate an object in 3-D space, the same principles apply as for 2-D rotations. In fact, you can reexamine the rotation of the shape in Figure 3.12 from a 3-D perspective. Figure 3.13 shows the 2-D shape drawn in 3-D space before and after it was rotated 90 degrees CCW about the pivot point, which is the origin of the xyz coordinate system.

Observe and understand how each line on the shape is rotated the same amount— 90 degrees CCW about the origin—and that the point on the shape originally in contact with the origin remains at the origin after rotation. One other thing you may notice is that the pivot point is the point view of the z-axis. The point view of a line is what you see as you look down the length of the axis. To illustrate this principle, take a pen or pencil and rotate it so you are looking directly at its point; notice that the length of the pen "vanishes" and only the "point" remains visible, as shown in Figure 3.14. As such, the original rotation of the 2-D shape, as shown in Figure 3.12, could be considered a 90 degree CCW rotation about the z-axis in 3-D space.

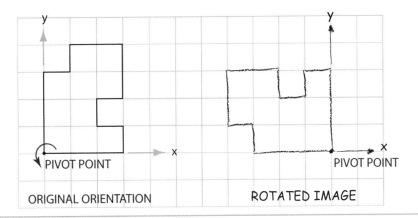

FIGURE 3.12. A shape rotated about a pivot point in 2-D space.

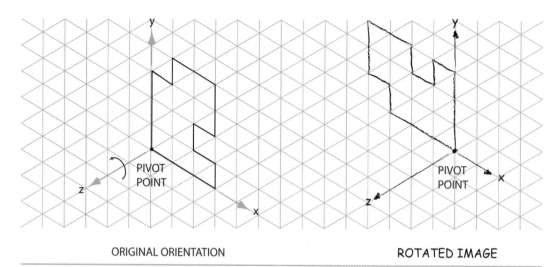

ORIGINAL ORIENTATION   ROTATED IMAGE

FIGURE 3.13. A 2-D shape rotated in 3-D space.

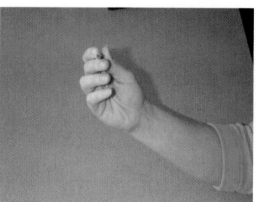

FIGURE 3.14. Looking down the end of a pencil.

Think back to what you learned in Chapter 2 about the right-hand rule. If you point the thumb of your right hand in the positive direction of the z-axis and curl your fingers, you will see that the 90 degree CCW rotation mimics the direction that your fingers curl, as illustrated in Figure 3.15. This CCW rotation of the 2-D shape represents a *positive* 90 degree rotation about the z-axis. The CCW rotation is positive because the thumb of your right hand was pointing in the positive direction of the z-axis as the shape was rotated. If you point the thumb of your right hand in the negative direction of the z-axis and the shape is rotated in the direction the fingers of your right hand curl, your fingers indicate a clockwise (CW) rotation of the shape about the z-axis, as shown in Figure 3.16. A CW rotation about an axis is defined as a negative rotation. Remember that the thumb of your right hand is pointing in the negative z-direction. Also remember that the pivot point of the shape remains at a fixed location in space as it is rotated in the negative z-direction.

You should now be ready to tackle rotations of 3-D objects in 3-D space. Imagine the 2-D shape from the past several figures is a surface view of a 3-D object. Assume you can extend the surface you have been seeing in the xy plane into the z-dimension. The result of extending that surface in the third dimension is a solid object. The terminology of 3-D CAD software says that the shape was extruded. You will learn more about extrusion later in this text. If this shape is "extruded" 3 units into the z-direction, the object will appear as shown in Figure 3.17. In this figure, notice that instead of a single point located on the axis of rotation (the z-axis in the figure), an entire edge of the object is located on that axis. The edge is hidden from sight in this view, but you can imagine it

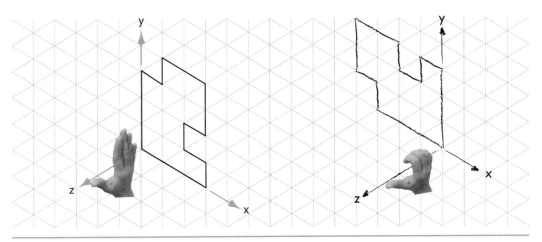

FIGURE 3.15. Positive rotation of a 2-D shape about the z-axis.

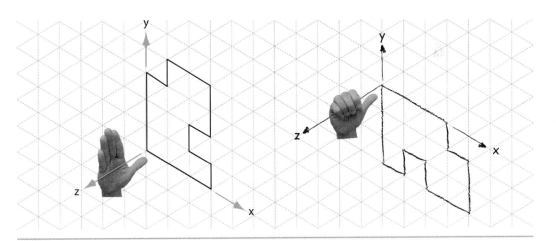

FIGURE 3.16. Negative rotation of a 2-D shape about the z-axis.

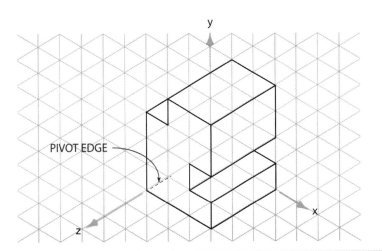

FIGURE 3.17. A 2-D shape from Figure 3.12 extruded three units in the z-direction.

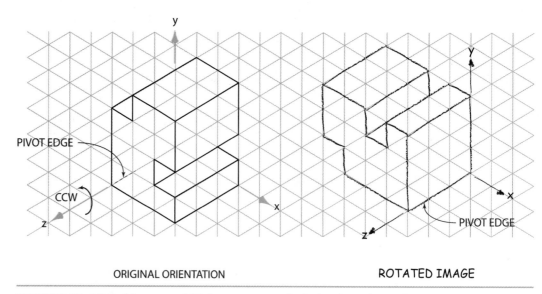

PIVOT EDGE

CCW

ORIGINAL ORIENTATION

PIVOT EDGE

ROTATED IMAGE

FIGURE 3.18. A 3-D object rotated 90 degrees counterclockwise about the z-axis.

nonetheless. Now think about rotating the entire object about the z-axis in a positive direction (or CCW) 90 degrees from its original position. When this happens, the image shown in Figure 3.18 appears. Instead of a single pivot point, the 3-D rotation has a pivot edge. Throughout the rotation, the edge remained in contact with the axis of rotation. All parts of the object also rotated by the same amount (90 degrees CCW about z) just as all parts of the surface were rotated when you were considering 2-D shapes.

Just as 2-D shapes can be rotated positively (CCW) or negatively (CW) about the z-axis, 3-D objects can be rotated in either direction. Figure 3.19 shows the same object after it has been rotated negative 90 degrees (CW) about the z-axis. This figure also makes clear that the pivot edge of the object remains in contact with the axis of rotation as the object is rotated.

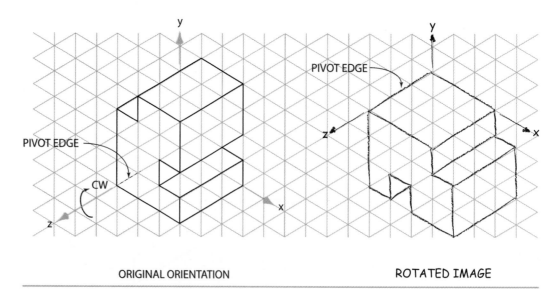

PIVOT EDGE

CW

PIVOT EDGE

ORIGINAL ORIENTATION

ROTATED IMAGE

FIGURE 3.19. A 3-D object rotated 90 degrees clockwise about the z-axis.

Any object can be rotated about the x- or y-axis by following the same simple rules established for rotation about the z-axis:

1. The edge of the object originally in contact with the axis of rotation remains in contact after the rotation. This edge is called the pivot edge.
2. Each point, edge, and surface on the object is rotated by exactly the same amount.
3. The rotation is positive when it is CCW about an axis and negative when it is CW about an axis. The direction is determined by looking directly down the positive end of the axis of rotation.
4. An alternative method for determining the direction of the rotation is the right-hand rule. Point the thumb of your right hand into the axis of rotation—into either the positive or negative end of the axis of rotation—and curl your fingers in the direction the object is rotated. The direction you obtain from the right-hand rule is the same as the direction defined in number 3 above, positive is CCW and negative is CW.

Figure 3.20 and Figure 3.21 illustrate the positive and negative 90 degree rotations obtained about the x-axis and the y-axis, respectively.

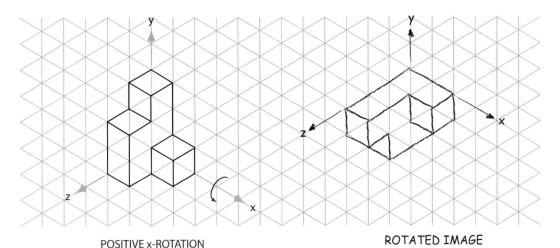

POSITIVE x-ROTATION   ROTATED IMAGE

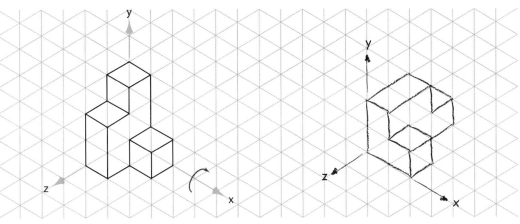

NEGATIVE x-ROTATION   ROTATED IMAGE

FIGURE 3.20. Positive and negative rotations about the x-axis.

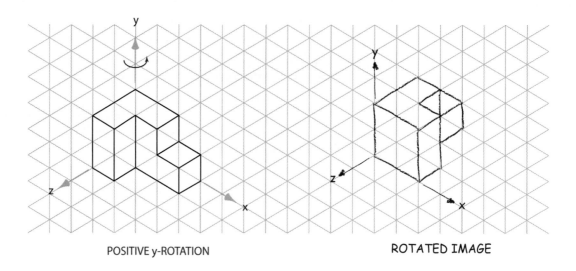

POSITIVE y-ROTATION ROTATED IMAGE

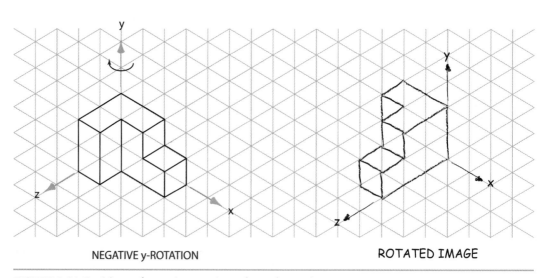

NEGATIVE y-ROTATION ROTATED IMAGE

FIGURE 3.21. Positive and negative rotations about the y-axis.

3.07.01 Notation

Specifying in writing a positive, or CCW, rotation about any axis is cumbersome and time-consuming. For this reason, the following notations will be used to describe object rotations in this text:

- To denote positive rotations of an object about the indicated axis.
- To denote negative rotations of an object about the indicated axis.
- Also, for simplicity in sketching, this text will always rotate an object in increments of 90 degrees about the indicated axis. Figure 3.22 illustrates the result when you rotate the object according to the notation given.

3.07.02 Rotation of Objects by More Than 90 Degrees about a Single Axis

In all examples and figures in the preceding sections, objects were rotated exactly 90 degrees about a single axis. In reality, you can rotate objects by any number of degrees. If you rotate an object in two increments of 90 degrees about the same axis, the total rotation will be 180 degrees. Similarly, if you rotate an object in three increments,

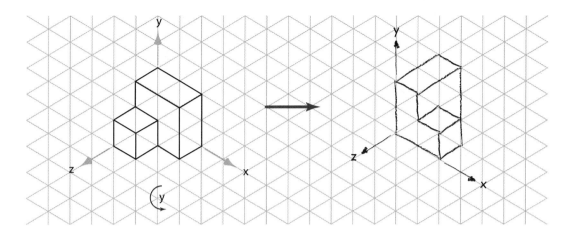

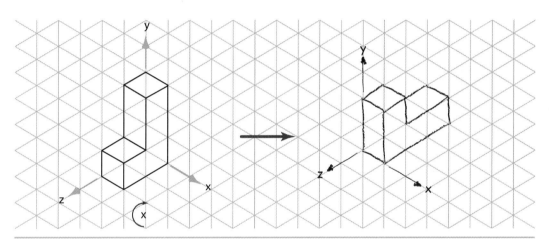

FIGURE 3.22. Object rotations specified by notation.

the total rotation will be 270 degrees. Figure 3.23 shows an object that has been rotated 180 degrees about a single axis, along with the symbol denoting the amount and direction of rotation. Notice that the two 90 degree positive x-axis rotations indicate the total 180 degree rotation achieved.

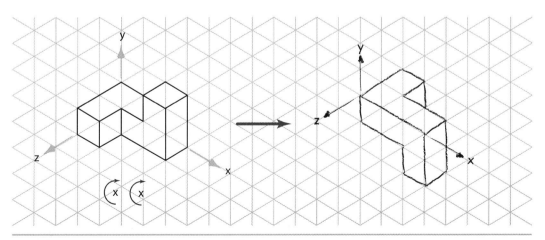

FIGURE 3.23. An object rotated 180 degrees about an axis.

Once you are free to rotate objects in multiple increments of 90 degrees, you can achieve several equivalent rotations. The term *equivalent rotations* means that two different sets of rotations produce the same result.

3.07.03 Equivalencies for Rotations about a Single Axis

When an object is rotated in multiple increments about an axis, the following equivalencies can be observed:

- A positive 180 degree rotation is equivalent to a negative 180 degree rotation.
- A negative 90 degree rotation is equivalent to a positive 270 degree rotation.
- A positive 90 degree rotation is equivalent to a negative 270 degree rotation.

These equivalencies are illustrated in Figures 3.24, 3.25, and 3.26, respectively.

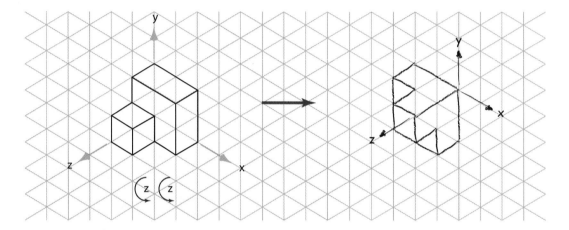

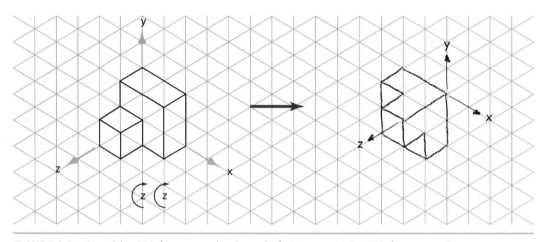

FIGURE 3.24. A positive 180 degree rotation is equivalent to a negative 180 degree rotation.

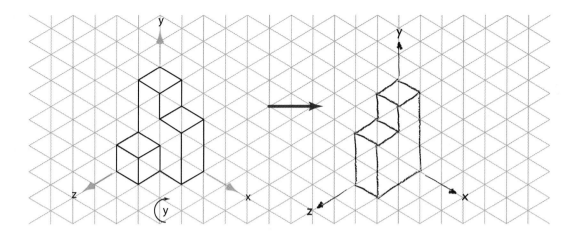

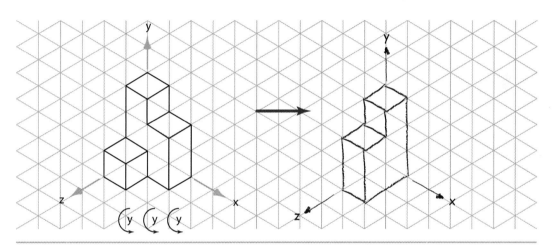

FIGURE 3.25. A negative 90 degree rotation is equivalent to a positive 270 degree rotation.

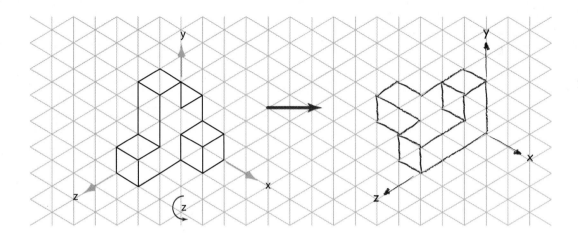

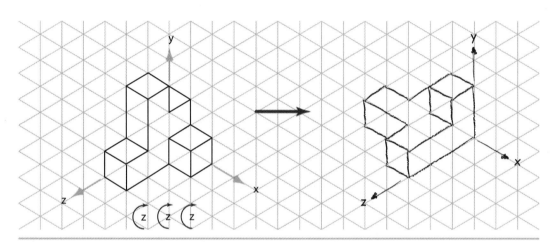

FIGURE 3.26. A positive 90 degree rotation is equivalent to a negative 270 degree rotation.

3.08 Rotation about Two or More Axes

In the same way you rotated an object about a single axis, you can also rotate the object about more than one axis in a series of steps. Figure 3.27 shows an object that has been rotated in the positive direction about the x-axis and then rotated in the negative direction about the y-axis. The rotation notation used in the figure indicates the specified two-step rotation. Figure 3.28 shows the same set of rotations, only this time they are shown in two single steps to achieve the final result. Notice that when an object is rotated about two different axes, a single edge no longer remains in contact with the axis of rotation (since there are now two of them). For rotations about two axes, only a single point remains in its original location, as shown in Figure 3.27 and Figure 3.28.

When rotating an object about two or more axes, you must be careful to perform the rotations in the exact order specified. If the rotations are listed such that you rotate the object CCW in the positive direction about the x-axis and then rotate it CW in the negative direction about the z-axis, you must perform the rotations in that order. Object rotations are not commutative. (Remember that the commutative property in math states that 2 + 3 = 3 + 2.) For object rotations, rotating about the x-axis and then rotating about the y-axis is *not* the same as rotating about the y-axis and then rotating about the x-axis.

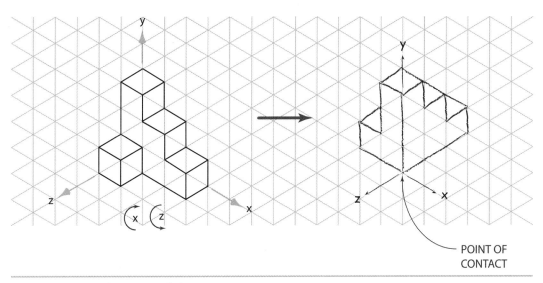

FIGURE 3.27. An object rotated about two axes.

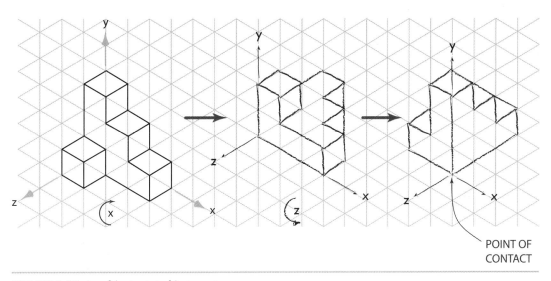

FIGURE 3.28. An object rotated in two steps.

In the top portion of Figure 3.29, the object has been rotated about positive y and then rotated about negative z to obtain its image. In the bottom portion of the figure, the object has been rotated about negative z and then rotated about positive y to obtain a new image of the rotated object. The second image is obtained by reversing the order of the rotations. The resulting images are not the same when the order of rotation is changed. Why? Because with the first set of rotations, the edge of the object on the y-axis serves as the pivot line for the first rotation, which is about positive y. For the second set of rotations, the edge of the object on the z-axis serves as the pivot edge for the first of the two rotations. When you rotate first about negative z, you are using an entirely different object edge than the initial pivot line; hence, the difference in rotated images.

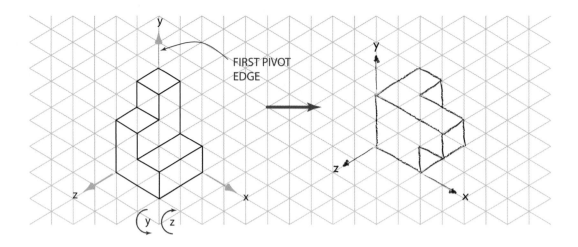

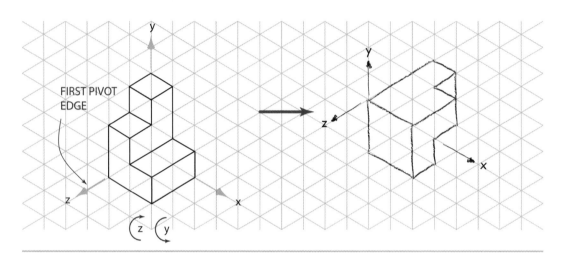

FIGURE 3.29. Object rotations about two axes—order not commutative.

3.08.01 Equivalencies for Object Rotations about Two or More Axes

Just as there are equivalencies for rotations of an object about a single axis, there are equivalencies for object rotations about two axes. Figure 3.30 shows one pair of rotational equivalencies. Can you find another set? How about positive x and then negative z? No! Or positive y and then positive z? Yes! There are several possibilities for each pair of rotations. But it is impossible to come up with simple rules for equivalency, as in the previous discussion of equivalent rotations about a single axis. Equivalent rotations for objects about two or more axes are likely to be determined through trial and error and a great deal of practice.

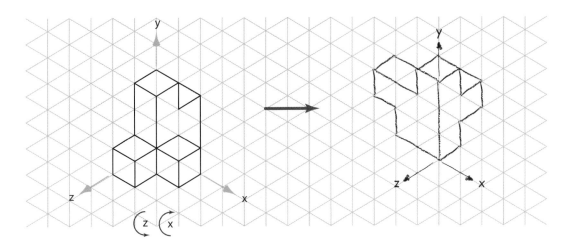

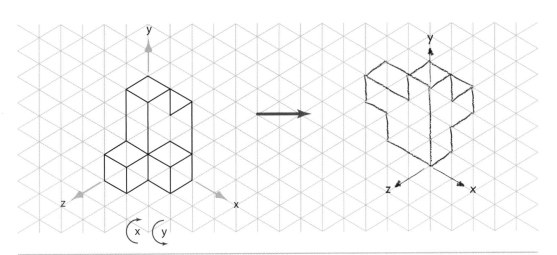

FIGURE 3.30. Equivalent rotations about two axes.

3.09 Reflections and Symmetry

Now that you know the basics of how to visualize an object rotated about an axis, you are ready to move on to visualizing reflections and symmetry. Visualizing planes of symmetry, for example, could save you a great deal of computation time when you are using analysis tools such as FEA. You will learn more about FEA in later chapters of this text.

You are probably familiar with the concept of **reflections** because you are used to looking at your image reflected back to you from a mirror. With a mirror, you see a reflected 2-D image of your face. If you have a mole on your right cheek, you will see the mole on the right cheek of the reflection. Even though your face is three-dimensional, your face in the mirror is a 2-D reflection—as if your face were projected onto a 2-D plane with your line of sight perpendicular to the plane. You may be able to see somewhat in the third dimension from this mirror plane; however, your depth perception will be a bit off because the image is only two-dimensional. Three-dimensional reflection of objects is different from 2-D reflections with mirrors. For one thing, you reflect a 3-D object *across* the plane so that a 3-D image ends up on the other side of the reflection plane.

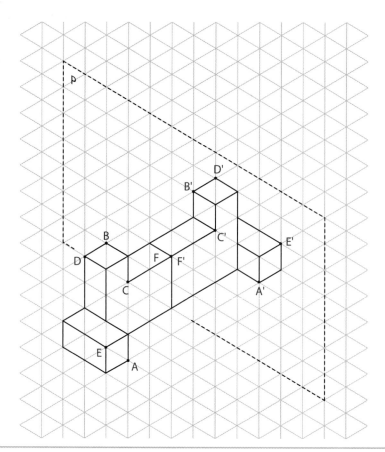

FIGURE 3.31. An object and its 3-D reflection.

Formally stated, in the case of 3-D object reflections, such as shown in Figure 3.31, each point A of the object is associated with an image point A´ in the reflection such that the plane of reflection is a perpendicular bisector of the line segment AA´. What this means is the distance between a point on an object and the reflection plane is equal to the distance between the corresponding point on the image and the reflection plane. The distances are measured along a line perpendicular to the plane of reflection. Figure 3.31 shows a simple object and its reflection across a reflection plane.

In this figure, several points on the original object are labeled, as well as their corresponding points on the reflected image. In this case, the plane of reflection coincides with one planar end of the original object; therefore, the corresponding planar end of the reflected image also coincides with the reflection plane. If you measure the distance between point A on the object and the reflection plane, you will find that it is 3 units. Then if you measure the distance between A´ and the reflection plane, you will find the distance to be 3 units again. It is also possible to reflect an object across a plane when the object is located some distance from the reflection plane, as illustrated in Figure 3.32.

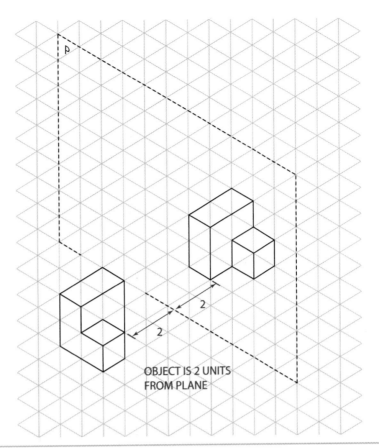

FIGURE 3.32. An object located at a distance from the plane and its reflection.

3.09.01 Symmetry

Your job as an engineer may be easier if you can recognize planes of symmetry within an object. A plane of **symmetry** is an imaginary plane that cuts through an object such that the two parts, one on either side of the plane, are reflections of each other. Not all objects have inherent symmetry. The human body is roughly symmetrical and has one plane of symmetry—a vertical plane through the tip of the nose and the belly button. The left side is a reflection of the right side. Some objects contain no planes of symmetry, some contain only one plane of symmetry, and still others contain an infinite number of planes of symmetry. Figure 3.33 shows several objects and their planes of symmetry: one object contains no planes of symmetry, one object has just one plane of symmetry, one object has two planes of symmetry, and the last object contains an infinite number of planes of symmetry.

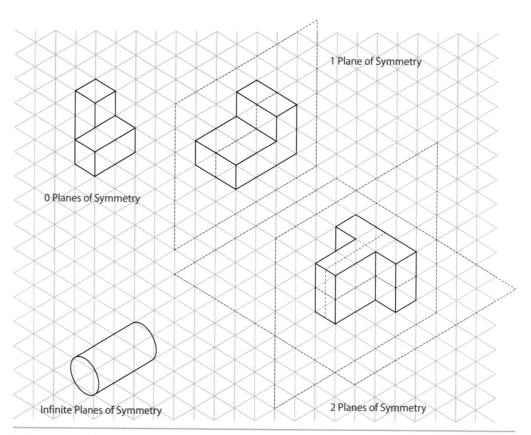

FIGURE 3.33. Objects and their planes of symmetry.

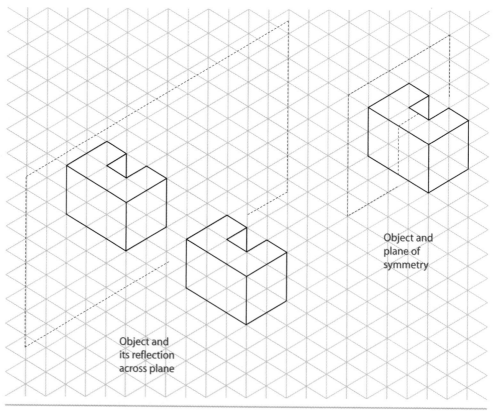

FIGURE 3.34. A comparison of object reflection and symmetry.

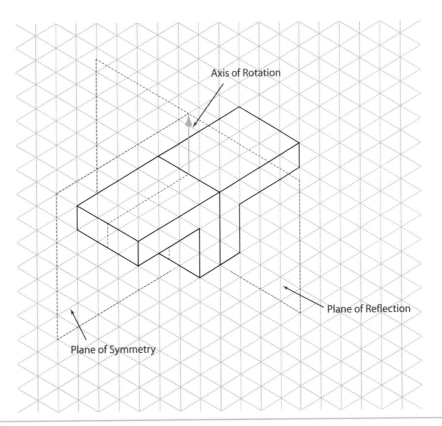

FIGURE 3.35. Object reflection through rotation.

There is one major difference between object reflection and object symmetry. With reflections, you end up with two separate objects (the original and its reflected image); with symmetry, you have a single object that you imagine is being sliced by a plane to form two symmetrical halves. Figure 3.34 illustrates the difference between the two.

For an object that is symmetrical about a plane, you can sometimes obtain its reflection by rotating the object 180 degrees. To do this, the axis of rotation must be the intersection between the plane of reflection and the plane of symmetry (two planes intersect to form a line). This concept is illustrated in Figure 3.35. Note that a reflection of an object that is not symmetrical cannot be achieved through a simple 180 degree rotation of the object. Hold up your hands in front of you to obtain an object (left hand) and its reflected image (right hand). Note that because your hands have no planes of symmetry, it is impossible to rotate one of them in space to obtain the other one.

3.10 Cross Sections of Solids

Visualizing cross-sections enables an engineer to figure out how a building or a mechanical device is put together. Visualizing cross-sections enables an electrical engineer to think about how circuit boards stack together within the housing that contains them. Chemical engineers and materials engineers think about the cross sections of molecules and the way those molecules combine with other molecules. Geological engineers and mining engineers visualize cross sections of the earth to determine where veins of rock and ore may be located. Most of the skills described in these examples are at an advanced level; in this section, you will learn about cross-sections of solids from a fundamental level. Then you can apply the principles to the visualization of more complex parts and systems in later courses and, of course, in your professional work.

Simply stated, a cross-section is defined as "the intersection between a solid object and a cutting plane." Because a plane is infinitely thin, the resulting intersection of the two planes is a planar section. The limits of the cross-sectional plane are the edges and

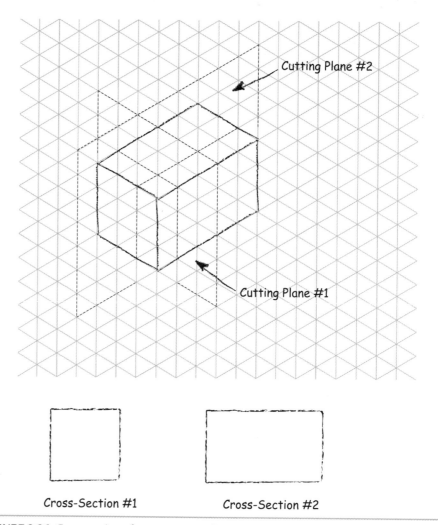

FIGURE 3.36. Cross sections from a square prism.

the surfaces where the plane cuts through the object. Consider a loaf of bread. Imagine a single slice of infinitely thin bread. One slice of bread would represent the cross section obtained by slicing a vertical plane through the loaf. Because most loaves of bread are not "constant" in shape along their lengths, the cross section changes as you go along the loaf. You know from experience that the cross sections, or slices, on the ends of the loaf are typically smaller than the slices in the middle.

The cross-section obtained by intersecting a cutting plane with an object depends on two things: (1) the orientation of the cutting plane with respect to the object and (2) the shape of the original object.

Consider the square prism shown in Figure 3.36. It is cut first by a vertical cutting plane perpendicular to its long axis to obtain the square cross section shown. If the cutting plane is rotated 90 degrees about a vertical axis, the result is the rectangular cross section shown in the figure. The two cross-sections are obtained from the same object. The difference in the resulting cross-sections is determined by changing the orientation of the cutting plane with respect to the object.

Now consider the cylinder shown in Figure 3.37. If a cutting plane is oriented perpendicular to the axis of the cylinder, a circular cross -section results; if the plane is located along the axis of the cylinder, a rectangular cross-section is obtained. Observe that this rectangular cross section through the cylinder is identical to the cross section obtained by slicing the rectangular prism along its long axis in Figure 3.36.

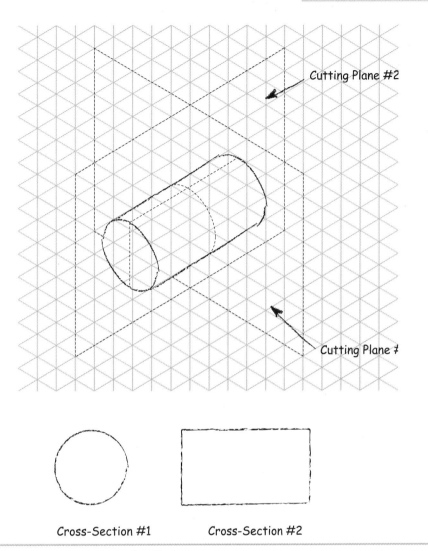

Cutting Plane #2

Cutting Plane #1

Cross-Section #1   Cross-Section #2

FIGURE 3.37. Cross sections of a cylinder.

Because a resulting cross-section through an object depends on the orientation of the cutting plane with respect to the object, most objects have several cross-sections associated with them. Figure 3.38 shows a cylinder with four possible cross sections. Can you imagine the orientation of the cutting plane with respect to the cylinder for each cross-section?

You already know that the first two cross-sections, rectangle and circle, were obtained by orienting the cutting plane perpendicular to and along the long axis of the cylinder, respectively.

What about the third cross-section? It was obtained by orienting the cutting-plane at an angle with respect to the axis of the cylinder.

The fourth cross-section was also obtained by angling the cutting plane with respect to the cylinder axis, but the angle was such that a portion of the cutting plane went through the flat circular end surface of the cylinder.

Figure 3.39 shows several cross-sections obtained by slicing a cube with cutting planes at different orientations.

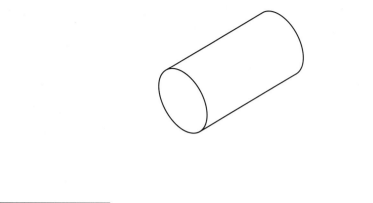

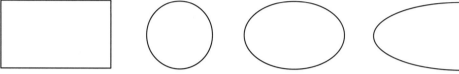

FIGURE 3.38. Various cross sections of a cylinder.

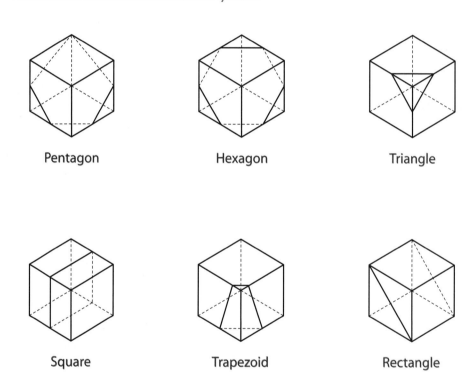

Pentagon   Hexagon   Triangle

Square   Trapezoid   Rectangle

FIGURE 3.39. Various cross sections of a cube.

3.11 Combining Solids

Another skill that will be helpful to you as an engineer is the ability to visualize how two solids combine to form a third solid. The ability to visualize **combining solids** will be helpful as you learn how to use solid modeling software. In early versions of 3-D CAD software, commands used to combine solids were sometimes known as **Boolean operations**. This terminology was borrowed from mathematics set theory operations, called Booleans, where basic operations include unions, intersections, and complements between sets of numbers. Boolean logic is now the foundation of many modern innovations. In fact, if you have performed a search on the Web using an AND or an OR operator, you have used Boolean logic to help you narrow or expand your search. In terms of 3-D CAD, the Boolean set operations typically correspond to software commands of Join, Intersect, and Cut. To help you become familiar with the terminology since you probably will be building 3-D computer models, this section will use the same terminology.

Two overlapping objects can be combined to form a third object with characteristics of each original object apparent in the final result. To perform any Cut, Join, and Intersect operations to combine objects, the objects must be overlapping initially. What is meant by overlapping is that they share a common volume in 3-D space—called the **volume of interference**. Figure 3.40a shows two objects that overlap; Figure 3.40b shows the volume of interference between the two objects. Notice that the volume of interference takes shape and size characteristics from each of the two initial objects.

When two objects are **joined**, the volume of interference is absorbed into the combined object. The result is a single object that does not have "double" volume in the region of interference. The Boolean Join operation is illustrated in Figure 3.41.

When two objects are combined by **intersecting**, the combined object that results from the intersection is the volume of interference between them, as shown in Figure 3.42.

In the **cutting** of two objects, the combined object that results from the cutting depends on which object serves as the cutting tool and which object is cut by the other object. The result of a cutting operation is that the volume of interference is removed from the object that is cut, as illustrated in Figure 3.43.

FIGURE 3.40. Overlapping objects and volume of interference.

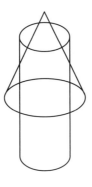

Overlapping
Objects

Volume of
Interference

FIGURE 3.41. Result of two objects joined.

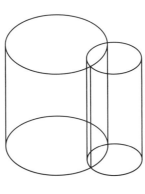
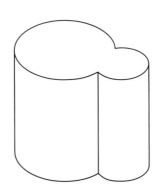

Overlapping Objects

Objects Joined

FIGURE 3.42. Result of two objects intersected.

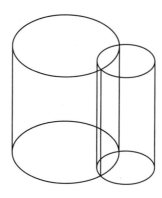

Overlapping Objects   Objects Intersected

FIGURE 3.43. Result of two objects cutting.

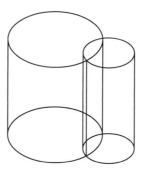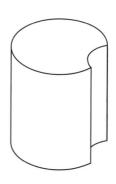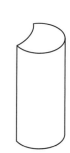

Overlapping Objects   Small Cylinder Cuts   Large Cylinder Cuts
                             Large Cylinder   Small Cylinder

3.12 Strategies for Developing 3-D Visualization Skills

In this chapter, you learned about several different types of exercises you might want to tackle in order to develop your 3-D visualization skills. In this section, you will learn how to get started with those exercises.

3.12.01 The Sketching of Corner Views

When you have a large task, such as constructing the isometric view of an object, the easiest way to get started is to complete an isometric view of a small piece first and then move on successively to other pieces of the object. You should follow this same process for almost every task in this chapter and throughout this textbook. In terms of objects, the basic building blocks are points, edges, and surfaces. To get started, you need to break down the object into its elements.

When sketching an isometric view of an object from its coded plan, you should look first at the corner from which you are sketching to determine which side of the object is on the left and which is on the right. The corner will be defined by a vertical line on the grid paper with the left and right sides emanating from there. Figure 3.44 shows a coded plan with the corners identified. If you want to sketch the Y-corner view, the arrows indicated show the left and right directions emanating from this corner. If you cannot immediately see this, turn the page so that *Y* is directly in front of you.

Next, you should sketch the height of the object from the corner you selected. As you move to the left from this corner, how does the height of the object change? For the coded plan in Figure 3.44, the height at the corner is 2; and as you go to the left, the object goes back two squares at the same height and then switches to a height of 3 for

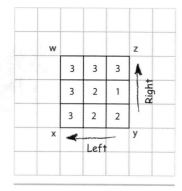

FIGURE 3.44. A coded plan.

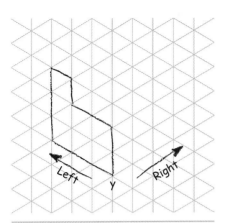

FIGURE 3.45. The left side surface of a building.

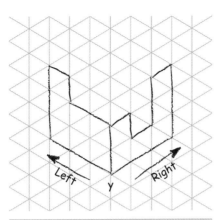

FIGURE 3.46. Left and right side surfaces of an object.

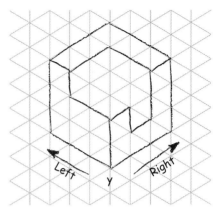

FIGURE 3.47. The top surface of the object.

one additional square. With this height information, you should be able to sketch the left-side surface of the object as shown in Figure 3.45.

You have now completed drawing one surface on the object. Go back to the original corner and think about moving in the other direction to define the surface on the object's right side. The height of the object goes from 2 to 1 to 3, one square deep at each height just indicated. Using this information, you can sketch the right-side surface going to the right from your chosen corner as illustrated in Figure 3.46.

Look again at the coded plan. You will see that the maximum height of the object is 3 units. At the same height, five blocks form an L going from the left side to the right side. You can sketch the L-shaped top surface at the given height as shown in Figure 3.47.

Look at the coded place once more, this time to determine where the object's height is 2. You will see three blocks at this height; together these three blocks trace another smaller L, as shown in Figure 3.48.

Finally, examine the sketch to determine where you need to add lines to complete the isometric. Add those lines. For the object you have been working with, you need to add lines to define the top surface that has a height of 1 and add whatever lines are needed at vertical corners to complete the isometric sketch. Figure 3.49 shows the completed sketch of the object.

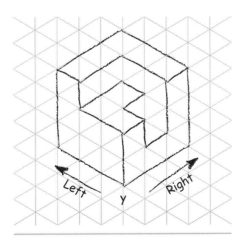

FIGURE 3.48. The second top surface of the object.

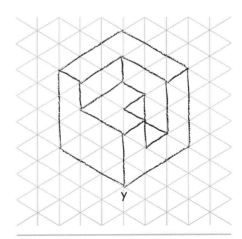

FIGURE 3.49. The completed isometric sketch.

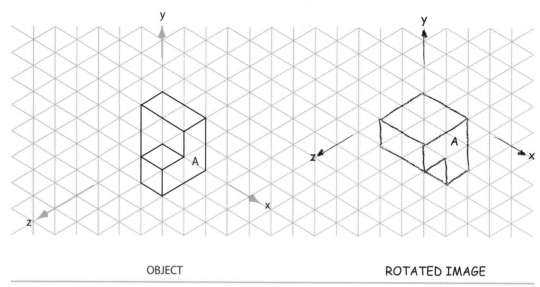

OBJECT   ROTATED IMAGE

FIGURE 3.50. An object in original position and its rotated image.

3.12.02 Object Rotations about One Axis

Once again, the simplest way to visualize rotation of an object is to focus on just one of the object's surfaces. You should look at the object and mentally select one surface to serve as your focal point for the rotation. This surface is called the key surface for purposes of this exercise. When you mentally rotate the key surface, you usually can let the remainder of the object follow. Figure 3.50 shows an object and its rotated image. What axis was the object rotated about, and was it a positive or a negative rotation?

This exercise will use the L-shaped surface, labeled *A*, as the key surface. By focusing on surface A on the original object, you can see that the surface was rotated positive 90 degrees about the x-axis. By definition, when an object is rotated in space, all points, edges, and surfaces on the object are rotated the same amount. This means that the entire object from Figure 3.50 is rotated 90 degrees about the x-axis, because surface A was rotated by that amount. Note that the surface you choose as the key surface could be any of those on the object, and this surface is likely to change from problem to problem.

Just as focusing on one surface can help you *identify* an object rotation, starting with one surface also can assist you in the task of *performing* an object rotation. Look at the object in Figure 3.51. Your task is to rotate the object negative 90 degrees about the z-axis and sketch the image that results.

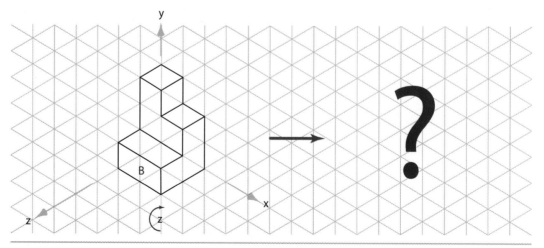

FIGURE 3.51. An object for rotation.

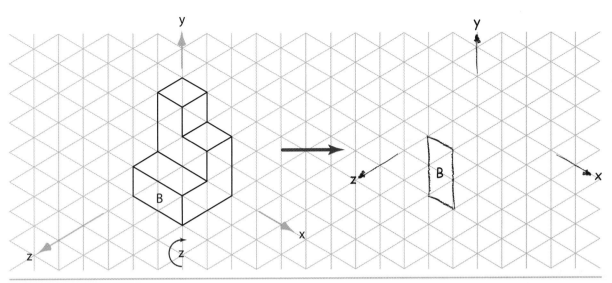

FIGURE 3.52. Rotation of surface B only.

To perform the task, you can select any surface; however, because the surfaces on the right side of the object will be hidden from view after the rotation is performed, they are probably not the best choice with which to begin this exercise. The surface of the object labeled *B* is probably the easiest one to begin with. Imagine surface B is rotated by the specified amount and sketch the surface only where it will appear after rotation. Figure 3.52 illustrates the rotation of the surface 90 degrees negatively (CW) about the z-axis.

Knowing the location of surface B after rotation, you can think about rotating surfaces C and D by the same amount as surface B and sketching the rotated surfaces C and D as shown in Figure 3.53. Notice that with 3-D rotations of an object, surfaces visible in the original view of the object are not always visible in the rotated image and surfaces that were hidden in the original view often become visible in the image of the rotated object.

Now you need to imagine what the "back" left-side surface of the object looks like after rotation so you can include it in your sketch. The back surface is hidden from view in the original orientation; but after rotation, it is the "top" surface of the object and is clearly visible. Going back to the object in its original position, you can see that this back surface starts at a height of 1 and jumps to a height of 3, meaning that it will

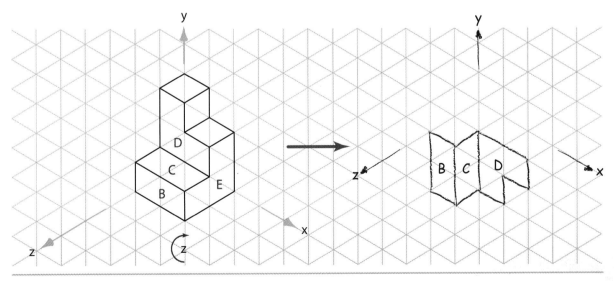

FIGURE 3.53. Rotation of surfaces C and D.

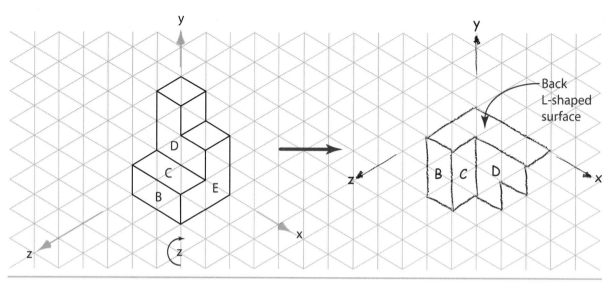

FIGURE 3.54. The back left-side surface after rotation.

appear L-shaped when rotated into position in the new view. This L-shaped surface can be sketched along with the other surfaces of the object as shown in Figure 3.54.

The last step is to clean up the drawing, adding lines as needed to complete the isometric sketch and to define the remaining surfaces on the image of the rotated object as illustrated in Figure 3.55.

3.12.03 Object Rotations about Two or More Axes

A step-by-step procedure for visualizing rotations about two or more axes is not as simple as the procedure for visualizing rotations of an object about one axis. The procedure is not simple because when rotating about two or more axes, many of the surfaces on the object that start out visible before rotation will be hidden after the first or successive rotations. One way to deal with the difficulty of visualizing rotation about two axes is to sketch the object as it appears after the first rotation and before the second rotation. For example, if an object is to be rotated positively about the x-axis and then negatively about the y-axis, sketch the intermediate step—the rotation about the x-axis—and complete the task from there. This way, the complex rotation is divided into a series of two single axis rotations. Figure 3.56 illustrates the method.

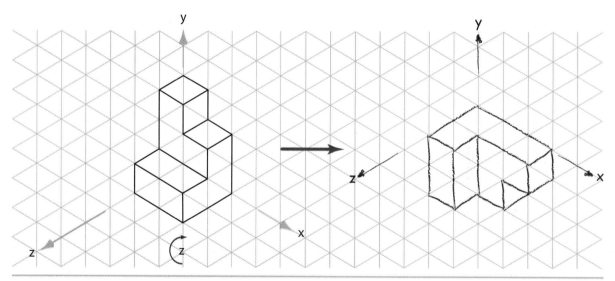

FIGURE 3.55. The completed sketch of the object after rotation.

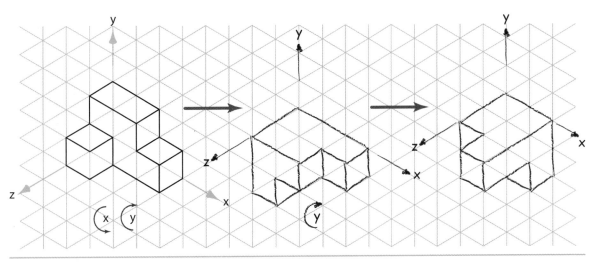

FIGURE 3.56. Intermediate rotation sketched.

You might be able to visualize the rotation about two or more axes by concentrating on a single key surface. But if you do try to do this, take care to assure that the key surface you choose to rotate remains visible after the rotation has been performed. Figure 3.57 shows an object and its rotated image. Note that surfaces A and B are no longer visible after the specified two rotations, so you would have to concentrate on surface C when mentally rotating the object.

One technique that may help you visualize rotations about two or more axes is to focus on a single surface that was not visible originally (instead of a visible one) and imagine its orientation after rotation. For example, the object shown in Figure 3.58 has a U-shaped surface on its back left side. Although you cannot see the surface in the original object orientation, the overall shape of the objects tells you that it is there. The surface of the object in its original position is hidden from view, but you should be able to visualize the surface nevertheless. Whenever you are asked to perform the rotations specified, you can think about rotating just the one surface and sketching it in its new position, similar to the way you started with the rotations about one axis. Figure 3.59 shows just the back surface rotated about both axes specified and into its final position.

When sketching the surface in the position after being rotated as specified, you can fill in the lines composing the entire object that corresponds to the same specified series of rotations as the single key surface. The complete sketch of the object after both specified rotations have been performed is shown in Figure 3.60.

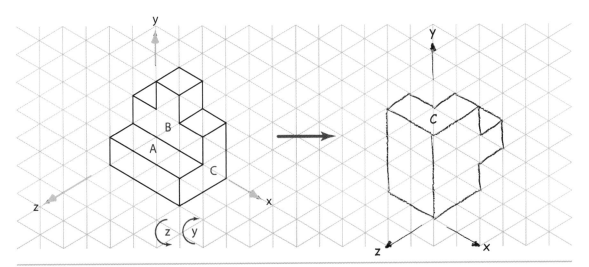

FIGURE 3.57. Visible surfaces before and after rotation.

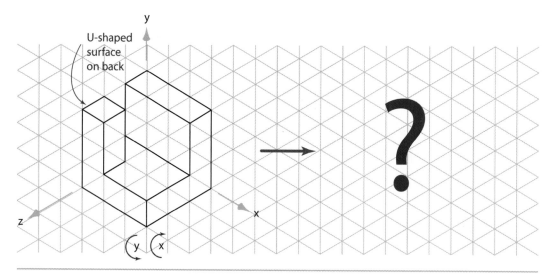

FIGURE 3.58. Original object position.

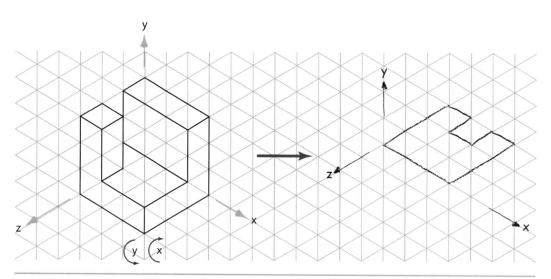

FIGURE 3.59. Rotation of U-shaped surface.

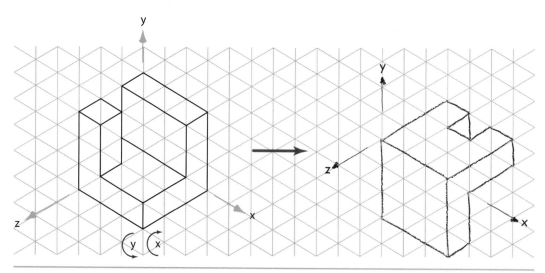

FIGURE 3.60. Completed object rotation.

3.12.04 Reflections

When creating a sketch of the image of an object as it appears on the other side of a reflection plane, you must remember that points on the object that are invisible in the original object may become visible in its reflection. The easiest way to create an object reflection is to start with one surface that is fully visible in the original view and will be fully visible in the reflection; then transfer that surface, point by point, from your view of the object to your view of the reflected image. (Usually, at least one surface on the object meets this criterion.) Since the object is the same distance from the reflection plane on either side of the plane, each point on the object and its corresponding reflected point on the image must be the same distance from the reflection plane on either side of the plane.

Figure 3.61 shows an object located 2 units from the plane of reflection. For this object, each of A, B, C, D, and E are located 2 units from the plane; another point hidden from view directly below A is the same distance from the plane of reflection. If each of these six points is reflected across the plane, they will be a total of 4 units—2 units to the plane and 2 units across the plane on the other side of it—from their location on the original object in a direction "perpendicular" to the plane. By "connecting the dots," you can sketch the surface they define, as in Figure 3.62, which shows the reflection of these points and the surface they form (the reflected surface) on the other side of the reflection plane.

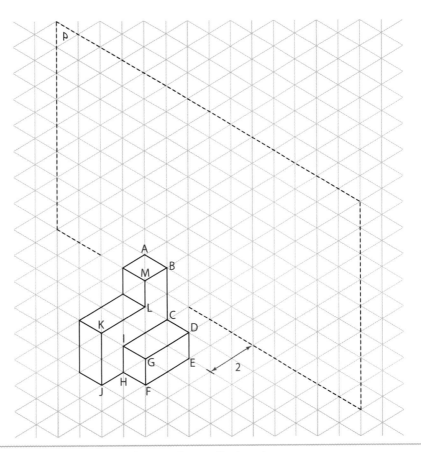

FIGURE 3.61. An object located 2 units from reflection plane.

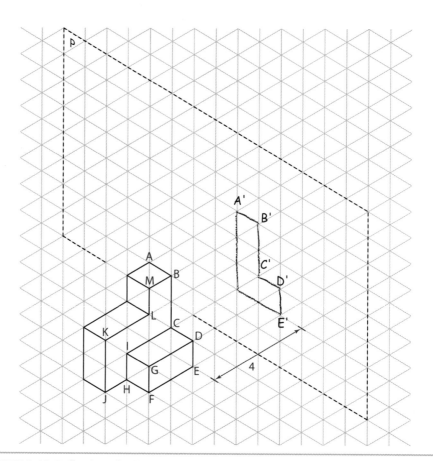

FIGURE 3.62. Reflection of points A, B, C, D, and E and the resulting surface.

For the object in this example, you can focus next on two surfaces that also will be visible in the reflection. One surface is defined by points D, E, F, and G; and the other surface is defined by points C, D, G, and I. Points C, D, and E have already been reflected, so the only points you have to consider to define the two surfaces are G, F, and I. Each point G, F, and I is located 4 units from the plane of reflection; thus, the reflection of each of these three points will be 8 units from its location on the original object in a direction perpendicular to the plane of reflection. The reflection of these points and the surfaces that result from connecting the reflected points are shown in Figure 3.63.

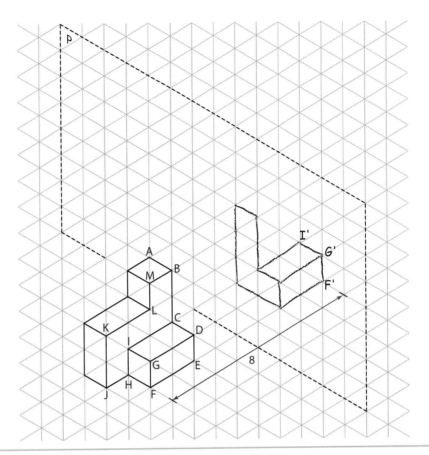

FIGURE 3.63. Reflection of two additional object surfaces.

Now consider the Z-shaped surface defined by points B, C, I, H, J, K, L, and M. You can reflect each of these points one at a time, realizing that H will be obscured from view in the reflected Z-shaped surface. Figure 3.64 illustrates the result of defining the reflected Z-shaped surface.

You now have enough of the object reflected that you can easily complete the sketch by adding the missing surfaces. The completed sketch is shown in Figure 3.65. Point labels have been excluded from the figure for clarity's sake. You could have reflected the object's other two surfaces point by point, but you can probably manage without that step.

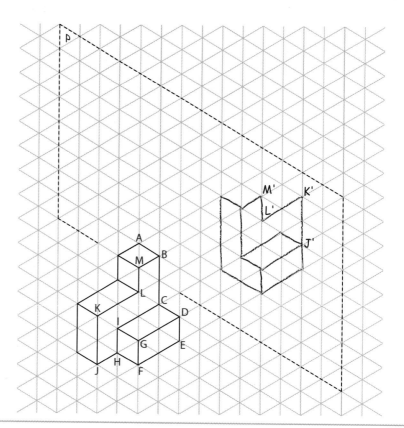

FIGURE 3.64. Reflection of Z-shaped surface.

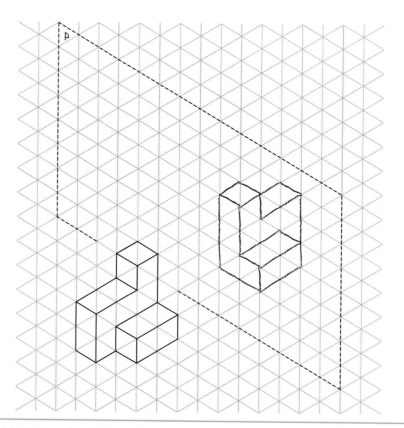

FIGURE 3.65. Completed object reflection.

3.12.05 Object Symmetry

To determine planes of symmetry for an object, you might want to sketch a dashed line on a surface of the object where you *think* a plane "splits" the object into two symmetrical parts. If you extend this line in your imagination, you can visualize an infinite plane. Look on each side of the dashed line you sketched on the object. Is one side a mirror image of the other side? If the sides are mirror images, then the dashed line you drew lies within a plane of symmetry; if the sides are not mirror images, then your dashed line does not lie within a plane of symmetry for the object.

You probably want to start with horizontal or vertical planes to identify an object's potential planes of symmetry. Figure 3.66 shows an object repeated three times with three potential planes of symmetry identified; two of the planes are vertical, and one is horizontal.

Notice that for the three planes identified, only planes 1 and 3, the vertical planes, are actually planes of symmetry. The part of the object on one side of plane 2 is not a mirror image of the part on the other side, so this plane cannot be a plane of symmetry. The object, then, has two planes of symmetry.

What about planes that are neither vertical nor horizontal? Those planes can be handled as was just shown for vertical and horizontal planes. First, sketch a line on the object that you think will lie within an imagined plane of symmetry; then examine each side of the object to see if the two halves sliced by the plane are mirror images of each other. This time the lines you sketch will be at an angle and not horizontal or vertical. Figure 3.67 shows an object with several planes of symmetry identified.

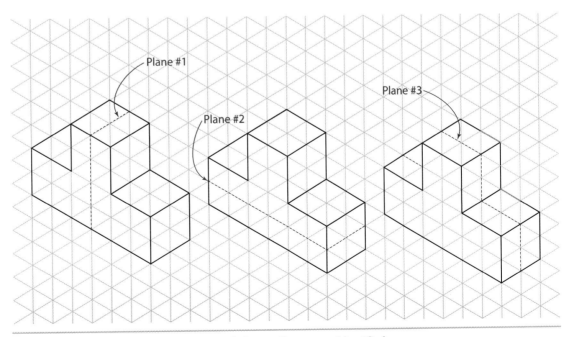

FIGURE 3.66. An object with three potential planes of symmetry identified.

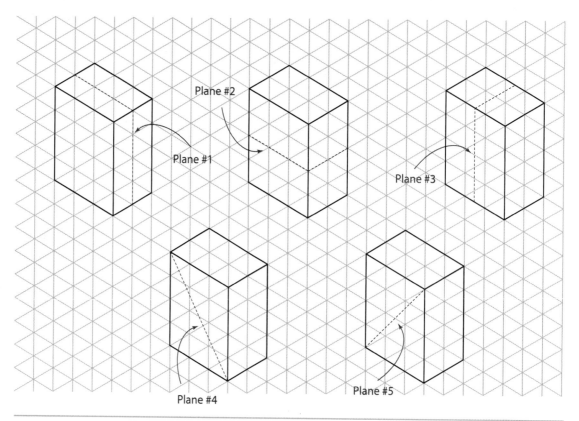

FIGURE 3.67. An object with five planes of symmetry identified.

3.12.06 Cross-Sections

When cutting planes are angled, the dimensions of the resulting cross-section "along" the plane becomes "stretched" compared with the dimensions of the cross section that results when the cutting plane is not angled. Figure 3.68 shows a simple object that has two cutting planes passing through it and the cross section corresponding to each cutting plane. For the vertical cutting plane, the shape of the cross section corresponds to the overall height and width of the object. When the cutting plane is angled, its height is stretched but its width remains the same. This point was illustrated previously in Figure 3.38. is, when the cylinder is cut along a plane perpendicular to its axis, a circular cross section results; however, when the cutting plane is angled, the diameter is stretched in one direction but remains the same in the other direction, resulting in the elliptical cross section.

To visualize the cross section that is obtained with an "angled" cutting-plane, think in terms of edges, either existing or imagined, on the object that are parallel to or perpendicular to the edges of the cutting plane. As the cutting-plane slices through the object, it intersects with the edges and surfaces of the object; the boundaries of

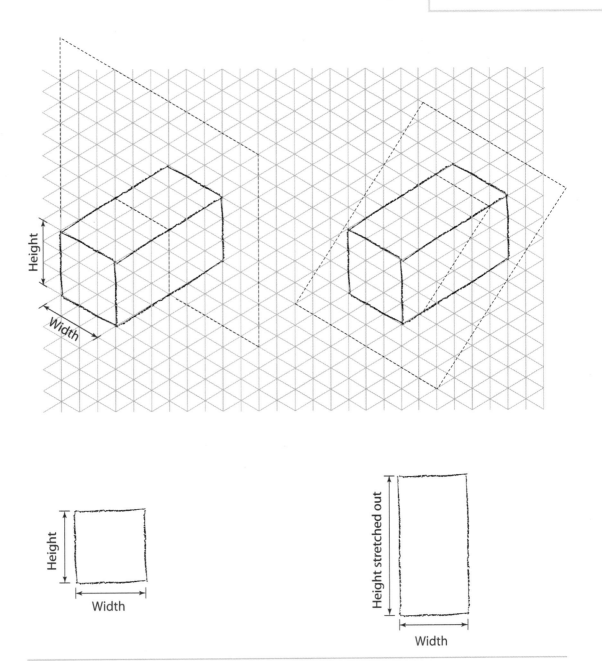

FIGURE 3.68. Effect of angling the cutting plane.

the cross-section will generally be parallel to the "edges" of the plane. (In reality, the cutting plane is infinite in size and, therefore, has no edges; but it is usually sketched as a finite size with edges so its orientation is shown.) After you have defined the edges of the cross section, you should mentally rotate the resulting planar cross section so it is perpendicular to your view direction. This allows you to "see" the cross section in its true shape and size. Obtaining the cross section for an object with an angled cutting plane is illustrated in Figure 3.69.

FIGURE 3.69. Cross section of an object with an angled cutting plane.

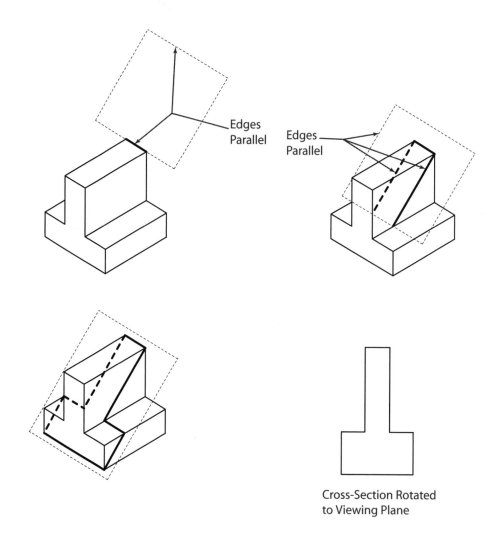

Edges Parallel

Edges Parallel

Cross-Section Rotated to Viewing Plane

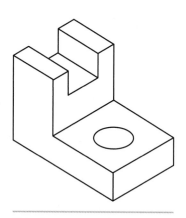

FIGURE 3.70. An object to be created through Boolean operations.

3.12.07 Combining Solids

The examples in the preceding three figures resulted from Boolean operations between simple objects combining to form a third, slightly more complicated object. The Cut, Join, and Intersect operations can be used in a series of steps to create a more complex object, which is often the case in 3-D modeling software applications. When creating a complex object using these methods, you first need to examine the final object you want to end up with; then visualize the steps needed to get to that final object. Figure 3.70 shows an object that you need to create using Boolean operations.

How would you create the object shown in Figure 3.70? One method you might employ is based on the concept of "material removal," which simply means cutting. Using this method, you need to create a block that is the overall size of the final object. Then you must create a smaller block that you will use to cut the larger block to form the basic staircase shape of the object. The first operation is illustrated in Figure 3.71.

Working with the newly formed object, now you need to create a cylinder and use it to cut the hole in the object, as shown in Figure 3.72. The final step is to create a block small enough to cut the "slot" in the top of the object, as illustrated in Figure 3.73. After completing all of these steps, you end up with the final object you set out to create.

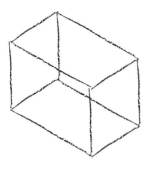

Create block

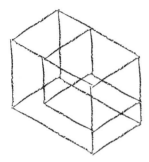

Create small block

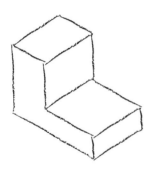

Small block cuts larger block

FIGURE 3.71. Creation of a stepped shape through cutting.

Most objects in 3-D modeling software can be created using many different methods. Can you think of a different series of steps you could use to create the object shown in Figure 3.70? Based primarily on joining operations, Figure 3.74 shows another method that uses Boolean operations to create the object.

Can you think of any other methods? As you gain familiarity with the use of 3-D modeling software, you will develop your own preferred methods for creating parts. Sometimes the method you use will depend on the object's final design characteristics. Other chapters in this text as well as texts devoted entirely to 3-D modeling software cover 3-D computer-aided modeling in greater detail and provide information about other types of operations that can be used to create solid models effectively and efficiently.

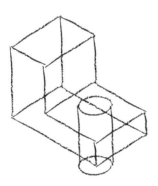

Create cylinder

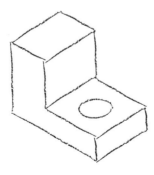

Cylinder cuts object

FIGURE 3.72. Cutting a hole in an object.

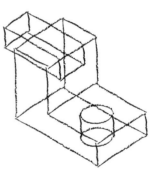

Create small block

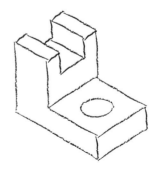

Small block cuts object -- desired result

FIGURE 3.73. Cutting an upper slot to achieve the desired result.

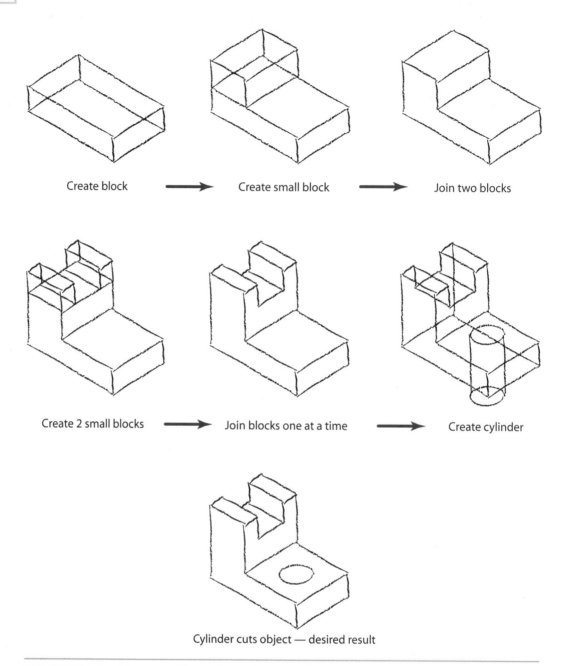

FIGURE 3.74. An object created by an alternative series of combinations.

CAUTION When creating corner views of simple objects, remember the general rules for creating simple isometric sketches described in an earlier chapter—that lines are included only at the intersection between surfaces, that no hidden lines are shown, and that only the visible portion of partially obscured surfaces are sketched. One common error novices often make is to include extra lines on a single surface of an object, especially when there are several changes in the height of the object. Figure 3.75 shows an improper sketch from a coded plan. Can you detect the "extra" unnecessary line?

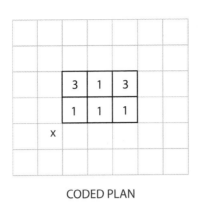

CODED PLAN

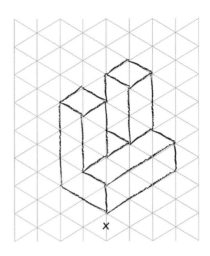

ISOMETRIC SKETCH

FIGURE 3.75. A common error: a sketch containing an extra line.

The extra line for the surface exists on the lower surface between the two "towers" on the object, as highlighted in Figure 3.76. Since a line defines the intersection of each of the towers with the lower surface, novices often extend the line through the gap even though there is no intersection between surfaces there. Figure 3.77 shows the correctly drawn object from the coded plan.

When rotating an object about an axis using the right-hand rule, right-handed people often forget that they must put down their pencil in order to rotate the object correctly in space. Right-handed people often use their left hand to define the rotation as they sketch with their right hand. If you forget to put down your pencil to define the direction of your rotation, you will end up with a rotation in the opposite direction of what you intended, as shown in Figure 3.78.

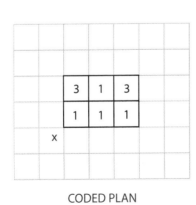

CODED PLAN

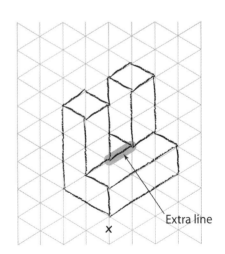

Extra line

ISOMETRIC SKETCH

FIGURE 3.76. A sketch with the extra line highlighted.

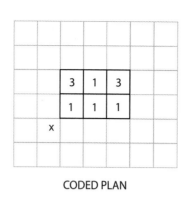

CODED PLAN

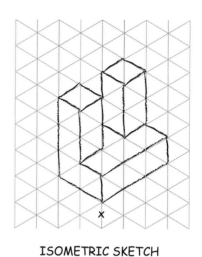

ISOMETRIC SKETCH

FIGURE 3.77. A correctly sketched object from a coded plan.

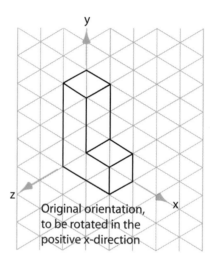

Original orientation, to be rotated in the positive x-direction

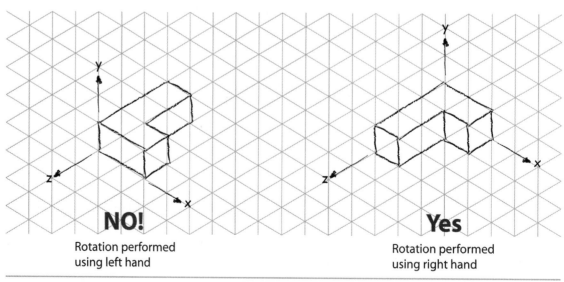

NO!

Rotation performed using left hand

Yes

Rotation performed using right hand

FIGURE 3.78. A common error: positive rotation (about the x-axis in this example) using the left hand instead of the right hand.

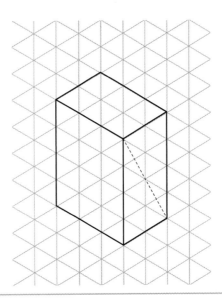

FIGURE 3.79. An object with a potential plane of symmetry identified.

When identifying angled planes of symmetry, be careful. Sometimes an angled plane produces two halves that look similar to each other but are not mirror images across the plane. For example, Figure 3.79 shows a potential plane of symmetry for an object. The two halves of the object appear to be identical halves; however, they are not mirror images across the plane. Therefore, the plane identified is not a plane of symmetry.

3.13 Chapter Summary

In this chapter, you learned about Gardner's definitions of basic human intelligences (including spatial intelligence) and the way spatial intelligence is developed and assessed. Spatial intelligence is important for engineering success, especially in engineering graphics and solid modeling courses. The chapter outlined several exercises that help develop spatial skills, including:

- Constructing isometric sketches from different corner views.
- Rotating 3-D objects about one or more axes.
- Reflecting objects across a plane and recognizing planes of symmetry.
- Defining cross sections obtained between cutting planes and objects.
- Combining two objects to form a third object by cutting, joining, or intersecting.

3.14 glossary of key terms

Boolean operations: In early versions of 3-D CAD software, commands used to combine solids.

combining solids: The process of cutting, joining, or intersecting two objects to form a third object.

corner views: An isometric view of an object created from the perspective at a given corner of the object.

cross-section: The intersection between a cutting plane and a 3-D object.

cut: To remove the volume of interference between two objects from one of the objects.

cutting-plane: An imaginary plane that intersects with an object to form a cross section.

3.14 glossary of key terms (continued)

intersect: To create a new object that consists of the volume of interference between two objects.

join: To absorb the volume of interference between two objects to form a third object.

mental rotations: The ability to mentally turn an object in space.

reflection: The process of obtaining a mirror image of an object from a plane of reflection.

spatial orientation: The ability of a person to mentally determine his own location and orientation within a given environment.

spatial perception: The ability to identify horizontal and vertical directions.

spatial relations: The ability to visualize the relationship between two objects in space, i.e., overlapping or nonoverlapping.

spatial visualization: The ability to mentally transform (rotate, translate, or mirror) or to mentally alter (twist, fold, or invert) 2-D figures and/or 3-D objects.

symmetry: The characteristic of an object in which one half of the object is a mirror image of the other half.

volume of interference: The volume that is common between two overlapping objects.

3.15 questions for review

1. What are some of the basic human intelligences as defined by Gardner?

2. What are the stages of development for spatial intelligence?

3. What are some of the basic spatial skill types?

4. What do the numbers on a coded plan represent?

5. What are some general rules to follow when creating isometric sketches from coded plans?

6. When a person is looking down a coordinate axis, are positive rotations CW or CCW?

7. Describe the right-hand rule in your own words.

8. Are object rotations about two or more axes commutative? Why or why not?

9. What is one difference between object reflection and object symmetry?

10. Are all objects symmetrical about at least one plane? Explain.

11. The shape of a cross section depends on two things. Name them.

12. What is the effect on the resulting cross section of a cutting plane that is tilted?

13. What are the three basic ways to combine solids?

14. In the cutting of two objects, does it matter which object is doing the cutting?

3.16 problems

1. For the following objects, sketch a coded plan, labeling the corner marked with an *x* properly.
2. Indicate the coded plan corner view that corresponds to the isometric sketch provided.

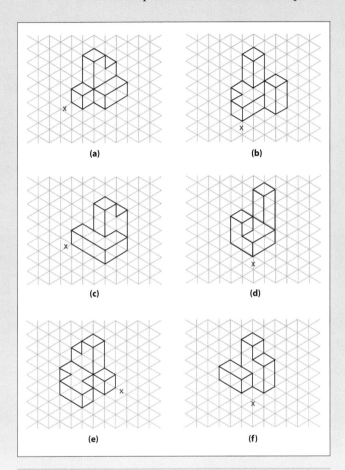

(a)

(b)

(c)

(d)

(e)

(f)

FIGURE P3.1.

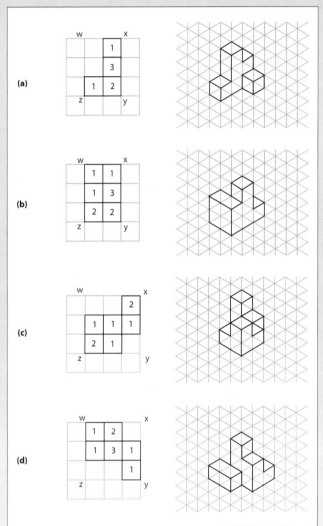

FIGURE P3.2.

3.16 problems (continued)

3. Use isometric grid paper to sketch the indicated corner view (marked with an *x*) for the coded plan.

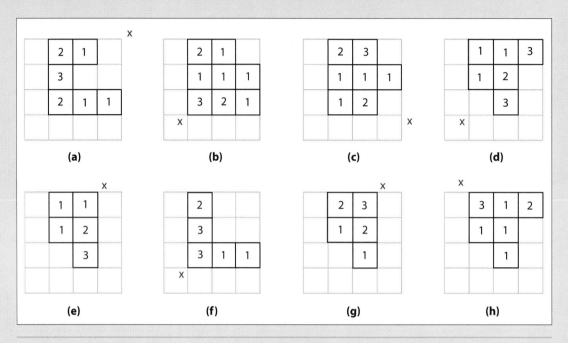

FIGURE P3.3.

3.16 problems (continued)

4. Using the notation developed in this chapter, indicate the rotation the following objects have experienced.

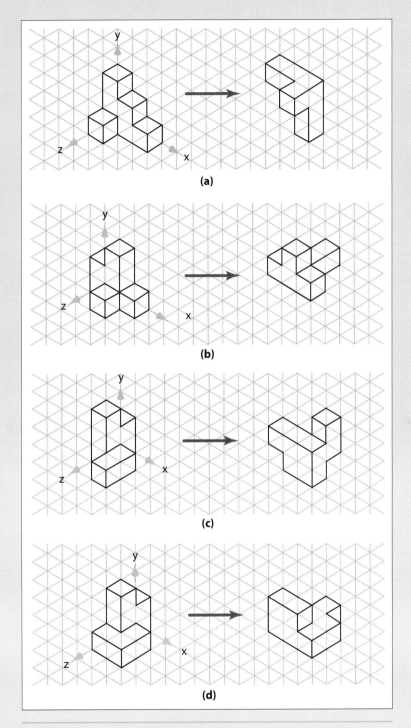

FIGURE P3.4.

3.16 problems (continued)

5. Rotate the following objects by the indicated amount and sketch the results on isometric grid paper.

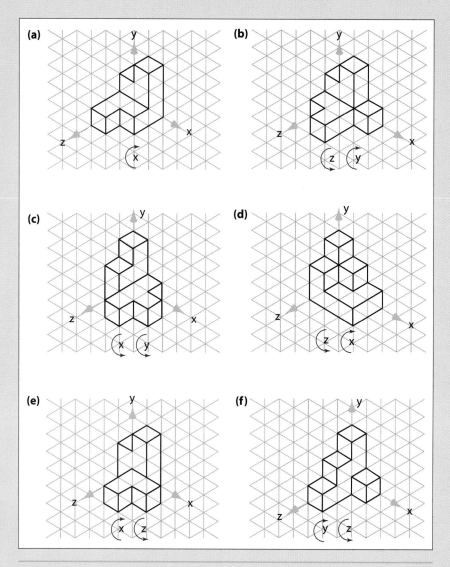

FIGURE P3.5.

3.16 problems (continued)

6. Copy the following object on isometric grid paper and sketch its reflection across the indicated plane. Note that the sketch of the reflection has been started for you.

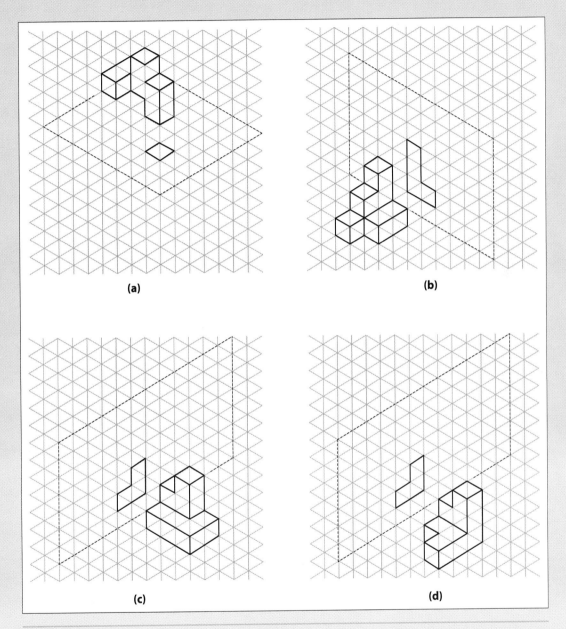

(a)

(b)

(c)

(d)

FIGURE P3.6.

3.16 problems (continued)

7. How many planes of symmetry do each of the following objects have?

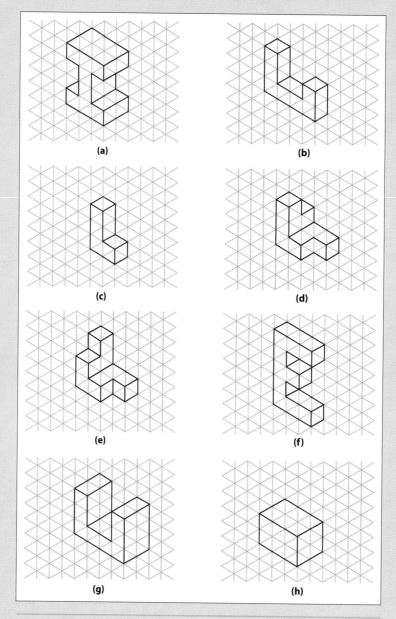

FIGURE P3.7.

3.16 problems (continued)

8. Sketch the cross section obtained between the intersection of the object and the cutting plane.

9. Sketch the result of combining the following objects by the indicated method.

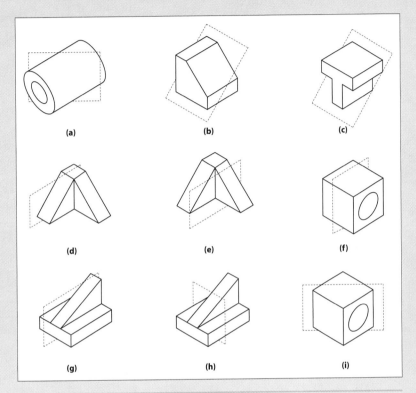

(a)   **(b)**   **(c)**

(d)   **(e)**   **(f)**

(g)   **(h)**   **(i)**

FIGURE P3.8.

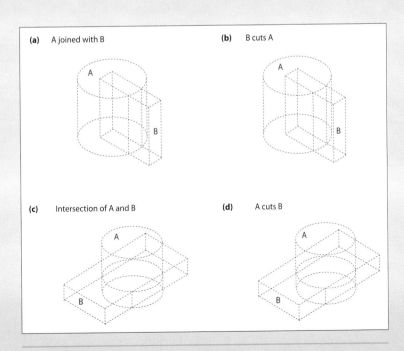

(a)   A joined with B   **(b)**   B cuts A

(c)   Intersection of A and B   **(d)**   A cuts B

FIGURE P3.9.

3.16 problems (continued)

10. Describe by words and sketches how you would create the following objects by combining basic 3-D shapes.

11. Create isometric sketches from these coded plans using the corner view that is circled or the corner prescribed by your instructor.

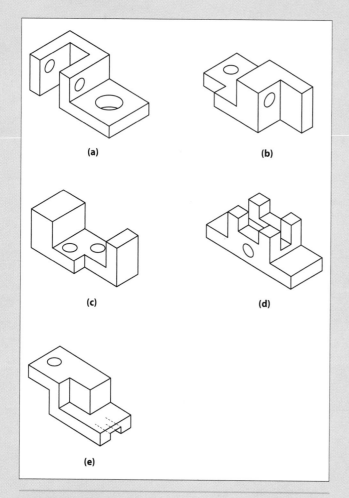

(a)   **(b)**

(c)   **(d)**

(e)

FIGURE P3.10.

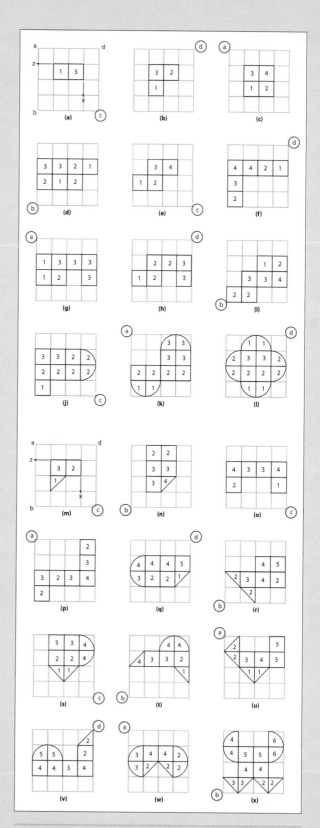

FIGURE P3.11.

3.16 problems (continued)

12. Add the reflected images or redraw these objects with symmetry using the xy, yz, or xz planes as indicated or the planes prescribed by your instructor.

13. The object shown in (a) is show again in (b) rotated by −90 degrees about the y-axis to reveal more detail. Rotate the object sequentially about the axes indicated or about the axes prescribed by your instructor.

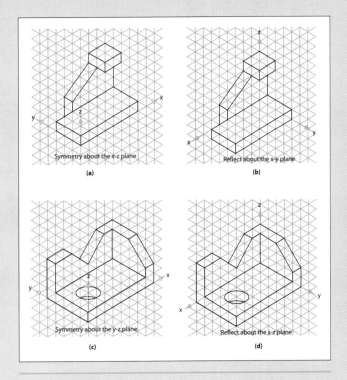

FIGURE P3.12.

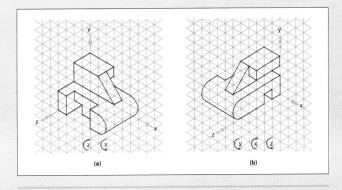

FIGURE P3.13.

3.16 problems (continued)

14. Create an isometric sketch of the objects created from coded plans A and B. Rotate object A sequentially about the axes indicated or about the axes prescribed by your instructor. Show the new object created by the indicated Boolean combination of object A and object B or the Boolean operation prescribed by your instructor when the coordinate axes of A and B are aligned.

15. Triangular volume A, triangular volume B, and rectangular volume C are shown intersecting in space. On the dashed outline drawings, darken and add edges to show all visible edges of the final volume created by the indicated Boolean operations.

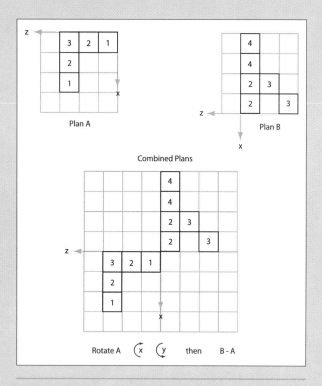

FIGURE P3.14.

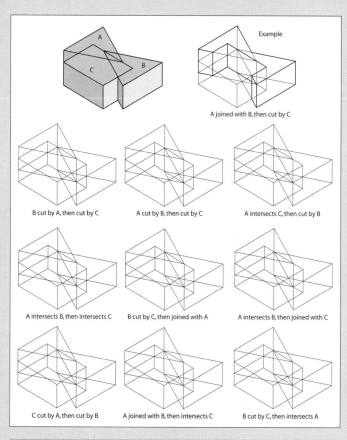

FIGURE P3.15.

6

Solid Modeling

objectives

After completing this chapter, you should be able to

- Introduce solid modeling as an engineering design graphics tool
- Explain how solid models are created
- Show how parts and models can be decomposed into features
- Develop strategies for creating a solid model
- Explain how solid models support the entire product life cycle

6.01 introduction

Solid modeling is a computer-based simulation that produces a visual display of an object as if it existed in three dimensions. **Solid models** aid in forming a foundation for the product development process by providing an accurate description of a product's geometry and are used in many phases of the design process and life cycle of the product. This chapter will focus on methods for creating robust solid models of mechanical parts; however, these methods can be applied to other domains as well.

Solid models are created with specialized software that generates files for individual as well as assembled parts. These models are then used in a variety of applications throughout the design and manufacturing processes, as shown schematically in Figure 6.01. During the product concept stage, solid models are used to visualize the design. As the product is refined, engineers use solid models to determine physical properties such as the strength of the parts, to study how mechanisms move, and to evaluate how various parts fit together. Manufacturing engineers use solid models to create manufacturing process plans and any special tools or machines needed to fabricate or assemble parts. Solid models also can be used to generate formal engineering drawings to document the design and communicate details of the design to others. People responsible for the product life cycle may depend on solid models to help create images for service manuals and disposal documentation. Even sales and marketing functions use graphics generated from solid models for business presentations and advertising. Thus, it is very important not only to learn how to create solid models but also to understand how others will use the models. Solid models must be built with sound modeling practices if they are to be useful in downstream applications. In this chapter, you will learn how to create robust solid models that not only look like the real thing but also support the entire product life cycle. You also will learn about the history of CAD tools and the importance of solid modeling as part of an engineering design graphics system.

6.02 Tools for Developing Your Idea

Many tools have been developed for creating accurate images of an object as an aid in analyzing its function, recording its history, or visualizing its appearance. One of the simplest tools is a pencil, which is used to make sketches of an object on paper. More formal tools include rulers, protractors, compasses, and various types of manually operated drafting machines. These tools are used to make more accurate, standardized drawings according to precise rules and conventions, as discussed in a previous chapter.

CAD systems are among the most sophisticated graphics and design tools available to engineers and designers. Many types of CAD systems are on the market today. The simplest systems are general purpose drawing or drafting packages that can be used to create 2-D images, similar to the way pencil images are created on paper (except faster and easier). More complex packages allow you to create simulations of 3-D models that can be used not only to generate conventional 2-D drawings of a design but also to create 3-D images for visualization. The core of a CAD model is a geometric **database**. The database includes information about the geometry and other engineering properties of an object. The CAD software uses the database to display the model and to conduct further engineering analysis. A short discussion of CAD history will demonstrate how these systems evolved and provide some insight into the modeling processes used by designers with various CAD systems.

FIGURE 6.01. Uses for a solid model database.

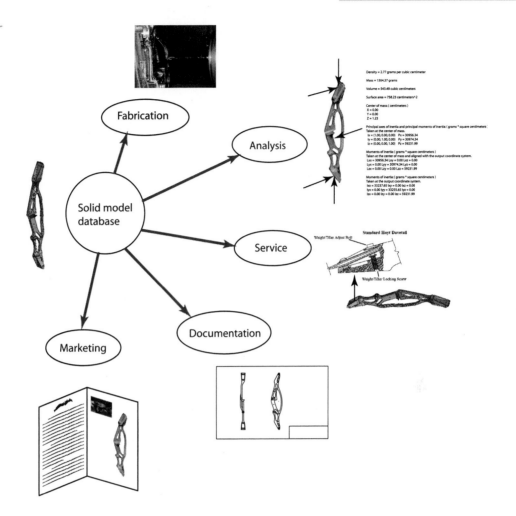

6.02.01 Two-Dimensional CAD

The first CAD systems were developed in the late 1960s at a time when computational resources were very limited. Graphics displays had refresh times measured in seconds, and the data storage capabilities were limited to fractions of a kilobyte. As a result, only very simple models could be created. Those models were basically electronic versions of conventional pencil-and-paper drawings. The user had to specify the location of each vertex in the model for the particular view desired. If the user wanted another view, she had to start from scratch, just as you would to do if you were creating a drawing on paper.

Since CAD models are used to define the geometry or shape and size of objects, the models are composed of geometric entities. In the earliest CAD models, those entities represented the edges of the object, just as you would draw the edges of an object with a pencil. In fact, at that time there was very little distinction between a 2-D drawing of an object and a 2-D CAD model of the object. The 2-D CAD model was simply a database that contains the edges of the object, dimensions, text, and other information that you would find on the drawing, but in electronic form instead of on paper.

The simplest geometric entity is a point. Points in two dimensions are defined according to their location in a coordinate system, usually Cartesian coordinates (x,y). In a CAD system, the coordinate system represents locations on the "paper," or computer screen. Points are generally used to locate or define more complex entities, such as the endpoints of a line segment or the center of a circle. A point on an entity that marks a particular position, such as the endpoint of a line segment or the intersection of two entities, is referred to as a **vertex**.

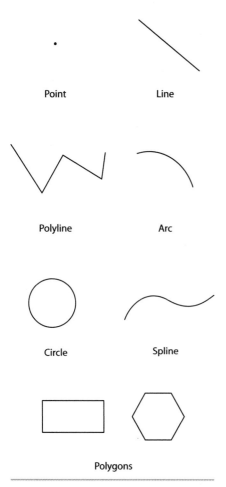

FIGURE 6.02. Some entities used for 2-D CAD.

FIGURE 6.03. With 2-D models, visualization of a 3-D object must be done mentally.

Two-dimensional geometric entities are those that can be created as a path or curve on a plane. Those entities include lines, circles, **splines**, arcs, polygons, and conic sections, which are shown in Figure 6.02. The entities can be assembled to create images of a desired object as it would be seen from different viewing directions, as shown in Figure 6.03.

One weakness of 2-D CAD systems is that to visualize and manipulate a 3-D model of the object, you must mentally assemble and reform the 2-D views. Another weakness of 2-D CAD (and pencil drawings) is that it is possible to create images of objects that are physically impossible to build, such as the three-pronged fork and the triangle shown in Figure 6.04.

6.02.02 Wireframe Modeling

In the early 1980s, 2-D CAD drafting packages evolved into 3-D modeling systems. In these newer systems, 3-D information could be included for the model. The computer could then perform the calculations needed to create views of an object as if it was seen from different directions. These systems were still limited to using entities such as

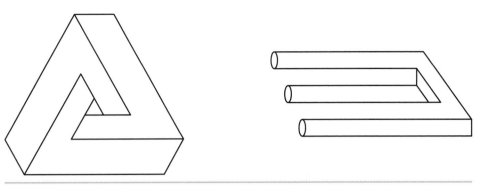

FIGURE 6.04. Impossible 3-D objects can be drawn with 2-D elements.

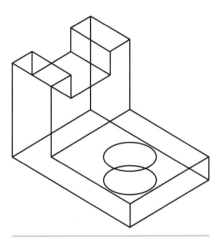

FIGURE 6.05. A wireframe model of a 3-D object.

lines, circles, and arcs; but the assemblage of the entities was no longer restricted to being on a single plane. The geometric entities were represented in a 3-D database within a 3-D coordinate system with x-, y-, and z-coordinates. Since simple curve or path entities were used to define the edges of an object, such models were called **wireframe models**. Think of a wireframe as being similar to a box kite. A wireframe model of a bracket is shown in Figure 6.05.

Wireframe models are still very limited in their representation of parts. The same wireframe model can represent an object from two different viewing directions, as demonstrated in Figure 6.06. Thus, the models were sometimes difficult to visualize as solids. Some models were ambiguous, being interpreted by viewers as different objects. Look at Figure 6.07 and try to imagine the solid object represented by the wireframe model in (a). Can you visualize the shape of the object? Does this figure represent more than one object? When the hidden edges are removed and the surfaces shaded, as in (b) and (c), it is much easier to see the desired shape.

FIGURE 6.06. Two possible view interpretations of the same wireframe model.

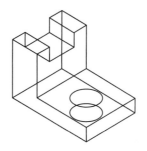

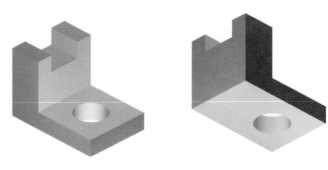

FIGURE 6.07. The wireframe model in (a) can represent the object in (b) or the object in (c).

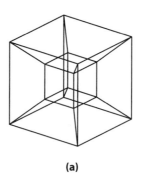

(a)

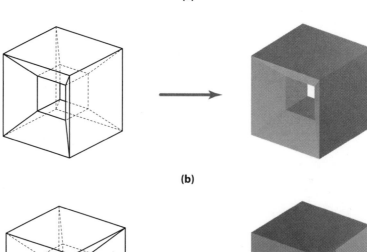

(b)

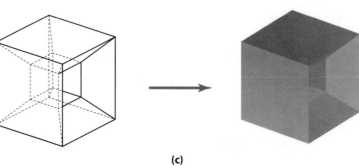

(c)

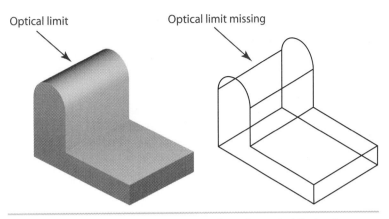

FIGURE 6.08. Wireframe models do not show the optical limit of a curved surface.

Another problem with wireframe CAD systems was that the geometry was limited to shapes with simple planar and cylindrical surfaces. Also, parts with cylindrical features, such as the one shown in Figure 6.08, generated wireframe models that did not show the optical limit or silhouette of the cylindrical surface. Even so, wireframe modeling represented a tremendous advance in technology compared to the drafting board. It is estimated that more than 75 percent of all common machined parts can be accurately represented using 3-D wireframe models.

6.02.03 Surface Modeling

As computers became more powerful and data storage capabilities increased, surface modeling techniques were developed. With a **surface model**, the designer could display the surfaces of a part, such as those shown in Figure 6.09, and use the model to perform engineering analyses such as calculating the part's mass properties. Such models also could be used to generate computer programs that controlled the fabrication of parts, for example, on a computer-controlled cutting machine called a mill.

Surface models evolved from wireframe models by mathematically describing and then displaying surfaces between the edges of the wireframe model. Thus, a surface model is a collection of the individual surfaces of the object. This modeling method is called **boundary representation**, or **b-rep**, because the surfaces "bound" the shape. The bounding entities of a simple part created using boundary representation are shown in Figure 6.10. The bounding entities can be planes, cylinders, and other surfaces in three dimensions. These surfaces are in turn bounded by simpler curve entities such as lines and arcs.

FIGURE 6.09. A surface model with semitransparent surfaces to reveal detail.

FIGURE 6.10. A surface model exploded to show individual surfaces.

The use of surface models eliminates most of the problems with visual ambiguity encountered with wireframe models.

6.02.04 Solid Modeling

Solid models are visually similar to surface models, so it is sometimes difficult to distinguish between them. With a solid model, however, the software can distinguish between the inside and outside of a part and the objects can have thickness. Thus, the information stored in the 3-D database is sufficient to distinguish between an empty shoe box and a brick. The software also easily computes information such as the object's volume, mass, center of mass, and other inertial properties. Early solid models, developed in the late 1980s, were made using a technique known as **constructive solid geometry (CSG)**. CSG models are composed of standard building blocks in the form of simple solids such as rectangular prisms (bricks), cylinders, and spheres, called **primitives**. The shapes are easy to define using a small number of dimensions. Figure 6.11 shows some of these basic solids. To create more complex solids, the primitives are assembled using Boolean operations such as addition (union), subtraction (difference), and interference. Examples of these operations are shown in Figure 6.12.

Surface and CSG models were very powerful tools for design, but their early versions were rather cumbersome to use. As computational resources improved, so did the capabilities of modeling software. Increasingly more sophisticated modeling methods, such as creating a solid model by moving or rotating a closed 2-D outline on a path

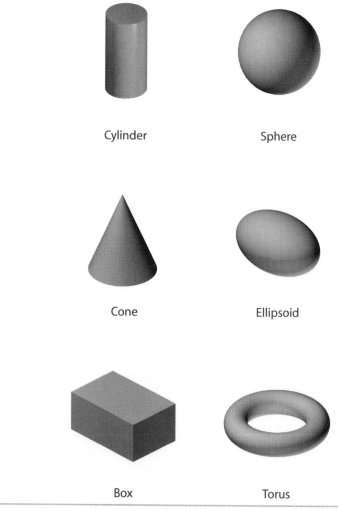

Cylinder

Sphere

Cone

Ellipsoid

Box

Torus

FIGURE 6.11. Some 3-D primitives used in solid modeling.

FIGURE 6.12. Steps in using solid primitives to build a more complicated solid model using Boolean operations.

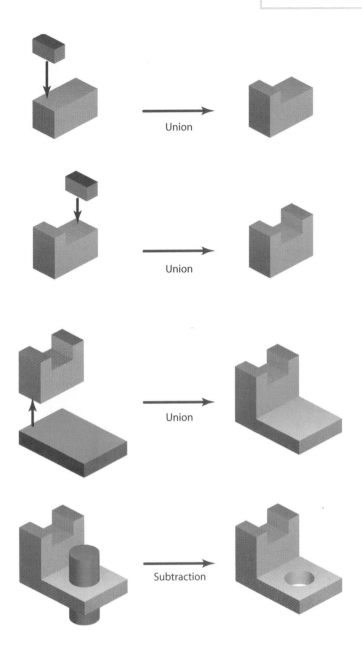

through space, as shown in Figure 6.13, were developed. Further developments included software tools for taking many individual solid model parts and simulating their assembly into a larger structure, as explained in Chapter 1, and for easily creating formal engineering drawings for parts and assemblies from their solid models.

A more accurate and efficient modeling tool called **feature-based solid modeling** was developed in the mid-1990s. This modeling method permitted engineers and designers to create a more complex part model quickly by adding common features to the basic model. Features are 3-D geometric entities that exist to serve some function. One common and easily recognizable feature is a hole. Holes in a part exist to serve some function, whether it is to accommodate a shaft or to make the part lighter. Other features, such as bosses, fillets, and chamfers, will be defined later in this chapter.

Parametric solid modeling is a form of feature-based modeling that allows the designer to change the dimensions of a part or an assembly quickly and easily. Since parametric feature-based solid modeling is currently considered the most powerful 3-D CAD tool for engineers and designers, the remainder of this chapter will be devoted to this modeling method.

FIGURE 6.13. Solids created by (a) moving and (b) revolving a 2-D outline through space.

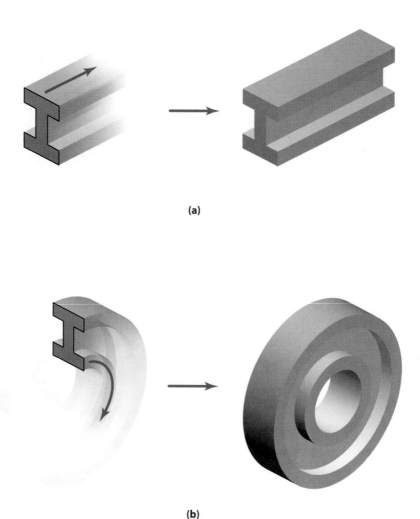

(a)

(b)

6.03 A Parametric Solid Model

So how does one go about creating a parametric feature-based solid model? In this section, a very simple model will be created to demonstrate basic concepts. More detail and sophistication will be presented in subsequent sections of this chapter. The tools that you need to create a parametric model are solid modeling software and a computer that is powerful enough to run the software. As you create the model, the software will display an image of the object which can be turned and viewed from any direction as if it actually existed in three dimensions.

Using the mouse and keyboard, you will interact with the software through a **graphical user interface (GUI)** on the computer's display device (i.e., the computer monitor). The GUI gives you access to various tools for creating and editing your models. GUIs differ slightly in different solid modeling software. However, most of the packages share some common approaches. When creating a new model (i.e., with nothing yet existing), you will probably be presented with a display of 3-D Cartesian coordinate x-, y-, and z-axes and the three **primary modeling planes**, which are sometimes called the **principal viewing planes** or **datum planes**. These planes help you visualize the xy, yz, and xz planes and are usually displayed from a viewing direction from which all three planes can be seen, as shown in Figure 6.14.

Nearly all solid modelers use 2-D **sketches** as a basis for creating solid features. Sketches are made on one of the planes of the model with a 2-D sketching editor similar to a drawing editor found on most 2-D CAD drafting software. When you begin a new model, you often make a sketch on the one of the basic modeling planes. When the sketching plane is chosen, some modelers will reorient the view so you are looking straight at the 2-D sketching plane. You can then begin sketching.

Line segments are usually inserted using mouse clicks, as shown in Figure 6.15(a). A sketch is initially created without much attention being paid to precise dimensions and exact orientations of the different segments. For convenience, the **sketching editor** in most solid models automatically corrects sloppy sketches by making assumptions about the intended geometry. For example, if a line segment is sketched almost vertically or almost horizontally, the sketching editor will force the line into a vertical or horizontal orientation. Figure 6.15(a) shows a sketch of a rectangle created by clicking the four corners, or vertices; Figure 6.15(b) shows the cleaned-up sketch after the sketching editor corrects the user input and reorients the line segments.

6.03.01 Valid Profiles

Before a solid feature can be created by extrusion or rotation, the final profile of the shape must be a closed loop. Extra line segments, gaps between the line segments, or overlapping lines create problems because the software cannot determine the boundaries of the solid in the model. Samples of proper and improper profiles are shown in Figure 6.16.

6.03.02 Creation of the Solid

A completed sketch that is used to create a solid is called a **profile**. A simple solid model can be created from the profile by a process known as **extrusion**, as shown in

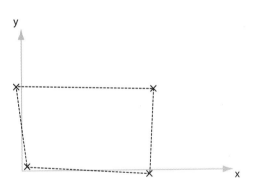

(a) corners of rectangle specified by user

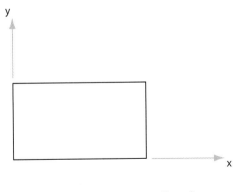

(b) rectangle corrected by software

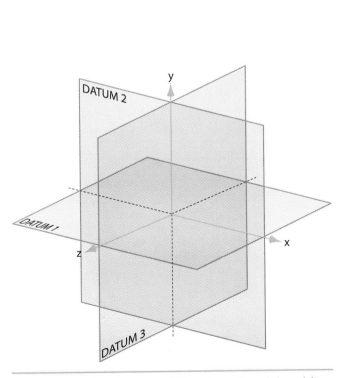

FIGURE 6.14. The primary modeling planes for solid modeling.

FIGURE 6.15. 2-D sketching.

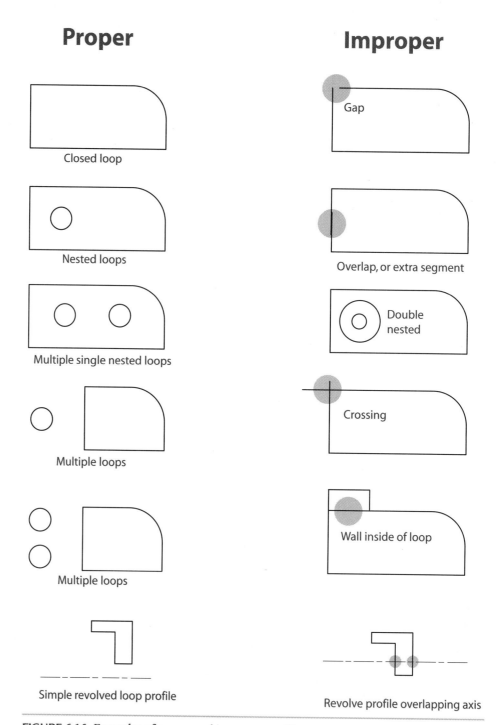

Proper   Improper

Closed loop

Gap

Nested loops

Overlap, or extra segment

Multiple single nested loops

Double nested

Multiple loops

Crossing

Multiple loops

Wall inside of loop

Simple revolved loop profile

Revolve profile overlapping axis

FIGURE 6.16. Examples of proper and improper profiles.

Figure 6.17. Imagine the profile curve being pulled straight out of the sketching plane. The solid that is formed is bound by the surfaces swept out in space by the profile as it is pulled along the path. Both the geometry of the profile and the length of the extrusion must be specified to define the model fully.

A different model can be created from the profile by a process called revolution. To create a **revolved solid**, a profile curve is rotated about an axis. The process is similar to creating a clay vase or bowl on a potter's wheel. The profile of a revolved part is also planar, and the axis of revolution lies in the profile plane (sketching plane). One edge of

(a)

(b)

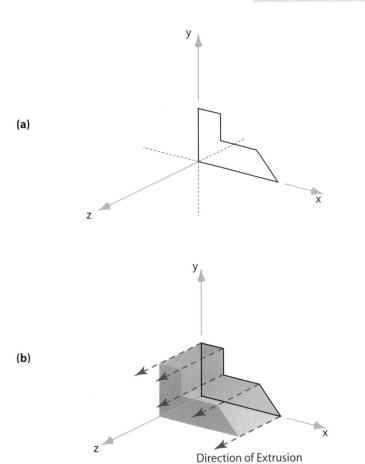

Direction of Extrusion

(c)

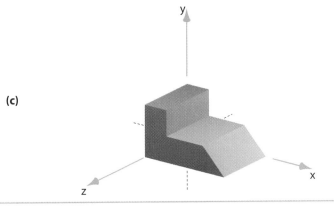

FIGURE 6.17. A solid created by extrusion of a 2-D profile.

the sketch may lie along the axis of revolution, as shown in Figure 6.18(a); or the sketch may be offset from the axis, as shown in Figure 6.18(b). It is important to make sure that the profile does not cross over the axis of revolution. This would create a self-intersecting model (i.e., a solid created inside another solid), which most solid modeling software interpret to be a geometric error. The geometry of the profile and the angle of rotation must be specified to define the model fully. The models shown in Figure 6.18 are revolved through a full 360 degrees.

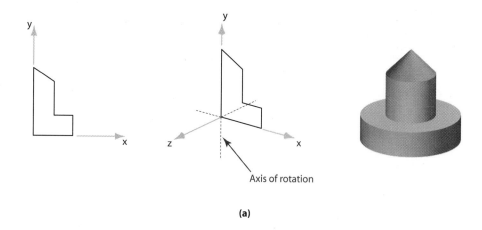

(a)

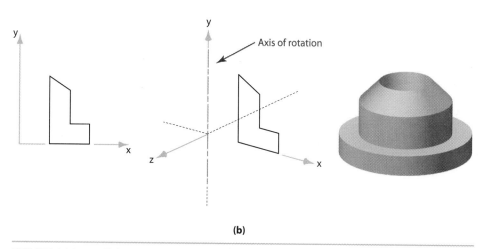

(b)

FIGURE 6.18. A solid created by rotation of a 2-D profile, with the axis on the profile in (a) and with the axis off the profile in (b).

6.04 Making It Precise

Before a part can be submitted for analysis or fabrication, the sizes and locations of all of its features must be completely specified. To see how this is done, let's back up a few steps in our discussion of the creation of the model.

6.04.01 Orientation of the Sketch

Before you begin to create the first extrusion or revolution, you must decide where to place the part in the space relative to the xyz coordinate system. With the model shown in Figure 6.17, the initial sketch was placed on one of the basic modeling planes. If the sketch was placed on one of the other basic modeling planes instead, the model would have the same geometry but with a different orientation in space, as shown in Figure 6.19.

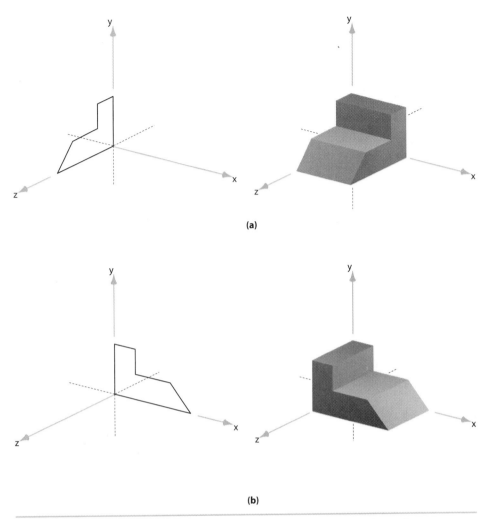

(a)

(b)

FIGURE 6.19. The same profile made in different sketching planes produces the same object but in different orientations. In (a), the profile is made in the yz plane; and in (b), the profile is made in the xy plane.

6.04.02 Geometric Constraints

Formally, **constraints** are the geometric relationships, dimensions, or equations that control the size, shape, and/or orientation of entities in the profile sketch and include the assumptions that the CAD sketcher makes about your sloppy sketching. Constraints that define the size of features will be discussed in the following section. The previous section provided a few examples of **geometric constraints** that were applied to a simple sketch: lines that were drawn as nearly horizontal were assumed to be horizontal, and lines that were drawn as nearly vertical were assumed to be vertical. Those assumptions reduce the number of coordinates needed to specify the location of the endpoints. Some solid modelers require you to constrain the profile fully and specify the sizes and locations of all of its elements before allowing the creation of a solid feature; others allow more free-form sketching. Geometric constraints may be either implicitly defined (hidden from the designer) or explicitly displayed so you can modify them. A set of geometric constraints is not unique, as demonstrated in Figure 6.20. In

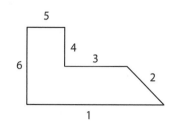

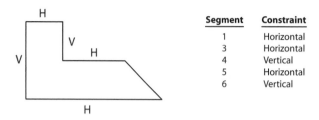

Segment	Constraint
1	Horizontal
3	Horizontal
4	Vertical
5	Horizontal
6	Vertical

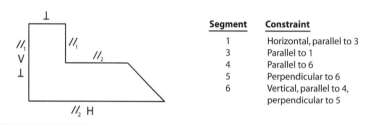

Segment	Constraint
1	Horizontal, parallel to 3
3	Parallel to 1
4	Parallel to 6
5	Perpendicular to 6
6	Vertical, parallel to 4, perpendicular to 5

FIGURE 6.20. The line segments in a profile are numbered in (a). The implied geometric constraints for each segment are shown in (b), and an equivalent set of applied constraints is shown in (c). A letter or symbol beside a segment signifies the type of geometric constraint applied to it.

this example, a set of geometric constraints that restricts some lines to being horizontal or vertical is equivalent to another set of constraints that restricts some lines to being either parallel or perpendicular to each other.

Geometric constraints specify relationships between points, lines, circles, arcs, or other planar curves. The following is a list of typical geometric constraints. The results of applying the constraints are shown graphically in Figure 6.21.

- Coincident—forces two points to coincide
- Concentric—makes the centers of arcs or circles coincident
- Point on Line—forces a point to lie on a line
- Horizontal/Vertical—forces a line to be horizontal/vertical
- Tangent—makes a line, a circle, or an arc tangent to another curve
- Colinear—forces a line to be colinear to another line
- Parallel—forces a line to be parallel to another line
- Perpendicular—forces a line to be perpendicular to another line
- Symmetric—makes two points symmetric across a centerline

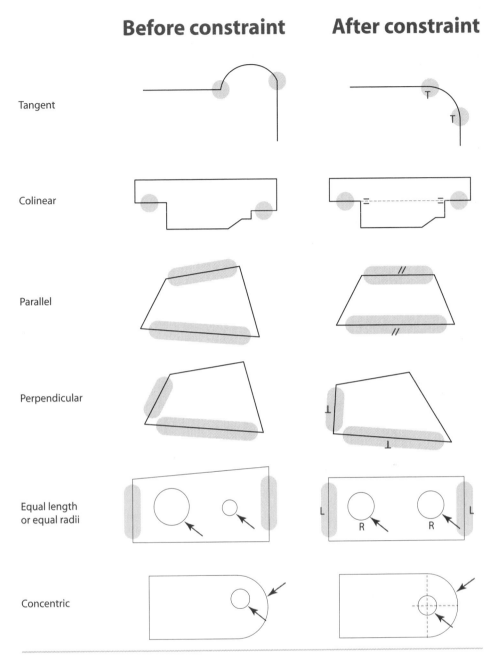

Before constraint   **After constraint**

Tangent

Colinear

Parallel

Perpendicular

Equal length
or equal radii

Concentric

FIGURE 6.21. Geometric constraints commonly found in sketching editors.

The sketching editors in most solid modeling software are usually configured to try to interpret the user's sketching intent such that certain constraints are created automatically. In addition to adjusting nearly horizontal or vertical lines into true horizontal or vertical lines, if two lines are nearly perpendicular or parallel or an arc and a line are nearly tangent at the common endpoint, the sketching editor will impose the assumed geometric relationship. These automatically applied geometric constraints can be changed at a later time if desired.

6.04.03 Dimensional Constraints

Each of the 2-D entities in the profile must have size and position. **Dimensional constraints** are the measurements used to control the size and position of entities in your sketch. Dimensional constraints are expressed in units of length, such as

FIGURE 6.22. A profile fully constrained with geometric and dimensional constraints.

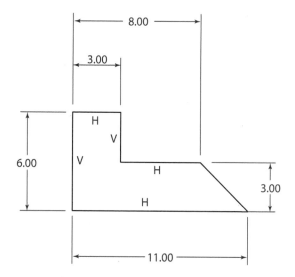

millimeters, meters, inches, or feet. For example, look at the profile in Figure 6.22, which shows dimensional constraints that define its size. If you, the designer, do not fully specify all of the necessary information, the software will default to some value that you may not want. It is better if you control the model, rather than have the software assign assumed parameters and conditions to the model.

Dimensional constraints can be created interactively while you are sketching, but also automatically as a result of a feature operation, an extrusion, or a revolution. There are three principal types of dimensional constraints:

- Linear dimensional constraints define the distance between two points, the length of a line segment, or the distance between a point and a line. Linear dimensions can be measured horizontally or vertically or aligned with the distance being measured.

- Radial and diametral dimensional constraints specify the radius or diameter of an arc or a circle.

- Angular dimensional constraints measure the angle between two lines. The lines do not need to intersect, but they cannot be parallel.

6.04.04 Uniqueness of Constraints

A set of dimensional constraints is not unique. It is possible to apply a different set of dimensional constraints on a profile to produce exactly the same geometry, as shown in Figure 6.23.

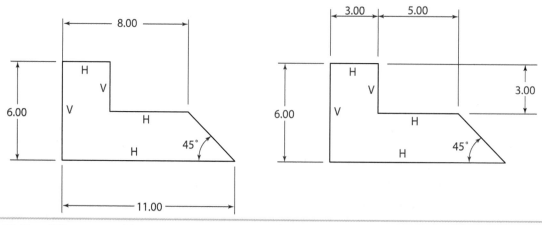

FIGURE 6.23. Two different sets of dimensional constraints that can be used to define the same geometry.

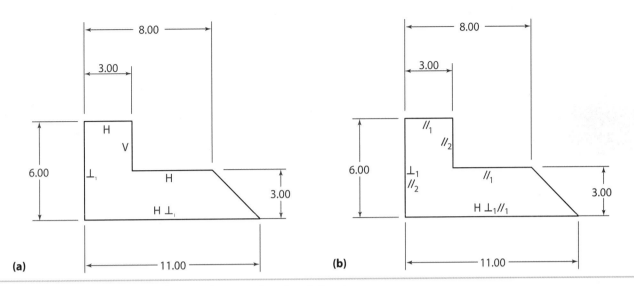

FIGURE 6.24. Two different sets of geometric constraints that define the same geometry.

Combinations of dimensional and geometric constraints also are not unique. It is possible to have different combinations of geometric constraints and dimensional constraints define exactly the same geometry, as shown in Figure 6.24.

The natural question then becomes, which set of constraints is correct or preferred? The answer depends on what the function of the part and the design intent is or how the designer wants to be able to change the model. You also should consider how the solid model will be used for analysis, manufacturing, and documentation when applying sets of constraints. One of the greatest advantages of a parametric solid model is that the model can be changed easily as the design changes. However, the constraints limit the ways in which the model can be changed.

6.04.05 Associative and Algebraic Constraints

Associative constraints, sometimes called **algebraic constraints**, can be used to relate one dimensional constraint to another. The dimensional constraints on a profile are expressed in terms of variables. Each dimensional constraint is identifiable by a unique variable name, as shown in Figure 6.25. Algebraic constraints can be used to control the values of selected variables as the result of algebraic expressions. Algebraic expressions consist of constants and variables related to each other through the use of arithmetic functions (+, −, *, absolute value, exponent, logarithm, power, square root, and sometimes minimum and maximum); trigonometric functions; and conditional expressions (if, else, or when) including inequalities comparisons (if A > B then . . .).

There are two different methods for solving sets of algebraic constraint equations. Software that uses **variational techniques** solves the equations simultaneously. A compatible solution for all of the variables can be calculated when there are a sufficient number of equations. In a system using **parametric techniques**, the equations are usually solved in sequential order. The equations will have only one unknown variable. All other variables in the algebraic expression must be known for the value of the unknown variable to be calculated, which is called the dependent or **driven dimension**. The known variables are called the **driving** dimensions. As shown in Figure 6.25, when the value of a driving dimensional constraint is changed, the value of its driven dimensional constraints are automatically changed too.

FIGURE 6.25. Dimensional constraints are shown in term of variables and a set of algebraic constraints in (a). Dimensions D3, D4, and D5 are automatically specified by specifying dimensions D1 and D2 in (b). Dimensions D3, D4, and D5 change automatically when D1 and D2 are changed in (c).

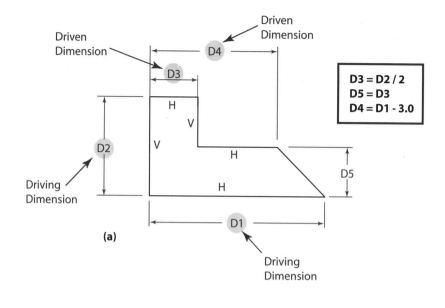

D3 = D2 / 2
D5 = D3
D4 = D1 - 3.0

(a)

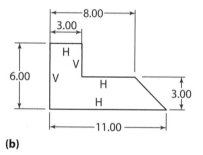

(b)

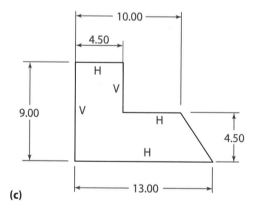

(c)

6.05 Strategies for Combining Profile Constraints

A completed profile is constrained using a combination of geometric and dimensional constraints and may include algebraic constraints as well. The constraint set must be complete for the geometry to be fully defined. If a profile is overconstrained or under-constrained, it may not be possible to create a solid feature from the profile. Some solid modeling software automatically applies constraints, but these constraints usually need to be changed to reflect the design intent. Furthermore, most software systems expect the user to apply constraints in addition to the automatically generated constraints; in particular, variational modelers allow underconstrained sketches and do not require user-applied constraints, but these systems can yield unpredictable results when the dimension values are changed. By gaining a thorough understanding of constraints (and how and when to apply them), you will be able to control the behavior of your models and capture your design intent. A strategy for applying geometric and dimensional constraints to a profile is demonstrated next.

The first constraint usually applied to a new sketch is a **ground constraint**. Ground constraints serve as anchors to fix the geometry in space. Ground constraints may have various forms. The most common type of ground constraint is a geometric entity such as a line or point on the profile having been made coincident with one of the basic modeling planes or with the origin of the coordinate system. For example, if the first feature of a model is created by extrusion, it may be convenient to place a corner of the profile on the origin of the coordinate system. This is usually done by placing one of the vertices of the sketch exactly at the origin. If the first feature is created by rotation, it may be convenient to place one of the endpoints of the center axis at the origin.

When the profile is closed and the automatically generated constraints have been applied the interactive constraint definition phase begins. Some software creates a fully constrained sketch, including both geometric and dimensional constraints; but the constraint set chosen by the software is usually not exactly what you want. Other software does not fully constrain the sketch, but leaves this task to the designer. Ground constraints should be specified if this was not already done when the profile was sketched. Next, geometric and dimensional constraints should be added and/or changed until the profile is fully constrained. Typically, your solid modeling software will alert you when the profile is fully constrained or when you try to overconstrain the profile. In particular, you should take care to delete any unwanted geometric and dimensional constraints that may have been automatically added. Finally, the profile should be changed to reflect the design intent and the dimensional constraints adjusted to the desired values. Some sketching editors automatically readjust the profile after each constraint is added; others wait until all of the constraints have been specified before readjusting the profile. Updating the profile to show its new shape after constraints are added or changed is called **regeneration**.

The way dimensional constraints are added depends largely on what the intended function of the part is, how it is to be fabricated, and how the geometry of the part may change in the future. What would a simple L-bracket look like if some of the dimensions were changed, as shown in Figure 6.26? In this case, d1 was changed from 30 to 40 and d2 was changed from 3 to 8. The result is shown in the figure. But if you want to make the bracket by bending a piece of sheet metal, the part should have a uniform thickness throughout. One way to do this is to force the length of line segments that define the thickness of both legs of the L to be equal. The geometric constraint shown in Figure 6.27 has this effect. The equal length geometric constraint replaces the dimensional constraint for the thickness of the vertical leg of the bracket. If you tried to apply the equal length constraint and the dimensional constraints on both line segments, the sketch would be overconstrained, a situation the software would not accept. In addition, an associative constraint needs to be added between the radius of the inside corner of the bracket and the radius of the outside corner to ensure that the thickness of the part is constant around the corner.

This constraint strategy demonstrates how to make your parts more robust. Through this simple example, you can see the importance of fully understanding the behavior of your model and the effects of your selection of dimensions and constraints. Your choices for geometric, dimensional, and algebraic constraints are not unique; but the decisions you make in selecting a set of constraints will have a big impact on the behavior of your model if you make changes to it. You must choose a modeling strategy that will reflect your design intent.

FIGURE 6.26. Changing the values of the dimensions changes the geometry of the model, without the need to reconstruct the model.

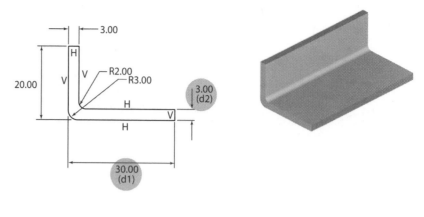

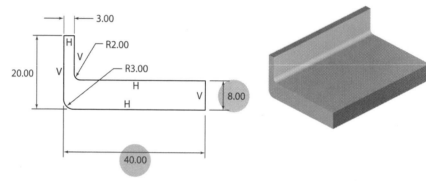

FIGURE 6.27. When compared to the original model in (a), the addition of the equality and associative constraints in (b) ensures a constant material thickness even if the dimensions are changed, thus adding functionality to the model if that is the intent.

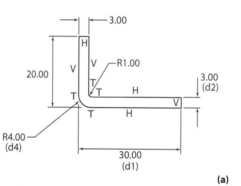

(a)

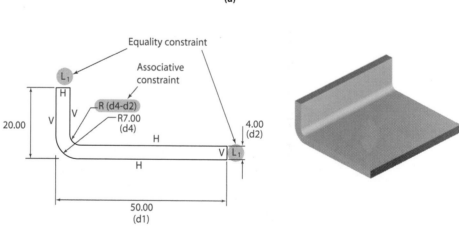

(b)

As an exercise for developing skill in the application of constraints, consider the rough sketch and the finished profile shown in Figure 6.28. For the profile to be fully constrained using only the dimensional constraints shown, certain geometric constraints are needed. Segment 1, for example, needs to be horizontal and tangent to Segment 2. Segment 2 needs to be tangent to Segment 1 as well as to Segment 3. Segment 3 needs to be tangent to Segment 2, perpendicular to Segment 4, and parallel to Segment 5. Segment 4 needs to be perpendicular to Segment 3 and equal in length to Segment 14. These constraints and the required geometric constraints on the remaining segments are shown in Figure 6.29. Keep in mind that a set of geometric constraints may not be unique. Can you specify another set of geometric constraints for this example that would create the same profile with the same dimensional constraints?

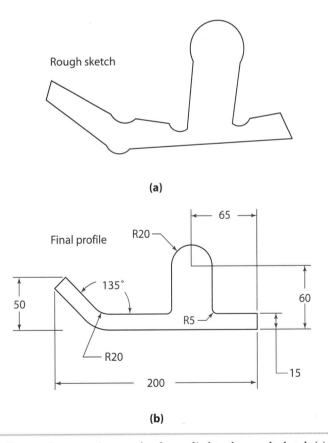

FIGURE 6.28. Geometric constraints need to be applied to the rough sketch (a) to produce the desired, fully constrained profile (b).

FIGURE 6.29. Applying geometric constraints to the first four segments of the sketch in Figure 6.28(a) to produce the finished profile in Figure 6.28(b).

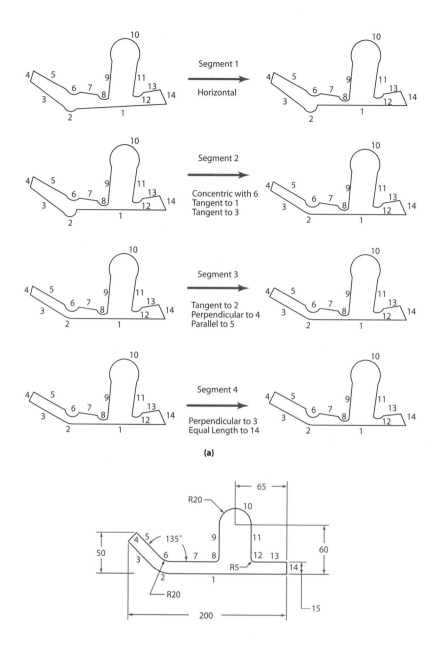

(a)

(b)

Segment	Constraint
1	Horizontal, Tangent to 2
2	Concentric with 6, Tangent to 1, Tangent to 3
3	Perpendicular to 4, Parallel to 5, Tangent to 2
4	Equal Length to 14, Perpendicular to 3
5	Parallel to 3, Tangent to 6
6	Concentric with 2, Tangent to 5, Tangent to 7
7	Horizontal, Tangent to 6, Tangent to 8
8	Tangent to 7, Tangent to 9
9	Vertical, Tangent to 8, Tangent to 10
10	Tangent to 9, Tangent to 11
11	Vertical, Tangent to 10, Tangent to 12
12	Tangent to 11, Tangent to 13
13	Horizontal, Tangent to 12
14	Vertical, Equal Length to 4

6.06 More Complexity Using Constructive Solids

You have seen how to create solid models by sketching a 2-D profile on one of the basic modeling planes and then using a single extrusion or a single rotation to create a 3-D model. Adding material to or removing material from the original model can create a more complex model. When material is added, a **protrusion** feature is created. When material is removed, a **cut** feature is created. Both protrusions and cuts begin with sketched profiles that are then extruded or revolved to form solid shapes that are added to or removed from the existing body of the model. For an extruded feature, the profile lies in the sketch plane and is extruded in a direction perpendicular to the sketching plane. For a revolved feature, the profile and the axis of revolution must be coplanar so both will lie on the sketch plane.

When protrusions or cuts are made on an existing model, sketches and profiles are no longer restricted to be located on one of the basic modeling planes. Instead, any planar surface on the model can be selected and used as a **sketching plane** on which sketches and profiles can be created. Once a sketching plane has been selected, any 2-D element that is created will be forced to lie on that plane. After a sketching plane is selected, the model can be reoriented to look directly into the sketching plane. Although you can sketch when not looking directly into the sketching plane, you need to be very careful when viewing from a different orientation. Edges of your sketch may not be shown in their true shape, and angles may appear distorted. Most people find it easier to create 2-D profiles when they are looking directly into the sketching plane, just as it is easier for someone to draw straight lines and angles with correct measurements when the paper is oriented straight in front of her.

Examples of profiles on various sketching planes on a model and resulting extruded protrusions are shown in Figure 6.30; examples of extruded cuts are shown in Figure 6.31. Examples of revolved protrusions are shown in Figure 6.32, and examples of revolved cuts are shown in Figure 6.33.

As with the first extrusion or revolution that created the main body of the model, the profiles for the added protrusions or cuts must be fully defined by geometric, dimensional, and algebraic constraints before they can be extruded or revolved. A common geometric constraint for protrusions or cut features is to make one or more edges or vertices of the new profile coincident with edges of the surface used as the sketching plane. In Figure 6.30(a), notice that one surface of the original object has been selected as a sketching plane and a rectangular profile has been sketched on the selected plane. The top and bottom edges of the sketched profile are coincident with edges of the sketching surface. The direction of extrusion is, by default, perpendicular to the selected sketching plane.

The length of the extrusion or angle of rotation also must be specified. There are several options for defining the length of the extrusion, as shown in Figure 6.30 and Figure 6.31. The simplest is to specify a **blind extrusion**. A blind extrusion is one that is made to a specified length in the selected direction, analogous to specifying a dimensional constraint, as shown in Figure 6.30(b). If your extrusion is the first feature used to create your initial model, it will be a blind extrusion. For a cut such as a hole, a blind extrusion creates a hole of a specified depth, as shown in Figure 6.31(b).

Another way to determine the length of the extrusion is to use existing geometry. One option for specifying an extrusion length is to **extrude to the next surface**. With this option, the extrusion begins at the profile and the protrusion or cut stops when it intersects the next surface encountered, as shown in Figure 6.30(c) and Figure 6.31(c). Another option is to **extrude to a selected surface**, where the protrusion or cut begins at the profile and stops when it intersects a selected surface, which may not necessarily be the first one encountered. See Figure 6.30(d) and Figure 6.31(d). For extruded cuts, there is an option to **extrude through all**. This option creates a cut or protrusion that starts at the profile and extends in the selected direction through all solid features, as shown in Figure 6.31(e). A **double-sided extrusion** permits the

FIGURE 6.30. Different ways to terminate an extruded protrusion from the profile in the sketching plane in (a). Blind extrusion in (b), extrude to next surface in (c), extrude to a selected surface in (d).

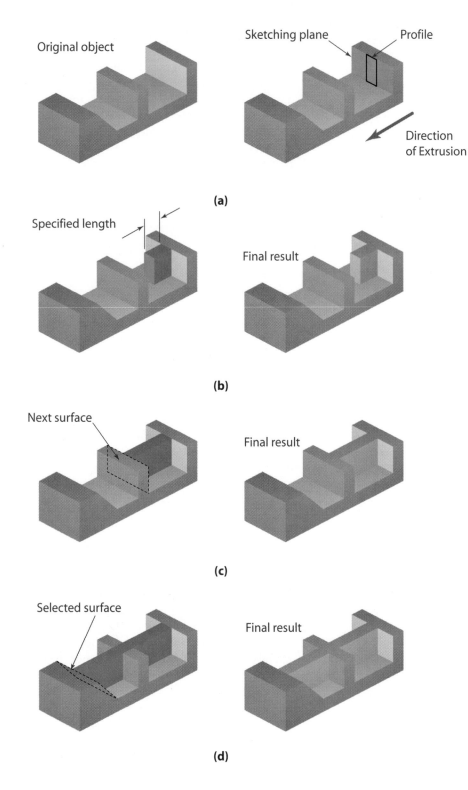

protrusion or cut to extend in both directions from a profile. The method of termination in each direction can then be specified independently. Other methods of terminating the extrusion length may be available depending on the specific solid modeling software used. You also can specify the angle of rotation of a revolved protrusion or cut in a similar manner by using a specified angle (blind revolution) or by revolving up to next or selected surfaces.

FIGURE 6.31. Different ways to terminate an extruded cut from the profile in the sketching plane in (a). Blind cut in (b); cut to next surface in (c). Cutting to a selected surface (d) and cutting through all (e).

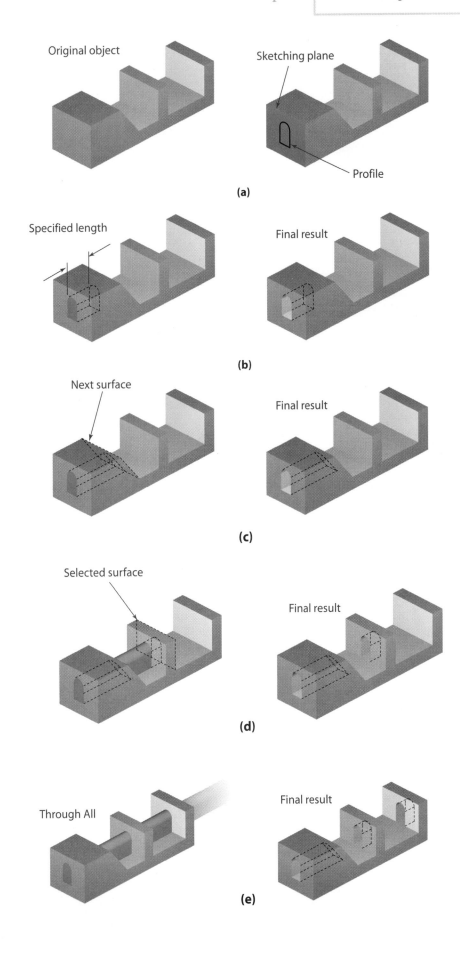

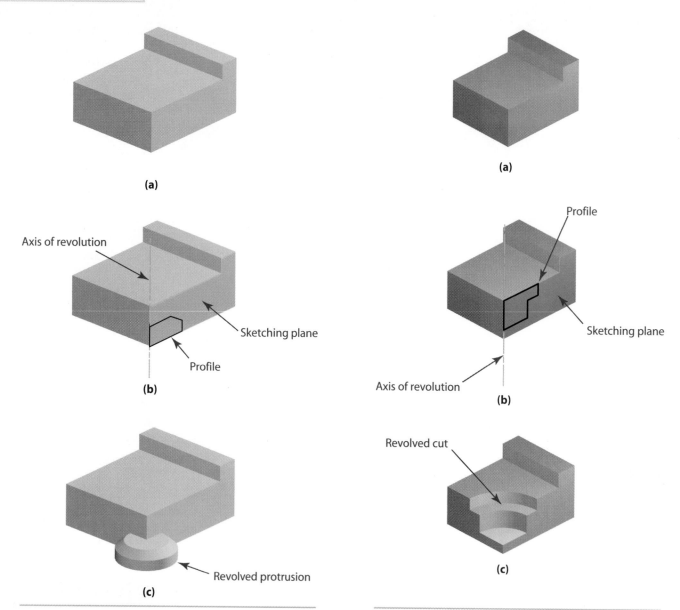

FIGURE 6.32. The addition of a revolved protrusion to an existing base in (a) by using one of its surfaces as a sketching plane to create a centerline and profile in (b) and revolving it to produce the final result in (c).

FIGURE 6.33. The addition of a revolved cut to an existing base in (a) by using one of its surfaces as a sketching plane to create a centerline and profile in (b) and revolving it to produce the final result in (c).

6.07 Breaking It Down into Features

When you build a solid model, you need to decide how to create the various shapes that compose the part. Very few parts can be modeled as a single extrusion or revolution. The various protrusions and cuts on the main body of a model are called **features**. What are features? If you consider your face, you might say that its features are your eyes, nose, lips, and cheeks. It is not much different on a manufactured part; a feature can be any combination of geometric shapes that make up the part and are distinctive in shape, size, or location. Features are characteristic elements of a particular object, things that stand out or make the object unique. Features often have characteristic geometric shapes and specific functions. A simple hole, for example, is a cylindrical cut that is often used as a receptacle for a fastener such as a bolt or screw. A manufactured part may have many different types of features. Since these features are the foundation of contemporary solid modeling systems, you must be able to recognize them.

Engineered parts also have features that are composed of repeated combinations of shapes. Most feature-based modelers have a collection of standard built-in features and may also allow you to define your own features. This can be handy when your products are designed with a particular shape that varies in size, such as gear teeth, airfoils, or turbine blades. The challenge for designers is to identify part features and build solid models that reflect the function of the part and design intent.

6.07.01 The Base Feature

All of your parts will be created from a collection of features, but you need to start your model with a basic shape that represents the general shape of the object. Your first step should be to study the part and identify the shape that you will use as the **base feature**. The base feature should be something that describes the overall shape of the part or something that gives you the greatest amount of functional detail that can be created with a single extrusion or rotation. Figure 6.34 shows several parts with the base features used to create the solid models.

After the base feature is created, you can modify the shape by adding or subtracting material to it to create form features. A **form feature** is a recognizable region or area on the part geometry that may have a specific function and/or method of manufacture. The geometric components or shapes within the feature usually have some geometric relationships or constraints. Different CAD systems use various names for these features, but you should become familiar with some of the common terms. The following section discusses common feature types.

FIGURE 6.34. Parts and their base features.

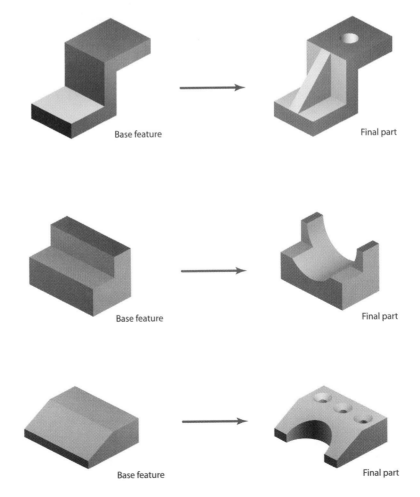

Base feature   Final part

Base feature   Final part

Base feature   Final part

FIGURE 6.34. (CONTINUED)
Parts and their base features.

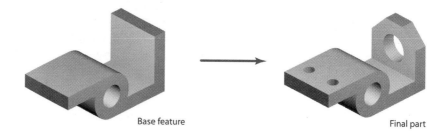

Base feature   Final part

Base feature   Final part

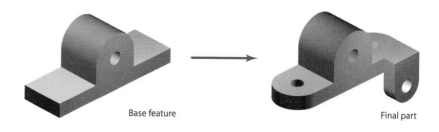

Base feature   Final part

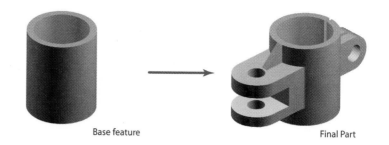

Base feature   Final Part

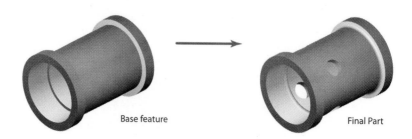

Base feature   Final Part

6.07.02 Chamfers, Rounds, and Fillets

Unless otherwise specified, adjoining surfaces on a virtual part can intersect to form sharp corners and edges, but real parts often have smooth transitions along the edges of these surfaces. The most common edge transitions are **rounds**, **fillets**, and **chamfers**. A round is a smooth radius transition of the external edge created by two intersecting surfaces. A fillet is a smooth transition of the internal edge created by two intersecting surfaces. Geometrically, the rounds and fillets are tangent to both intersecting surfaces. Examples of rounds and fillets are shown in Figure 6.35. Fillets and rounds are specified by the size of their radii and the edge(s) that are rounded.

Chamfers also provide a transition between two intersecting surfaces, but the transition is an angled cut instead of a radius. Examples of chamfers are shown in Figure 6.36. Chamfers can be specified by the distance along each intersecting surface to the original edge or by the distance along one of the original surfaces and the angle made with that surface.

Functionally, on an inside edge, a fillet may be necessary to facilitate fabrication or to reduce stresses at the corner so the part does not break as easily. On an outside edge, rounds and chamfers are usually used to eliminate sharp edges that can be easily damaged or that can cause injury or damage when the part is handled. Rounds, fillets, and chamfers are generally small when compared to the overall size of the associated base or parent feature.

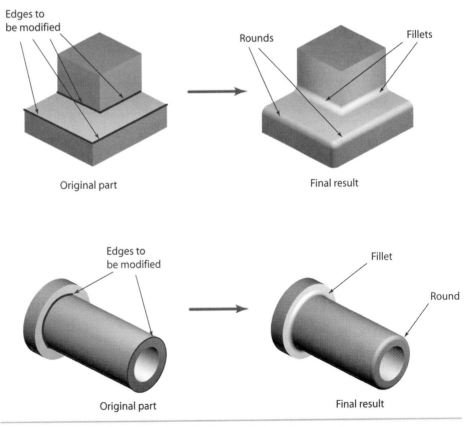

FIGURE 6.35. Examples of rounds and fillets applied to the edges of a part.

FIGURE 6.36. Examples of chamfering applied to the edges of a part.

Edges to
be modified

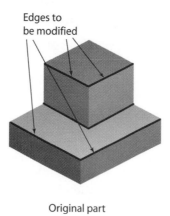

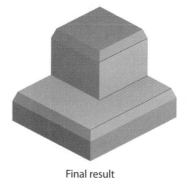

Original part

Final result

Edges to
be modified

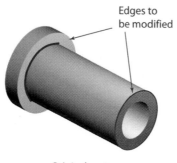

Original part

Final result

6.07.03 Holes

Holes are ubiquitous in nearly all manufactured parts and, therefore, can be inserted into a model as features by most solid modeling software. Holes are often used with bolts or screws to fasten parts together. Many different types of holes can be used with specific fasteners or can be created using different manufacturing processes. Some special types include holes that are blind, through, tapped, counterbored, or countersunk, as shown in Figure 6.37. Each type of hole has a particular geometry to suit a specific function. You should study the hole types so you recognize them when you model your parts.

Many solid modeling software packages include standard or built-in features to help you with your modeling task. When you use a standard hole feature, the solid modeling software makes certain assumptions about the geometry of a hole so you do not need to specify all of the dimensions and constraints that make up the feature. A countersunk hole, for example, can be made as a revolved cut. What do you need to do to create this feature? You begin by selecting a sketching plane, then create and constrain the sketch and revolve the sketch about a specified axis. Many things can go wrong if you are not careful. There might not be a plane on which to sketch. Your sketch might not have the proper shape, or the axis might not be perpendicular to the desired surface. However, a countersunk hole feature can often be created from a standard feature by selecting the location of the axis of the hole on the desired surface, the diameter of the hole, the diameter and angle of the countersink, and the depth of the hole. The shape of the profile, axis of revolution, and angle of revolution are included automatically in the feature definition. No sketching plane is needed.

FIGURE 6.37. Cross sections of various types of holes to reveal their geometry.

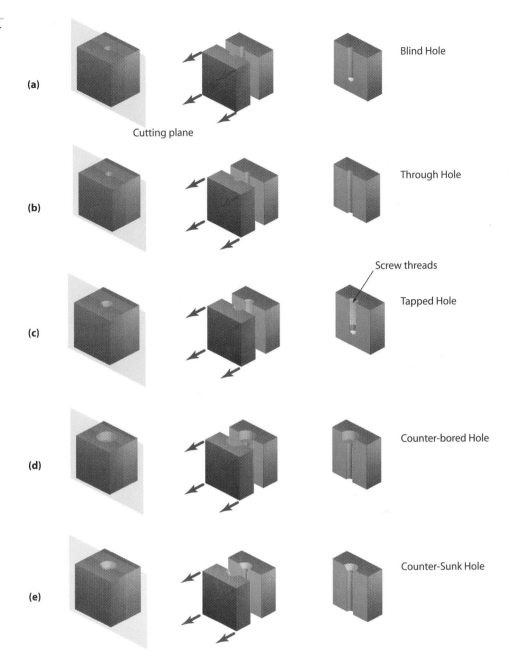

(a)

Cutting plane

Blind Hole

(b)

Through Hole

Screw threads

Tapped Hole

(c)

Counter-bored Hole

(d)

Counter-Sunk Hole

(e)

Figure 6.38 illustrates the use of a cut feature compared to the use of a built-in hole feature to create a countersunk hole. In most cases, it is more desirable to create a hole using the built-in hole feature instead of a general purpose cut feature. Besides being a more natural way to place a hole in a model, you avoid potential errors in creating the desired geometry. Furthermore, using a general cut feature does not incorporate the specific geometry and function of a "hole" in the knowledge base of the model, which may be useful in downstream applications such as process planning for manufacturing the hole.

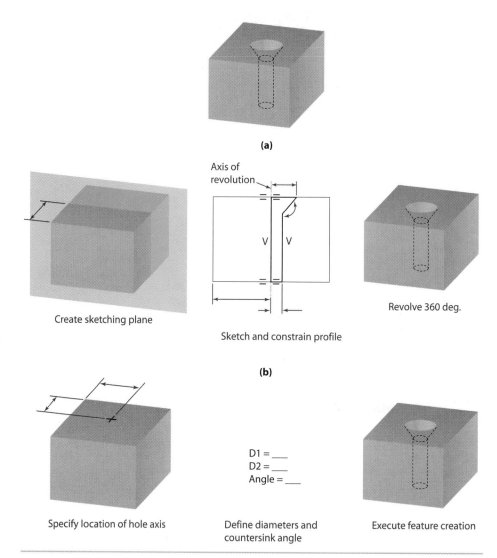

(a)

Axis of revolution

V V

Create sketching plane

Sketch and constrain profile

Revolve 360 deg.

(b)

Specify location of hole axis

D1 = ___
D2 = ___
Angle = ___

Define diameters and countersink angle

Execute feature creation

FIGURE 6.38. The countersunk hole shown in (a) can be created by using a general revolved cut, as shown in (b), or by specifying the hole as a built-in feature, as shown in (c).

6.07.04 Shells

The process of creating a shell, or **shelling**, removes most of the interior volume of a solid model, leaving a relatively thin wall of material that closely conforms to the outer surfaces of the original model. Shelled objects are often used to make cases and containers. For example, a soda bottle is a shell, as are cases for electronic products such as cell phones and video displays. The walls of a shell are generally of constant thickness, and at least one of the surfaces of the original object is removed so the interior of the shell is accessible. Figure 6.39 shows examples of a model that has been shelled.

Shelling is sometimes considered an operation rather than a feature. It is usually performed on the entire model, including all of its features, by selecting the surfaces to be removed and the thickness of the shell wall. Any feature not to be shelled should be added to the model after the shelling operation is complete. The order of feature creation and shelling operations may have a dramatic effect on the shape of the part, as will be shown later in this chapter.

FIGURE 6.39. Examples of shelling.

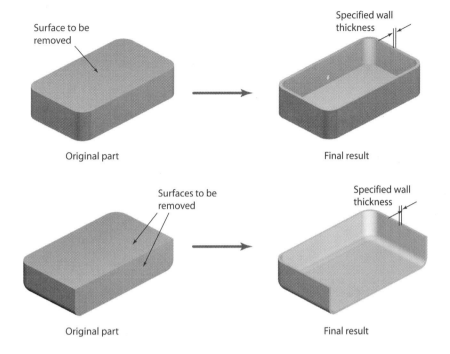

6.07.05 Ribs and Webs

Ribs are small, thin, protrusions of constant thickness that extend predominantly from the surface of a part. Ribs are typically added to provide support or to stiffen a part. Sometimes they are added to improve a part's heat transfer ability. **Webs** are areas of thin material that connect two or more heavier areas on the part. Examples of ribs and webs are shown in Figure 6.40. These features are usually specified by their flat geometry, thickness, and location.

FIGURE 6.40. Ribs (a) added to parts to reinforce them, and webs (b) connect thicker sections on parts.

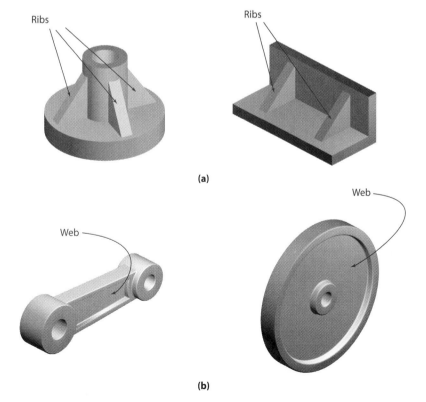

6.07.06 Other Feature Types

The features that follow (and that are shown in Figure 6.41) are less commonly found in solid modelers. When available, they should be used as needed. When such features are not available in the solid modeler, the geometric shapes can still be created from sketched profiles as protrusions or cuts. Note that special feature types usually imply a particular shape, function, manufacturing process, or other feature attribute.

- Boss—a slightly raised circular area, usually used to provide a small, flat, clean surface
- Draft—a slight angle in the otherwise straight walls of a part, usually used to facilitate its removal from a mold
- Groove—a long, shallow cut or annulus
- Island—an elongated or irregularly shaped raised area, usually used to provide a flat, clean surface
- Keyseat—an axially oriented slot of finite length on the outside of a shaft
- Keyway—an axially oriented slot that extends the entire length of a hole
- Slot—a straight, long cut with deep vertical walls
- Spot face—a shallow circular depression that has been cut, usually used to provide a small, flat, clean surface
- Taper—a slight angle in the otherwise cylindrical walls of a part, usually used to facilitate its insertion or removal into another part

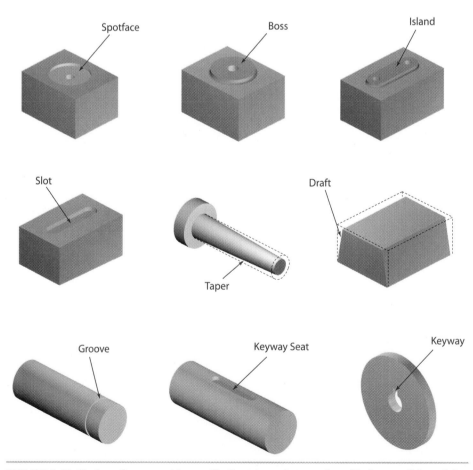

FIGURE 6.41. Various features with specific functions that may be added to a solid model.

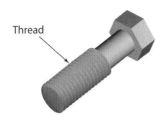

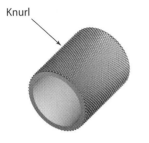

FIGURE 6.42. Some cosmetic features.

6.07.07 Cosmetic Features

Parts can be modified by altering their surfaces characteristics. These characteristics are called **cosmetic features** because they generally modify the appearance of the surface but do not alter the size or shape of the object, just like lipstick or hair coloring. Cosmetic features are necessary to the function of the part and may be included in the model so they can be used in later applications, such as fabrication. Some common cosmetic features include threads and knurls. Since the geometric changes are small and detailed, the cosmetic features usually are not modeled in their exact geometric form in the database of the object, but are included as notes or with a simplified geometric representation. You will learn more about simplified representations on drawings in later chapters. Some cosmetic features are shown in Figure 6.42.

6.07.08 An Understanding of Features and Functions

As a design engineer, you need to become familiar with the different types of features on various parts. Doing so will help you communicate with other engineers as well as imbed more of a part's engineering function into your models. For example, if you look at Figure 6.43, you will notice a rectangular cut on the edge of the hole. This cut is a geometric feature called a keyway. Why is it there? What purpose does it serve? In Figure 6.44, the gear is mounted to a shaft, which also has a rectangular cut. A small part called a key is used to line up the shaft and the gear and transmits torque from the shaft to the gear. If you were to create a feature-based solid model of the gear, you could identify the rectangular cut as a keyway feature. If the model parts were to be assembled with assembly modeling software (which is explained in detail in a subsequent chapter), the computer and software would recognize the models as mating parts and orient the gear, key, and shaft automatically.

FIGURE 6.43. A gear with teeth, a bore, and a keyway as functional features.

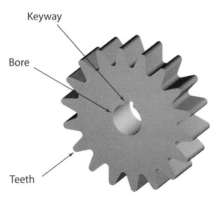

FIGURE 6.44. A gear and shaft assembly. The key functions to transmit torque. The keyseat receives the key in the shaft, and the keyway receives the key in the gear.

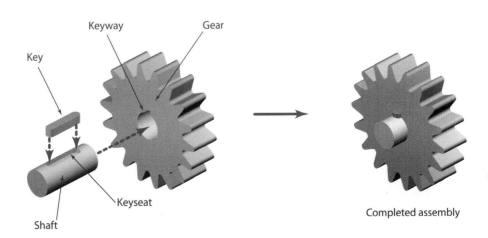

6.08 More Ways to Create Sophisticated Geometry

Creating protrusions and cuts by extending the sketch profiles made on either the basic modeling plane or one of the existing surfaces of the model results in a wide variety of possible models. Even more sophisticated models, however, can be created by using reference geometries called datums, which can be added to the model, displayed, and used to create features. Generally, solid modelers offer at least three types of **datum geometries** that can be placed into a model: datum points, datum axes, and datum planes. These datum geometries do not actually exist on the real part (i.e., they cannot be seen or felt) but are used to help locate and define features. Consider, for example, the part shown in Figure 6.45(a). The angled protrusion with the hole would be easy to create if an angled sketching plane could be defined as shown. The extrusion could be made to extend from the sketching plane to the surface of the base feature. This feature would be more difficult, although not impossible, to define using extruded protrusions and cuts that extended only from the basic modeling planes or one of the surfaces on the existing model. In Figure 6.45(b), the uniquely shaped web would be easy to create if a sketching plane could be placed between the connected features as shown. An extruded protrusion could extend from both sides of the sketching plane to the surfaces of the connected features.

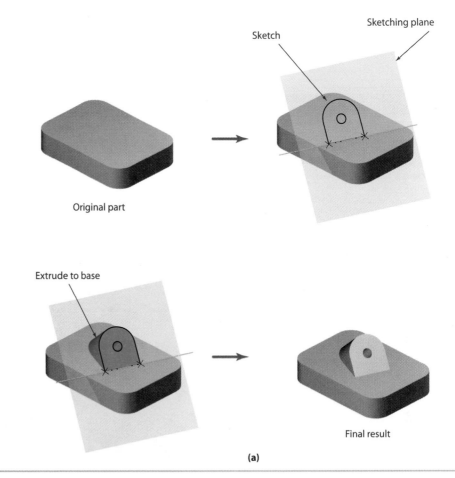

FIGURE 6.45. Using a sketching plane and profile, which are not on an existing surface of the object, to create a protrusion feature (a).

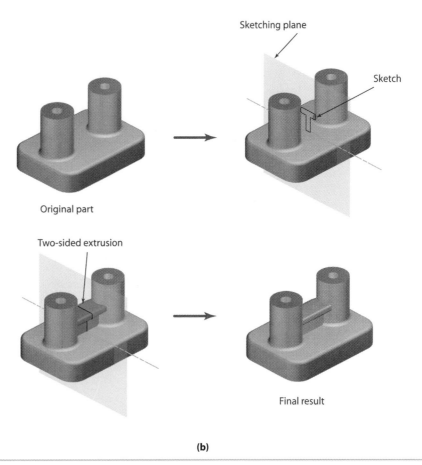

(b)

FIGURE 6.45. (CONTINUED) Using a sketching plane and profile, which are not on an existing surface of the object, to create a web feature (b).

The next few sections will describe methods in which the three different types of datums can be defined geometrically and how the datums can be used to create a variety of new types of features. Depending on the specific solid modeling software being used, some of the methods described here for datum definition may or may not be available.

6.08.01 Defining Datum Points

Following are some of the different ways a datum point can be defined and created. The definitions are shown graphically in Figure 6.46.

- At a vertex
- On a planar surface at specified perpendicular distances from two edges
- At the intersection of a line or an axis and a surface that does not contain the line

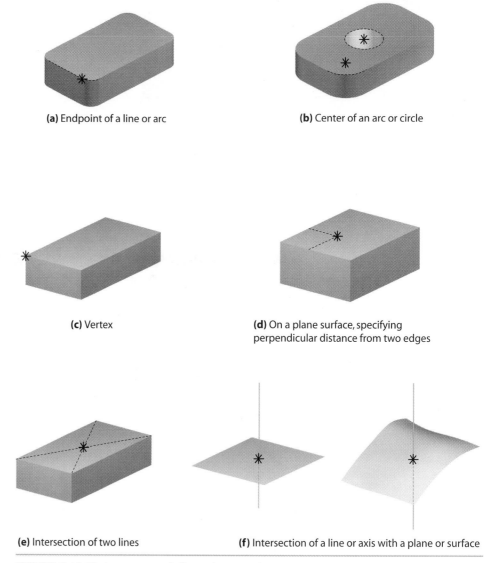

(a) Endpoint of a line or arc

(b) Center of an arc or circle

(c) Vertex

(d) On a plane surface, specifying perpendicular distance from two edges

(e) Intersection of two lines

(f) Intersection of a line or axis with a plane or surface

FIGURE 6.46. Various ways to define a datum point.

6.08.02 Defining Datum Axes

Following are some of the different ways a datum axis can be defined and created. The definitions are shown graphically in Figure 6.47.

- Between two points (or vertices)
- Along a linear edge
- At the intersection of two planar surfaces
- At the intersection of a cylinder and a plane through its axis
- Along the centerline of a cylinder or cylindrical surface

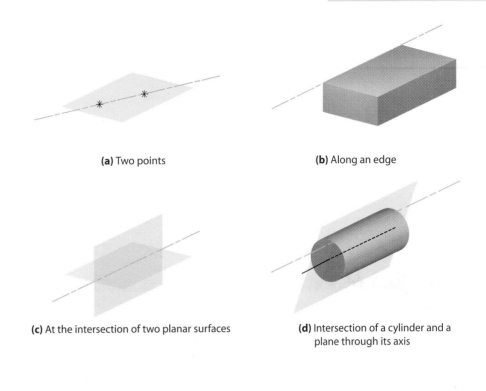

(a) Two points

(b) Along an edge

(c) At the intersection of two planar surfaces

(d) Intersection of a cylinder and a plane through its axis

(e) At the centerline of a cylinder or cylindrical surface

FIGURE 6.47. Various ways to define a datum axis.

6.08.03 Defining Datum Planes

Following are some of the different ways a datum plane can be defined and created. The definitions are shown graphically in Figure 6.48.

- Through three noncolinear points
- Through two intersecting lines
- Through a line and a noncolinear point
- Offset from an existing flat surface at a specified distance
- Through an edge or axis on a flat surface at an angle from that surface
- Tangent to a surface at a point on that surface
- Perpendicular to a flat surface and through a line parallel to that surface
- Perpendicular to a flat or cylindrical surface through a line on that surface
- Tangent to a cylindrical surface at a line on that surface

FIGURE 6.48. Various ways to define a datum plane. More ways to define a datum plane.

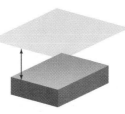

(a) Offset from Existing flat surface, and a distance

(b) A flat surface, through an edge or axis on that surface, and an angle from that surface

(c) Tangent to a surface at a point on that surface

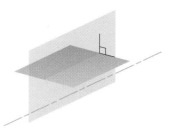

(d) Perpendicular to a flat surface, and through a line parallel to that surface

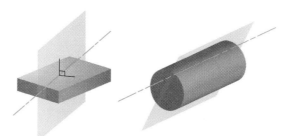

(e) Perpendicular to a flat or cylindrical surface and through a line on that surface

(f) Tangent to a cylindrical surface at a line on that surface

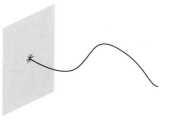

(g) Perpendicular to a curve at a point on that curve

(h) Three points

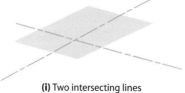

(i) Two intersecting lines

(j) A Line and a point

6.08.04 Chaining Datums

Series of simply defined datums are often used for creating more complex datums. In the example shown in Figure 6.45(a), the angled protrusion was created in this manner: On the top surface of the base extrusion, two datum points were created by defining each of their locations from the edges of the base extrusion. A datum axis was then created using the two datum points as the endpoints of the axis. Finally, the desired datum plane was defined using the top surface of the base extrusion, using the datum axis created in that plane, and specifying the angle that the new datum plane makes with the top surface.

Another example is shown in Figure 6.49, where a datum plane is created to be tangent to the surface of a cylindrical extrusion. An intermediate datum plane is defined by one of the basic planes; the axis of the cylinder, which lies on that basic plane; and the angle the intermediate datum plane makes with the basic plane. The final datum plane is then created to be tangent to the surface of the cylindrical extrusion at its intersection with the intermediate datum plane. A datum plane tangent to the surface of a cylinder is commonly used to create cuts that extend radially into a cylindrical surface, such as holes or slots, and protrusions that extend radially from the cylindrical surface, such as spokes or vanes. Note that with protrusion from a tangent datum plane, the extrusion must be specified to extend in both directions from that datum; otherwise, there will be a gap between the extrusion and the curved surface.

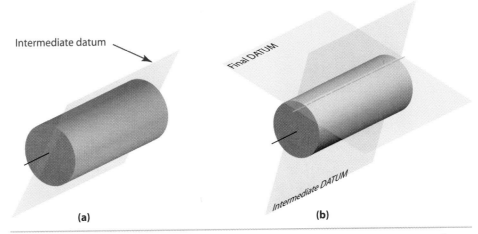

(a)   **(b)**

FIGURE 6.49. To create a datum plane that is tangent to a cylindrical surface at a specific location, an intermediate datum plane, shown in (a), can be created through the centerline of the cylinder. The intersection of the intermediate datum with the cylinder creates a datums axis that is used to locate the final datum plane.

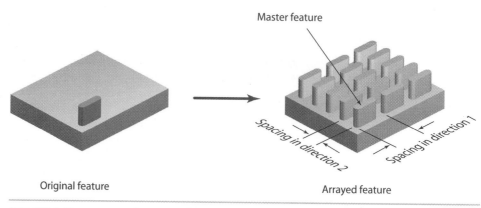

Master feature

Spacing in direction 2

Spacing in direction 1

Original feature

Arrayed feature

FIGURE 6.50. A rectangular array of protrusions created from a master feature.

6.08.05 Using Arrays (Rectangular and Circular)

One method of creating multiple identical copies of a feature in a model is to create a **feature array**, which is sometimes called a **feature pattern**. A feature array takes one feature, called the **master feature**, and places copies of it on the model at a specified spacing. The copied features are identical to the master feature, and changing the geometry of the master at a later time also changes the geometry of the copies at that time. Including features in this manner can save time and effort in creating the entire model, especially when the features are rather complex. An example of a model with a rectangular array of features is shown in Figure 6.50. An array of rectangular cuts is shown in Figure 6.51. As shown, rectangular arrays can generate copied features in two directions. These directions must be specified, as well as the spacing of the copied features in each direction. Finally, the number of copies in each direction must be specified. Care must be taken to ensure that there is enough room on the model to accommodate all of the copied features.

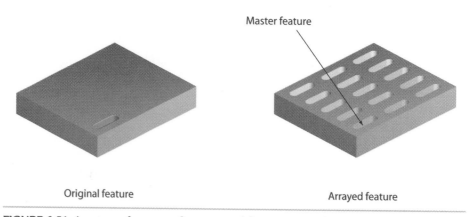

Master feature

Original feature

Arrayed feature

FIGURE 6.51. A rectangular array of cuts created from a master feature.

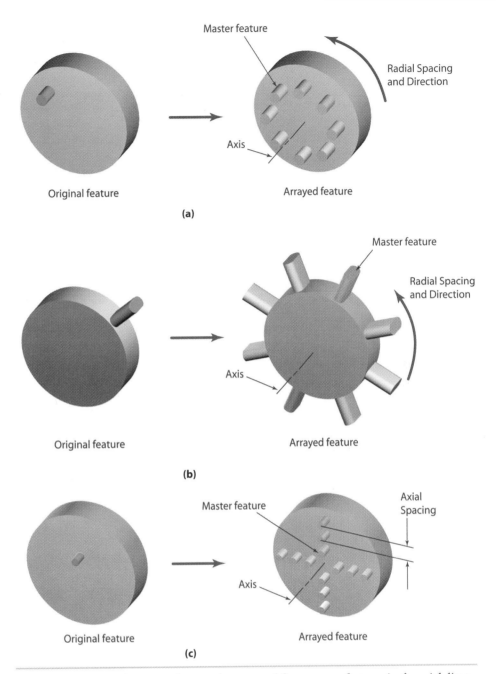

Master feature

Radial Spacing
and Direction

Axis

Original feature

Arrayed feature

(a)

Master feature

Radial Spacing
and Direction

Axis

Original feature

Arrayed feature

(b)

Master feature

Axial
Spacing

Axis

Original feature

Arrayed feature

(c)

FIGURE 6.52. A circular array of protrusions created from master features in the axial direction (a) and (b), both in the axial and radial direction (c).

Examples of models with radial arrays of protrusions are shown in Figure 6.52. Radial arrays can extend radially or axially. For radial arrays, in addition to the master feature being selected, the axis of revolution for the array must be selected. If such an axis does not already exist on the model, one must be created from an added datum axis. The number of copies, the direction of the array, and the radial and axial spacing of the copies must be specified.

6.08.06 Using Mirrored Features

Another method of creating a feature, when applicable, is to create its mirrored image. To create a **mirrored feature**, you must first identify a mirror plane. You can use an existing plane or define a new datum plane to use as the mirror plane, as shown in Figure 6.53. A mirrored duplicate of the master feature can then be created on the model on the opposite side of the mirror plane. Mirrored features can be cuts or protrusions; however, keep in mind that the copied feature will be a mirror image of the master, not an identical copy. Changing the master feature at a later time also will change the mirrored feature correspondingly. As with arrayed features, using mirrored features can save a great deal of time in model creation, especially when the mirrored feature is complex.

6.08.07 Using Blends

Not all models can be created using just extruded or revolved features. One complex feature is a **blend**. Figure 6.54 shows models with blended surfaces. A blend requires at least two profile sketches, and the model is formed by a smooth transition between

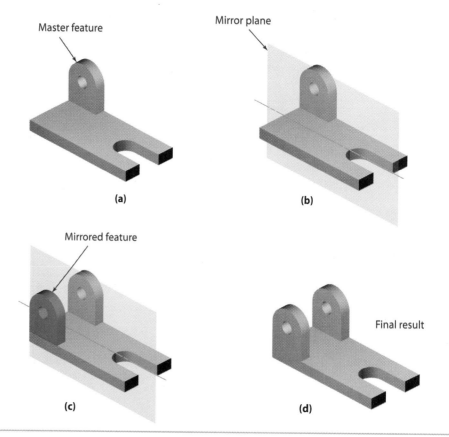

FIGURE 6.53. Creation of a mirrored feature. The master feature in (a) is mirrored by creating a datum plane as a mirror plane (b). A mirror image of the feature is produced on the opposite side of the datum plane in (c), and the final result is shown in (d).

these profiles. The profiles can be sketched on the basic modeling planes, on surfaces of an existing model, or on datum planes. In the simplest blends, the profiles are sketched on parallel planes. Many software packages require the number of vertices on each of the sketched profiles to be equal. If your profiles do not have the same number of vertices, you will have to divide one or more of the entities to create additional vertices. In some sketching editors, circles include four vertices by default. The vertices in all profiles are usually numbered sequentially, and the software usually tries to match the vertices to create an edge between vertices with the same number, as shown in (a) and (b) of Figure 6.54. Rotating the profiles or redefining the vertex numbering can control twisting of the blended transition, as shown in Figure 6.54(c). Further control on the model transition usually can be performed by specifying the slope of the transition at each vertex for each shape.

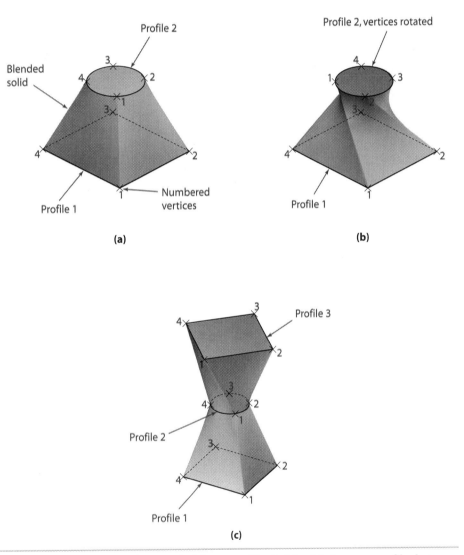

FIGURE 6.54. Blended solids created with two profiles in (a), with the same profiles but rotated vertices in (b), and with three profiles in (c).

6.08.08 Sweeps

Swept features, as with simply extruded or revolved features, are created with a single profile. The difference is that a swept feature does not need to follow a linear or circular path, but can follow a specified curve called a **path** or **trajectory**. The profile is created at an endpoint of the path on a sketching plane that is perpendicular to the path at that endpoint. In sweeping out a solid volume, the profile is imagined to travel along the path. Usually the profile is constrained to remain perpendicular to the path. A good example of a swept solid is a garden hose. The cross section or profile is a simple circle, but the path can be curved. Figure 6.55(a) shows the path and profile of a swept feature where the path is open. Figure 6.55(b) shows a swept feature where the path is closed. Care must be taken in defining the profile and path of a swept solid. Just as you cannot bend a garden hose around a sharp corner without creating a kink, if the path of your sweep contains a sharp corner or a small radius, the feature may fail by trying to create a self-intersecting solid. A special case of a swept solid is a coil spring. In this case, the path is a helix, as shown in Figure 6.56. Many solid modelers include a hel-

FIGURE 6.55. Features created by sweeps. The sketching plane is perpendicular to the path. The path in (a) is open, and the path in (b) is closed.

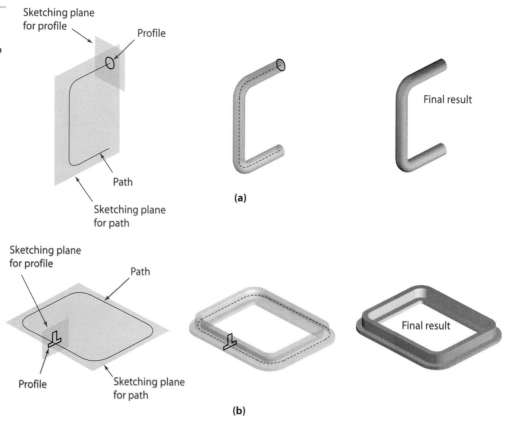

FIGURE 6.56. A tapered spring created by sweeping a circular profile on a helical path.

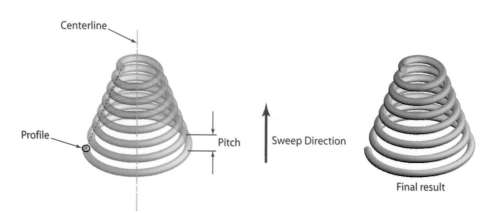

ical sweep as a special feature so you do not have to sketch the helix. In this case, you sketch the profile and specify an axis on the sketching plane. The helix is specified by a pitch dimension, which is the distance between coils, and the direction of the sweep. To avoid self-intersection, the pitch must be larger than the maximum size of the profile in the sweep direction.

6.09 The Model Tree

An extremely useful editing tool included in most solid modeling software is the **model tree**, sometimes called the **feature tree**, **design tree**, or **history tree**. The model tree lists all of the features of a solid model in the order in which they were created, providing a "history" of the sequence of feature creation. Further, any feature in the model tree can be selected individually to allow the designer to edit the feature. An example of a model tree and its associated solid model are shown in Figure 6.57. Usually new features are added at the bottom of the model tree. Some software allows the designer to "roll back" the model and insert new features in the middle of the tree. In this case, the model reverts to its appearance just before the insertion point, so any inserted feature cannot have its geometry or location based on features that will be created after it.

FIGURE 6.57. A typical model tree showing the features of a model in the order in which they were created.

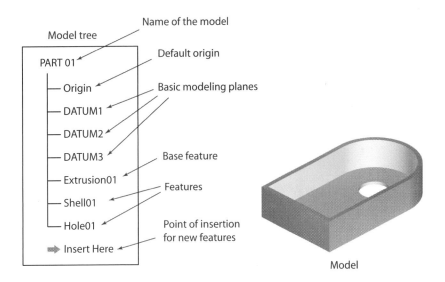

FIGURE 6.58. The result of reversing the order of creating the hole and shell features.

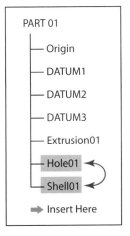
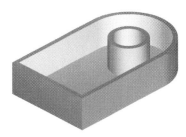

The order in which features are created may have a profound effect on the results. In the previous example, a shell feature, which has the effect of hollowing out a part, was performed with the top surface of the part removed from the feature. A hole was then added to the model after the shelling operation. If the hole was added to the block before the shelling operation, the result would be different, as shown in Figure 6.58, because the surface around the hole through the block would have been considered a part of the shell. In most solid modeling software, removing the feature from one location in the model tree and inserting it in a new location changes the order of creation of the feature.

The model tree also provides access to the editing of features. Each feature item on the model tree can be expanded. The base extrusion in the previous example is composed of a fully constrained rectangular sketch profile that has been extruded to a specified length. The feature can be expanded in the model tree, as shown in Figure 6.59, to give access to the profile so it can be selected for editing. The sketch can then be edited by restarting the sketching editor. The dimensional constraints can be changed by selecting and editing their numerical values. Access to the sketching editor and feature parameters may vary with different software, and changes made through the model tree may be one of several different ways to modify your model.

In many models, certain features are dependent upon the existence of other features. For example, consider the features shown in the model in Figure 6.60. The location of the counterbored hole is measured from the edges of the rectangular base.

FIGURE 6.59. Use of the model tree to access and edit the sketch used to create the base feature (Extrusion01).

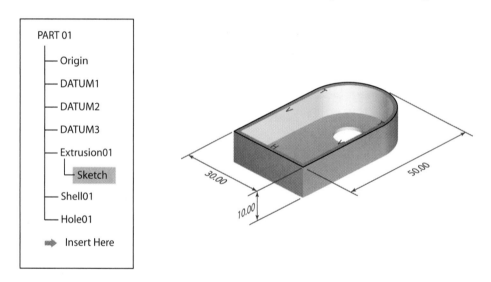

FIGURE 6.60. The holes in the model show parent-child dependencies. The existence of the straight hole depends on the existence of the countersunk hole, which depends on the existence of the counterbored hole. Elimination of a parent also eliminates its child.

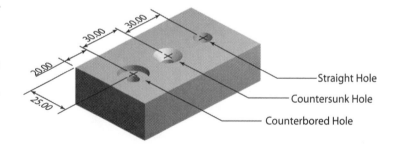

However, the location of the countersunk hole is measured from the location of the counterbored hole and the location of the straight hole is measured from the location of the countersunk hole. Imagine what would happen to the straight hole if the countersunk hole were deleted. There would be no reference for placing the straight hole; therefore, it could not be created. Similarly, if the counterbored hole was deleted, neither the countersunk hole nor the straight hole could be created. This relationship is often referred to as a parent-child relationship. The straight hole is considered the **child feature** of the countersunk hole, and the countersunk hole is considered the child of the counterbored hole. The counterbored hole is considered the **parent feature** of the countersunk hole, and the countersunk hole is considered the parent of the straight hole. Just as you would not be reading this text if your parents did not exist, neither can features in a solid model exist without their parent (or grandparent) features. On the model tree, if you try to delete a particular feature, its progeny also will be deleted. However, different software behaves differently; and while some software provides specific warnings about the deletion of features, other software does not.

Understanding parent-child relationships in solid models is important if your model needs to be flexible and robust. As a designer, you undoubtedly will want to change the model at some time. You might need to add or delete features to accommodate a new function for the part or reuse the model as the basis of a new design. If you minimize the number of dependencies in the feature tree (like a family tree), it will be easier to make changes to your model. When it is likely that some features will be deleted or suppressed in a future modification of the part, those features should not be used as parents for other features that must remain present. The most extreme example of this strategy is called **horizontal modeling**, where the feature tree is completely flat; that is, there are no parent features except the base feature. This type of modeling strategy was patented by Delphi and has been used successfully by many companies. In Figure 6.61, the locations of three holes have been redefined so they are measured from the edge of the rectangular base instead of relative to one another. The base then becomes the parent to all three holes, and deleting any one of the holes does not affect the others.

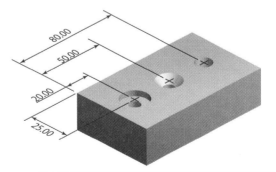

FIGURE 6.61. This model demonstrates horizontal modeling. Each hole has no parent-child dependencies except to the base feature.

6.10 Families of Parts

Groups of engineered parts often have very similar geometry. An everyday example is bolts and screws. A group of bolts may have the same head and thread geometries, but differ in their available length. Another example is the family of support brackets shown in Figure 6.62. Each bracket has a rough L-shaped base feature, holes, and a support rib (except for Version 3). Only the size and number of holes are different for each version.

When a group of parts is similar, it is possible to represent the entire group with a **family model**, with different versions of that model selected to specify particular parts. Such a model includes a **master model**, which has all of the features that are in any of the members of the group, and a **design table**, which lists all of the versions of that model and the dimensional constraints or features that may change in any of its versions. The attributes that may change are sometimes called **parameters**. The first

Version 1

Version 2

Version 3

FIGURE 6.62. A family of three parts with similar features and geometry.

step in building a family model is to identify all of the features and parameters that can be varied in the members of the family. In addition to a numerical value, every dimensional constraint in a model has a unique **dimension name**, which can be shown by selecting the appropriate display option. In Figure 6.63, all of the dimensional constraints have been changed to show their dimension names and the features have been identified by the feature names that appear on the design tree.

The next step is to select the option for the construction of a design table, which is usually an internal or external spreadsheet, in the solid modeling software. The spreadsheet table should look similar to that shown in Figure 6.64. The first column usually contains the names of the different versions of the model. In Figure 6.64, these versions are called Version 1, Version 2, and Version 3 for convenience. The first row usually contains the names of the parameters that can change with each version. The individual cells of the spreadsheet show what the corresponding numerical values are of the

FIGURE 6.63. The master model showing the numerical values of its dimensions in (a) and the names of the features and dimensions in (b).

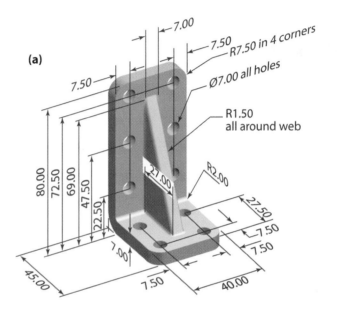

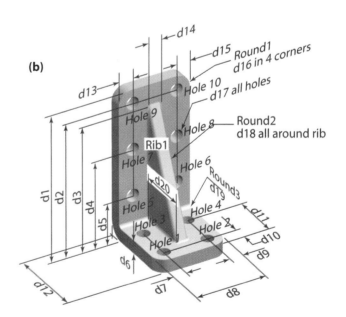

	Hole 3	Hole 4	Hole 7	Hole 8	Hole 9	Hole 10	Rib1	d1	d3	d12
Version 1	U	U	U	U	U	U	U	80.00	69.00	45.00
Version 2	U	U	U	U	S	S	U	60.00	50.00	45.00
Version 3	S	S	S	S	S	S	S	30.00	N/A	30.00

S = Suppressed
U = Unsuppressed

FIGURE 6.64. The design table for the parameters that change within the three versions of the family of parts in Figure 6.62 and Figure 6.63.

dimensional constraints for each version and whether a particular feature is present in that version. When a particular feature is present, it is specified as being **unsuppressed**. When that feature is not present, it is specified as being **suppressed**. When the version of the part to be displayed has been selected, the corresponding model with its specified parameters is shown.

With the existence of a design table, editing the values in the table can change the numerical values of those dimensional constraints for any model version. In Figure 6.65, selecting and editing the appropriate cell in the design table changed the height of the L-bracket. In Figure 6.66, the support rib is no longer present because it was suppressed in the design table. When suppressing a feature, remember to be cautious, because suppressing a feature will also suppress its entire progeny.

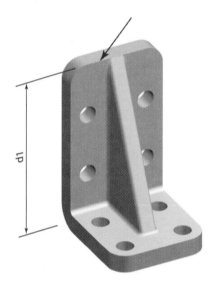

	Hole 3	Hole 4	Hole 7	Hole 8	Hole 9	Hole 10	Rib1	d1	d3	d12
Version 1	U	U	U	U	U	U	U	69.00	69.00	45.00
Version 2	U	U	U	U	S	S	U	60.00	50.00	45.00
Version 3	S	S	S	S	S	S	S	30.00	N/A	30.00

S = Suppressed
U = Unsuppressed

FIGURE 6.65. The height of the L-bracket in the model has been changed by changing the value of the cell in the design table associated with this parameter.

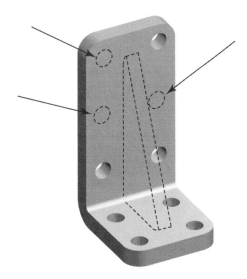

	Hole 3	Hole 4	Hole 7	Hole 8	Hole 9	Hole 10	Rib1	d1	d3	d12
Version 1	U	U	S	S	S	U	S	80.00	69.00	45.00
Version 2	U	U	U	U	S	S	U	60.00	50.00	45.00
Version 3	S	S	S	S	S	S	S	30.00	N/A	30.00

S = Suppressed
U = Unsuppressed

FIGURE 6.66. Features in the model can appear or not appear by changing their suppression states in the design table.

6.11 Strategies for Making a Model

You have a blank computer display in front of you, and your solid modeling software is running. So where do you start? The first step in modeling a solid part is to decompose it into features. Study the part and try to identify the base feature. Expanding on a previous statement, the base feature should be something that describes the overall shape of the part or something that gives you the greatest amount of functional detail that can be created with a single extrusion, rotation, sweep, or blend. Next, break the rest of the part into subsections that can be created using extruded, revolved, swept, or blended shapes. Look for standard features such as holes and slots that are manufactured using a particular process. Identify the edge features such as chamfers and rounds. Once you have studied the part, you can create the model using the following eight-step procedure:

1. Create any datum geometries or paths required to create the base geometry.
2. Sketch and constrain profiles needed for the base.
3. Extrude, rotate, sweep, or blend to create the base.
4. Create any necessary datum geometries or paths to create the next feature.

5. For sketched features, sketch and constrain or otherwise specify the feature profiles; then extrude, rotate, sweep, or blend to create the feature.

6. For standard features such as holes and edge features, specify the desired parameters and placement on the existing geometry.

7. Array or mirror the feature if necessary to create identical features.

8. Repeat steps 4–9 until the model is complete.

Once the model is complete, it can be modified to become more robust. For example, additional associative constraints may be added in place of dimensional constraints or design tables may be created for families of parts.

6.11.01 Step-by-Step Example 1—The Guide Block

Consider the guide block in Figure 6.67 as an example. How would you build a solid model for this part? What should be its base feature? What are its secondary features?

One reasonable base feature would be an extrusion made with the profile shown in Figure 6.68. This extrusion would capture many details of the part in a single operation and is representative of the general shape of the part. The sketch is made on one of the basic planes and is geometrically and dimensionally constrained. Note the use of horizontal and vertical geometry constraints, which would likely be applied automatically if the segments were sketched approximately in the orientations shown. Also note that a corner of the profile is grounded by constraining the vertex to be coincident with the origin of the coordinate system; therefore, dimensional constraints locating the profile on the plane are not needed. Note the use of the colinear constraint on the two short horizontal sketch segments, which eliminates the need to place separate dimensional constraints on the height of the segments. Once the profile is complete, it can be extruded to the width of the part, as shown in Figure 6.68(d).

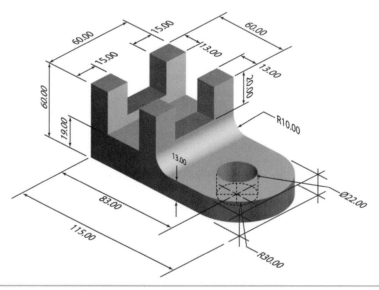

FIGURE 6.67. A solid model of this part is to be created. What operations should be performed, and in what sequence should they be made?

FIGURE 6.68. The base feature is created by sketching on one of the basic modeling planes (a), constraining the sketch to create a profile (b), and extruding the profile (c) to the required depth to obtain the desired result (d).

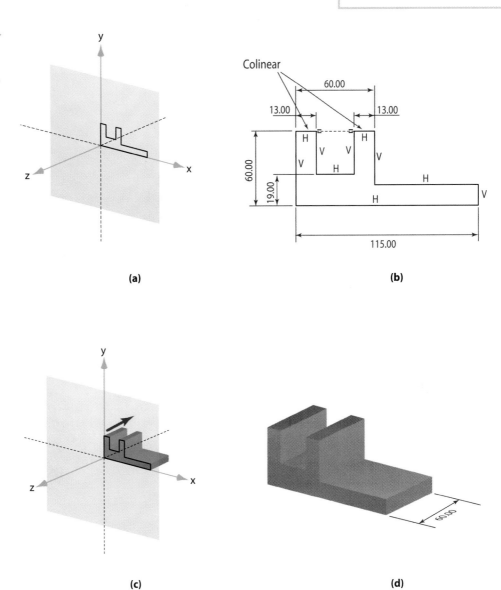

(a)

(b)

(c)

(d)

The first feature to be added is the slot across the upper portion of the part. The slot can be made on the model by an extruded cut using a rectangular profile on the sketching plane shown in Figure 6.69. Geometric and dimensional constraints are added to the sketch. One edge of the sketch is constrained to be colinear with the top edge of the base feature, guaranteeing that the slot always will be a slot (and not a square hole) if the height of the part increases. An extruded cut is then made by extruding the completed profile to the limit of the part or through the entire part. If this extruded cut was made to a specific length just beyond the limit of the part (e.g., with a blind extrusion extending past the part), the resulting model would appear identical to the desired model. However, blind extrusions like this are usually considered poor modeling practice, because if selected length constraints of the part are increased, the slot no longer extends entirely through the part.

Next, the hole is added. Simple through holes can be created as a cut feature by selecting the desired plane or face of the existing solid, sketching a circle, and extruding a cut or negative feature. However, a better way to make a hole is to use the standard

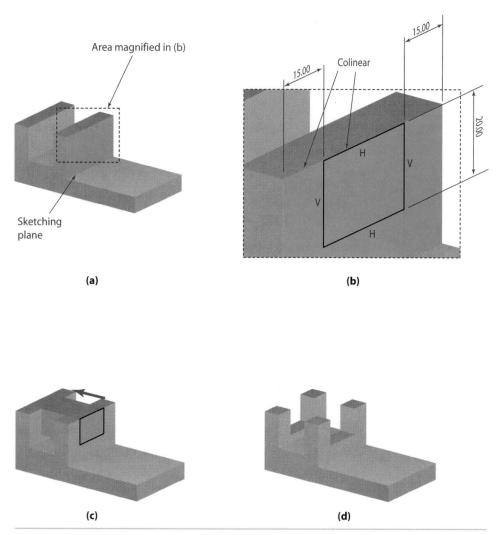

FIGURE 6.69. A slot is created by selecting a surface on the model to be the sketching plane in (a), on which a sketch is created and constrained in the magnified view in (b). The profile is extruded to the end of the part in (c), and the material is removed to create the result in (d).

hole feature, which will identify the feature as a hole in the database. Therefore, if your part is to be manufactured by an automated production system, the holes can be recognized and automatically drilled or bored. The way that the location dimensions of the hole are included in the model is also important. Why does this matter? Looking at the part, you might assume that the hole should stay centered on the width of the part. What will happen if the width of the part changes? Wouldn't you want the hole to remain centered on the width of the part? Using an associative constraint on the width location of the hole, making it always equal to one-half the part's width, ensures that the design intent will be maintained. No matter who uses your model or changes the dimensions, the intended symmetry will remain embedded in the part. Adding the hole with its associative constraint is shown in Figure 6.70.

Finally, the round and fillet features need to be added to the model geometry. Rounds and fillets are associated with particular edges, so no sketching is involved for this step. Simply pick the desired edge and apply the round or fillet feature, specifying the desired radius. The result of adding the rounds is shown in Figure 6.71, and the fillet is shown in Figure 6.72. There are no array or mirror features, so the model is now complete.

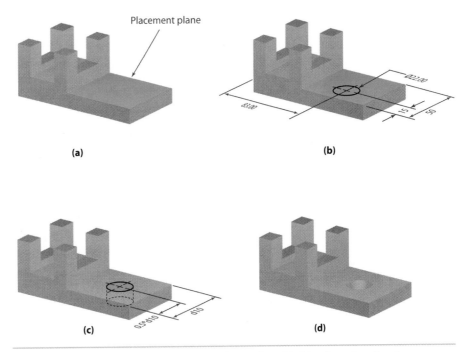

FIGURE 6.70. The surface to which the hole is to be added is selected as the placement plane in (a). The location and diameter of the hole are specified in (b). An associative constraint is used on the variable names to ensure that it remains centered in (c), and the final result is shown in (d).

FIGURE 6.71. The edges to be rounded are selected in (a), and the radius is specified in (b) as an associative constraint to ensure a full radius across the part. The result of the rounding operation is shown in (c).

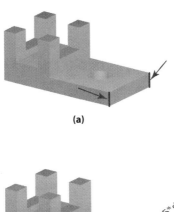

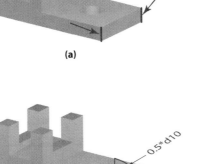

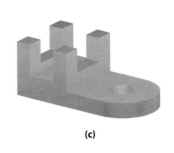

FIGURE 6.72. The edge to be filleted is selected in (a), and the radius is specified in (b). The result of the fillet operation is shown in (c).

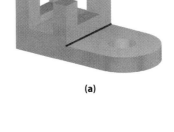

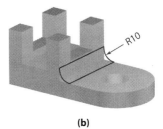

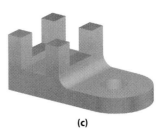

Depending on the design intent, several different modeling strategies can be used for the same part. If the designer wants the entire part to be symmetrical, another way to achieve the desired symmetry would be to create a two-sided extrusion of the base profile from the original sketching plane. By creating a two-sided extrusion, no extra datum planes are needed to ensure symmetry. Then the slot is constrained to be symmetrical across the plane, and the hole center is constrained to lie in the symmetry plane.

6.11.02 Step-by-Step Example 2—The Mounting Brace

The mounting brace shown in Figure 6.73 includes two mounting plates with holes connected by a cross-shaped web. The base feature is not as easily identifiable as in the previous example. Also, one mounting plate is set at an angle with respect to the other mounting plate, which is located on the bottom of the part. Note that no dimensions are given for the location of the web on either mounting plate because the web is assumed to be centered on both plates. The height of the web is measured at the center of the cross section. Creating the model of this part provides a good example of how datum axes and datum planes are used to help create and locate geometry.

A rectangular block that will help form the bottom mounting plate is selected as the base feature. Even though this rectangular block does not dominate the overall part shape, it is easy to locate and create; and the other features can be easily located and created from it. The sketch, profile, and extrusion of this simple base using the basic modeling planes are shown in Figure 6.74. The initial sketch is made on datum plane 1. Note that the origin is not used to constrain the location of the profile. The sketch is to be symmetrical across datum planes 2 and 3. The strategy used to achieve symmetry may vary depending on your software. Some software allows you to place symmetry constraints across the basic datum planes that appear as edges in the sketch view, such as datums 2 and 3 in this example. Otherwise, a datum axis must be used as a centerline. With some solid modeling software, datum axes are present at the intersections of the basic modeling planes and need not be created. Sometimes you may need to create datum axis 1 at the intersection of datum planes 1 and 3 and datum axis 2 at the

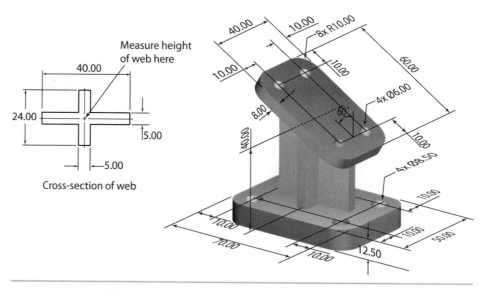

FIGURE 6.73. A solid model of this part is to be created. What operations should be performed, and in what sequence should they be made?

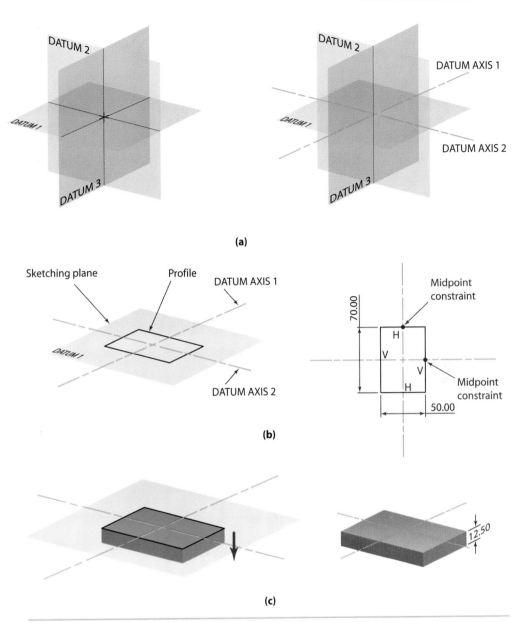

FIGURE 6.74. To create the base feature, datum axes are added to the intersections of the basic modeling planes in (a). Those axes are used to help center the base profile in (b) by constraining the midpoints of the segments to be colinear with the axes. The base feature is extruded to the required depth in (c).

intersection of datum planes 2 and 3. Now the midpoints of two adjacent legs of the rectangle can be constrained to lie on the datum axes using either coincidence or colinearity constraints. With these constraints, the rectangular profile will be centered about the axes and will remain centered about the axes if the design is modified in the future. The extrusion direction is chosen to be downward from datum plane 3, thus putting that datum plane on top of the base.

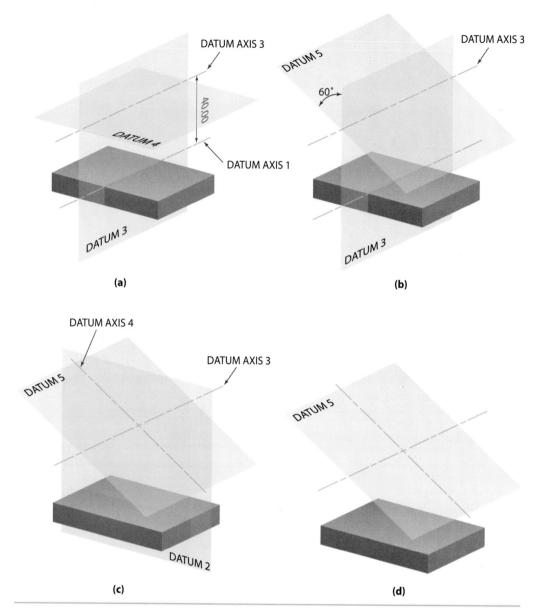

FIGURE 6.75. To create the angled feature, datum axis 3 is created in (a) above the midline of the model using intermediate datum plane 4 created above and parallel to the top of the base extrusion. Angled datum plane 5 is created through the new datum axis in (b). Datum axis 4 is created at the intersection of datum plane 5 and basic modeling plane 2 in (c) to create datum axes that can be used to locate the center of the angled feature, as shown in (d).

The next major feature to be added is the angled mounting plate. It may seem peculiar to create disconnected geometry, but you will soon see how useful this strategy can be. No sketching plane is available for creating the angled plate; so before the extrusion is created, some additional datum geometries need to be created. In addition to the datum (sketching) plane, some datum axes are needed to position the sketch at the center of the web. These datum geometries, shown in Figure 6.75, are as follows:

- Datum plane 4—located 40 mm above and parallel to datum plane 1
- Datum axis 3—at the intersection of datum plane 3 and datum plane 4

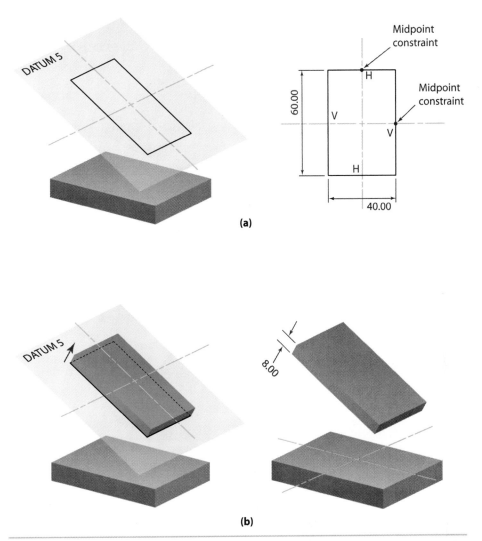

FIGURE 6.76. The profile for the angled feature is sketched and constrained on the angled datum plane in (a), constraining the midpoints of the segments to be colinear with the axes. The profile is extruded to the required depth in (b).

- Datum plane 5— through datum axis 3, 60 degrees from datum plane 3
- Datum axis 4—at the intersection of datum plane 2 and datum plane 4

Datum axes 1 and 2 mark the center of the base; and datum axes 3 and 4 mark the center of the angled mounting plate, where the web will be located.

To create the angled mounting plate, a sketch of its rectangular profile is constrained and dimensioned on datum plane 5, as shown in Figure 6.76. Note that each of the midpoints of two adjacent edges of the profile have been constrained to be colinear with datum axis 3 or 4. In this way, the rectangular profile is always centered about the axes. The sketched profile is then extruded to form the angled mounting plate.

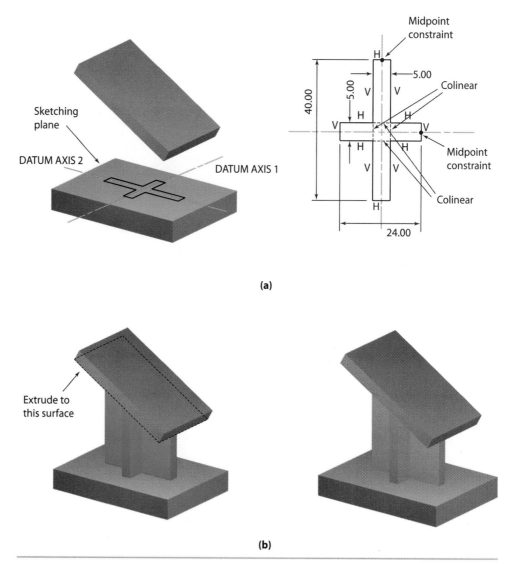

(a)

(b)

FIGURE 6.77. To create the web, the top of the base is selected as the sketching plane in (a) and the profile of the web is constrained using midpoint and colinear constraints to ensure symmetry. The profile is extruded to the underside of the angled feature in (b).

The top of the base feature is used as the sketching plane for the profile of the web. A cross-shaped profile is used, as shown in Figure 6.77. The midpoints of the line segments representing the thickness of two adjacent legs of the cross are constrained to be coincident with datum axis 1 or with datum axis 2. Note the use of colinear constraints on the edges of opposing legs of the cross. These constraints make the thickness of the legs the same on opposite sides when one of the legs is dimensioned. The profile is extruded up to the next surface that it intersects, which is the bottom of the angled mounting plate.

The rounds are added using the round and fillet feature creation tool by selecting the edges shown in Figure 6.78 and specifying the desired round radius. By grouping the rounds in one feature, their radii will be equal and will remain equal as the part is modified in the future. Adding holes to both mounting plates using a hole feature creation tool is shown in Figure 6.79. The centers of the holes are located on the upper surface of each plate, with their locations specified relative to the edges of the plates. The holes are then defined by their diameters and depth (all the way through to the next surface on each plate). Note that you would not want to use the "through all" option on these holes, as the holes from the angled plate would extend through the baseplate as well. The model is now complete.

FIGURE 6.78. The edges for rounding are selected in (a), and the desired radius of the rounds is applied in (b).

(a)   **(b)**

FIGURE 6.79. The holes are added to the base feature in (a) and to the angled feature in (b).

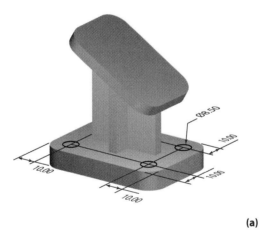

(a)

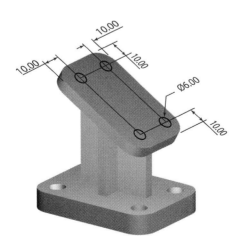

(b)

6.11.03 Step-by-Step Example 3—The Handwheel

The part shown in Figure 6.80 is a handwheel. It consists of a cylindrical hub with a D-shaped hole at its center, a circular rim with a circular cross section, and spokes that connect the hub to the rim. The handwheel is a good example of a model that should be created with a combination of rotation, sweep, and array.

A good base feature might be either the hub or the rim. Both of these features can be created by revolving a suitable profile. Some solid modelers will let you create both features in the same operation, as will be shown here. One of the basic modeling planes is selected as the sketching plane. A centerline will be required on the same sketch as the profiles, as shown in Figure 6.81. The centerline is placed coincident with the intersection of the sketching plane and another basic modeling plane. The length of the centerline is unimportant. The rectangular profile for the hub is sketched and constrained as shown in Figure 6.81(a). The circular profile of the rim is sketched and

FIGURE 6.80. The handwheel to be modeled is shown in (a). It is cut away in (b) to help reveal all of its dimensions. The D-shaped center hole and a cross section of a spoke are magnified in (c) to show their dimensions.

(a)

(b)

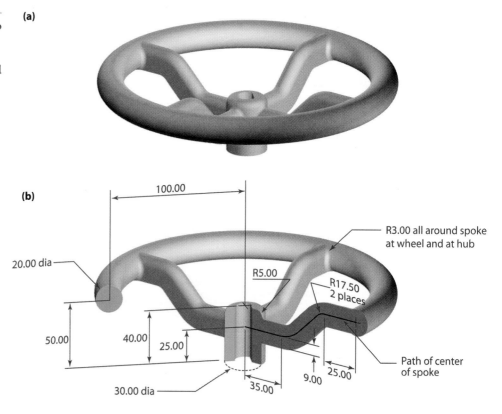

(c)

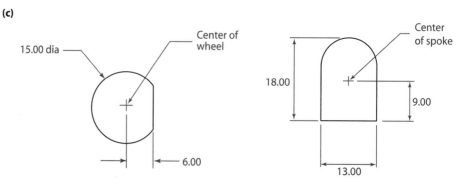

Dimensions of D-shaped hole (enlarged view)

Cross-section of spoke (enlarged view)

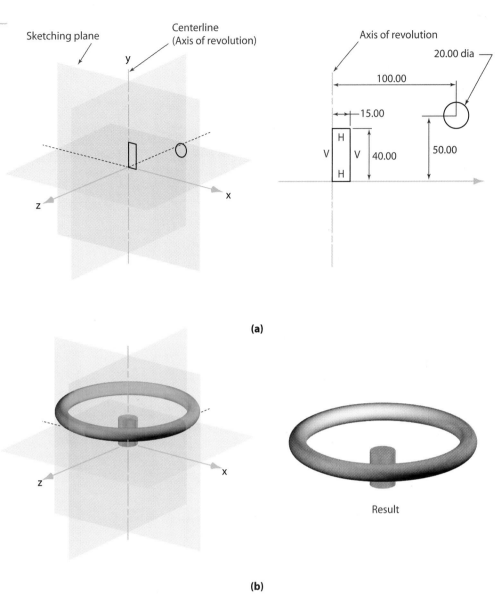

FIGURE 6.81. The profile for the base feature is sketched in (a), and the base feature is created by revolution in (b).

constrained. Notice that the two profiles are not constrained to each other, but only to the basic planes and centerline or axis of revolution. Thus, if the shape of the hub or rim is changed, the other profile in the sketch will not change. Both profiles are rotated 360 degrees about the centerline in the same operation to produce the base feature. The base feature appears as two disconnected solids, but this is fine as long as you remember to connect them later.

The next feature to be created is one of the spokes. Because it will be created using a sweep, a path will be required in addition to the cross-section profile, as shown in Figure 6.82(a). The path can be created on the same basic modeling plane that was used for sketching the base profiles. Even though the same sketching plane is used, the profiles for the base and the path are considered separate entities. The spoke cross section must be sketched on a plane perpendicular to the path. The only planes available for sketching in this example are the basic modeling planes. Therefore, you will start the swept profile on the basic modeling plane at the center of the hub, which is perpendicular to the desired path.

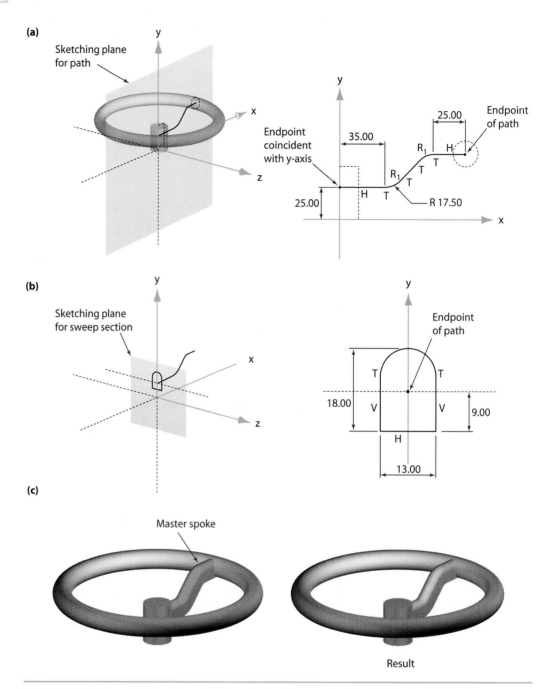

FIGURE 6.82. The profile for the path is sketched and constrained in (a). The profile for the sweep section is sketched and constrained in (b). The master spoke is created by sweeping in (c).

Some software requires the designer to create the path first, then the cross-section profile; other software reverses the order. For this example, the creation of the path will be described first. The path is comprised of three line segments and two arcs. The starting point on the hub is constrained to be coincident with the rotation axis, and the endpoint is constrained to be coincident with the center of the circle that represents the profile of the rim. Additional geometric and dimensional constraints are added, as shown in Figure 6.82(a). The profile must be created on a sketching plane that is perpendicular to the path at one of its endpoints. As previously noted, another one of the basic modeling planes satisfies this requirement, as shown in Figure 6.82; so creating a new datum plane is not necessary. The profile is sketched and constrained. Notice that the bottom of the cross-section profile does not lie on the basic modeling plane; its

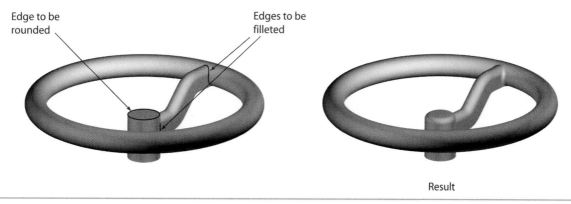

FIGURE 6.83. The edge at the top of the hub is rounded, and the intersections of the spoke are filleted to the specified dimensions.

vertical location is controlled by a dimensional constraint that is measured from the endpoint of the path curve. A sweep operation using the just-created path and profile is performed to create a solid spoke. A round is added to the top of the hub, and fillets are added at the intersections of the spoke with the hub and rim, as shown in Figure 6.83.

Multiple spokes are created with a circular array. The axis for the array is selected to be the same as the axis of rotation of the base. The features to be arrayed are selected to be the swept spoke as well as all of the fillets on it. Most solid modeling systems allow multiple features to be arrayed or patterned in a single operation. This is particularly useful when a parent feature has children that should be included in the pattern. In fact, some software systems automatically include the child features in the pattern. Some software requires a separate pattern operation for each feature. In either case, four spokes are made with equal rotational spacing, as shown in Figure 6.84.

The final feature to be added is the D-shaped hole. This feature is created as an extruded cut, as shown in Figure 6.85. The top surface of the hub is selected as the sketching plane. The profile is sketched and constrained. Note that the center of the arc for the hole is constrained to be coincident with the center axis of the hub. The profile is extruded to the next intersecting surface to create the cut and thus completes the model. Notice that the D-shaped cut for the hole was performed after the creation of the spokes. What would happen if the hole was created before the spokes were modeled? Since the path of the master spoke starts at the axis of revolution of the hub, the spoke is essentially embedded in the hub. If the hole was created first, material would be created in this region and would fill up portions of the hole when the spokes were created. A good rule of thumb to remember when modeling is to create solid geometry first (protrusions), then remove material (cuts) whenever possible.

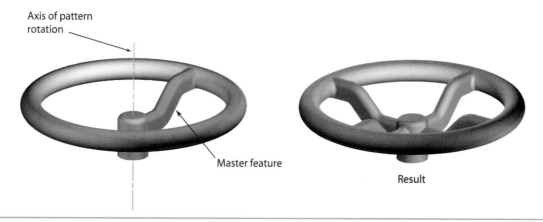

FIGURE 6.84. Multiple spokes are created by a circular pattern, or array, using the center of the wheel as the axis of rotation.

FIGURE 6.85. The D-shaped hole is created by selecting the top of the hub as the sketching plane in (a). The profile is sketched and constrained in (b). The profile cut is extruded through the hub in (c).

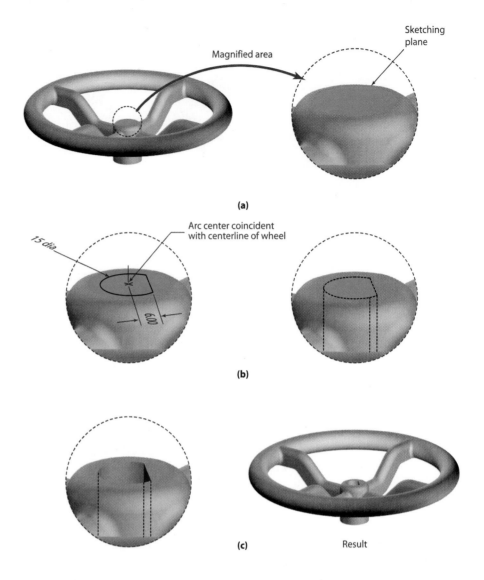

6.12 Extraction of 2-D Drawings

Nearly all solid modeling software packages have a facility for easily creating 2-D engineering drawings from solid models. Formal engineering drawing, which is covered in detail in later chapters, displays the part with all of its features in multiple predesignated views. It also displays the sizes and locations of the features. Solid modelers, which display a model from any viewpoint, can easily create the required views and display dimensions, thus greatly reducing the time and effort required to produce a drawing. Note that the dimensional constraints used in creating the solid model may be different from the dimension values that should be displayed on the engineering drawing. For example, the drawing is required to display all of the dimensions that are necessary for manufacturing the part. Some of these dimension values may be controlled by geometric constraints and are not included in the model as dimensional constraints. You will learn more about proper dimensioning practices in later chapters of this text. An example of a 2-D engineering drawing produced from a solid model is shown in Figure 6.86.

FIGURE 6.86. A typical solid model and a formal working drawing extracted from the model.

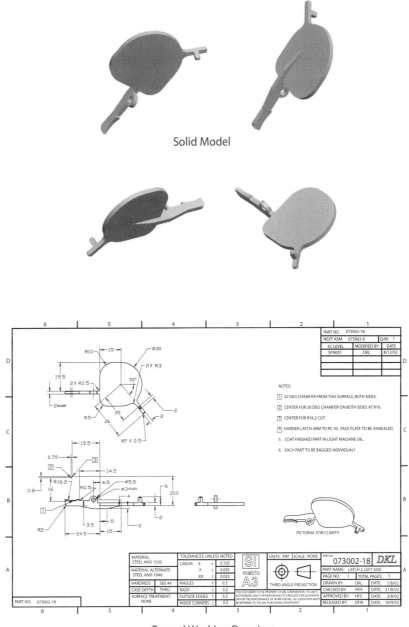

Solid Model

Formal Working Drawing

CAUTION   Inexperienced users of solid modeling software usually commit common errors in creating models. Some of these errors are merely a nuisance, such as generating extra unnecessary dimensions. Other errors do not let the user proceed with the creation process and must be resolved before the user can proceed. Still other errors let the user create a model that may appear like the one desired; however, problems manifest themselves later when the model is edited or when the part is fabricated. The following sections are a compilation of common errors made in solid modeling.

Base Profile Not Properly Positioned

A 3-D model is defined not only by its geometry but also by its location in space. When a solid model is built, the location of the model should be defined relative to the origin of the model's coordinate system. Defining this location is done by defining the location of the profile used for the base feature, most commonly by making one vertex (or point on the centerline) on the profile coincident with the origin. If this is not done, as shown in Figure 6.87, the profile will not be fully constrained and extra dimensional constraints would have to be added to define the location of the profile. These extra dimensional constraints are meaningless and add confusion to the model.

Invalid Profile

Valid profiles were discussed earlier in the chapter. Often invalid profiles are created inadvertently, usually through careless use of the computer's pointing device. Three common errors are shown in Figure 6.88. In Figure 6.88(b), the user attempted to close the sketch to make a valid profile, but missed the target endpoint and left the sketch open. Valid profiles must be closed. In Figure 6.88(c), while attempting to close the sketch, the user crossed over the first sketch element with the final sketch element. Valid profiles cannot cross, overlap, or self-intersect. A similar problem occurs when the profile contains a duplicate line segment. Overlapping lines can be very difficult to

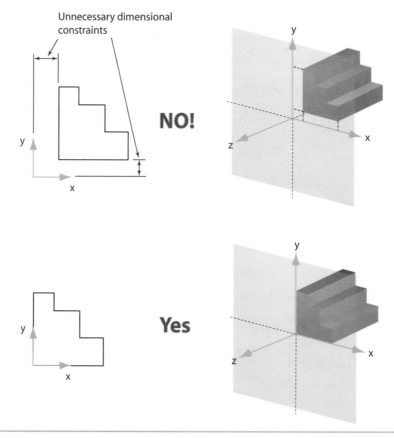

FIGURE 6.87. The base feature should be aligned with the origin whenever possible to avoid the need for extra dimensions.

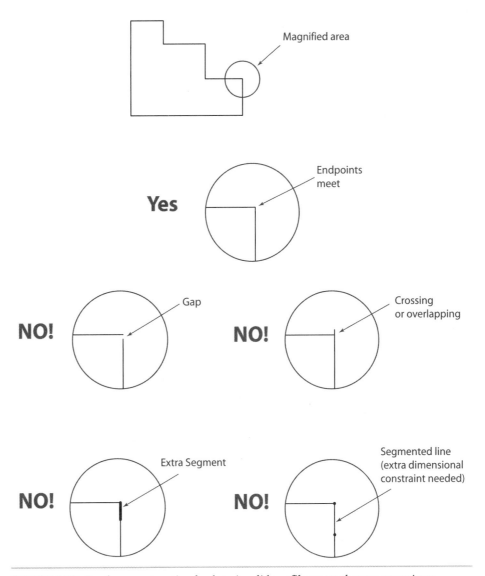

FIGURE 6.88. Careless construction leads to invalid profile errors that are sometimes difficult to find.

find; you may want to delete a line segment if you suspect that it might be duplicated, then redraw the line if no duplicate is found. In Figure 6.88(d), the user inadvertently used two line segments in place of one continuous line segment, resulting in an internal vertex along the desired edge. The profile cannot be fully constrained until the lengths of both line segments are defined. This results in an unnecessary and meaningless dimensional constraint. A profile with a segmented line like this is considered poor modeling practice. Invalid profile errors are usually difficult to see and, therefore, difficult to resolve. Some sketching editors alert the user by highlighting the location of gaps or intersections. Otherwise, you may be faced with the tedious task of searching for the source of the problem. Careful use of the computer's pointing device usually keeps these errors to a minimum.

Profile Not Constrained with Design Intent

It is sometimes tempting to use dimensional constraints instead of geometric constraints that reflect the intent of the design, because application of dimensional constraints follows traditional drafting practice and is typically easy to do in a sketching editor. The availability of geometric constraints in solid modelers offers an opportunity to include aspects of design intent that were previously unavailable in 2-D drafting. Consider the profile for the base feature of a rod clamp, shown in Figure 6.89. The profile is fully constrained, specifying the location of the center of the circular cutout. The design intent, however, is for the circular cutout to be concentric with the rounded part of the exterior of the clamp. If the overall height of the profile was changed, this design intent would not be maintained. In replacing the location dimensions of the circular cutout with a concentricity constraint (coincident arc centers), the design intent is maintained as the overall height of the profile changes. Also note that symmetry constraints on the lower edge of the part ensure that the gap is centered along the axis of the clamp and that both sides have equal thickness.

FIGURE 6.89. The desired behavior is for the outer radius of this part to be concentric with the hole. A geometric constraint rather than a dimensional constraint is preferred to guarantee this behavior, even if other dimensions are changed.

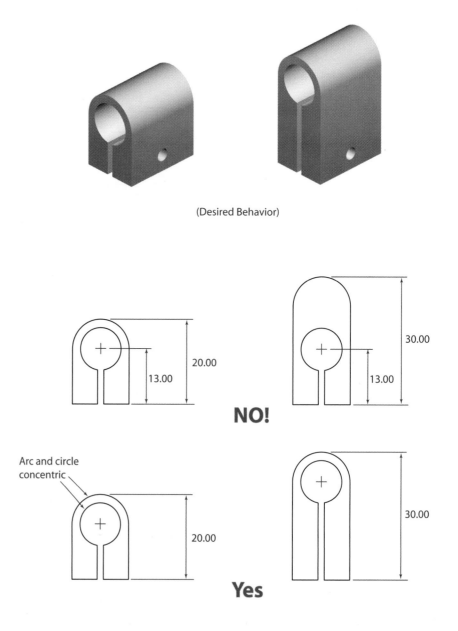

(Desired Behavior)

Profile Overconstrained by Automatic Constraints

For the most part, sketching editors that intelligently apply presumed geometric constraints are very useful. For example, a great deal of time is saved when lines that are sketched to be almost horizontal or almost vertical have these constraints applied automatically. However, automatic constraint application can sometimes lead to problems, particularly when the constraints are applied inadvertently. If your sketching editor has been set to search automatically for equal element sizes, as in Figure 6.90, line segments created to almost the same length in the sketch will automatically be constrained equal in length to each other. Arcs created to almost the same radius as other arcs also will be automatically constrained equal in radii to each other. If that is your intent, then fine. But if that is not your intent, then you must be careful not to create line segments or arcs that are too close in size to each other or you must delete the unintentional constraints when they appear and replace them with separate dimensional constraints on each entity. Figure 6.91 shows a case where an intelligent colinear constraint has been unintentionally applied. In Figure 6.92, an unintentional perpendicularity constraint has been applied. In all cases of unintentional constraints, the addition of the desired geometric constraints or dimensional constraints cause the profile to be overconstrained. In this case, you need to delete the unintentional constraints and then add constraints to capture your design intent.

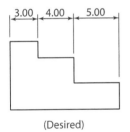

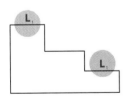

FIGURE 6.90. Automatic geometric constraints in the sketching editor sometimes cause equal length constraints to be applied inadvertently.

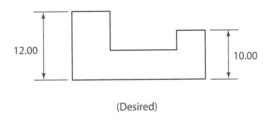

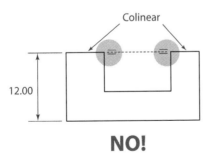

FIGURE 6.91. Automatic geometric constraints in the sketching editor sometimes cause colinear constraints to be applied inadvertently.

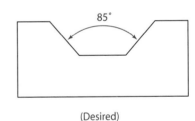

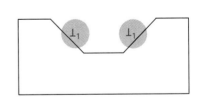

FIGURE 6.92. Automatic geometric constraints in the sketching editor sometimes cause perpendicular constraints to be applied inadvertently.

Dimensional, Instead of Geometric, Constraints

A common error in making extruded cuts and protrusions is to use a blind depth to extrude the feature a specific distance, when what is really desired is to extrude the feature to a particular surface. In the model shown in Figure 6.93, for example, the design intent is for the extruded cut to extend all the way through the base. However, the cut was created by specifying a dimensional constraint for the length of the extrusion. The specified length of the extrusion is an unnecessary, meaningless dimension, because the cut was to extend all the way through. Also, if the thickness of the base increases, as sometimes occurs when the design changes, the extruded cut may no longer extend all the way through the base. By specifying, instead, that the extruded cut is to continue until it intersects the bottom of the base, the design intent is always fulfilled.

In the model shown in Figure 6.94, the design intent is for the protrusion to extend from the angled datum plane to the top of the base. However, it was created by specifying a dimension for the length of the extrusion. The specified length of the extrusion is a meaningless dimension, because the protrusion was to extend to the top surface of the base. Also, if the thickness of the base decreases, as may occur if the design ever

FIGURE 6.93. When a cut is to extend to a specific surface or all the way through a part, cutting to a specified distance should not be done.

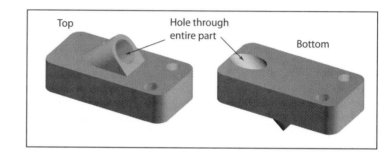

FIGURE 6.94. When a protrusion is to extend to a specific surface, extending to a specified distance should not be done.

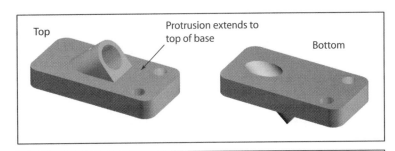

changes, the extruded protrusion may extend beyond the bottom of the base. By specifying, instead, that the extruded protrusion is to continue until it intersects the top of the base, the design intent is always fulfilled.

Using a Cut or Protrusion Instead of a Built-in Feature

A common practice for beginning designers is to use a cut feature to create a hole, for example. Figure 6.95 shows the creation of a counterbored hole using two concentric circular cut features compared to using the built-in counterbored hole feature. Even though the geometry of the resultant holes is identical, the use of cut features can result in undesired results. What if you decreased the diameter of the counterbore to a value that was smaller than the diameter of the through hole? What if the location constraints for the two cut features had different values? The resulting geometry would not represent your intent, a counterbored hole. The built-in counterbored hole feature does not permit such changes in the geometry. Another reason to use the built-in features is to capture more design information. While it may seem easy to sketch a circle on a given surface to create

FIGURE 6.95. Functional features such as this counterbored hole should be created as features and not constructed from extruded cuts or protrusions.

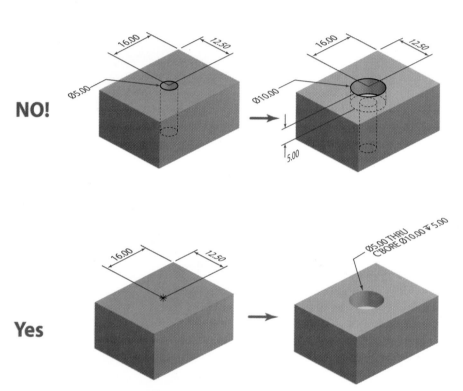

a hole, the solid modeler may be integrated with a larger, more sophisticated CAD/CAM system that might not recognize the feature as a hole. If the CAD system has intelligent assembly capabilities, it may automatically align the axis of the hole with the shaft of a bolt or screw. If you are creating manufacturing plans from your solid model, the software may recognize certain types of holes and specify the appropriate fabrication sequences automatically. But when you create the hole using a cut feature, the CAD system does not know it is a hole; and you will have to specify the assembly and fabrication sequences yourself. That leaves a great deal of room for errors such as putting bolts in upside down or omitting one of the machining operations. To save time and avoid errors in later applications, it is prudent to use the appropriate feature type that imbeds the special attributes of the feature in your solid model.

6.13 Chapter Summary

In this chapter, you learned about features and parametric solid modeling. Features are distinctive shapes that compose a solid model. Parametric models have the capability to be modified by changing the sizes and other attributes of the features in the model. The history of solid modeling shows how CAD has evolved from wireframe to solid models and provides some insight regarding the strategies used to create solid models.

Part modeling can be a very complicated process, but some general strategies make it easier to create good, robust solid models. But before you go to the computer, you need to consider how the part model will be used. Later applications such as manufacturing and documentation will be easier when the part is modeled properly. Thus, you need to plan carefully and ask yourself some questions before the first feature is created: How can you decompose that complicated widget into simpler features that are available on your solid modeler? Which feature should you create first? Which features are related to each other? How is the part used? Manufactured? Can standard features such as holes be modeled to imbed design intent and/or manufacturing information in addition to simple geometric characteristics? How does the part fit into an assembly? What will the engineering drawing look like? These are just a few questions you need to consider before you begin. For now, you may not know the answers to all of these questions; but as you gain experience, you will develop an appreciation for the importance of building a robust solid model that captures your design intent.

The solid modeling process begins with identification of the features of the part, followed by selection of the base feature. Profiles for extrusion, rotation, sweeps, and blends are created with sketches and are controlled using different types of geometric, dimensional, and associative constraints. After the base feature is created, other features are added to the model; these features are dependent upon the base feature or other previously created features. Care must be taken in the creation of solid models to make flexible models that are robust and that can be used for purposes such as analysis, manufacturing, and documentation.

As modeling systems continue to develop, designers and engineers want to include more information in the model to better simulate the physical characteristics of the parts. These models, called behavioral models, might include features such as physical properties, manufacturing tolerances, surface finish, and other characteristics of the parts. Besides a person's appearance, you would need to know something about his or her education or physical abilities to determine whether the person might be able to do a particular job. Likewise, a designer or an engineer may need to know more than just the shape of an object or assembly model to determine whether it will perform its intended function. As they become more realistic and can simulate the actual behavior of the parts and assemblies, product models of the future will contain even more characteristics and features.

6.14 glossary of key terms

algebraic constraints: Constraint that define the value of a selected variable as the result of an algebraic expression containing other variables from the solid model.

associative constraints: *See* algebraic constraints.

base feature: The first feature created for a part, usually a protrusion.

blend: A solid formed by a smooth transition between two or more profiles.

blind extrusion: An extrusion made to a specified length in a selected direction.

boundary representation (b-rep): A method used to build solid models from their bounding surfaces.

chamfers: Angled cut transitions between two intersecting surfaces.

child feature: A feature that is dependent upon the existence of a previously created feature.

constraints: Geometric relationships, dimensions, or equations that control the size, shape, and/or orientation of entities in a sketch or solid model.

constructive solid geometry (CSG): A method used to build solid models from primitive shapes based on Boolean set theory.

cosmetic features: Features that modify the appearance of the surface but do not alter the size or shape of the object.

cut: A feature created by the removal of solid volume from a model.

database: A collection of information for a computer and a method for interpretation of the information from which the original model can be re-created.

6.14 glossary of key terms (continued)

datum geometries: Geometric entities such as points, axes, and planes that do not actually exist on real parts, but are used to help locate and define other features.

datum planes: The planes used to define the locations of features and entities in the construction of a solid model.

design table: A table or spreadsheet that lists all of the versions of a family model, the dimensions or features that may change, and the values in any of its versions.

design tree: *See* model tree.

dimensional constraints: Measurements used to control the size or position of entities in a sketch.

dimension name: The unique alphanumeric designation of a variable dimension.

driven dimension: A variable connected to an algebraic constraint that can be modified only by user changes to the driving dimensions.

driving dimension: A variable used in an algebraic constraint to control the values of another (driven) dimension.

double-sided extrusion: A solid formed by the extrusion of a profile in both directions from its sketching plane.

extrude through all: An extrusion that begins on the sketching plane and protrudes or cuts through all portions of the solid model that it encounters.

extrude to selected surface: An extrusion where the protrusion or cut begins on the sketching plane and stops when it intersects a selected surface.

extrusion: A solid that is bounded by the surfaces swept out in space by a planar profile as it is pulled along a path perpendicular to the plane of the profile.

family model: A collection of different versions of a part in a single model that can display any of the versions.

feature array: A method for making additional features by placing copies of a master feature on the model at a specified equal spacing.

features: Distinctive geometric shapes on solid parts; 3-D geometric entities that exist to serve some function.

feature-based solid modeling: A solid modeling system that uses features to build models.

feature pattern: *See* feature array.

feature tree: *See* model tree.

fillets: Smooth transitions of the internal edge created by two intersecting surfaces and tangent to both intersecting surfaces.

form feature: A recognizable area on a solid model that has a specific function.

geometric constraints: Definitions used to control the shape of a profile sketch through geometric relationships.

graphical user interface (GUI): The format of information on the visual display of a computer, giving its user control of the input, output, and editing of the information.

ground constraint: A constraint usually applied to a new sketch to fix the location of the sketch in space.

history tree: *See* model tree.

holes: A cut feature added to a model that will often receive a fastener for system assembly.

horizontal modeling: A strategy for creating solid models that reduces parent-child relationships within the feature tree.

master feature: A feature or collection of features that is to be copied for placement at other locations in a model.

master model: In a collection of similar parts, the model that includes all of the features that may appear in any of the other parts.

mirrored feature: A feature that is created as a mirror image of a master feature.

model tree: A list of all of the features of a solid model in the order in which they were created, providing a "history" of the sequence of feature creation.

parameters: The attributes of features, such as dimensions, that can be modified.

parametric solid modeling: A solid modeling system that allows the user to vary the dimensions and other parameters of the model.

parametric techniques: Modeling techniques where all driven dimensions in algebraic expressions must be known for the value of the dependent variables to be calculated.

parent feature: A feature used in the creation of another feature, which is called its child feature.

path: The specified curve on which a profile is placed to create a swept solid.

primary modeling planes: The planes representing the XY-, XZ-, and YZ-planes in a Cartesian coordinate system.

primitives: The set of regular shapes, such as boxes, spheres, or cylinders that are used to build solid models with constructive solid geometry methods (CSG).

principal viewing planes: The planes in space on which the top, bottom, front, back, and right and left side views are projected.

profile: A planar sketch that is used to create a solid.

6.14 glossary of key terms (continued)

protrusion: A feature created by the addition of solid volume to a model.

regeneration: The process of updating the profile or part to show its new shape after constraints are added or changed.

revolved solid: A solid formed when a profile curve is rotated about an axis.

ribs: Constant thickness protrusions that extend from the surface of a part and are used to strengthen or stiffen the part.

rounds: Smooth radius transitions of external edges created by two intersecting surfaces and tangent to both intersecting surfaces.

shelling: Removing most of the interior volume of a solid model, leaving a relatively thin wall of material that closely conforms to the outer surfaces of the original model.

sketches: Collections of 2-D entities.

sketching editor: A software tool used to create and edit sketches.

sketching plane: A plane where 2-D sketches and profiles can be created.

solid model: A mathematical representation of a physical object that includes the surfaces and the interior material, usually including a computer-based simulation that produces a visual display of an object as if it existed in three dimensions.

splines: Polynomial curves that pass through multiple data points.

suppressed: Refers to the option for not displaying a selected feature.

surface model: A CAD-generated model created to show a part as a collection of intersecting surfaces that bound a solid.

swept feature: A solid that is bound by the surfaces swept out in space as a profile is pulled along a path.

trajectory: *See* path.

unsuppressed: Refers to the option for displaying a selected feature.

variational techniques: Modeling techniques in which algebraic expressions or equations that express relationships between a number of variables and constants, any one of which can be calculated when all of the others are known.

vertex: A point that is used to define the endpoint of an entity such as a line segment or the intersection of two geometric entities.

webs: Small, thin protrusions that connect two or more thicker regions on a part.

wireframe models: CAD models created using lines, arcs, and other 2-D entities to represent the edges of the part; surfaces or solid volumes are not defined.

6.15 questions for review

1. What are some of the uses of solid models?
2. What is a feature?
3. Why are features important in solid modeling?
4. What types of features can be used as base features for your solid models?
5. Why are wireframe models inferior to solid models?
6. What are the steps in creating a solid model?
7. What are some errors that make a sketch invalid for creating a solid?
8. Why is it necessary to constrain a 2-D sketch?
9. What are the different types of geometric constraints?
10. What are associative constraints?
11. What are dimensional constraints?
12. What does it mean when a feature is a child of another feature? A parent of another feature?
13. What are some errors that constitute poor modeling practices?
14. What are some examples of good modeling-strategies?

6.16 problems

1. Create the following closed-loop profiles using the 2-D drawing capabilities of your solid modeling software. Define the geometry and sizes precisely as shown, using the necessary geometric constraints. Do not over- or underconstrain the profiles.

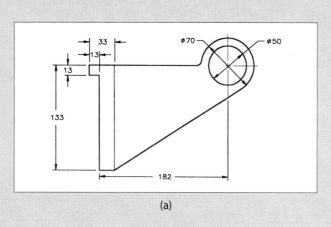

(a)

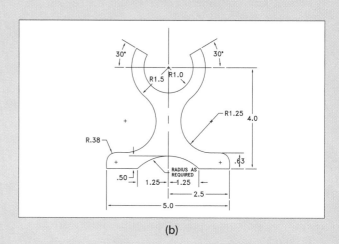

(b)

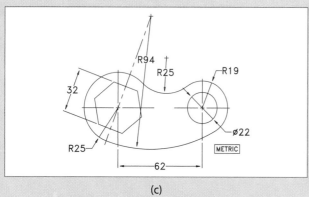

(c)

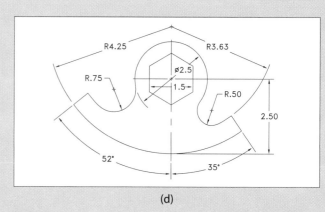

(d)

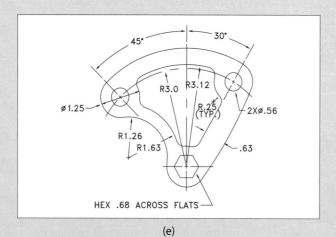

(e)

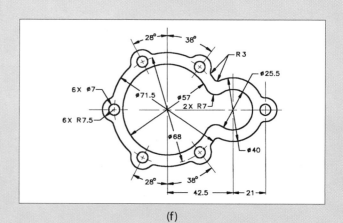

(f)

6.16 problems (continued)

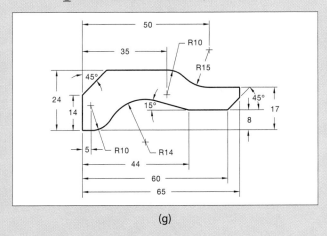

(g)

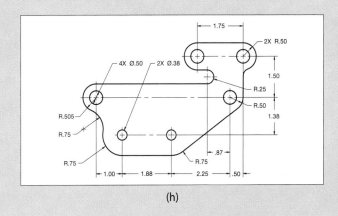

(h)

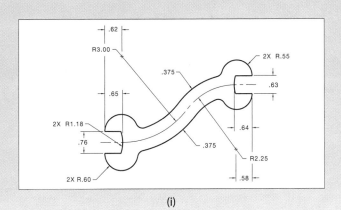

(i)

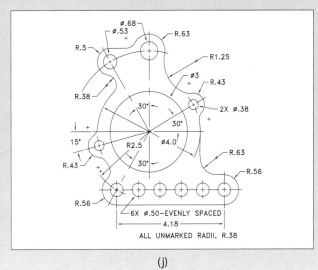

(j)

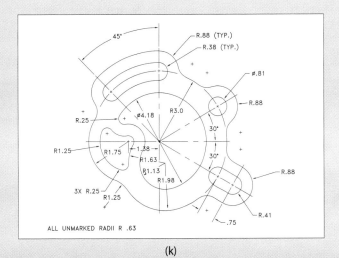

(k)

FIGURE P6.1.

6.16 problems (continued)

2. Study the following closed-loop profiles for which geometric constraints have not been added. Number each segment of the profiles and specify the necessary geometric constraints on each segment to create the final profile. Do not over- or underconstrain the profiles.

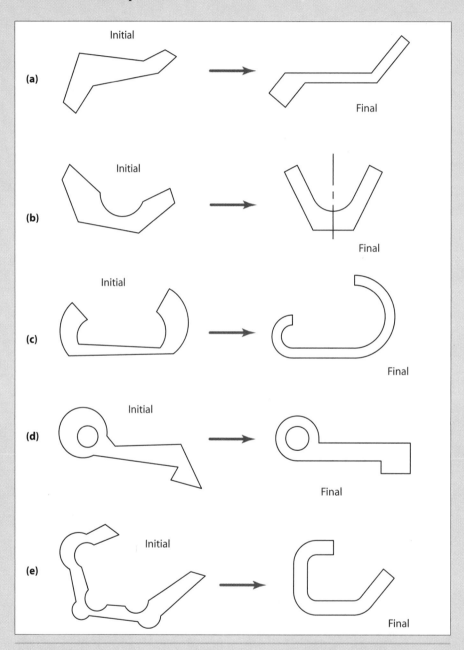

FIGURE P6.2.

6.16 problems (continued)

3. At first glance, these profiles may appear to be missing key dimensions. However, they are fully constrained by the addition of geometric constraints. Number each segment of the profiles. What were the geometric constraints used for each segment?

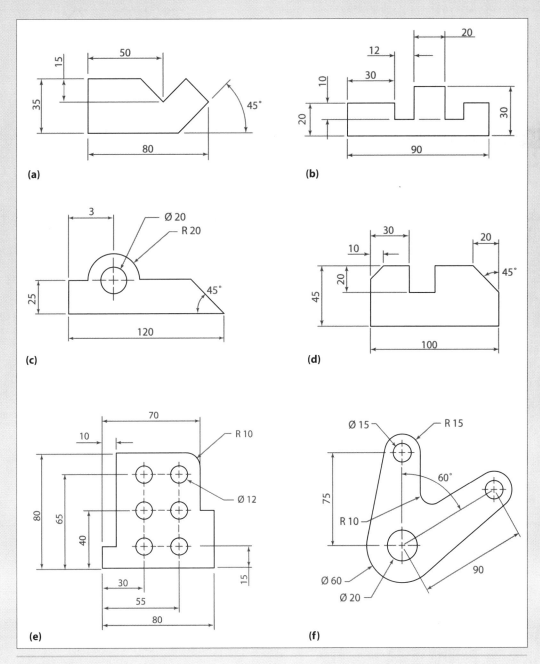

FIGURE P6.3.

6.16 problems (continued)

4. Create solid models of the following parts in your CAD system. Identify what you consider to be the base geometry for each part. Are any (child) features dependent upon the existence of other (parent) features? If so, specify the hierarchy.

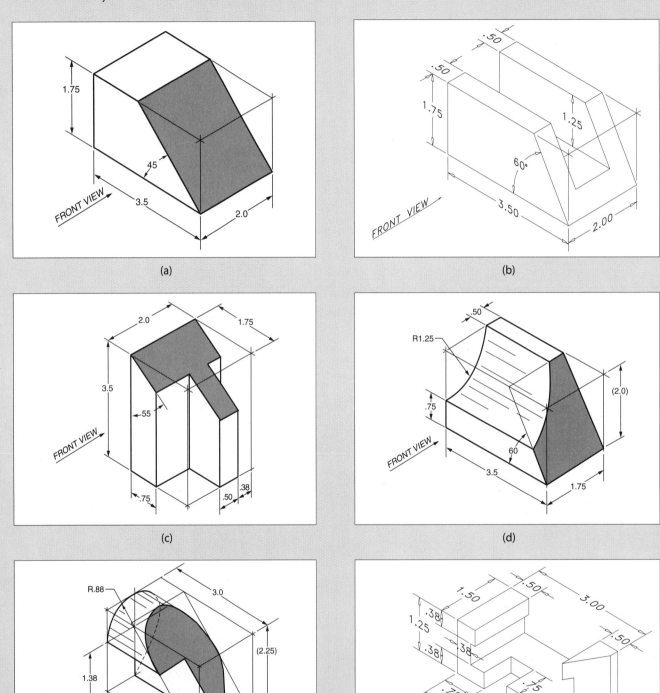

(a)

(b)

(c)

(d)

(e)

(f)

6.16 problems (continued)

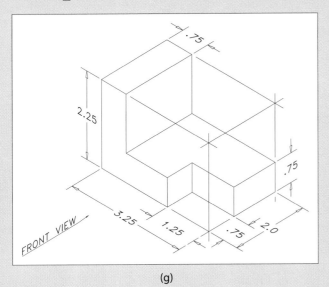

(g)

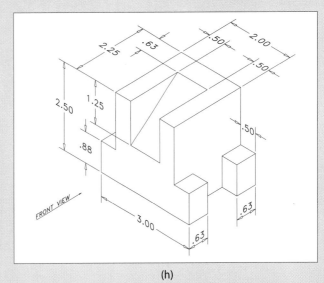

(h)

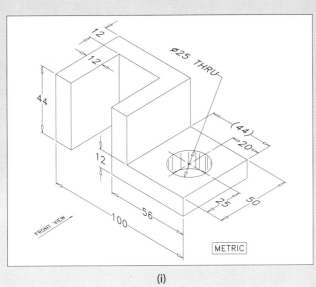

METRIC

(i)

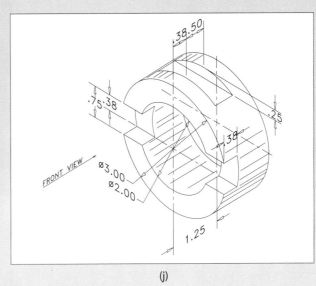

(j)

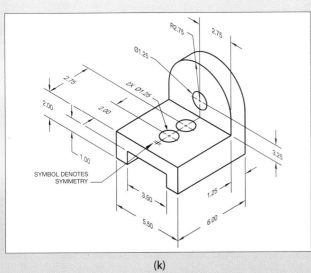

(k)

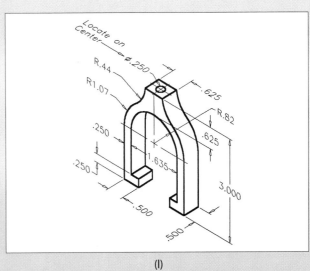

(l)

6.16 problems (continued)

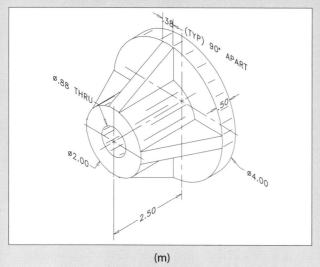

(m)

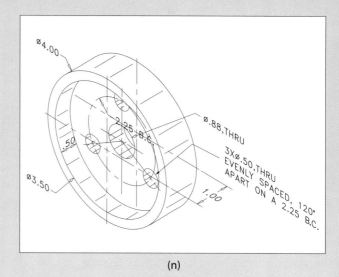

(n)

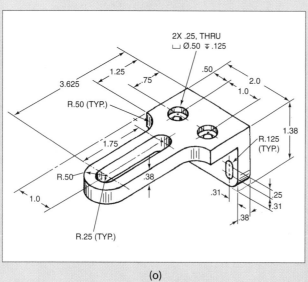

(o)

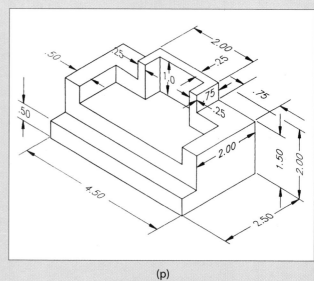

(p)

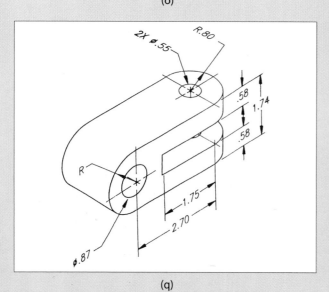

(q)

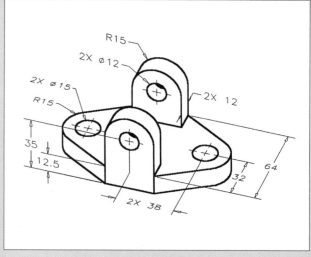

(r)

6.16 problems (continued)

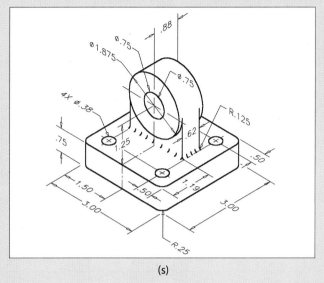

(s)

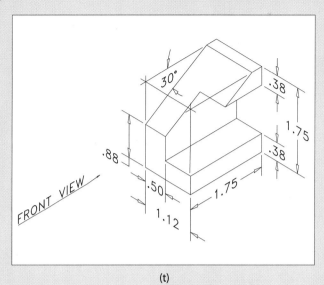

(t)

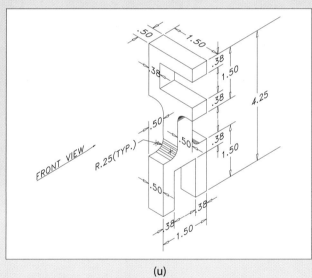

(u)

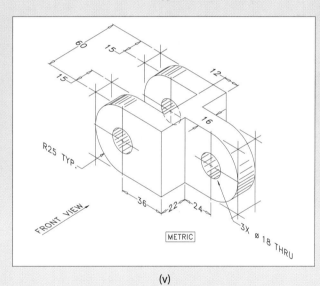

(v)

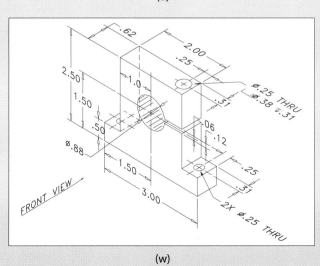

(w)

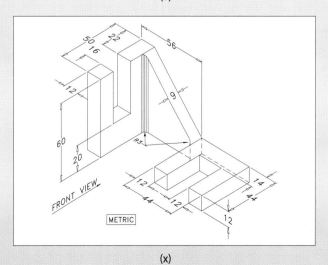

(x)

6.16 problems (continued)

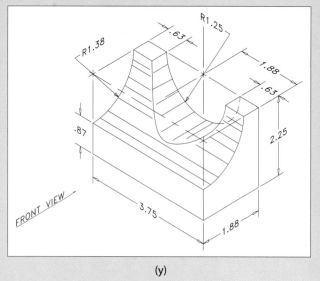

(y)

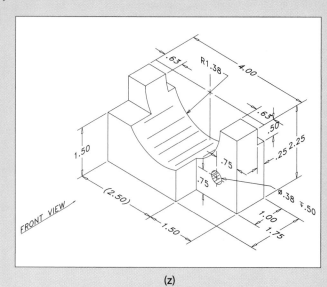

(z)

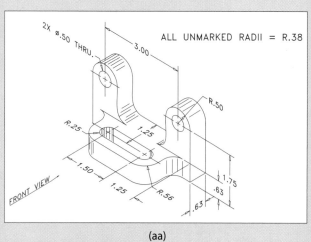

(aa)

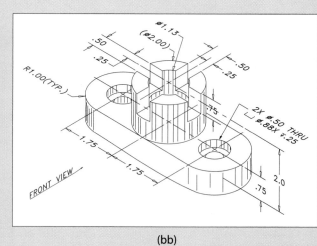

(bb)

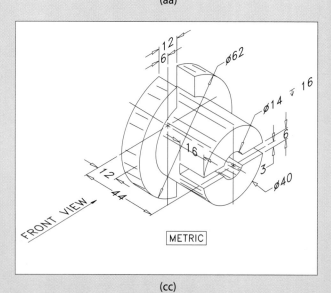

(cc)

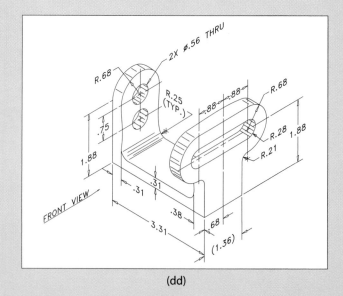

(dd)

6.16 problems (continued)

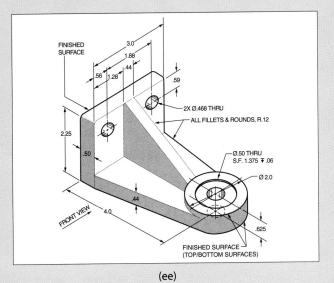

(ee)

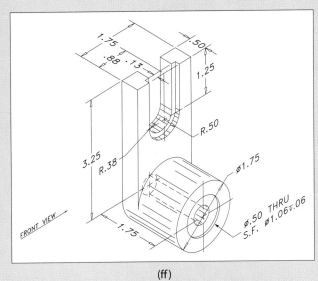

(ff)

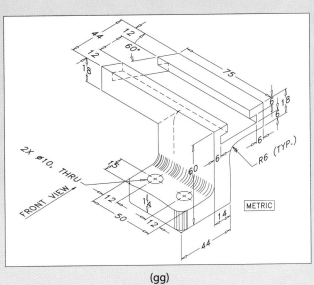

(gg)

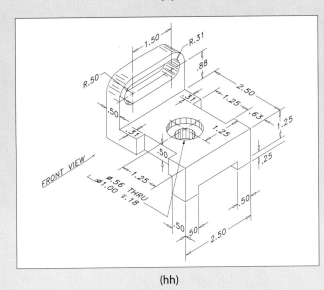

(hh)

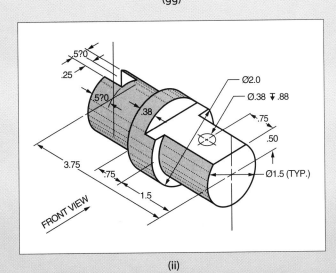

(ii)

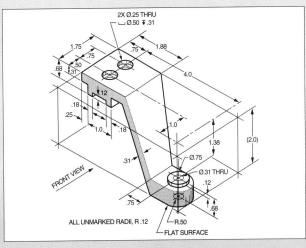

(jj)

6.16 problems (continued)

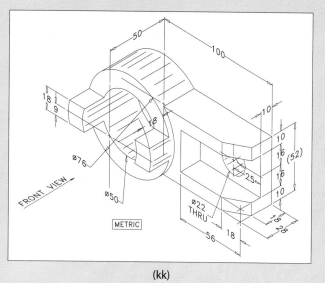

(kk)

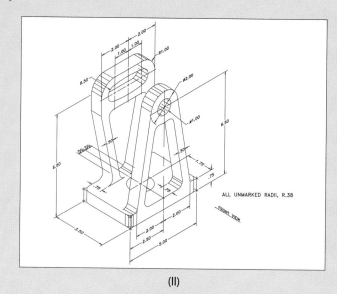

(ll)

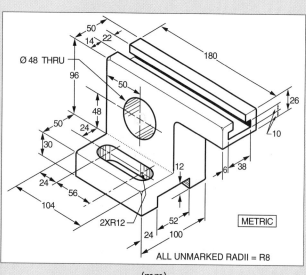

(mm)

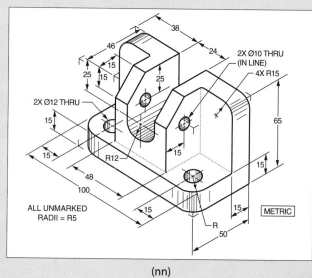

(nn)

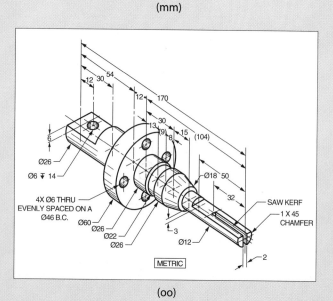

(oo)

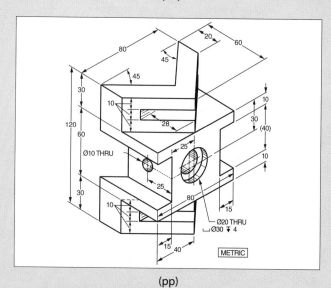

(pp)

6.16 problems (continued)

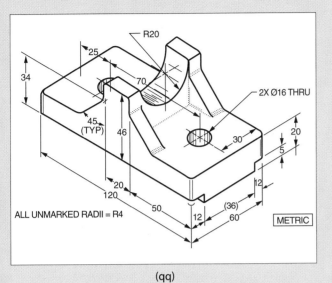

(qq)

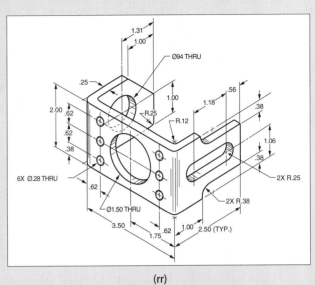

(rr)

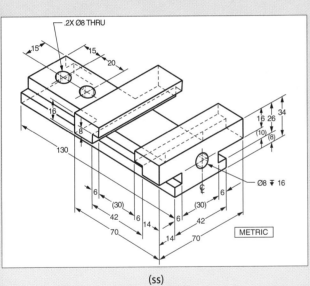

(ss)

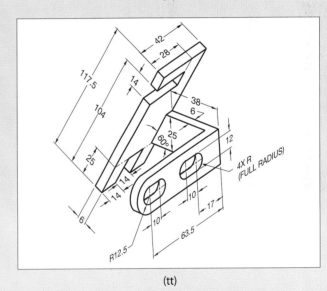

(tt)

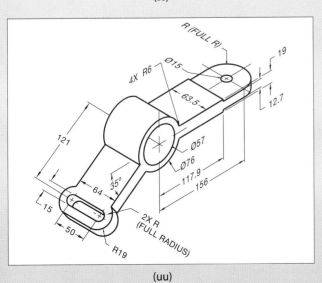

(uu)

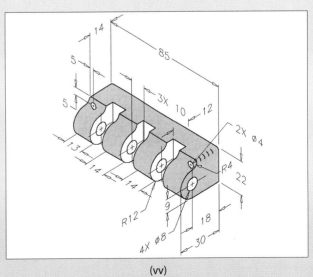

(vv)

6.16 problems (continued)

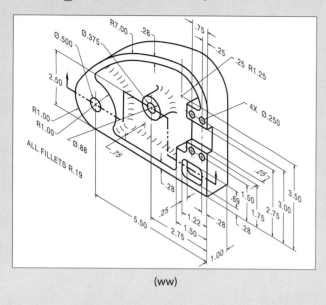

(ww)

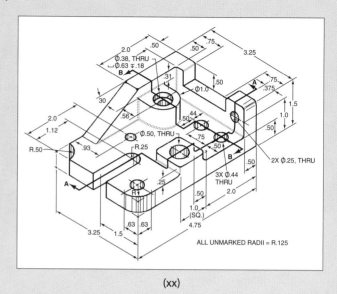

(xx)

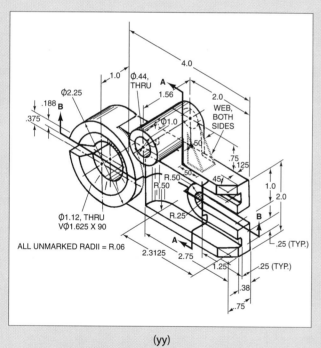

(yy)

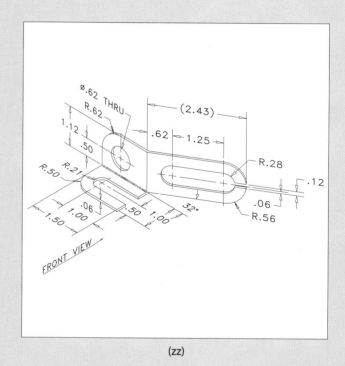

(zz)

6.16 problems (continued)

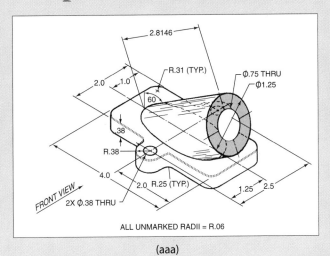

(aaa)

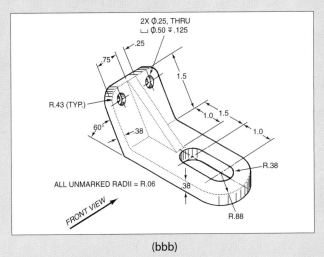

(bbb)

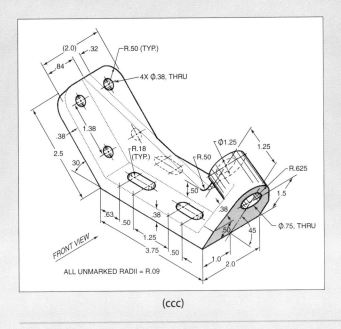

(ccc)

FIGURE P6.4.

7

Assembly Modeling

objectives

After completing this chapter, you should be able to

- Apply new terminology in the context of assembly modeling
- Create an appropriate hierarchy for effective assembly modeling
- Apply assembly constraints between instances
- Create a bill of materials and an assembly drawing
- Determine interferences and clearances between instances in an assembly

7.01
introduction

In a previous chapter, you learned about the techniques used to create solid models with computer tools. Most engineered systems, however, do not consist of a single part, but comprise multiple parts that work together and form the system or assembly. Think of a bicycle. It is used for personal transportation, and its purpose is to allow an individual to get from point A to point B through pedaling. It is composed of several subsystems, each of which serves a distinct purpose in allowing a person to operate the bicycle in a safe and consistent manner. Some of the subsystems found on a bicycle are the pedal system, the gear system, the tire system, and the frame. Each subsystem is composed of other subsystems or parts. For example, the gear system contains many single parts (e.g., the individual gears and the cables), as well as other subsystems (e.g., the derailleur).

This chapter describes how systems or assemblies are created with the use of CAD software and what type of information can be extracted from the assembly models. Because the foundation of assembly modeling is most often the initial creation of the components that make up the assembly, the assumption is that you are already familiar with the creation of solids.

7.02 Assembly Terminology

As with most categories in engineering design and analysis, one of the first things you must learn is the terminology particular to the topic. For assembly modeling, you need to learn a few new terms so you can work productively. Some of these terms will be discussed in the subsequent paragraphs.

In the creation of solid models, computer-generated geometry was referred to as parts, features, or objects; however, the objects that make up a system are referred to as **components**. A system component is identical to its referenced object geometry, and the change in terminology is to avoid confusion between two closely related modeling tasks. Think of a component as a 3-D part that has been brought into an assembly model. For example, consider the footbridge shown in Figure 7.01. Notice that the assembly model consists of abutments, approaches, a bridge deck, and handrails.

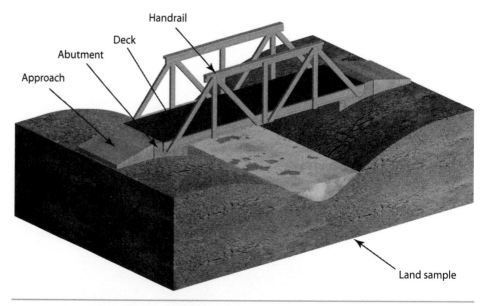

FIGURE 7.01. An assembled footbridge placed on a sample cutout section of land.

You can create a solid model of the abutment within solid modeling software. In this case, the solid model of the abutment is the desired final outcome of the modeling process. When you are working on assembly modeling where the desired final outcome is a bridge assembly, the parts brought into the model that you are working on (the assembly) are called components. When the solid model of the abutment is brought into the assembly model, it is referred to as a component and is no longer thought of as a "part."

In the case of the bridge assembly model, two abutments are in the desired final result. It would be cumbersome to bring a new abutment component into the assembly each time it is required. Further, the abutments are identical to each other (they are just oriented differently in space), so you want it to be clear that the abutments in the final assembly are copies of the same component. In assembly modeling, the copies of a component within the system are called **instances**. Thus, for the bridge, an abutment can be an overall component associated with the system with two instances of the particular component within the assembly. Figure 7.02 illustrates the concept of instances of components in an assembly model.

In reality, system components do not actually appear on the computer screen—they are stored in memory within the assembly model, waiting for you to instance them into the system, but are not displayed in the work area. It is similar to having certain vocabulary words stored in your brain. You can put the words on a sheet of paper to form sentences and paragraphs, but the words do not physically exist anywhere in space—they exist only in your memory. When you want to put a copy of a component in an assembly, you *instance* it into your workspace.

FIGURE 7.02. The concept of parts, components, and instances in assembly modeling.

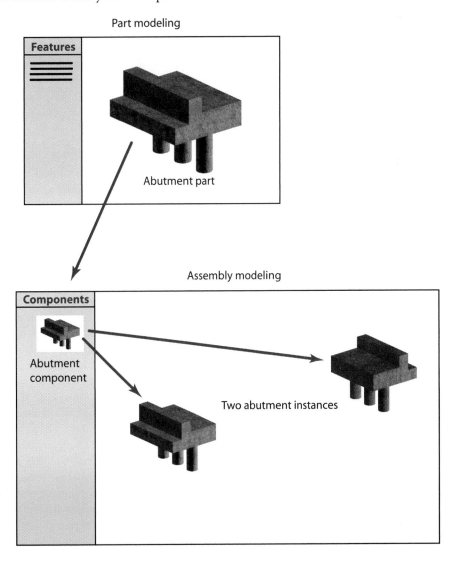

Part modeling

Features

Abutment part

Assembly modeling

Components

Abutment component

Two abutment instances

FIGURE 7.03. The handrail subassembly (with the bridge deck shown in phantom for reference only).

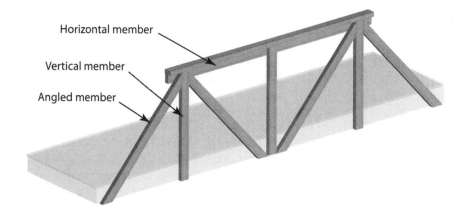

FIGURE 7.04. The second handrail subassembly as an instance of the first handrail subassembly.

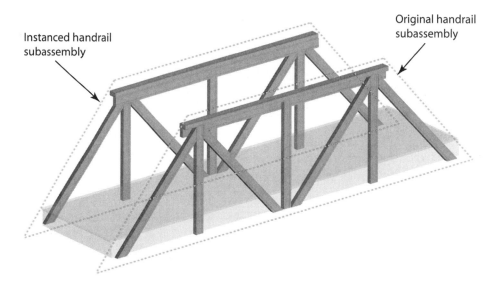

Another new term for you to consider in assembly modeling is the concept of a **subassembly**. A subassembly is a grouping of components that serves a single purpose within the overall assembly. Going back to the bridge example, a subassembly could be created to represent the handrail. Notice that the handrail consists of vertical members, angled members, and the horizontal crossbar at the top, as shown in Figure 7.03.

Instead of instancing each of the individual members that make up the handrail into the overall assembly, you could create one subassembly of the handrail that includes appropriate instances of all of its components—including the vertical, angled, and horizontal members—and just instance that subassembly into the overall system two times. The completed handrail subassembly is shown in Figure 7.04.

Since it is unlikely that the horizontal member of the handrail will act independently of the vertical or angled members, it makes sense to put them into a subassembly together so you can work with them as a single unit. You might think it would be easier to make the handrail a single part. But because the individual components may be made of different materials, you want to keep them as separate objects for any analysis you perform later on. Linking them in a subassembly allows you the flexibility to alter properties of components independent of one another, but also affords you the efficiency of treating them as one unit in the assembly modeling process.

Subassemblies are unique in that they are composed of instances, but subassemblies also can be instances. When you are creating the overall system, you can insert instances that are individual components or that are subassemblies made up of several individual components. Subassemblies also can contain other subassembly instances. For the handrail subassembly, you could choose to combine two angled members and one vertical member as one subassembly, as shown in Figure 7.05. The subassembly

FIGURE 7.05. The web subassembly composed of two angled components and one vertical component.

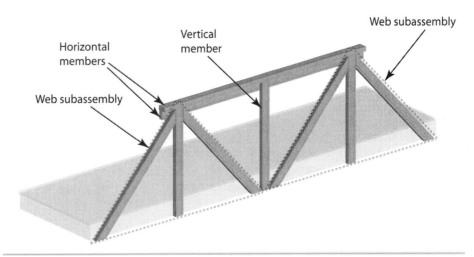

FIGURE 7.06. The complete handrail subassembly composed of one vertical member, two horizontal members, and two web subassemblies (with the bridge deck shown in phantom for reference only).

could be instanced into the overall handrail subassembly two times, along with one additional vertical member and the horizontal bar, to make up the overall handrail subassembly shown in Figure 7.06.

It may seem that the change in terminology between solid modeling and assembly modeling is picky and overly complicated. Why not just put multiple copies of the abutment part within the assembly? Why do you have to learn about components and instances? Why are subassemblies that are made up of instances and that are instances themselves important? The main reasons for the changes are to improve assembly modeling efficiency and to save computer storage space. Saving computer storage space may seem like a trivial matter; however, the less memory a model takes up, the faster your computer modeling software will work. Files that are too large (in terms of memory) are difficult and slow to work with. The improvement in assembly modeling efficiency through the use of subassemblies should be apparent. But how do you save on computer storage space or memory?

To answer that question, consider just the horizontal member of the handrail subassembly. Depending on the design of the member, the computer must "remember" many points to define the model. Each time there is a vertex where two or three edges intersect, the software must remember where the point is located in 3-D space. If the edges of the member are rounded, not sharp, corners, several points on the rounded edge must be remembered for the part geometry to be defined completely. Because some designs for a horizontal handrail are fairly complex, the number of geometric data points used to define it can be large; and the number of 3-D locations in space for the part the computer model must remember also is large. If you were to put the horizontal member directly into the assembly model, each time you moved the member in space within the assembly model, the computer would have to remember the new location of each multiple point that defines the horizontal member. In the case of a bridge with two handrails, the number of points to be remembered is relatively large.

By organizing with components and instances, however, the data to be stored is significantly reduced. The component is referenced to an object, and all the component has to remember is that the component looks exactly like the object. When an instance of the component is placed in the assembly (or subassembly), all that has to be remembered is location of the instance relative to that of the component. In other words, when the instance is located 6 units along the x-axis and 0 units along both the y- and z-axes and it is rotated 90 degrees about Z relative to the component definition, the only thing to be remebered is the location of the instance compared to the location of the component. Thus, for each instance, only six pieces of data must be remembered by the computer—translations in X, Y, and Z and rotations about X, Y, and Z. The amount of data stored

FIGURE 7.07. A schematic representation of a horizontal member part (a) and an instance (b).

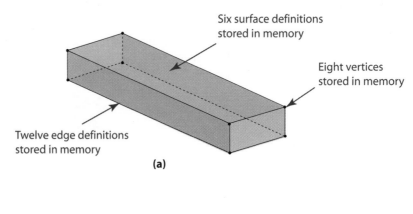

Six surface definitions stored in memory

Eight vertices stored in memory

Twelve edge definitions stored in memory

(a)

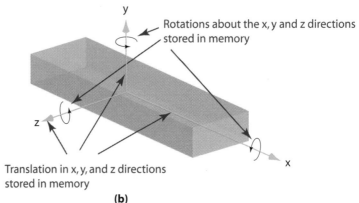

Rotations about the x, y and z directions stored in memory

Translation in x, y, and z directions stored in memory

(b)

under this scheme is significantly less than what would be stored if copies of an object were placed directly into the system. Figure 7.07 shows the object for the horizontal handrail member and an instance of it in a subassembly. Also shown in the figure are the data points defining the location of the instance that define its location within the subassembly.

7.02.01 Associativity

In the solid modeling chapter, you learned about associativity between parts and drawings. When an object changed, any associated drawings also changed in the same way. Associativity also can exist between parts, components, and assemblies. In assembly modeling, **associativity** means that if you change the geometry of a part, the component and all instances of it also will change by the same amount. With some software, when you change a component within assembly modeling, the object geometry also changes by the same amount. That also means that any drawings, finite element models, or manufacturing models associated with the part also will be updated.

Associativity greatly increases your computer modeling efficiency for complex parts and systems. Thinking back on the footbridge example, imagine you are working for a company that designs and produces footbridges for parks and recreation areas. The company might have several bridge models that use the same bridge deck. If the bridge deck design division of the company changes its design, the changes can be reflected throughout all bridge models simultaneously as long as the associative relationships between parts and assemblies have been maintained throughout the company's product line. If the associations have been broken, the engineers working with the various models must be aware of the changes in the bridge deck design and then make the required changes model by model. If the engineers forget one of the models, the overall design will be incorrect, which could have a significant impact when the production phase of the project is initiated.

7.03 Assembly Hierarchy

Assembly models are easier to work with when they are organized in a logical manner. An assembly is usually thought of as a composition of several smaller subassemblies, each of which may consist of other subassemblies or individual components. The organization or structure of a system is referred to as its **hierarchy**. The hierarchy is similar to an inverted family tree. Another way to think of an assembly hierarchy is as a corporate structure. The president of the company is at the top of the hierarchy and at the next level has several vice presidents reporting to him. Each vice president, in turn, is responsible for several managers; and structure of the organization continues until you reach the lowest level in the company hierarchy, where the laborers are located. In this analogy, the individual laborers can be thought of as subassembly instances, the managers would be the first level of subassemblies, the vice presidents would be the next level of subassemblies, etc., until the entire assembly is defined. The top-level assembly could be considered the company president.

As with objects and features, the associations between components and subassemblies are often called parent-child relationships. Going back to the handrail subassembly, the handrail would be a parent whose children are the horizontal member, the subassembly of two angled members and a vertical one, etc. The overall bridge would be the parent whose children consist of two handrails, two approaches, two abutments, the bridge deck, etc. As with objects and features, to work effectively, you must understand the various parent-child relationships defined in assembly modeling. A schematic of a possible hierarchy for the footbridge is shown in Figure 7.08.

Organizing an assembly in a logical hierarchy enables you to work more efficiently with the assembly. The technique is similar to the way you organize files on a computer, establishing folders to group files together in your work space. As stated previously, one advantage of creating an assembly hierarchy is that subassemblies can be dealt with as a whole rather than as separate components. For example, one subassembly can be moved as a single unit within the system, rather than individual components of the system being moved separately, just like the way you move folders and all of the files in them on your computer workstation.

FIGURE 7.08. The footbridge assembly hierarchy.

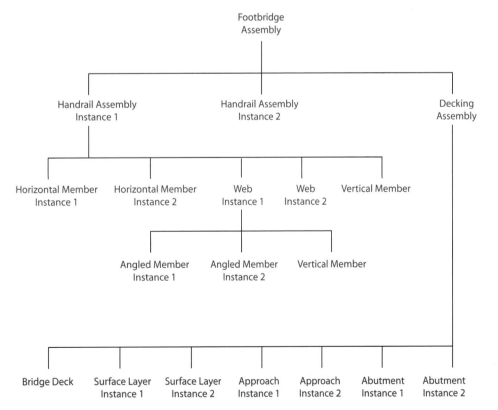

7.04 Assembly Constraints

The first thing you want to do after setting up your system hierarchy is to orient the instances so they are properly located in space relative to one another. To do that, you need to select one component to serve as the **base instance**. The base instance remains stationary with the other instances moving into place around it. For example, if your assembly model was a car, you might choose the chassis as the base instance. Usually the choice of a base instance is fairly obvious; however, in some cases, you may have to choose one from among several choices.

After selecting the base component, you should establish reference planes for the assembly that are connected to the base component. These reference planes will serve as the coordinate planes for the space defined by the system. For the footbridge assembly, the bridge deck was selected as the base component, with the reference planes established as shown in Figure 7.09. You will use these reference planes as you orient the various components within the system.

When creating parts, you used constraints to establish geometric and dimensional relationships between 2-D entities or features. Thus, you constrained two lines to be parallel or perpendicular to each other. Or you constrained the diameter of a circle to be a specific size and its center to be located given distances from lines on the drawing or from edges on an object. In assembly modeling, you can apply **assembly constraints** between two 3-D instances so the instances maintain dimensional or geometric relationships with respect to each other within the assembly.

Each time you bring an instance of a component into an assembly, you introduce six degrees of freedom (DOF). The instance will have a set of coordinate axes associated with it, and the six new DOFs will correspond to the three translational DOFs (distance along X, Y, and Z from the instance origin to the base component origin) and to the three rotational DOFs (rotations about X, Y, and Z) relative to the coordinate planes associated with the base component. Each time you apply a constraint to the assembly, you remove one or more DOFs. As with part modeling, you can continue to apply constraints until all of the DOFs are removed from the assembly model.

7.04.01 Concentric Constraints

One of the more useful applications of assembly constraints is to define two different instances to be concentric with each other. This is especially useful in dealing with cylindrical shafts that fit within a cylindrical hole in another part. You can constrain the centerline of one instance to coincide with the centerline of a different instance,

FIGURE 7.09. The bridge deck as the base instance, with reference planes and axes.

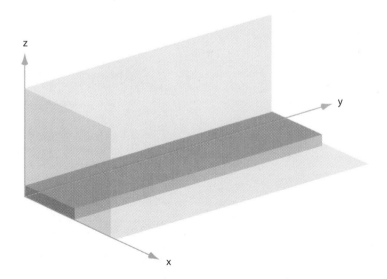

FIGURE 7.10. Concentric constraint used to locate a bolt in its hole. Before application of constraint (a) and after constraint (b).

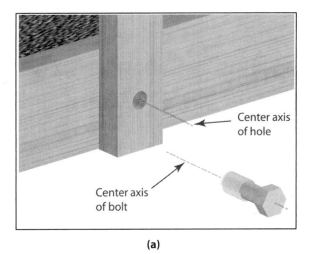

(a)

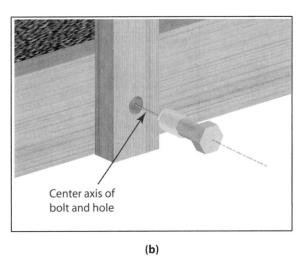

(b)

forcing the two instances to be concentric. After constraining the instances to be concentric, you only need to determine how far along each centerline the instances are located relative to each other. For the bridge assembly, nuts and bolts are used to fasten the instances of the system together. (The nuts and bolts were not shown in previous figures of the bridge assembly to simplify the discussion.) Figure 7.10 shows a concentric constraint applied between two instances in the bridge assembly. Note that when the concentric constraint is applied to the system, several DOFs are removed, since the x-, y-, and z-rotations are now fixed and one of the translation DOFs also has been removed.

In some modeling packages, an "insert" constraint is a special type of concentric contraint used to insert a fastener such as a bolt into a hole in a different part. When the bolt is inserted into the hole, the system automatically applies a concentric constraint between the two components.

7.04.02 Mating Surfaces Constraints

Another useful constraint available in most assembly modeling software is used to define two surfaces as mating surfaces. Mating surfaces coincide with each other—in other words, they line up on top of each other. Usually that type of constraint works only with flat or planar surfaces. When creating a mating surface constraint, you are essentially working with the surface normals. A surface normal is defined as "a vector that is perpendicular to the surface and points away from it." So when you are applying a mating surface constraint, you are forcing the normals of the two surfaces to be parallel to each other. Depending on the final desired result, you may have to flip one of the instances around in order to apply the mating surface constraint to achieve the correct orientation between instances. Figure 7.11a shows a mating surface constraint applied between the inner face of the hex head at the end of the bolt and the outer surface of the handrail member for the bridge. Figure 7.11b shows the result of incorrect mating surface orientation. Figure 7.11c shows the correct surface orientation, with bolt flipped in the final result. Also notice that when the constraint is applied, several DOFs for the system are removed, including both rotational and translational DOFs.

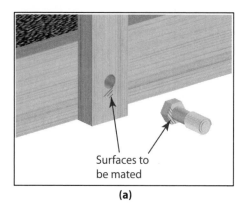

(a)

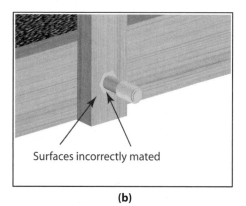

(b)

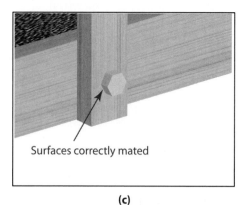

(c)

FIGURE 7.11. Applying mating surfaces constraint after concentric constraint to the bolt and hole. The mating surfaces are identified in (a). The incorrect mating orientation is shown in (b); the correct orientation, in (c).

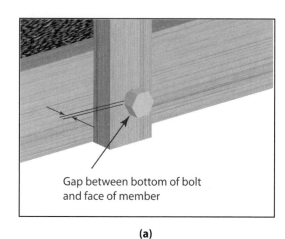

(a)

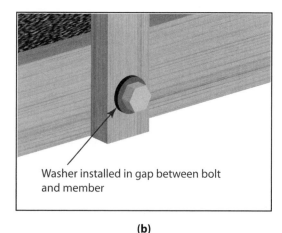

(b)

FIGURE 7.12. Applying an offset constraint between the bolt and member to permit a washer instance.

Another type of constraint that is related to the mating surfaces constraint is one whereby you include an "offset" from one surface to the other. Basically, you are saying that the surface normals for the two surfaces are still parallel to each other, but now the surfaces do not line up on top of each other. Figure 7.12a shows the bolt and handrail member after an offset constraint has been included between the instances to make room for the washer that is included in Figure 7.12b.

7.04.03 Coincident Constraints

One definition of *coincidence* is that two entities take up the same space. For that type of constraint in assembly modeling, coincidence can occur between two lines, between two points, or between a point and a line. (Note that coincidence of two planes has already been defined with the mating surfaces constraint.) In assembly modeling, defining coincident constraints often means that you select a corner or an edge on one instance to be coincident with a corner or an edge on another instance. When applying this type of constraint, you typically are required to input offset distances between points in order to achieve your final desired result. Figure 7.13a shows the effect of making one edge on a vertical handrail member coincident with an edge on the horizontal member, and Figure 7.13b shows the final result achieved after including a dimensional constraint between corresponding endpoints of the edges. Figure 7.14a and Figure 7.14b show the effect of making the edges of two members coincident and then making the two corresponding corner points coincident to achieve the desired final result.

When applying coincident constraints, you may again have to flip one instance around to achieve the desired final result. Figure 7.15a shows two instances with a coincident constraint applied, and Figure 7.15b shows the same two instances after one has been flipped to put it into its desired orientation.

FIGURE 7.13. A coincident edge constraint is used in (a) to align the edges of the horizontal and vertical members. A dimensional constraint is used in (b) to perform the final location of the horizontal member with respect to the vertical member.

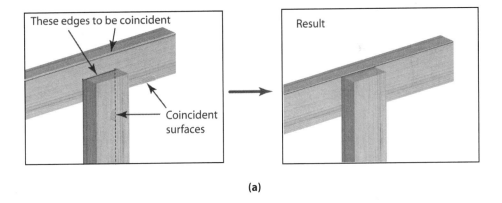

(a)

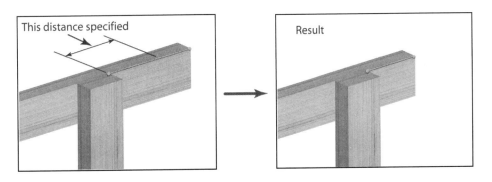

(b)

FIGURE 7.14. A coincident edge constraint is used in (a) to align the edges of the vertical and angled members. A coincident vertices constraint is used on the vertices shown in (b) to perform the final location of the angled member with respect to the vertical member.

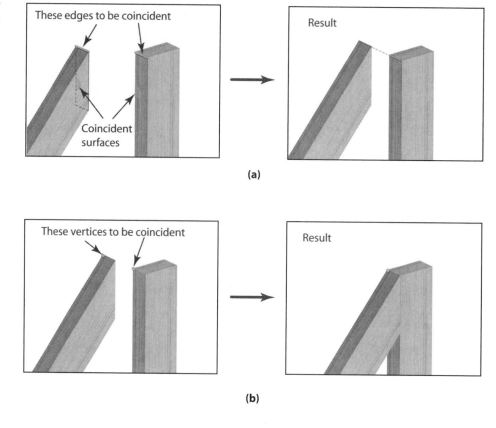

(a)

(b)

FIGURE 7.15. The effect of flipping a coincident surface constraint. Coincident surfaces, edges, and vertices are used in (a) to align the vertical and angled members. The coincident surface constraint is flipped in (b) to realign the members.

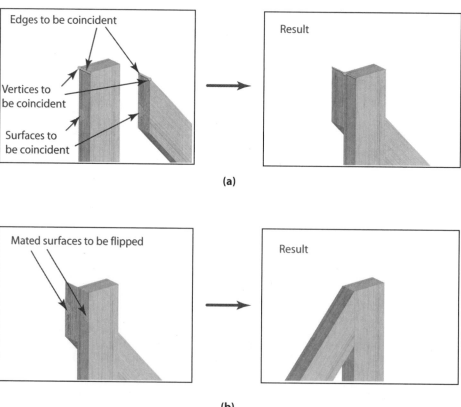

(a)

(b)

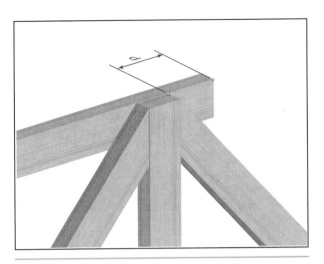

FIGURE 7.16. A distance constraint between vertices to locate the horizontal member with respecte to the angled member.

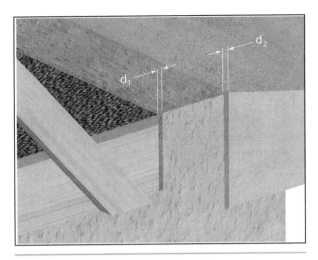

FIGURE 7.17. Parallel distance constraints used to create clearance gaps between the deck and the abutment and between the abutment and the approach.

7.04.04 Distance Constraints

When creating a 3-D solid model, you often add dimensions between features to define sizes of parts. With assembly models, you add distance constraints to define the relationship between two instances. When adding the distance constraints, you use points, edges, and surfaces to define the distances between the instances. Often a distance constraint is used in conjunction with a second or third assembly constraint. For example, for the two instances shown in Figure 7.16, a coincident constraint was applied between the point on the angled member and the edge on the horizontal crossbar. A distance constraint was then applied between the endpoint of the two instances, as shown in the figure.

A distance constraint also can be applied between parallel surfaces on two separate instances, as shown in Figure 7.17.

7.04.05 Adding Constraints to Your Assembly

In addition to putting your parts together to see how they look, certain types of analysis that are best performed on an assembled system will aid you in your engineering design tasks. One predominant type of analysis that you can perform with an assembled model is to model it as a mechanism. With this type of analysis, you add joints such that two parts are able to rotate freely about an axis or you add a joint such that two parts slide relative to each other. Consider a piston in a cylinder. The piston can slide in and out; and as is illustrated schematically in Figure 7.18, the cylinder and the connecting rod are also free to pivot about the piston pin and the connecting pin.

Mechanism analysis is important for a piston assembly. The analysis allows you to determine whether the connecting rod bumps up against the walls of the cylinder as the mechanism goes through its cycle of motion or whether the piston bumps up against the fixed end of the cylinder. For you to accomplish this type of analysis, however, your assembly must be properly constrained.

When you learned about including constraints with sketches or models as you were studying part creation, you learned that sketches could be unconstrained, fully constrained, or partially constrained. Similarly, assemblies can be unconstrained, fully constrained, or partially constrained. You should avoid unconstrained systems since all instances in the assembly are free to move relative to one another. If you have an unconstrained assembly, you need to move each instance and subassembly one at

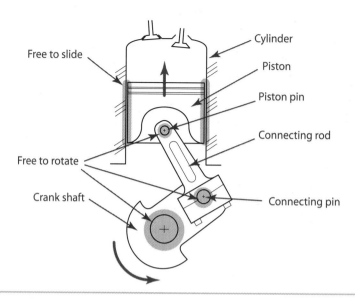

FIGURE 7.18. Schematic drawing of piston/cylinder assembly.

a time—a tedious task—to perform your analysis. An assembly that is fully constrained is rigid and unable to move. Each time you try to move one instance, the entire system reverts to its original orientation to satisfy all of the constraints on it. Like Goldilocks, you want a system that is "just right"—with just enough constraints to define the permissible motion in the assembly but not too many constraints that its ability to function properly is hindered.

Going back to the piston/cylinder assembly, you want the constraint between the piston and the pin to be rigidly defined—these two instances should not be able to move relative to each other (ever!). However, the cylinder and piston should be partially constrained such that they remain concentric to each other but the piston is still free to move up and down along the centerline of the cylinder. Likewise, the connecting rod should be partially constrained such that the pin remains concentric to the pin hole but is free to rotate about its axis as the system moves. To achieve the balance between systems that are over- or underconstrained, you should think about the types of motion your assembly will go through in computer analysis as well as in real life. If you think about the bridge assembly presented earlier in this chapter, the instances in this system should never move relative to one another—a bridge is a rigid structure that is built to remain rigid its entire life cycle. In the case of the footbridge, having a fully constrained assembly is permissible.

Some software requires assembly models be fully constrained. In this case, you are usually permitted to include "assumptions" with your constraints in order to satisfy the need for system flexibility and movement. For example, in the case of the connecting rod and piston pin, you could include the concentric constraint and then add an "assumption" that the two instances are able to rotate relative to each other. In this case, the assumption will eliminate DOFs in the system and the software will be satisfied that the assembly is "fully" constrained.

7.05 Exploded Configurations

For most mechanical systems, an assembly drawing is necessary in order to put the system together. You probably saw that kind of drawing if you ever put together a furniture kit or a model. Once you assemble your system, you can create an **exploded configuration** that will essentially be an assembly drawing for the system. Figure 7.19 shows an exploded configuration for a small flashlight assembly. Note that the configuration shows how all of the parts in the system will be put together, or assembled.

FIGURE 7.19. An exploded view of a small flashlight assembly.

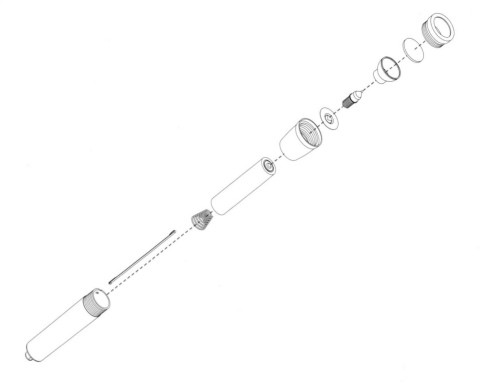

7.06 Interferences and Clearances

One of the main advantages to be gained from assembling a system of parts is that you are able to determine whether two parts overlap or interfere with each other. Since different engineering teams often work on separate parts of an assembly and since communication between groups may not always be clear, being able to determine overlap is especially important when working collaboratively on a large design. The amount that two instances overlap is referred to as the **interference** between them. Another advantage is that you can determine **clearances**, or minimum distances, between parts. You can use that information to optimize the assembly. You can change the size of features as appropriate to remove interference or to increase clearances between parts. For some systems, you may choose to perform a kinematic analysis of the parts in the assembly. You can then check each part for interference or clearance problems as the parts move through the kinematic analysis. For example, if you are designing a piston and cylinder system, in the initial position, none of the parts will overlap. However, as the crankshaft is rotated and the piston slides in or out of the cylinder, you may find that the connecting rod interferes with the end of the cylinder, as illustrated in Figure 7.20. Since that is a problem with the design, you can modify the design to alleviate the problem and re-check the interferences and clearances.

One other consideration in accomplishing interference or clearance checks for an assembly is the *number* of checks you want to perform. If you have a system with twenty-five parts, you probably will not want to check for interference between all parts in the assembly; that would require $(25 - 1)!$ (24 factorial, or more than 6×10^{23}) checks. With most CAD software, you can specify two groups of parts. The software will perform the interference or clearance checks, checking all of the parts in one group against all of the parts in the second group.

Only one of the two, interference or clearance, is possible between two instances. If two parts overlap, there is an interference; and a clearance is not defined between the two. Conversely, if two instances have a clearance, or distance, between them, they do not overlap; and an interference is not defined.

One common place where you need to check interferences and clearances is between shafts and circular holes. When you align shafts in holes by making them concentric, you may not realize that the shaft is too large or too small for the hole. In a later chapter, you will learn about classes of fits between holes and shafts. In that chapter, you will learn that sometimes you want the shaft to be larger than the hole and other times you want the shaft to be smaller than the hole. The class of fit you need depends on your design intent. Figure 7.21 shows an end view of two shafts in holes—in one case, the shaft is larger than the hole; in the other case, the shaft is smaller than the hole. The clearance and interference between the shaft and the hole in each case are shown in the figure.

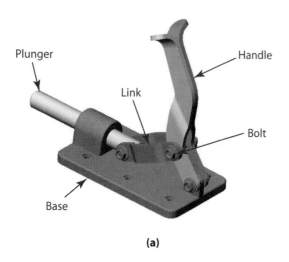

(a)

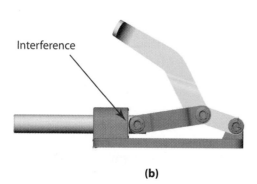

(b)

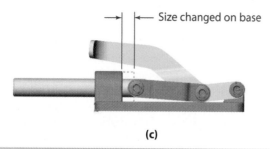

(c)

FIGURE 7.20. The completed toggle clamp assembly is shown in (a). In its original form, the link and the base interfere, as shown in (b), preventing the handle from being pushed all the way down into a closed and locked position. The base has been modified in (c) to eliminate the interference, allowing the toggle to work properly.

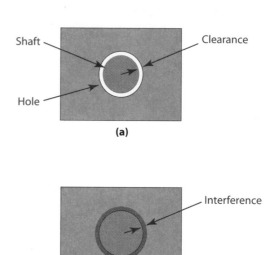

(a)

(b)

FIGURE 7.21. When the shaft has a smaller diameter than the hole, as in (a), there is clearance between the two parts. If the shaft has a larger diameter than the hole, as in (b), there is interference between the parts.

7.07 Bill of Materials

Most real-life assembly drawings contain a **bill of materials**, which consists of a table listing all parts in the assembly as well as the quantity of each part required to put the assembly together. If you were to begin assembling a system, you could look at the bill of materials and easily determine how many screws, how many washers, etc., you needed to gather to assemble the system. Figure 7.22 shows an assembly drawing (exploded configuration) for a system, along with the associated bill of materials.

In some cases, a bill of materials lists subassembly items, as shown in Figure 7.23. In that case, the assembly drawing for the subassembly is usually shown on a different sheet of paper and you are expected to have constructed the subassembly before you begin putting the entire assembly together.

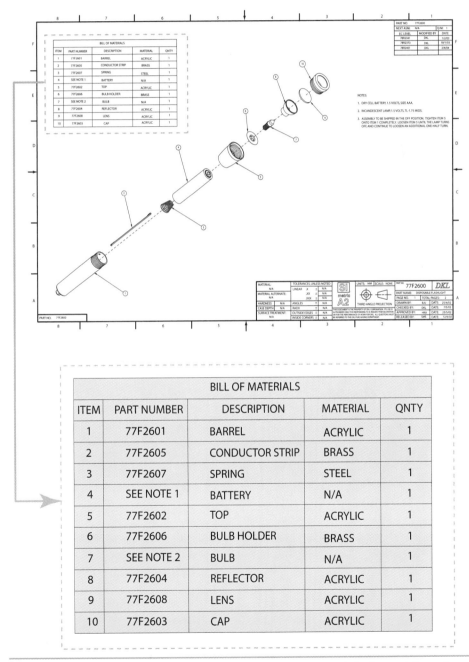

BILL OF MATERIALS				
ITEM	PART NUMBER	DESCRIPTION	MATERIAL	QNTY
1	77F2601	BARREL	ACRYLIC	1
2	77F2605	CONDUCTOR STRIP	BRASS	1
3	77F2607	SPRING	STEEL	1
4	SEE NOTE 1	BATTERY	N/A	1
5	77F2602	TOP	ACRYLIC	1
6	77F2606	BULB HOLDER	BRASS	1
7	SEE NOTE 2	BULB	N/A	1
8	77F2604	REFLECTOR	ACRYLIC	1
9	77F2608	LENS	ACRYLIC	1
10	77F2603	CAP	ACRYLIC	1

FIGURE 7.22. The assembly drawing for a small flashlight, with its bill of materials on the drawing.

FIGURE 7.23. The bill of materials for two levels of subassembly, leading to the final assembly of the footbridge.

BILL OF MATERIALS, PART NUMBER XKZ0030, WEB ASSEMBLY				
ITEM	PART NUMBER	DESCRIPTION	MATERIAL	QNTY
1	XKZ0001	VERTICAL MEMBER	WOOD	1
2	XKZ0002	ANGLED MEMBER	WOOD	2

BILL OF MATERIALS, PART NUMBER XKZ0015, HANDRAIL ASSEMBLY				
ITEM	PART NUMBER	DESCRIPTION	MATERIAL	QNTY
1	XKZ0001	VERTICAL MEMBER	WOOD	1
2	XKZ0003	HORIZONTAL MEMBER	WOOD	2
3	XKZ0030	WEB ASSEMBLY	WOOD	2

BILL OF MATERIALS, PART NUMBER XKZ0009, DECKING ASSEMBLY				
ITEM	PART NUMBER	DESCRIPTION	MATERIAL	QNTY
1	XKZ0006	DECK	WOOD	1
2	XKZ0007	SURFACE LAYER	FIBER REINFORCED CONCRETE BOARD	2

BILL OF MATERIALS, PART NUMBER XKZ0001, FOOTBRIDGE ASSEMBLY				
ITEM	PART NUMBER	DESCRIPTION	MATERIAL	QNTY
1	XKZ0023	ABUTMENT	POURED CONCRETE	2
2	XKZ0013	APPROACH	POURED CONCRETE	2
3	XKX0009	DECKING ASSEMBY	WOOD, CONCRETE	1
4	XKZ0015	HANDRAIL ASSEMBLY	WOOD	2

7.08   Assembly Strategy

When creating an assembly, you can choose from two modeling methods—top-down or bottom-up. Bottom-up assembly modeling was used extensively in the past; however, top-down modeling is now gaining in popularity. A description of each method follows.

7.08.01 Bottom-up Assembly Modeling

With **bottom-up modeling**, you create all of the parts required for the system. When more than one copy of a given part is in an assembly, you do not have to create more than one copy of the part—you include multiple instances of the component in the system. You then establish the assembly hierarchy, making sure you organize instances into smaller subassemblies as appropriate. You orient all of the instances using constraints to establish relationships between instances. Next, you check for clearances and interferences between instances to make sure your constraints were properly applied and you achieved your design intent. If you so choose, you obtain a bill of materials for the assembly. Your final step is to create an exploded view of the system as necessary to create its assembly drawing.

7.08.02 Top-down Assembly Modeling

Top-down assembly modeling has evolved in recent years in much the same way concurrent engineering evolved—both were facilitated through the modern computer tools and CAD systems. With **top-down modeling**, the system is first defined, including its hierarchy. In some cases, physical space may be assigned to the assembly as well as to all subassemblies and components contained in it. The function of the system and its components also is articulated at this time. After the framework of the system has been established, engineering teams then work on creating the individual parts and subassemblies that go into the overall system. For example, because the engineers working on subassembly A know that their subassembly connects and interacts with subassemblies B, D, and G, they can collaborate through e-mails or other means as they create their assigned subassembly. Further, the team members working on subassembly A know that the space they occupy cannot encroach on the space occupied by subassembly C and must take that fact into account when they do their design work. Teams working on subassembly B know that they must work with teams working on subassemblies A and C as they complete their assigned task. In this way, efficiency in assembly design is achieved—problems can be solved before they arise. With the bottom-up design approach, problems between subassemblies A and D might not be apparent until the entire design is completed, meaning that all teams need to start from scratch to solve the problem. Top-down assembly modeling is especially effective when multiple teams, many times in different parts of the world, are working on a single design. Most modern-day CAD systems have the tools necessary to implement a system of top-down assembly modeling; however, as a student, you may not have the opportunity to work in this efficient environment.

7.09 Strategy for Bottom-up Assembly Modeling

Suppose you needed to model the assembly shown in Figure 7.24. The distinct components that make up the assembly are shown in Figure 7.25. Note that the bottom-up approach will be employed in the assembly modeling of this case, since all of the parts have already been created and must simply be put together to form the assembly model.

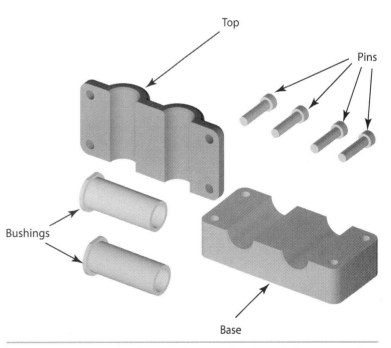

FIGURE 7.24. A fully assembled model of a bearing block.

FIGURE 7.25. An exploded view of the parts that form the bearing block assembly.

FIGURE 7.26. Two possible
hierarchies for the bearing
block assembly, with no
subassemblies (a) and with a
housing block subassembly (b).

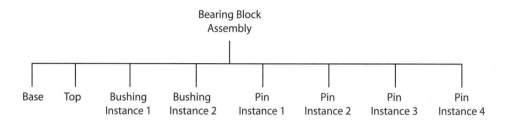

(a)

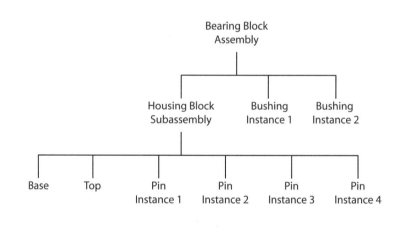

(b)

With the bottom-up assembly modeling approach, after the individual components have been modeled, you need to define a hierarchy for the system. For this particular assembly, it might make sense to link the four pins into one subassembly; however, this is probably not necessary. Since the bushings have a flat surface for alignment, you probably need to know if they should be aligned independent of each other before you decide whether they make up a subassembly. Since the base block and the cap block will likely be considered a single unit, the two components should be put into a subassembly. Two possible hierarchies for the system are shown in Figure 7.26.

For purposes of demonstration, you will work with the hierarchy established in Figure 7.26a. In this case, your first step is to assemble the base subassembly. This subassembly consists of the base block and the cap block. You should establish the base block as the base instance for the assembly, setting the coordinate planes for the system as shown in Figure 7.27.

If you bring the cap block onto the screen, you can put it in place within the system through the use of coincident constraints. For this subassembly, the edges of the half circles of the cap and base should coincide. If this constraint is applied, notice the two possible orientations for the cap where this constraint is satisfied, as shown in Figure 7.28.

To achieve the desired orientation for the cap block, you need to apply one more coincident constraint using any of the remaining edges, or you can use the endpoints of the corresponding half circles. Figure 7.29 shows the second coincident constraint applied, which leads to the desired final result.

Now you put the pin subassembly in place within the overall system. The pin subassembly consists of four instances of the pin component. You can bring the pins on-screen one at a time and locate each of them relative to the base subassembly that is

FIGURE 7.27. Definitions of coordinate axes and datum planes for the base as the first object in the assembly model.

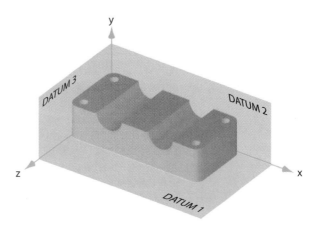

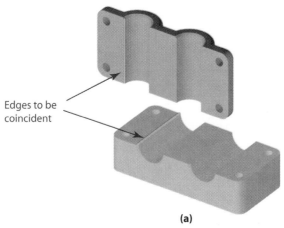

Edges to be coincident

(a)

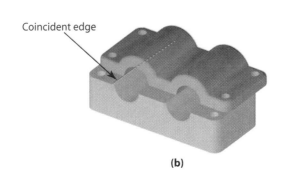

Coincident edge

(b)

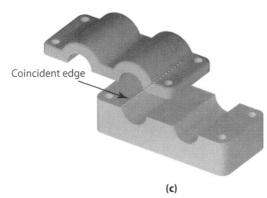

Coincident edge

(c)

FIGURE 7.28. A coincident constraint applied to the edges shown in (a) can result in two possible orientations of the top, as shown in (b) and (c).

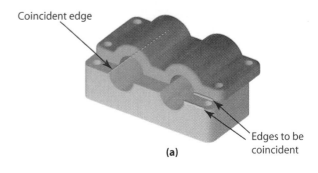

Coincident edge

Edges to be coincident

(a)

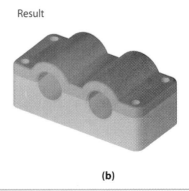

Result

(b)

FIGURE 7.29. Adding a coincident edge constraint to the edges shown in (a) is one method used to create the final alignment between the base and the top, as shown in (b).

already in place. If you bring the first instance of the pin on-screen, you need to establish two constraints to put it in its final location. The two constraints to be added are a concentric constraint between the axis of the pin and the axis of the corresponding hole, and a mating surfaces constraint can be applied between the "bottom" surface of the pinhead and the top surface of the cap, block. These two constraints are shown in Figure 7.30a, with the final result shown in Figure 7.30b.

Using a similar strategy, the remaining three instances of the pin component can be oriented within the assembly, with the result shown in Figure 7.31.

Finally, the two bushings can be inserted one at a time into the assembly using a strategy similar to the one used in locating the pins—applying a concentric constraint between the centerlines of the bushing and the base-block semicircular cutout and a mating surfaces constraint between the corresponding surfaces of the bushing and the base block. Figure 7.32a shows the constraints applied to the leftmost bushing, and Figure 7.32b shows the result of applying these constraints.

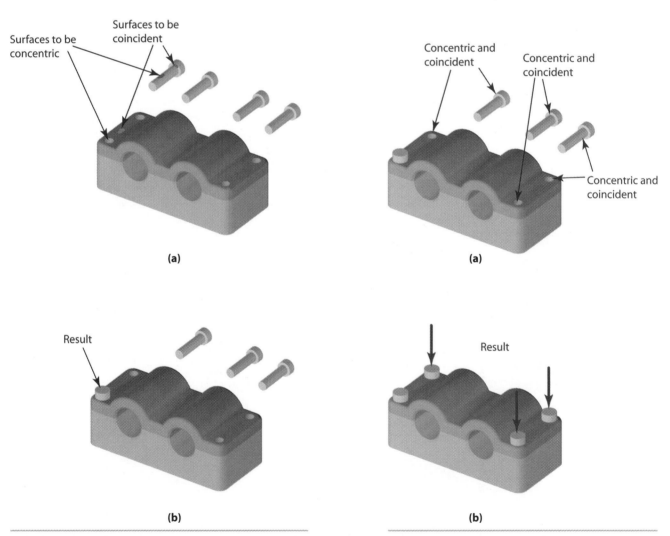

FIGURE 7.30. Applying a concentric constraint between the shaft of the pin and the hole in the top and a coincident constraint between the bottom of the pinhead and the top, as shown in (a), locates the pin in the hole, as shown in (b).

FIGURE 7.31. The remaining three pins are inserted in their holes by applying the same types of concentric and coincident constraints used for the first pin.

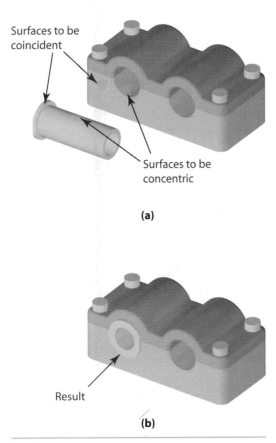

(a)

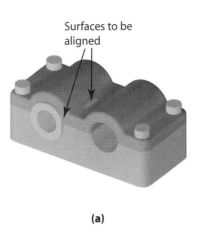

(a)

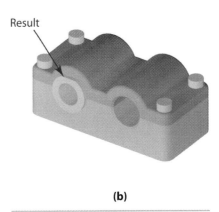

(b)

(b)

FIGURE 7.32. The bushing is placed by applying the concentric and coincident constraints to the surfaces indicated in (a) to produce the result shown in (b).

FIGURE 7.33. An alignment constraint is applied between the flat on the bushing and the top surface, as shown in (a), to create the desired orientation of the bushing, as shown in (b).

When the pins were added to the assembly, it did not matter what angular orientation they had with respect to the axis of the pin; however, the bushing instances include a flat surface that can be used for alignment. To align the surface properly, you want to include a distance constraint between the flat surface on the bushing and the bottom (or top) flat surface on the base. In this case, the distance constraint forces the two surfaces to be parallel to each other. Figure 7.33a shows the constraint applied between the flat surface of the bushing and the upper flat surface of the top, and Figure 7.33b shows the result of applying this constraint.

Finally, the second instance of the bushing can be brought into the assembly and oriented with the use of appropriate constraints. The final assembly model is shown in Figure 7.34.

Once your assembly model is complete, you may want to check for interferences or clearances between instances. Figure 7.35 includes the results from an interference and clearance check for the instances in the assembly. Since there is a relatively small number of instances in the assembly, all instances were checked against all others.

Other items you might need from this model include an assembly drawing and a bill of materials. Most modern-day software can generate these automatically. Figure 7.36 shows an assembly drawing with the bill of materials for the block assembly you have been working with thus far.

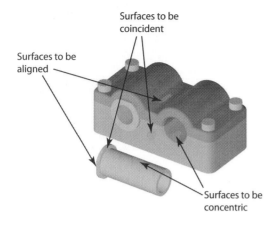

Surfaces to be coincident

Surfaces to be aligned

Surfaces to be concentric

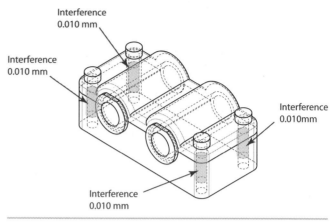

Interference 0.010 mm

Interference 0.010 mm

Interference 0.010mm

Interference 0.010 mm

FIGURE 7.35. The result of an interference check between all of the parts in the bearing block assembly, showing the interference from the forced fit between the pins and the base block.

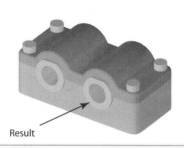

Result

FIGURE 7.34. The second bushing is placed by applying the same type of concentric, coincident, and aligned constraints as were used to place the first bushing, as shown in (a). The final position of the second bushing is shown in (b).

FIGURE 7.36. An assembly drawing of the block assembly (removed from its drawing header) identifying its parts in its bill of materials.

BILL OF MATERIALS, PART NUMBER CDX010, BEARING BLOCK ASSEMBLY				
ITEM	PART NUMBER	DESCRIPTION	MATERIAL	QNTY
1	CDX011	BASE BLOCK	ALUMINUM, 6061 T6	1
2	CDX012	CAP BLOCK	ALUMINUM, 6061 T6	1
3	CDX089	PIN	STEEL, 1060	4
4	CDX076	BUSHING	BRONZE, SINTERED	2

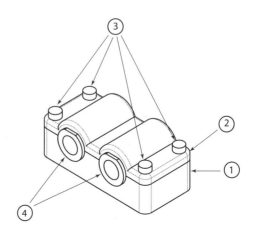

FIGURE 7.37. A fully assembled model of a table vise.

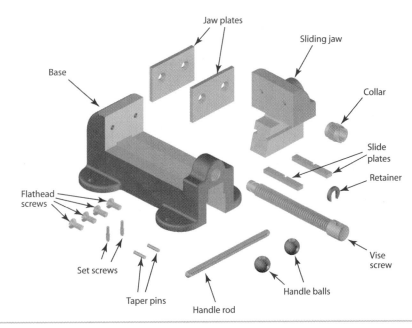

FIGURE 7.38. The various pieces of the table vise prior to assembly.

As another example, consider the vise assembly shown in Figure 7.37, with the individual components shown in Figure 7.38.

The first step is to establish the hierarchy for the system. In this case, you can consider the vise base to be the base instance. The sliding jaw is a subassembly that consists of two subassemblies—a jaw plate subassembly and a handle subassembly. A jaw plate subassembly also attaches to the base. Each subassembly includes several screws that are used for fastening. The overall hierarchy for that assembly is shown in Figure 7.39.

FIGURE 7.39. The assembly hierarchy for the table vise.

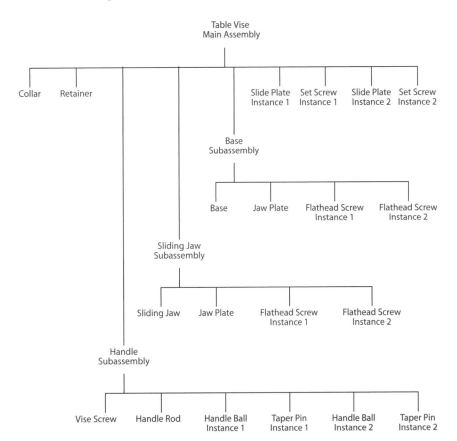

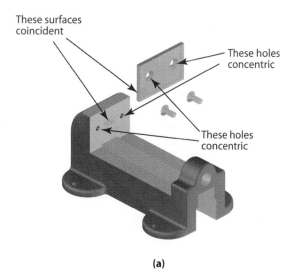

These surfaces
coincident

These holes
concentric

These holes
concentric

(a)

Result

(b)

FIGURE 7.40. Adding assembly constraints between
the jaw plate and the base on the base subassembly
(a) to get the assembled results in (b).

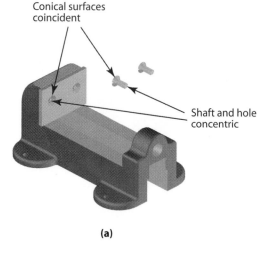

Conical surfaces
coincident

Shaft and hole
concentric

(a)

Result

(b)

FIGURE 7.41. Adding assembly constraints to
one flathead screw (a) to get the assembled
results in (b). The second flathead screw is
constrained in a similar manner within the
other hole.

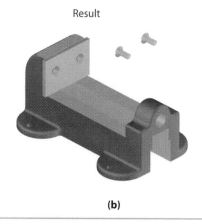

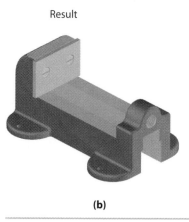

To put this assembly together, you once again start with the base instance.
Attached to the base instance is the jaw plate subassembly that consists of a jaw plate
and two screws that hold the jaw plate in place. Using concentric and mating surfaces
constraints, you can assemble the jaw plate subassembly as shown in Figure 7.40; and
that subassembly can be added to the base instance through coincident constraints as
shown in Figure 7.41.

At this point, it is probably easier to put the base instance (along with the attached
jaw plate subassembly) away and work only with the sliding jaw subassembly. When
you start with the sliding jaw as the "base" of the subassembly, you can insert another
instance of the jaw plate subassembly and put it in place using coincident constraints
between the appropriate elements, as shown in Figure 7.42.

The handle subassembly can be put together with a concentric constraint between
the handle and the vise screw, as shown in Figure 7.43.

FIGURE 7.42. The sliding jaw subassembly is created from its parts. The jaw plate is constrained in (a); and the flathead screws are constrained, first one and then the other, in (b).

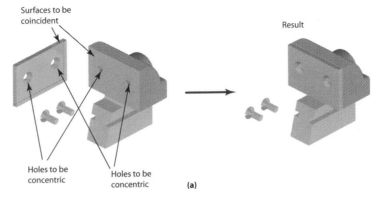

Surfaces to be coincident

Result

Holes to be concentric

Holes to be concentric

(a)

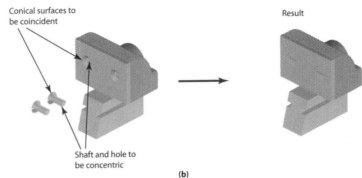

Conical surfaces to be coincident

Result

Shaft and hole to be concentric

(b)

FIGURE 7.43. The handle subassembly is created by applying constraints to the rod (a), the end balls (b), and the pins that retain the end balls (c).

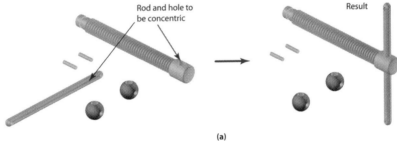

Rod and hole to be concentric

Result

(a)

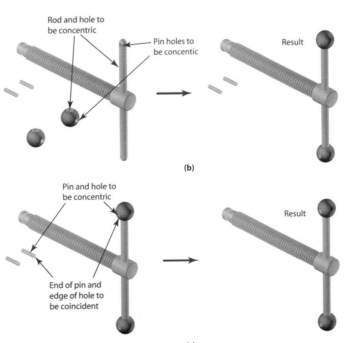

Rod and hole to be concentric

Pin holes to be concentic

Result

(b)

Pin and hole to be concentric

Result

End of pin and edge of hole to be coincident

(c)

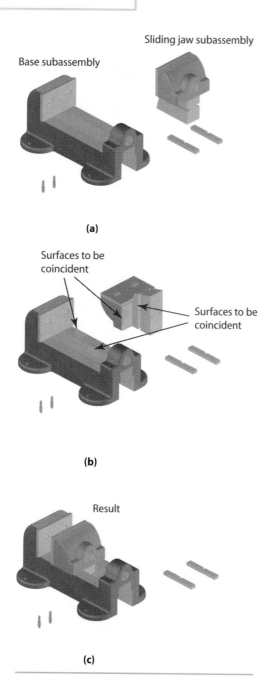

(a)

(b)

Result

(c)

FIGURE 7.44. The base subassembly and sliding jaw subassembly are brought together in (a). The sliding jaw subassembly is rotated to expose the surfaces to be constrained in (b). The final result is shown in (c).

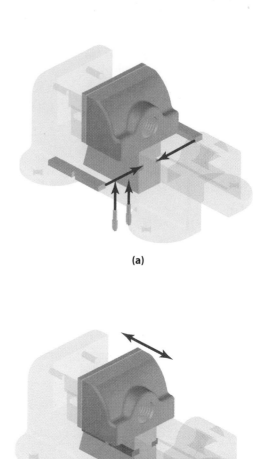

(a)

(b)

FIGURE 7.45. By applying coincident constraints between the two slide plates and the sliding jaw and concentric and coincident constraints between the two setscrews and the sliding jaw in (a), the sliding jaw can move freely in one direction only, as shown in (b).

Next, the handle subassembly and the set screws that hold it in place can be added to the sliding jaw through use of mating surfaces and concentric constraints, as shown in Figure 7.44.

Finally, the sliding plate and associated screws can be added to the bottom of the sliding jaw through the use of coincident and distance constraints, as shown in Figure 7.45.

You now can retrieve the base component and orient the sliding jaw subassembly through the use of coincident constraints between appropriate edges on the base and

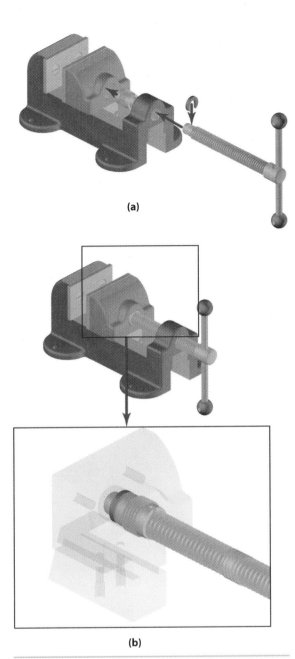

(a)

(b)

FIGURE 7.46. The retainer and collar are assembled onto the screw and sliding jaw in (a) to complete the vise, shown in (b). The detail in (b) shows the final positions of the retainer and collar in the sliding jaw.

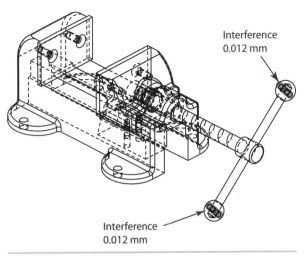

Interference
0.012 mm

Interference
0.012 mm

FIGURE 7.47. An interference check on the entire vise assembly warns that there will be interference between the taper pins and the pin holes on the end balls on the handle rod. The interference, in this case, is desirable for the purpose of keeping the end balls on the handle rod.

the sliding jaw. Note that you do not want to include any distance constraints at this time, enabling the sliding jaw to be located anywhere along its "track." Figure 7.46 shows the completed assembly of the vise model.

If you like, you can check for clearances and interferences (Figure 7.47) or create an assembly drawing and a bill of materials for the assembly (Figure 7.48).

FIGURE 7.48. The bill of materials and assembly drawing for the table vise.

ITEM	PART NUMBER	DESCRIPTION	MATERIAL	QNTY
	BILL OF MATERIALS, PART NUMBER RNP1000, TABLE VISE ASSEMBLY			
1	RNP050	BASE	STEEL, CAST	1
2	RNP051	SLIDING JAW	STEEL, CAST	1
3	RPN010	JAW PLATE	STEEL, AISI 1020	2
4	RPN015	SCREW	STEEL, AISI 1060	1
5	RPN017	COLLAR	BRASS	1
6	RPN018	RETAINER	STEEL, AISI 1060	1
7	RPN020	HANDLE ROD	STEEL, AISI 1040	1
8	RPN022	HANDLE BALL	STEEL, AISI 1040	2
9	RPN012	SLIDE PLATE	STEEL, AISI 1060	2
10	RPN008	TAPER PIN	STEEL, AISI 1060	2
11	RPN009	FLATHEAD SCREW	STEEL, AISI 1060	4
12	RPN007	SETSCREW	STEEL, ASIS 1060	2

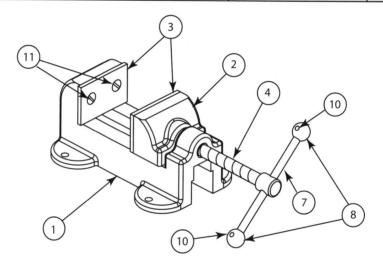

CAUTION   One thing to avoid when working with assembly models is the creation of a flat hierarchy. With a flat hierarchy, the main assembly is the parent and every instance is a child of the main assembly—there are no subassemblies, just individual instances. With a flat hierarchy, you cannot treat several instances as one, but must deal with each one individually. Creating a flat hierarchy may save you time in the planning stages, but it is likely to cost you a great deal of time when you work with the assembly. To avoid a flat hierarchy, make sure you logically group instances together in subassemblies to save time later. Figure 7.49 shows an undesirable flat hierarchy for the footbridge assembly, in contrast to Figure 7.08 at the beginning of this chapter which shows a hierarchy that advantageously employs subassemblies to link instances together logically.

As discussed previously, another situation you should avoid in assembly modeling is the creation of a system that is too rigid. A rigid system consists of instances that are fixed in space and not fixed relative to one another. To avoid an overly rigid system, make sure you establish relationships between instances with constraints rather than merely locate instances by moving them in 3-D space. Using constraints will add flexibility to your assembly model. For example, consider the bolt used to hold together two

FIGURE 7.49. A "flat" assembly hierarchy, such as this one for the footbridge model, should be avoided. A more reasonable hierarchy is shown in Figure 7.08.

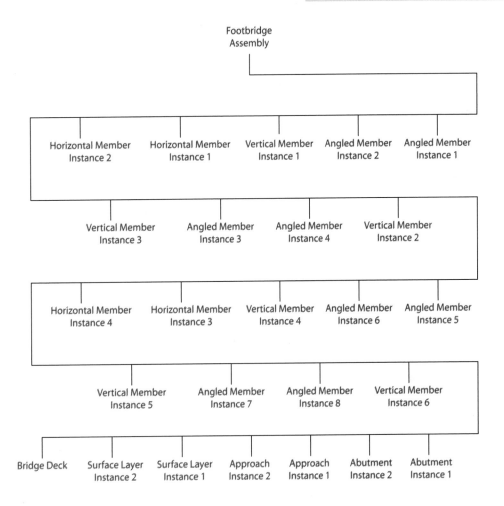

NO!

members of the handrail for the footbridge. If you use a concentric constraint between the bolt and the holes in the members, as you move the members around, the bolt will move with them. However, if you put the bolt in the hole without a constraint, when you move the members, the bolt will stay where you put it and will not move with the members. Without a constraint, you would have to move the members and then move the bolt in an additional step.

7.10 glossary of key terms

assembly constraints: Used to establish relationships between instances in the development of a flexible assembly model.

associativity: The situation whereby parts can be modified and the components referenced to the parts will be modified accordingly.

base instance: The one fixed instance within an assembly.

bill of materials: A tabular list of the components, with quantities of each for the parts, that make up an assembly.

bottom-up modeling: The process of creating individual parts and then creating an assembly from them.

clearances: The minimum distances between two instances in an assembly.

components: References of object geometry used in assembly models.

exploded configuration: A configuration of an assembly that shows instances separated from one another. An exploded configuration is used as the basis for an assembly drawing.

7.10 glossary of key terms (continued)

hierarchy: The parent-child relationships between instances in an assembly.

instances: Copies of components that are included within an assembly model.

interference: The amount of overlap between two instances in an assembly.

subassembly: A logical grouping of assembly instances that is treated as a single entity within the overall assembly model.

top-down modeling: The process of establishing the assembly and hierarchy before individual components are created.

7.11 questions for review

1. Describe the differences between an object and a component.

2. What is an instance?

3. What does the term *associativity* mean in the context of assembly modeling?

4. What type of relationships are made when an assembly model is established?

5. Name and describe three types of assembly constraints.

6. Define *interference* and *clearance* in the context of assembly modeling.

7. What is a bill of materials?

8. What is the primary difference between bottom-up assembly modeling and top-down assembly modeling?

7.12 problems

1. The two parts in Figure P7.1 are to be mated together as shown. Using only the features labeled, apply assembly constraints to mate the two pieces so that the top part is fully constrained and assembled correctly with the bottom part. Assume the bottom part is already fixed in position. Specify five ways of doing that using only coincident and concentric constraints. An example follows:

   Constraint set 1: hole 1 concentric with hole 2

   surface 1 coincident with surface 3

   surface 2 coincident with surface 4

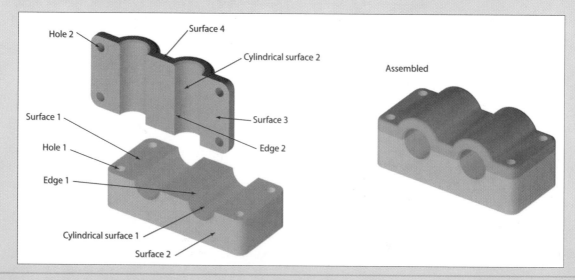

FIGURE P7.1. Constrain the edges and surfaces of (a) to create the assembled position (b).

7.12 problems (continued)

2. The parts shown in Figure P7.2 are to be assembled into a screw clamp. Create a solid model for each part and apply assembly constraints to create an assembly model of the clamp. All parts are made of steel. The notation "M10" designates a standard metric screw thread with a 10 mm outer diameter. (You will learn more about this in a later chapter.)

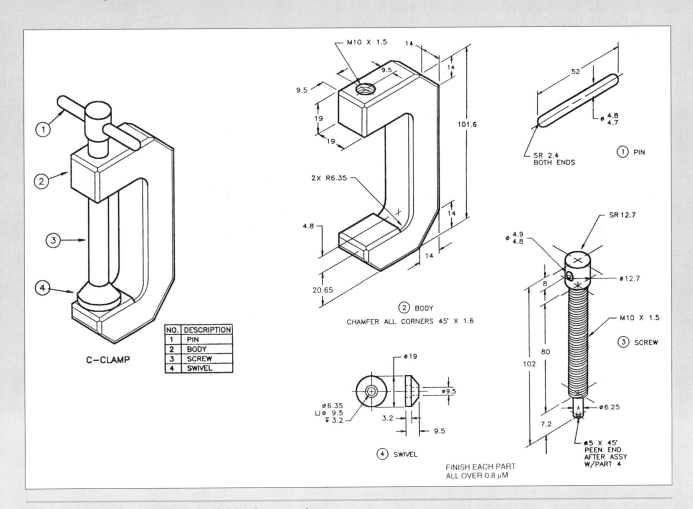

FIGURE P7.2. Create an assembly model for the screw clamp.

7.12 problems (continued)

3. Figure P7.3 shows a conceptual model for a pen-type eraser in whole and in cutaway view. Using reasonable materials and dimensions of your choice, expand the concept to create solid models of the individual parts. Using assembly constraints, create an assembly model of the eraser.

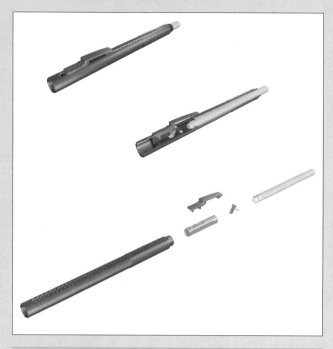

FIGURE P7.3.

4. Figure P7.4 shows a conceptual model for a garden hose nozzle in whole, cutaway, and exploded views. Using reasonable materials and dimensions of your choice, expand the concept to create solid models of the individual parts. Using assembly constraints, create an assembly model of the nozzle.

FIGURE P7.4.

5. Conceptual sketches (top view, front view, and side view) for a toggle clamp are shown in Figure P7.5. Using reasonable materials and dimensions of your choice, expand the concept to create solid models of the individual parts. Using assembly constraints, create an assembly model of the toggle clamp.

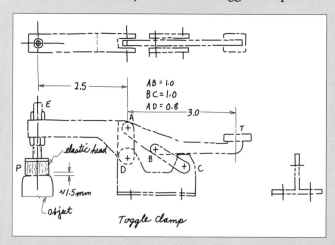

FIGURE P7.5.

7.12 problems (continued)

6. Conceptual sketches (top view, front view, and side view) for a wheelbarrow are shown in Figure P7.6. Using reasonable materials and dimensions of your choice, expand the concept to create solid models of the individual parts. Using assembly constraints, create an assembly model of the wheelbarrow.

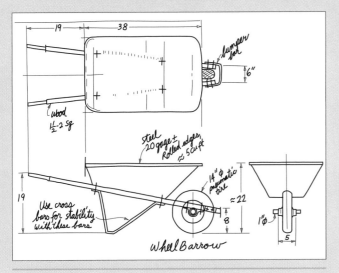

FIGURE P7.6.

7. Conceptual sketches (top view, front view, and side view) for a caster are shown in Figure P7.7. Using reasonable materials and dimensions of your choice, expand the concept to create solid models of the individual parts. Using assembly constraints, create an assembly model of the caster.

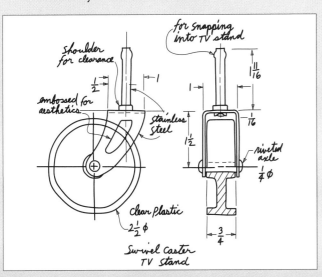

FIGURE P7.7.

8. Conceptual sketches (top view, front view, and side view) for a gear puller are shown in Figure P7.8. Using reasonable materials and dimensions of your choice, expand the concept to create solid models of the individual parts. Using assembly constraints, create an assembly model of the gear puller.

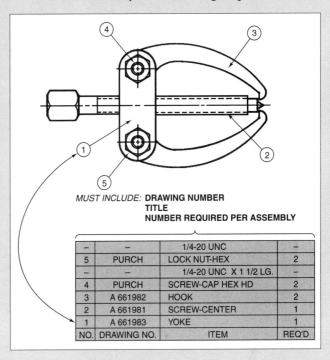

MUST INCLUDE: **DRAWING NUMBER**
TITLE
NUMBER REQUIRED PER ASSEMBLY

NO.	DRAWING NO.	ITEM	REQ'D
–	–	1/4-20 UNC	–
5	PURCH	LOCK NUT-HEX	2
–	–	1/4-20 UNC X 1 1/2 LG.	–
4	PURCH	SCREW-CAP HEX HD	2
3	A 661982	HOOK	2
2	A 661981	SCREW-CENTER	1
1	A 661983	YOKE	1

FIGURE P7.8.

10

Orthogonal Projection and Multiview Representation

objectives

After completing this chapter, you should be able to

- Discuss the principles of orthogonal projection
- Show how orthogonal projection is used to create multiple views of an object for formal engineering drawing
- Explain why orthogonal projection is necessary to represent objects in formal engineering drawing
- Create a multiview drawing from a 3-D object

10.01

introduction

The best way to communicate the appearance of an object (short of showing the object itself) is to show its image. For the purposes of the object's fabrication, analysis, or record keeping, this image must be precise. A precise description of an object begins with an accurate graphical representation of that object, which is what a formal engineering drawing is all about. It is a series of images that show the object viewed from different angles, every view accurately depicting what that object would look like from each view.

Whether you originated a drawing or you received one from the originator, the images represented in any engineering drawing must be interpreted the same way. Consistency is achieved by adhering to nationally and internationally accepted methods for creating and interpreting the images. Pictorial images, such as the isometric drawings first presented in Chapter 2 (and detailed in Chapter 12), quickly convey large amounts of qualitative information. However, pictorial images have the disadvantage of distorting the true size, configuration, and geometry of their features.

For an object to be represented without distortion or ambiguity, enough views must be provided such that all of the object's features can be clearly seen and accurately measured. In an engineering drawing, the choice of views is not arbitrary. Also, the views are carefully chosen such that the features on the object are aligned between the views and the geometries of the features are shown without distortion. With these views, size specifications can be added later to complete the description of the object.

10.02 A More Precise Way to Communicate Your Ideas

You have a wonderful idea for a new device. You believe in your idea. You want to have it fabricated. However, you must communicate to another party your thoughts about what the parts in the device will look like when they are fabricated. The other party may be another engineer who subjects your device to a more detailed analysis of what it should look like. The other party may be a fabricator who makes the device to your exact specifications. The other parties may be located in another area of the country or in another country. With the international scope of business today, design, analyses, and fabrication are commonly done in different locations around the world.

If questions arise concerning your idea, you may not be around to answer them. That is why all other parties involved in fabricating the object must envision it exactly as you do. One of your goals as the engineer or designer of a product, device, or structure is to represent it graphically in such a way (i.e., accurately) that it can be fabricated without any party misinterpreting how you want it to appear.

During the development of the Aerotec riser, the engineers at Hoyt USA faced the possibility that the product's geometry would be misinterpreted due to insufficient representation of what it would look like after fabrication. Creating a graphical image of the object in the form of a sketch or drawing as seen from only a single direction was not a good idea. The riser, which is shown in Figure 10.01, contains many features, such as cutouts and protrusions that could remain hidden when viewed from only one direction. The object had to be viewed from multiple directions to ensure that all of its features were revealed. If you were the engineer responsible for the design and manufacturing of a similar product, what would you do? How would you communicate what you want built to those who build it? How would you ensure that different people interpret and build the product the same way every time?

FIGURE 10.01. Viewing the Aerotec riser from different directions reveals previously hidden features. The arrows indicate details in each view that cannot be fully seen and described in the other views. (Model courtesy of Hoyt USA Archery Products).

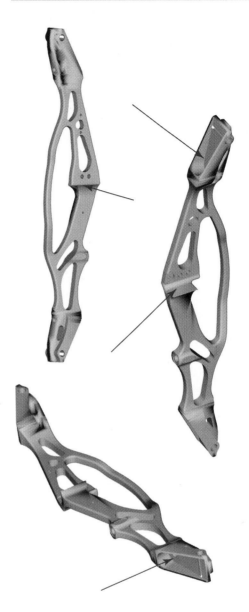

10.02.01 Problems with Pictorials

One solution would be to use pictorials such as isometric or perspective view. These types of representations of an object offer the advantage of quickly conveying the object's 3-D aspects from one view. Even people who do not have a technical background can easily and quickly understand pictorials.

However, pictorial representations present problems that are inherent in the use of one view of an object's three dimensions. One problem is the distortion of angles, as shown in Figure 10.02. The use of right angles and perpendicularity between surfaces is common on many fabricated objects because surfaces having those relationships are easy to construct with machine tools. However, on pictorials, 90° angles do not appear as 90° angles. In fact, depending on the angle of viewing, a 90° angle can appear as more or less than 90°. On a pictorial, it is difficult to depict an object's angles correctly when angles are not 90°.

Another problem with pictorials is the distortion of true lengths. In any pictorial, a length of 1 m on an object, for example, is neither depicted nor clearly perceived as a 1 m length.

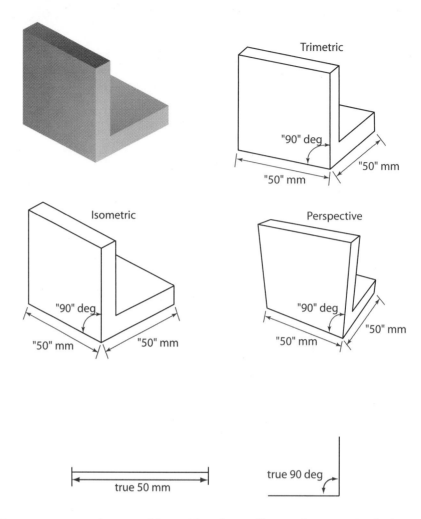

In some cases, such as an object with only rectilinear edges seen in the isometric view, this length distortion is the same in every direction. In this case, the real length can be obtained by multiplying the distorted edge length by a single correction factor. In Figure 10.02, for example, the length of each edge of the object shown in the isometric would need to be the actual edge length multiplied by a scaling factor of 0.612 if the object were drawn its full size. The formulas for getting this particular scaling factor is complicated, so do not worry about it for now. In general, however, the correction is not just a simple scaling factor. In a dimetric view, the correction factor for an edge of the object is dependent upon direction. The correction factor is more complicated for a trimetric representation, and the correction factor is even more complicated for a perspective representation.

Internal measurements also are distorted in pictorials. This distortion is dependent upon the direction of measurement, as shown in Figure 10.03. The location of the center of a hole placed at the center of a square face is, in reality, equidistant from each vertex of the square. However, in an isometric pictorial, the center of the hole must be drawn such that it is located a different distance from one vertex than from its adjacent vertices.

Figure 10.03 also shows the problem of curve distortion. The simplest curve—a circle or an arc of a circle—appears elliptical on a pictorial. On an isometric pictorial, the conversion from a circle to its representation as an ellipse is a matter of figuring out the scaling factors to calculate the major and minor axes and the orientation of the ellipse, both of which are dependent upon the circle's orientation in space. The calculation or construction is more complicated on a trimetric view because the scaling and orientation factors are different for different plane orientations on the object. On a perspective representation, the construction is more complicated

FIGURE 10.03. Distortion of internal lengths in pictorials. These different lengths on the same object represent the same length, which is the diameter of the holes in the cube.

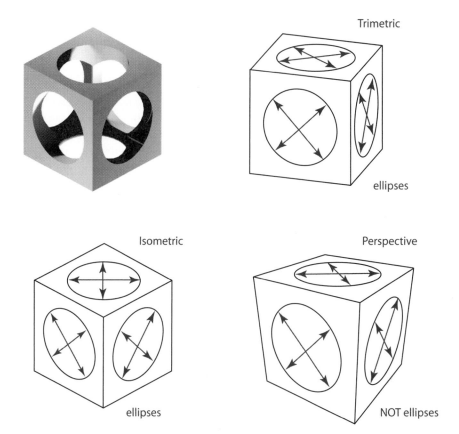

FIGURE 10.03. Distortion of internal lengths in pictorials. These different lengths on the same object represent the same length, which is the diameter of the holes in the cube.

because the circle does not appear as an ellipse, but rather as an oval, or egg shape. (Remember, an egg shape is not an ellipse.)

The sum of the previous discussion is that although pictorials have the advantage of looking realistic, it is difficult or impractical to create an object with precision from them. Pictorials are subject to misinterpretation and errors in analysis and fabrication because the angles and distances are distorted. The most universally accepted solution to these problems is to use multiview representations, which are explained next.

10.02.02 Viewing Planes

A **multiview** representation depicts in one plane, such as a sheet of paper, many images of the same object, each viewed from a different direction. Pictorials can be used to enhance the clarity of the 3-D perception of an object; but the sizes of the object and its details are shown in a series of views, each view showing the sizes in their true length or shape. Any fabrication or analysis of the object's measurements can then be based on what is shown in the multiview projections, not on what is shown in the pictorial.

When you visualize an object in space, its appearance changes depending on the direction from which you view it. The lines and curves that form the graphical presentation of the object, such as the lines and curves shown in Figure 10.03, represent edges that are the intersections of surfaces. Now visualize a transparent plane, perhaps a sheet of glass, fixed in space between you and the object. This plane is called a **viewing plane**. Imagine the image of the object as seen through the plane is somehow painted onto the plane. Continuing to imagine, remove the object and look at the image painted on the viewing plane. What you see on that plane is a 2-D image of a 3-D object. The appearance of the image, however, would depend on the viewing angle of your head in front of that plane when you created the image. The simplest and most accurate view is from your head looking directly forward at the object. In general, to be accurate about the appearance of the object as seen through the plane, you would need to define the locations and orientations of the object, the viewing plane, and the viewer.

This is a great deal of information. But you would not need all of that information if you defined the image as one created by orthogonal projection, which is explained next.

10.02.03 Orthogonal Projection

In orthogonal projection, the image of an object is composed of points projected from individual points on the object onto the viewing plane such that the projection of each point is perpendicular to the viewing plane. Orthogonal projection of an object onto a transparent viewing plane is shown in Figure 10.04, where you can see the perpendicular relationship between the projection lines and the viewing plane when the plane is turned on edge.

An image created in this manner has two advantages. One advantage is that such an image is easy to create because you do not have to worry about defining the location or orientation of the viewing plane relative to the line-of-sight. The line-of-sight from a point on the object to the viewing plane is like the projection path; that is, it is always perpendicular to the viewing plane. The other advantage is that by turning the object such that an edge of the object is parallel to the viewing plane, the image of that edge shows its true length. Furthermore, the length of a projected edge is independent of its distance from the viewing plane. Both of these properties are shown in Figure 10.05.

10.02.04 A Distorted Reality

An image created by orthogonal projection is merely a convenience that allows you to analyze the image more easily when you are ready to make the object depicted. In the strictest sense, orthogonal projection does not accurately represent an image of the way a real object looks. In reality, parts of an object that are farther away appear smaller than the same-sized parts of an object that are closer. With orthogonal projection, all parts of the object appear in the same scale no matter how far the object is placed from

FIGURE 10.04. Using orthogonal projection to create an image of an object on a viewing plane. The object in (a) is in front of the viewing plane. The object in (b) is behind the viewing plane. In either case, the projection lines are perpendicular to the viewing plane, as shown in (c).

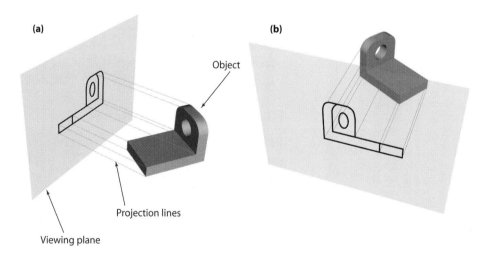

(a)

(b)

Object

Projection lines

Viewing plane

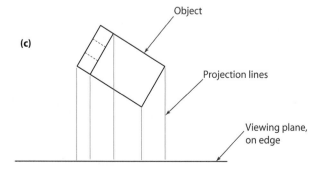

(c)

Object

Projection lines

Viewing plane, on edge

FIGURE 10.05. With orthogonal projection, the projected length of an edge is independent of its distance to the viewing plane. For this particular object orientation, the true lengths of the vertical edges are shown.

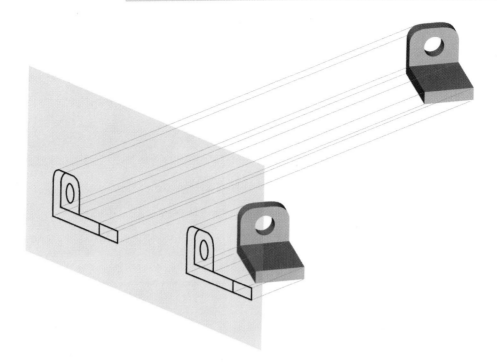

the viewing plane. But as in the case that follows and in most cases, the approximation is close and the convenience and ease of image creation and analysis far outweigh the need to see the image as it really appears.

The effect of an image created by orthogonal projection is similar to a photograph of an object taken at a long distance using a powerful telephoto lens. That type of picture lacks depth; that is, the object appears flat. This lack of depth is attributable to the fact that although the light rays actually extend radially from the surface of an object, the reflected light rays appear less like radial rays and more like parallel rays viewed at a great distances from the object. The greater the distance, the more parallel the light rays. At a long distance, where the light rays compose the image of the object, such as at a camera lens, the light rays are very nearly parallel to each other and very nearly perpendicular to the plane of the lens. This effect is shown in the bottom photograph in Figure 10.06; both photographs are the same object, each taken from a different camera distance. Even though the overall image size of the object is about the same, in the close-up photo, you should be able to see that the parts (for example, the wheels) of the object that are closer appear magnified when compared to the parts that are farther away.

10.02.05 Choice of Viewing Planes

From what was just explained, you should understand that an orthogonal projection of an object is a 2-D drawing of that object as it would appear on a viewing plane. To get a different view of the object, you need to move the object and/or the viewing plane to a different location.

Consider the case of keeping the viewing plane in the same place and rotating the object. One advantage of orthogonal projection is that an object's lines and curves can be seen in their true shape. For example, when the viewing plane is parallel to a circle, the circle actually appears as a circle rather than an ellipse. This may be important, for example, when you want to see how close the edge of a hole in an object actually comes to the edge of the object. It makes sense, therefore, to rotate the object into an orientation where the measurements, such as the diameter of the hole or its distance to the edge, can be seen to represent the true shape, distance, and size. Figure 10.07 shows an object rotated into the best position for this specific analysis versus the same object in

FIGURE 10.06. The top photograph was taken from up close. The bottom photo was taken from a long distance and enlarged so feature sizes could be compared. Can you see the lack of perspective in the long-distance photo?

a poor orientation. In general, in the creation of the first view of an object, it has become common practice to orient the object in a position that shows as many as possible of its lines and curves in their true shape.

However, a single view of an object is usually insufficient to specify all of its features and measurements fully. Figure 10.08 shows how different objects can appear the same using a single view only.

FIGURE 10.07. Good part placement shows most of the part edges in their true length.

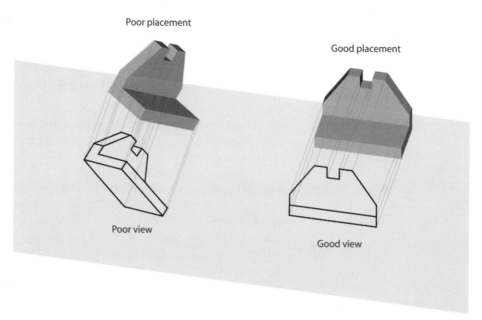

FIGURE 10.08. A single view of a part may have many different interpretations.

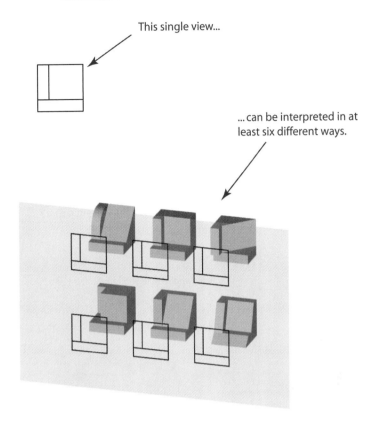

This single view...

... can be interpreted in at least six different ways.

To fully define the 3-D geometry of an object, it is necessary to depict the object in **multiple views**. This means there must be a viewing plane for each of the views. Specifying the location and orientation of each of the additional viewing planes must be done in a standardized way so that 2-D images can be extracted from the object easily. Also, the multiple 2-D images must contain enough information so that the original 3-D image can be re-created from them. One way to do this is to locate and orient the additional viewing planes so that each is orthogonal to the first viewing plane, as shown with a second and third viewing plane in Figure 10.09(a). The images on all of these viewing planes are created using orthogonal projection.

When the location and orientation of the intersection line between the first viewing plane and any one of the additional viewing planes are known, the location and orientation of each of the other additional images can be specified. The intersection line between the first viewing plane and any of the additional viewing planes can be imagined as a hinge between the two planes. By "unfolding" the additional planes at their imaginary hinges, as shown in Figure 10.09(b), the images on all of the viewing planes can be shown on a single plane, or in other words, a 2-D drawing.

Used this way, orthogonal projection and viewing planes offer you the advantage of seeing multiple views of the same object at the same time on a single sheet of paper. Orthogonal projection also can precisely identify the position and orientation of the viewing planes used to create those views by specifying on the single sheet the location of the intersection lines between the viewing planes.

10.02.06 Size and Alignment

When the second and third planes are completely unfolded and are coplanar with the first viewing plane, as shown in Figure 10.09(c), three images can be seen on a single plane. The images from the second and third planes are considered adjacent to (i.e., created immediately next to) the image from the first plane. Note that the size and orientation of the images are not arbitrary. Each image has the same scale (or magnification);

FIGURE 10.09. Two viewing planes that are orthogonal to the first (front) viewing plane (a) can be unfolded (b) to present the images on a single plane (c). The imaginary hinges for the two viewing planes are at the intersections of these planes with the front viewing plane.

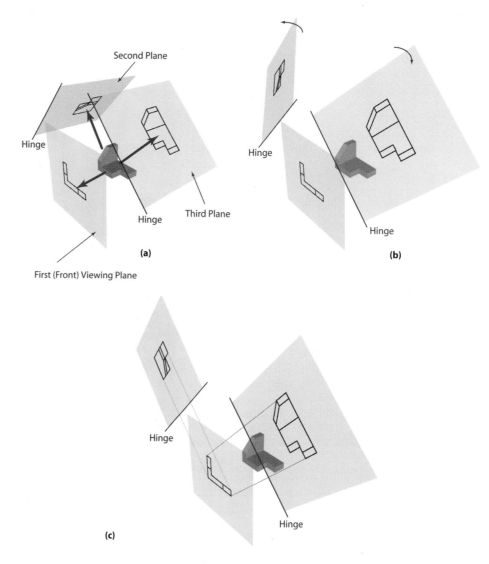

and the orientation of the image is dependent upon the original location of its viewing plane as defined by the location of the intersection line between the viewing planes, or their hinge. This alignment of the vertices of the object images in **adjacent views** is shown in Figure 10.10, where the three views are presented on a single sheet.

FIGURE 10.10. Viewing planes completely unfolded showing proper size, location, and orientation of the images on a single plane.

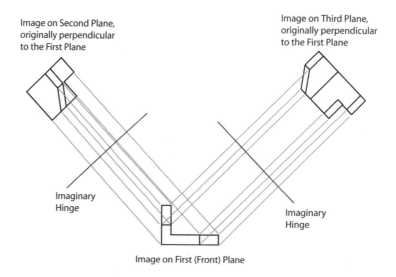

10.03 **The Glass Box**

Only three or four views are required to fully define most objects. Simple objects may require only one view; complicated objects may require six or more views. Objects such as engineered parts can usually be fully defined when they are viewed through a set of six viewing planes that together form a **glass box**, as shown Figure 10.11(a). The glass box has the unique property that for any viewing plane, all of its adjacent planes are perpendicular to each other and opposite viewing planes are parallel to each other.

When you open (or unfold) the panels of the box, as shown in Figure 10.11(b), you can view all six sides of the object simultaneously on a single plane, as shown in Figure 10.11(c). There is more than one way to unfold the box. Unfolding in the manner shown in Figure 10.11 is the standard way to do it according to accepted drawing practices. The top and bottom and right- and left-side views open about the front view; and the rear view is attached to the left-side view.

Make sure you see and understand that when the viewing planes are completely unfolded, the size and orientation of each image is not arbitrary. The scale in each view is the same. In the case of the complete glass box, each viewing plane is orthogonal to its adjacent viewing planes. When the box is unfolded and presented on a single sheet,

FIGURE 10.11. Viewing an engineered part through a glass box (a) that opens (b) to present the images on a single plane (c).

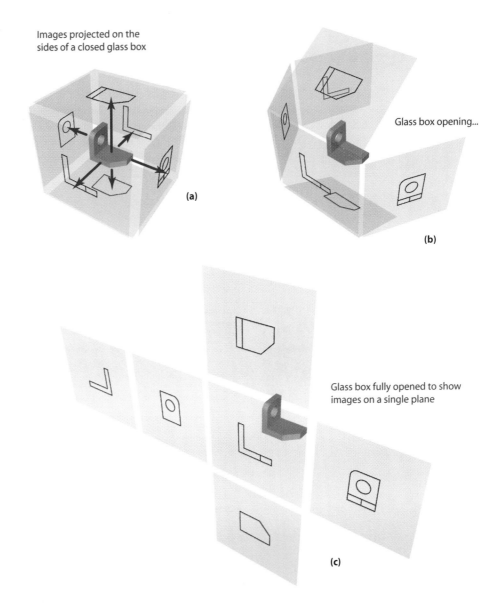

Images projected on the sides of a closed glass box

(a)

Glass box opening...

(b)

Glass box fully opened to show images on a single plane

(c)

as in Figure 10.12, adjacent images are aligned horizontally for horizontally adjacent views or vertically for vertically adjacent views. These alignment properties are very important when the object is analyzed. If you select any point on the object (assume point A on Figure 10.12), the images of that point will be horizontally aligned with each other on horizontally adjacent views and those images will be vertically aligned with each other on vertically adjacent views.

In general, the same point in space seen in adjacent views is aligned along a path that is perpendicular to the intersection line of the viewing planes, as shown in Figure 10.10. What this means for engineering drawing is that features on an object, such as edges or holes, shown in one view can be easily located on the adjacent view because the features are aligned between adjacent views. For complex objects with many features, the ability to identify the same feature on adjacent views is of tremendous utility.

10.03.01 Standard Views

The glass box yields six different views of an object. For a large percentage of engineered parts, six views are more than sufficient. Engineers typically like to design things that are easy and therefore inexpensive to make. Three-axis milling machines and single-axis lathes are common machines in any fabrication shop. These machines easily create surfaces on the workpiece that are parallel, perpendicular, or concentric to each other and that easily cut holes, slots, or other features that are perpendicular to the working surface.

The six views represented by the glass box are the front, top, left side, right side, bottom, and rear views. These views are known as the six standard orthogonal views or the six principal orthogonal views or more simply as the **six standard views** or the **six principal views**, respectively. When a formal drawing is created showing these views, the intersection lines and projection lines between views are not shown because these lines do not add much information to the drawing when it is already understood that adjacent views are orthogonal to each other. Also, each view does not need to be labeled as the front, top, right side, etc., views.

FIGURE 10.12. Alignment of points on adjacent views for all six standard views.

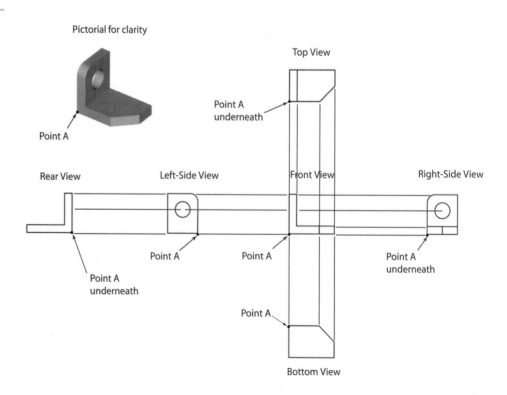

FIGURE 10.13. The preferred presentation configuration showing the front, top, and right-side views of an object. Other views are added only when necessary to show features that cannot be defined in the preferred configuration.

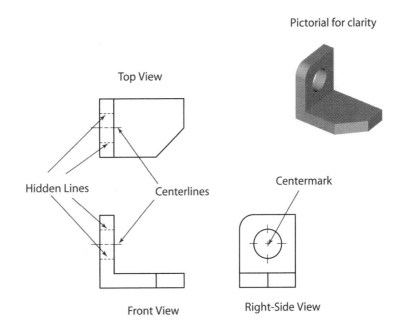

Pictorial for clarity

Top View

Hidden Lines   Centerlines

Centermark

Front View   Right-Side View

10.03.02 The Preferred Configuration

Are all six views necessary? Usually not. The great percentage of engineered parts can be fully defined geometrically with fewer than all six of the standard views. In fact, most engineered parts can be completely defined for fabrication using only three views.

Although there are no defined rules as to which views must be included or excluded in a formal engineering drawing, there is a **preferred configuration**—the front, top, and right-side views. Additional views are presented only when necessary to reveal and define features that cannot be shown in the preferred views. The preferred configuration for the object in Figure 10.12 is shown in Figure 10.13. Only the front, top, and side views are shown. Make sure every edge of the object can be seen in its true length in at least one view.

It is becoming increasingly popular to include an isometric or trimetric pictorial of the object somewhere on the drawing. When a pictorial is included, it serves only to aid in clarity; it does not need to be properly aligned or scaled with the standard views.

10.04 The Necessary Details

Only the minimum number of views needed to quickly and accurately communicate the geometry of an object should be created. Whenever possible, the preferred configuration of a front, top, and side view should be used unless fewer than three views are needed to see and define all of the features of the object. To minimize the number of required views on complicated objects and to reduce any possible ambiguity, some shorthand notation that describes common geometries such as certain types of holes and screw threads is used in drawing practice. Such notation is detailed in later chapters in this book. There will, however, be cases where additional views become necessary or when the preferred configuration may not be the best.

10.04.01 Hidden Lines and Centerlines

The dashed lines you see on the views shown in Figure 10.13 represent internal features or edges that are obscured by the object. These obscured features or edges are called **hidden lines** in these views. Hidden lines, which are denoted as equally spaced dashed lines on a drawing, represent the edges of an object or its features that cannot be seen on the real object but would be visible if the object were partially transparent. Hidden lines are used to emphasize an object's unseen geometry and thus speed the interpretation of its presentation. Hidden lines also are used to reduce the need for creating additional views. Although hidden edges cannot be seen on an opaque object, they are represented graphically the same way hidden lines are included in a view to emphasize that a feature cannot be seen in that view or to show that a feature cannot be seen from any of the other views. Later in this chapter, hidden lines will be discussed further as you encounter examples of the advantages and problems associated with them.

Looking closely at Figure 10.13, you will see lines located at the center axis of the hole. These are not hidden lines. They are **centerlines**, which are represented graphically by alternating short and long dashes along the length of the center of the circular hole. Centerlines cannot be seen on the real object, but they must be included on the drawing to identify where the center of the circular hole is located on the object. More generally, centerlines are used where there is a cylindrical surface such as a hole or a tube.

The reason for including centerlines is to make it easier for the reader to distinguish between edges, visible or hidden, that are part of a cylindrical surface and edges that result from the intersections of planes. Using centerlines also makes it easier to locate features such as holes, which are commonly defined by their diameters and center locations.

A **centermark**, the end view of a centerline, is identified by a right-angle cross such as that shown in the center of the circular hole in the right-side view of the object in Figure 10.13. Typically, centerlines and centermarks are used where the arc of a cylindrical surface is 180° or greater, although they can be used for lesser arcs as required for clarity in a drawing.

10.04.02 The Necessary Views

How many views should be created to fully define a object? In engineering practice, it is considered poor practice to create more views than are needed. Creating unneeded views means more work for which there is no payoff. However, having too few views can create problems when the fabricator tries to make the part. In the worst-case scenario, the fabricator will try to guess what you want, get it wrong, and deliver a potentially expensive part that cannot be used. In that case, the creator of the drawing would be at fault, not the fabricator. The party responsible for creating the drawing also may be legally responsible for paying for the services of the fabricator.

So how many views are needed to fully define an object? The number depends on how complicated the object is to depict in three dimensions. Start by creating the front, top, and right-side views. Remember, they represent the preferred configuration, which all engineering personnel like to see. Try to orient the object in such a way that these three views reveal as much of the object's features as possible. If you are lucky, these three views will fully define the object; but that is not always the case.

You should ask yourself the following two questions when you finish creating the drawing views:

1. Can the true size of all of the measurements needed to define all of the features of this object be seen in at least one of the views just created?

2. Is it impossible for the geometry of any feature to be misinterpreted as another type of geometry?

Yes to both questions means you have enough views. No to either question means you have more work to do.

FIGURE 10.14. Formal multi-view presentation of the Aerotec riser as would be seen in an engineering drawing. The measurements, text, and other specifications are not shown in this example so you can see the views more clearly. (Model and drawing courtesy of Hoyt USA Archery Products)

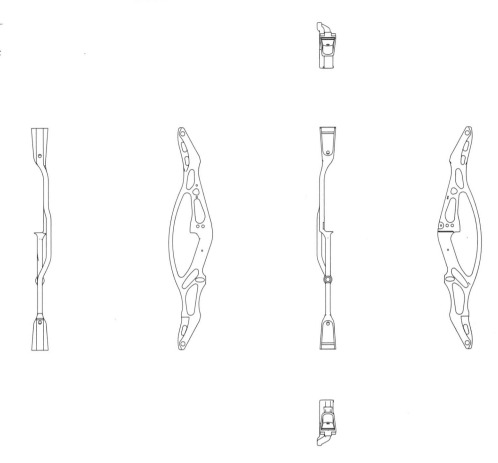

The multiview production drawing for the Hoyt Aerotec riser is shown in Figure 10.14. The complexity of this object requires that all six standard views be used because it has features that can be seen only from each of the six viewing directions.

Objects that are flat can be defined with a single view along with some sort of note specifying the thickness of the object. Flat sheet metal objects and objects that can be cut from a plate of uniform thickness fall into this category. The cuts must be through the entire thickness of the sheet or plate. An example of this type of object is shown in Figure 10.15. Because this object is made of very thin material, the adjacent orthogonal views would appear as lines.

Even when the thickness of the object is constant, a fabricator may find it helpful to see a second view; for example, to emphasize that the thickness of the object is a significant fraction of the object's planar geometry. See how the second view in Figure 10.16 helps depict the relatively large and uniform thickness of the object.

For objects that have 3-D features such as protrusions and cuts, each with a different depth, the problem of finding the proper number of views for a drawing becomes more difficult. Figure 10.17 shows an example of a drawing with two views. In this case, more than one interpretation of the object is possible. The addition of a third view is necessary to completely specify the desired object.

Figure 10.18 shows three original views that, in the absence of hidden lines, could be used to represent two possible objects. A fourth orthogonal view, a bottom view, is required in this case to distinguish between the two possibilities.

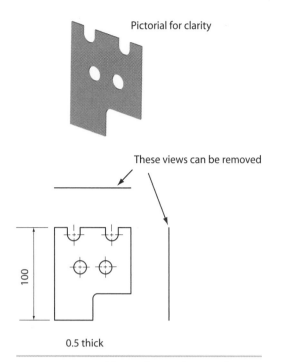

Pictorial for clarity

These views can be removed

100

0.5 thick

FIGURE 10.15. Additional views for very thin parts, such as sheet metal, add little information.

Second View

Pictorial for clarity

Original View

FIGURE 10.16. For a part with a constant but significant thickness, including a second view is a good idea to emphasize the 3-D nature of the part.

FIGURE 10.17. Different interpretations of a drawing with two views. A third view is necessary.

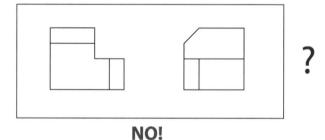

?

NO!

These two views alone are insufficient to define a three-dimensional object

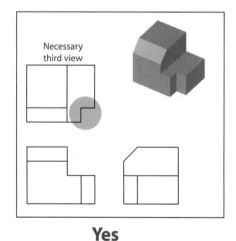

Necessary third view

Yes

Adding the third view uniquely defines the object shown

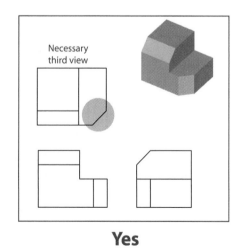

Necessary third view

Yes

Adding the third view uniquely defines the object shown

FIGURE 10.18. In the absence of hidden lines, four views are required to distinguish between these two parts. The fourth view is needed to distinguish the cutout on the underside as being diagonal instead of square.

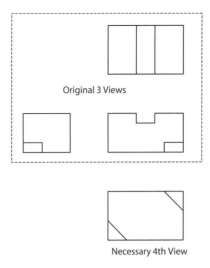

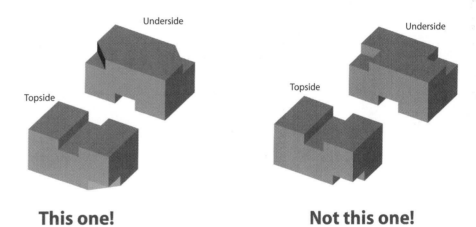

Figure 10.19 shows an example of an object where, in the absence of hidden lines, five views are necessary.

As a rule of thumb, when an object contains inclined surfaces with respect to the standard viewing directions, each of those inclined surfaces must appear inclined in at least one of the orthogonal views representing the object. When the inclined surface is not shown in one of the orthogonal views, a view needs to show the surface as being inclined (i.e., with at least one of its edges at an angle that is not 0° or 90°).

10.04.03 Hidden Lines versus More Views

One way to reduce the number of required views is to use hidden lines. The object shown in Figure 10.20 has some unique features. Try to imagine representing the object without using hidden lines. Without the hidden lines, five views would be required to define all of its features. With only the front, top, and right-side views and no hidden lines, the geometry of the keyway seen on the underside of the object cannot be defined. Moreover, without hidden lines, additional views would be required to show that the hole and slot extend all the way through the object.

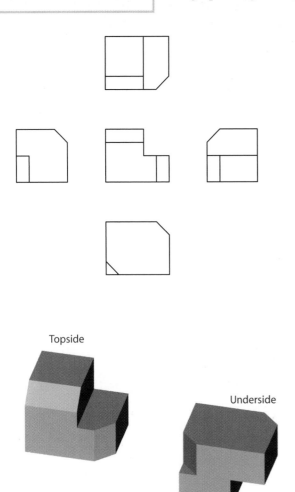

FIGURE 10.19. Without the benefit of hidden lines, five views are required to describe this object.

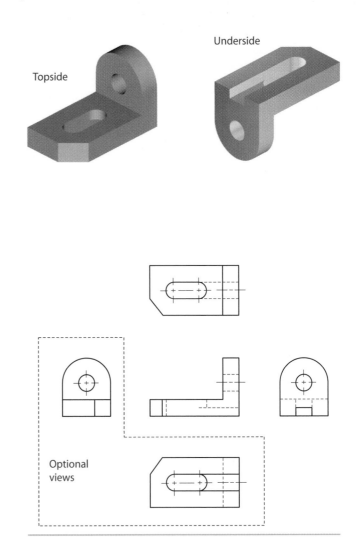

FIGURE 10.20. Hidden and internal features on a part. Using hidden lines makes the left side and bottom views optional.

By using hidden lines, only three views are required—the preferred configuration of front, top, and side views. Whether you use all five views shown in Figure 10.20 or the preferred three-view presentation depends on your answer to this question: Which presentation would be clearer? You always select the presentation that has, in your opinion, the least ambiguity (and not necessarily the least amount of work to produce). In the case of the five-view presentation, although it would not be an absolute requirement, adding hidden lines would emphasize the internal geometry of the object. For the three-view presentation, adding the hidden lines would be an absolute necessity.

Another use of hidden lines is to reveal the details of internal features that cannot be easily seen in any of the standard orthogonal views. Such details would be, for example, the depth or the profile of holes and slots, as shown in Figure 10.21. Figure 10.20 demonstrates how hidden lines can be used instead of additional views, making the drawing easier to create and more compact without the loss of any information. For the object shown in Figure 10.21, the depth of the slot cannot be seen in any of the standard orthogonal views. If you look carefully at the views for the object shown in Figure 10.21, you see that hidden lines for different features can be separated into different views. But if all of the hidden lines were shown on all of the views, the result would be a jumble of so many hidden lines that it would be difficult to distinguish the different features that they represent.

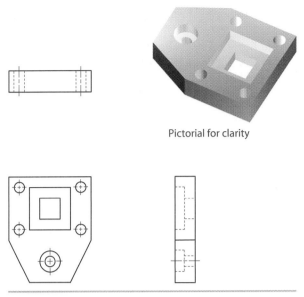

Pictorial for clarity

FIGURE 10.21. Use of hidden lines to reveal internal features.

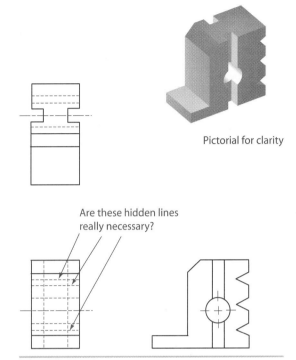

Pictorial for clarity

Are these hidden lines really necessary?

FIGURE 10.22. Overuse of hidden lines causes confusion. Exercise judgment. It might be better to create another view, such as a rear view in this case.

A common problem for inexperienced designers is deciding when to use hidden lines. Hidden lines should be used to add clarity to a drawing. Hidden lines should be used to emphasize a feature, even if that feature can be seen and defined in the existing orthogonal views. The goal of the creator or the drawing is to increase the speed at which the drawing can be interpreted. However, hidden lines must be used to add information when there is no way to obtain this information from the rest of the drawing.

Because hidden lines can be used to avoid creating another view, it is sometimes tempting to do just that, even when using another view would be better. Figure 10.22 shows that adding too many hidden lines create a complex, confusing drawing. With this result, it would be better to create extra views. When deciding whether to use hidden lines or to add additional views, simply do whatever will cause less confusion for the reader of the drawing. However, it is usually not a good idea to create hidden lines of different features such that the hidden lines cross each other, lie on top of each other, or even come close to each other.

The purpose of hidden lines is to define or emphasize details that cannot be seen, which is accepted as standard practice. Deleting unnecessary hidden lines and adding additional views are considered optional methods of reducing ambiguity when the use of hidden lines makes the presentation confusing. There must be no confusion as to which feature a hidden line represents.

10.05 First-Angle Projection versus Third-Angle Projection

The glass box representation of multiviews of an object is formally referred to as **third-angle projection**. Whenever third-angle projection is specified on a drawing, each view of the object was created by projecting the image of the object onto the glass box's transparent viewing plane between you and the object—the object is behind the transparent viewing plane. The viewing planes are then rotated about their intersection lines until all of the views are shown on a single plane or sheet. This interpretation is the one most commonly used in the United States.

However, in some parts of Asia and Europe, **first-angle projection** is commonly used. In first-angle projection, each viewing plane is behind the object, which means the object is between you and the viewing plane. With first-angle projection, the viewing plane is opaque and the image is projected back and transferred onto the viewing plane. One way to interpret first-angle projection is to imagine the object in front of the opaque panels, as shown in Figure 10.23(a). The image of the object, as seen by a viewer located directly in front of each panel (with the object directly in line between the two panels), is transferred to that panel. Opening the panels, as in Figure 10.23(b), begins to show how the front, top, and right-side views are presented on a single plane, as shown in Figure 10.23(c).

For drawings created using either first-angle or third-angle projection, the primary view is considered to be the front view. The front view in either projection is usually selected as the view containing the most features in their true sizes and shapes, thereby allowing for the most measurement extraction. As you saw earlier, for the six standard views using third-angle projection, the top view appears above the front view and the

FIGURE 10.23. Viewing an object in front of opaque panels for first-angle projection. The images are projected onto the panels (a), which open (b) to present the images on a single plane (c).

Images projected onto opaque panels

Panels opening...

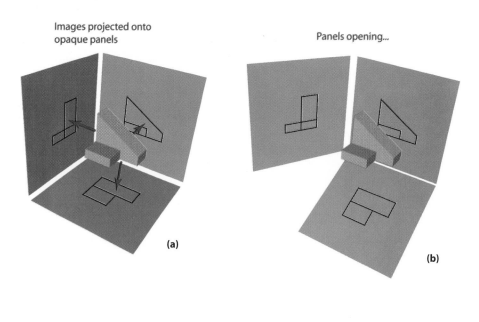

(a)

(b)

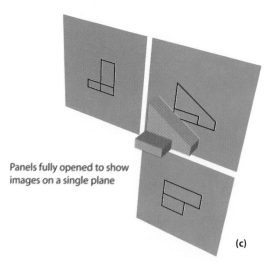

Panels fully opened to show images on a single plane

(c)

bottom view appears below the front view. The right-side view appears to the right of the front view, and the left-side view appears to the left of the front view. The rear view appears, by practice and convention, attached to the left-side view and appears to its left.

Using first-angle projection, the top view of an object appears below the front view and the bottom view appears above the front view. The right-side view appears to the left of the front view, and the left-side view appears to the right of the front view. The rear view appears, by practice and convention, attached to the left-side view and appears on its right. The location of the first-angle projection views is shown in Figure 10.24.

The differences between first-angle projection and third-angle projection are sometimes subtle and confusing, particularly because the front view of the object is the same in both cases. To add further confusion, for a large percentage of engineered parts, the left side and right-side views or the top and bottom views are identical. These reasons explain why drawings need to clearly specify whether first-angle or third-angle projection must be used to interpret the views. Many large companies operate internationally, with engineering and fabrication facilities worldwide. In international business, drawings are often created in one country and the parts fabricated in another country. When a drawing is interpreted incorrectly, the resulting fabricated part may be the mirror image of what was desired. Figure 10.25 shows a multiview drawing of an object and the two different objects that are created when the drawing is interpreted using first-angle projection and third-angle projection.

The symbol added to a drawing to specify first-angle projection or third-angle projection is two views of a truncated cone, shown in Figure 10.26. This symbol depicts how a truncated cone would appear if a drawing of it were made using the projection method used for the entire drawing. The appropriate symbol and/or wording must be added to a formal drawing, usually somewhere in the title block (for which more detail can be found in Chapter 18) to eliminate ambiguities that may arise from misinterpreting which projection was used.

FIGURE 10.24. The six standard views, using first-angle projection, presented on a single sheet.

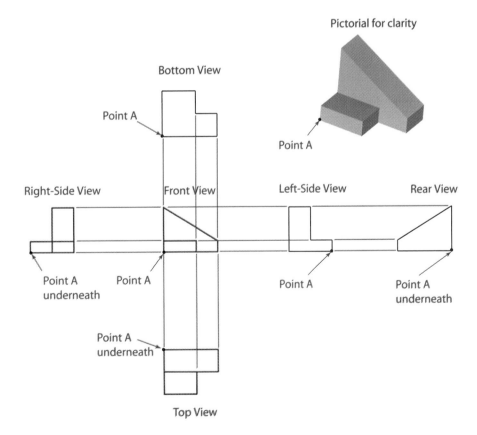

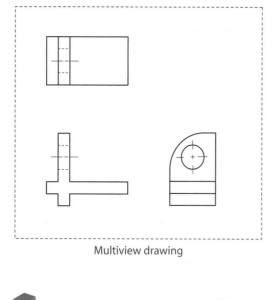

Multiview drawing

Object Represented

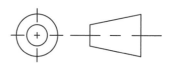

Symbol for First-Angle Projection

Symbol for Third-Angle Projection

FIGURE 10.26. Drafting symbols for specifying the use of either first-angle or third-angle projection in a drawing.

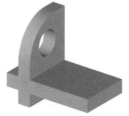

Interpretation using third-angle projection

Interpretation using first-angle projection

FIGURE 10.25. Drawing interpretation using first-angle or third-angle projection may lead to different parts.

10.06 Strategies for Creating Multiviews from Pictorials

Few people think of an object in terms of its multiview representation. If you are thinking about a pencil, for example, you probably do not imagine it in terms of a front, top, and side view. The image you have is likely to be three-dimensional, perhaps as a pictorial of some sort. Transforming that image into its multiview representation requires some skill. To develop this skill, some rules (and a great deal of practice) are required. And you need to remember that a pictorial image contains 3-D information that must be extracted from the way the pictorial looks in a 2-D medium. A multiview representation is merely a different, more accurate way of presenting this information. Exercises in converting pictorials to multiviews and multiviews to pictorials will help you develop practical skills, as well as improve visualization skills. Engineers should be able to quickly visualize 3-D objects from multiview drawings and quickly create multiview drawings for proposed or existing 3-D objects. You can begin developing these skills using the following step-by-step procedures. For the first few examples that follow, sketching techniques will be used because sketching, as opposed to drawing with instruments or CAD, is an excellent method for developing visualization skills. Later examples in this section will use more formal graphics so the drawings can be more clearly detailed.

Transforming a pictorial image into a multiview drawing usually involves keeping track of the vertices, edges, or surfaces of the object. Regardless of which elements are tracked, the process starts the same way. An eight-step process is used to create the drawing. The first two steps are as follows:

Step 1: On the pictorial, specify the viewing directions that you intend to create (e.g., front, top, right side, etc.) and create a sheet with areas reserved (and labeled) for the appropriate orthogonal views based on the projection method used.

Step 2: Find the maximum size of the object in each of the three directions of your coordinate system and in each view, sketch the limits of a rectilinear box that will contain only the entire object in all three directions.

A typical problem of multiview creation is shown in Figure 10.27. An isometric image of an object is presented, and the goal is to create the necessary orthogonal views to specify all of its features completely. Assume that all of the hidden surfaces are flat and that there are no hidden features.

This object is basic, considering all of its surfaces are perpendicular or parallel to each other. When this is the case, the edges of all of the surfaces will appear to be horizontal or vertical in all of the orthogonal views created. The true length of each feature must be shown in at least one view. For convenience in measuring the lengths of the edges on the object, an isometric grid has been placed on the isometric view. Placed on each of the orthogonal views is a corresponding rectangular grid that in each plane direction represents the same grid spacing as the isometric grid, as shown in Figure 10.28. The edge lengths as seen in the isometric view then can be conveniently transferred to the corresponding edges on the orthogonal views.

As an alternative to creating grids, you also can measure the edges in the isometric view using drafting instruments or CAD and transfer these measurements to the corresponding edges on the orthogonal views. When the edge lengths are otherwise specified, such as with notes, the specified edge lengths should be used in the orthogonal views. Carefully note the viewing directions for each view on the orthogonal views and the pictorial and make sure these directions are consistent.

You need to make clear from which point to which other point you are measuring any line in the pictorial —that is, the direction of your measurement—so you can incorporate the same information (direction of point-to-point measurement) in any of the

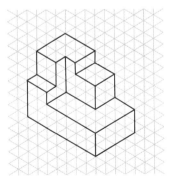

FIGURE 10.27. How would you create a multiview drawing of this object? The isometric grid is to be used for sizing.

FIGURE 10.28. Defining the foundation space, axes, viewing directions, and anchor point A.

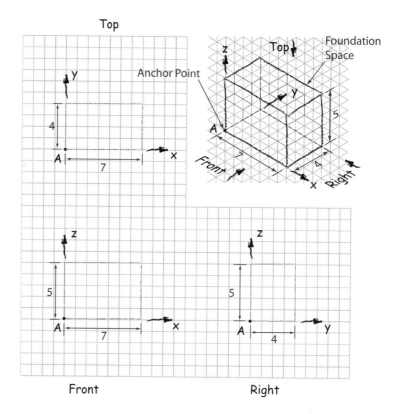

orthogonal views. For example, in Figure 10.28, as you measure from one point to another in the pictorial, you must be able to follow the same direction of measurement in the orthogonal views. For this purpose, it may be convenient to use a set of coordinate axes initially to help you with the directions of measurements until you become more familiar with the directions in the orthogonal views in your drawings. In Figure 10.28, a right-handed Cartesian coordinate system is placed with the origin coincident to one of the corners of the object in the pictorial. This same coordinate system is placed in all three orthogonal views. Make sure you maintain alignment of the origin of the coordinate system in each of the three views (step 1).

For this point to be in the same place in each view, it must be aligned on a vertical line between the top and front views and on a horizontal line between the front and right-side views. The top view looks straight onto the xy plane, so the z-axis points out of the page. The front view looks straight onto the xz plane, so the y-axis points into the page. The right-side view looks straight onto the yz plane, so the x-axis points out of the page.

The next step in creating the multiview drawing is to mark the limit of the size of the object in all three directions (step 2). These limits define a **foundation space**, which represents the rectilinear limits occupied by the object in each view. Although the foundation space is not the outline of the object itself, it helps you visualize the object in each view by delineating the volume that the object can and cannot occupy. If in the process of creating the orthogonal views you start creating lines or points for the object outside its foundation space, you will know you are doing something wrong. The foundation space for the object in Figure 10.27 is shown in Figure 10.28. Examine the foundation space on the pictorial. It extends 7 units in the x-direction, 4 units in the y-direction, and 5 units in the z-direction. Make sure these limits are marked off properly in each of the orthogonal views.

Once the foundation space is defined, there are different ways you can proceed. Students who have practiced and completed many problems in drawing orthogonal views from pictorials are able to proceed intuitively. Most beginners need a little help getting started before intuition kicks in.

10.06.01 Point Tracking

One way of continuing beyond step 2 is to label each vertex on the pictorial as a point, keep track of each point on every orthogonal view, and then connect the points in the views to form an image of the object in these views. (Keep in mind that all of an object's points may not be visible on the pictorial.) This process is called the **point tracking** method. Here is how it works.

After you have established the viewing directions and foundation volume in step 1 and step 2, you are ready to follow the next six steps to complete the drawing. The general procedure is outlined below. Each step is explained in detail in the paragraphs that follow.

Step 3: Define an anchor point.

Step 4: Locate a vertex adjacent to the anchor point and draw that edge.

Step 5: Successively locate other vertices and draw the edges between those vertices.

Step 6: Convert hidden lines.

Step 7: Add internal features.

Step 8: Check model validity.

A point on the object must be selected as an **anchor point** (step 3). There is an anchor point in each of the orthogonal views, and it is the same point in space as is seen from the different views. An anchor point is a point whose location you feel certain you can identify on each of the orthogonal views. Such a point is commonly a vertex located on one of the bottom corners of the object. Call this point A; then locate and label the point on each of the orthogonal views and on the pictorial. Remember, point A in views that are left or right of each other must be aligned horizontally; and in views that are above or below each other each, point A must be aligned vertically. In this case, but not necessarily in all cases, point A also is the origin of the coordinate axes.

Select another point on the pictorial (step 4) near point A, which can be located by traveling along one edge of the object, as shown in Figure 10.29. Call this point B; then locate it with respect to point A in each orthogonal view. You do this by noting on the

FIGURE 10.29. Defining and tracking points on the same surface near the anchor.

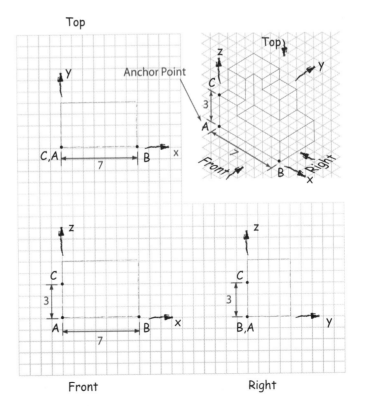

pictorial the direction and distance from point A to point B. From the measurements on the pictorial, you can see that to reach point B from point A, you need to travel 7 units in the positive x-direction. In the top view, the location for point B is 7 units to the right on a horizontal line from point A, which is the x-axis in that viewing plane. In the front view, the location of B also is 7 units to the right on a horizontal line from point A, which is the x-axis in that viewing plane. In the right-side view, the x-axis points out of the page; so point A and point B appear coincident in that view, although point B would actually be closer to you. Finally, connecting point A and point B in each orthogonal view creates an edge in each view.

Next, select another point (step 5) on the object near point A or point B that can be located by traveling along an edge of the object. It does not matter if the point is closer to point A or to point B because eventually all of the points on the object will be selected. Call this point C and locate it on each of the orthogonal views by noting the distance and direction you must travel to get to it from point A or point B. Point C is located 3 units from point A in the positive z-direction. In the front and right-side views, this direction is upward on a vertical line from point A. On the top view, point A and point C appear coincident because the z-axis points out of the page. Once point C is located in each view, its corresponding edge can be created.

The object's other edges are created in the same manner. You should select the points and edges to outline one entire surface of the object before moving to another surface of the object, as shown in Figure 10.30. In this way, you can see the surfaces appear one at a time instead of having a series of connected edges that extend in different directions. This process continues until the entire object is created in all of the views, as shown in Figure 10.31.

Inspecting the object's pictorial for any hidden edges (step 6) reveals that all edges shown are visible; they should be shown with solid lines. There are no internal features (step 7) on the object. As a final check (step 8), make sure each vertex in every view has at least three edges connected to it. Remember, one of these edges may be oriented into the page and thus appear as a point coincident with the vertex. If you determine that no

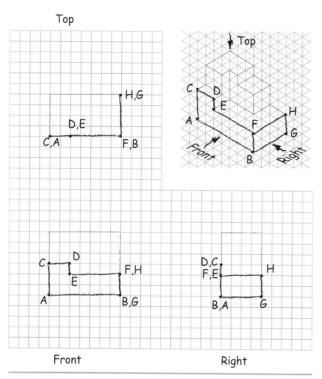

FIGURE 10.30. Connect the points to form edges of a complete surface before proceeding.

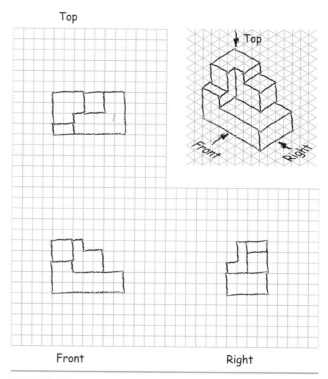

FIGURE 10.31. Continue tracking points, creating edges and surfaces until all points are accounted for.

edges are oriented into the page and only two edges are connected to a vertex, then a line must be missing.

You may have realized that even though three orthogonal views were created, this particular object could have been described using only two orthogonal views—the front and right-side views, shown in Figure 10.32. When only two views are used, it makes a difference as to which two views are used. In the example shown in Figure 10.32, specifying the front and right-side views is correct. If you were to use the front and top views, the possibility exists of either an inclined surface or a step feature, as shown in Figure 10.33.

FIGURE 10.32. Two orthogonal views, the front and the right, define all of the features of the object and are an acceptable presentation on an engineering drawing. The use of three views is more common.

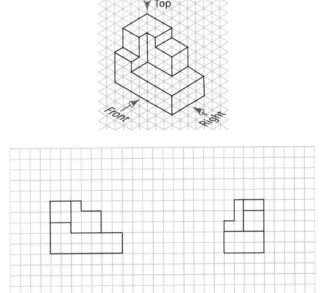

FIGURE 10.33. The wrong two views, the top and the front, lead to ambiguity. These views can represent either of two objects.

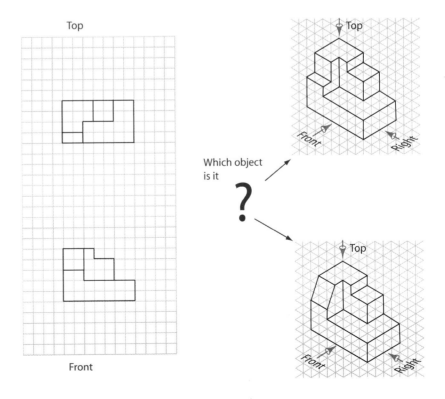

FIGURE 10.34. By keeping track of individual points, how would you create a multiview drawing of this object?

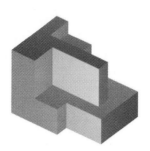
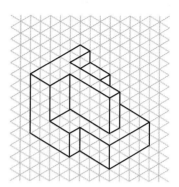

A slightly more complicated object is shown in Figure 10.34. You will try to build the multiview drawing of this object with three views.

The three views and their directions are shown in Figure 10.35. Note that the definitions of the viewing directions for this object are different from the definitions of the directions for the object in the preceding example. This does not matter as long as the definitions are consistent within the same presentation; that is, the right-side view is always on the right of the front view, the top view is always above the front view, etc., on the drawing. Whenever possible, the front, top, and right-side views should be used to represent the object unless one or more of the other standard views offers a better representation of the object's features. This example will proceed using the front, top, and left-side views to show how other views can be created and used.

A set of coordinate axes is defined on the pictorial and then transferred to the orthogonal views (step 1). Note that these directions are different from the coordinate directions in the preceding example. The location and orientation of these axes must be consistent in all views—that is what matters. In fact, as long as you are sure of the travel directions in each view, you can skip the use of coordinate axes altogether.

The foundation space is outlined in each view (step 2); and a convenient anchor point, designated A in the views, is selected (step 3). This time assume you know how to locate points on the pictorial and then transfer the location of each point to its corresponding place in each of the orthogonal views. Points near the anchor are identified on the object and then located on each of the orthogonal views (step 4), as shown in Figure 10.36.

Correctly joining the points creates the edges. The process of successively locating the object's vertices and creating edges on the multiview drawing is then extended to the rest of the object, as shown in Figure 10.37 (step 5). If you carefully examine Figure 10.37, you will notice that although the left-side view shows all of the edges of the object that can be seen in that view, some of the edges would not be seen if the object were solid and opaque. The edges that cannot be seen are hidden lines and should be shown as dashed lines for clarity (step 6).

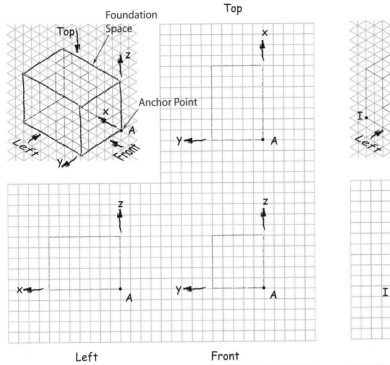

FIGURE 10.35. Defining the foundation space, viewing directions, and anchor point.

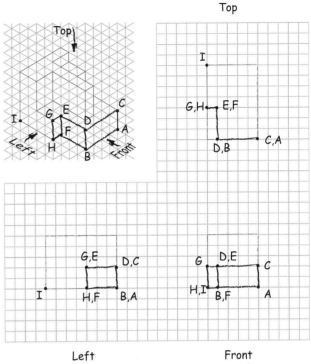

FIGURE 10.36. Designate each vertex as a point. Working with one surface at a time, locate the points and then the edges that make up each surface.

An alternative presentation is shown in Figure 10.38, where the right-side view has been added. This additional view allows you to see solid edges that are hidden in the left-side view. Note that the right-side view also has hidden lines, which are edges seen as solid lines in the left-side view. When you add the right-side view in this example, the hidden lines on both side views are no longer mandatory; but it would be wise to keep them since they do not clutter the drawing and would speed its interpretation. With the use of hidden lines, either the left- or right-side view can be deleted without harming the information conveyed about the object's geometry. Or both side views can be presented for additional emphasis to this geometry.

When internal features in this object are examined, none are found (step 7). As a final check, make sure each vertex in every view has at least three edges connected to it (step 8), keeping in mind that one of these edges may be oriented into the page and thus appear as a point coincident with the vertex. When this is not the case, a line is missing.

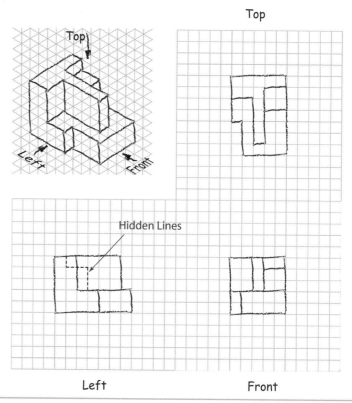

FIGURE 10.37. Continue tracking points, creating edges and surfaces until all points are accounted for. Edges that are obscured are represented with hidden lines.

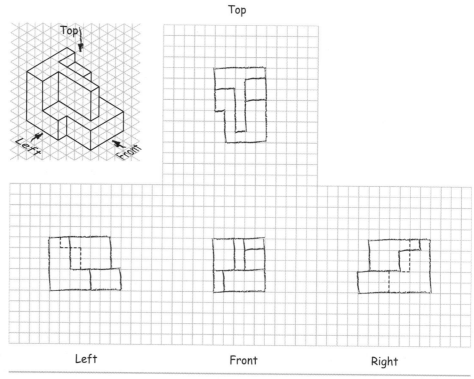

FIGURE 10.38. When a right-side view is added, the hidden lines are no longer necessary but still recommended to show all of the edges of the object.

10.06.02 Edge Tracking

Tracking individual points on an object to create its orthogonal views is a reliable method of creating the views. However, this process is slow and boring. After several trials at using this method, you will be anxious to try something faster. One way is to track an edge instead of tracking two points along the edge. This process is called **edge tracking**. It is like the eight-step process used for point tracking, where steps 1, 2, 6, 7, and 8 are the same, but steps 3, 4, and 5 are modified as follows:

Step 3: Define an anchor edge.

Step 4: Locate an edge adjacent to the anchor point, and draw that edge.

Step 5: Successively locate other adjacent edges.

To create a multiview drawing of the object in Figure 10.39, decide how many orthogonal views you may need; then create the foundation space and directions (steps 1 and 2), as shown in Figure 10.40. Locate and label all of the edges on the object pictorial, keeping in mind that all of its edges may not be visible.

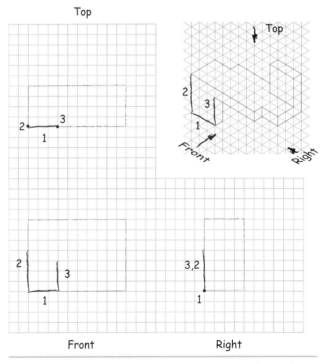

FIGURE 10.39. By keeping track of individual edges, how would you create a multiview drawing of this object?

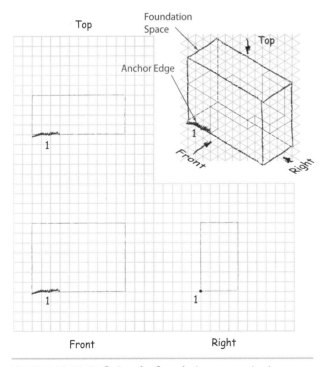

FIGURE 10.40. Defining the foundation space, viewing directions, and anchor edge. The selected anchor edge must be identifiable with confidence in all views.

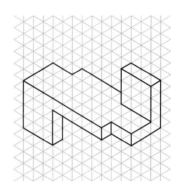

FIGURE 10.41. Defining and tracking edges near the anchor edge on the same surface.

Next, instead of selecting a convenient anchor point, select a convenient edge to use as an **anchor edge** (step 3). A good choice would be an edge whose length, location, and orientation you can easily and confidently find on each of the orthogonal views. For the object in this example, such a choice might be a straightedge on the bottom of the object. Call this edge 1 and locate and label the edge on each of the views, as shown in Figure 10.40.

Next, select an edge on the object that is connected to edge 1 (step 4). Call this edge 2 and note the size, location, and orientation of this edge with respect to edge 1. Find the same location and orientation of edge 2 in each of the orthogonal views and create this edge in those views. Keep in mind that if the edges of the object are parallel to a viewing plane, it will appear as its true length when it is viewed through that plane. If an edge on the object is perpendicular to a viewing plane, that edge will appear with both of its endpoints coincident when viewed through that plane. Note that edge 2 on the object is parallel to the front and side views; so in those views, that edge appears as its true length. Edge 2, however, is orthogonal to the top view. In that view, edge 2 appears as coincident endpoints, which would be drawn as a single point.

Continue to locate each of the object's edges on the respective orthogonal view until the object is completely represented in all orthogonal views (step 5). In the edge tracking method, you should select the edges to outline one entire surface of the object before moving on to outline another surface, as shown in Figure 10.42.

Notice on the completed multiview drawing in Figure 10.43 that for the object in this example, an edge that was originally visible during its creation later became obscured by another surface. The resulting hidden line (step 6) can be removed because the existence of that edge can be easily ascertained from the information already in the drawing. However, in this case, it would be better to leave this hidden line in place because its inclusion would facilitate the interpretation of the drawing.

There are no internal features (step 7) on this object. As a final check, make sure each vertex in every view has at least three edges connected to it (step 8).

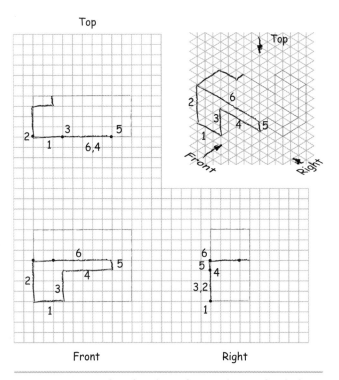

FIGURE 10.42. Define the edges of a complete surface before proceeding to the next surface.

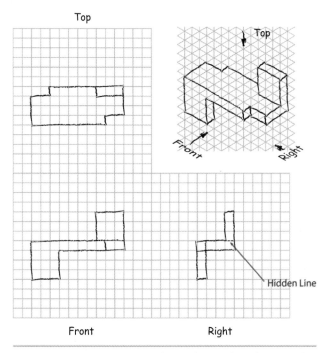

FIGURE 10.43. Continue tracking edges and surfaces until all edges are accounted for.

10.06.03 Surface Tracking

As you gain more experience and become faster at creating orthogonal views using the point tracking or the edge tracking approach, you may want to use an even faster technique. Instead of tracking an object's points or edges, you may want to track its surfaces. This is called **surface tracking**. The initial steps are the same as for point and edge tracking: first, decide how many orthogonal views you may need; then create the foundation space and directions on those views (step 1 and step 2). Steps 6, 7, and 8 are also the same; but steps 3, 4, and 5 are modified as follows:

Step 3: Define an anchor surface.

Step 4: Locate a surface adjacent to the anchor surface and draw its boundary.

Step 5: Successively locate other adjacent surfaces and draw those boundaries.

For the object shown in Figure 10.44, the viewing directions and foundation are shown in Figure 10.45 (steps 1 and 2).

Note that two pictorial views are required to reveal all of the features of this object. This is a clue that more than three orthogonal views (or some use of hidden lines) will be required to specify all the features of this object completely. In addition to front, right side, and top views, the left side and bottom views also will be included. Later the drafter can eliminate views that are unnecessary if she decides they will provide no useful information or function. For surface tracking, you must locate and label all of the surfaces on the object's pictorial, keeping in mind that all of the surfaces may not be visible.

For surface tracking, the first surface selected will be the **anchor surface** (step 3). A good choice would be a surface whose length, location, and orientation you can easily and confidently find on each of the orthogonal views, such as one of the surfaces located on the bottom of the object in this example. Call this surface A and locate and label this surface on each of the orthogonal views. Note that on the top and bottom views, surface A appears as its true shape. On the front and two side views, the surface appears on edge and is represented by a line.

FIGURE 10.44. By keeping track of individual surfaces, how would you create a multiview drawing of this object?

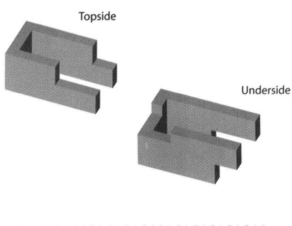

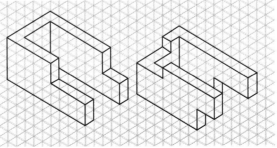

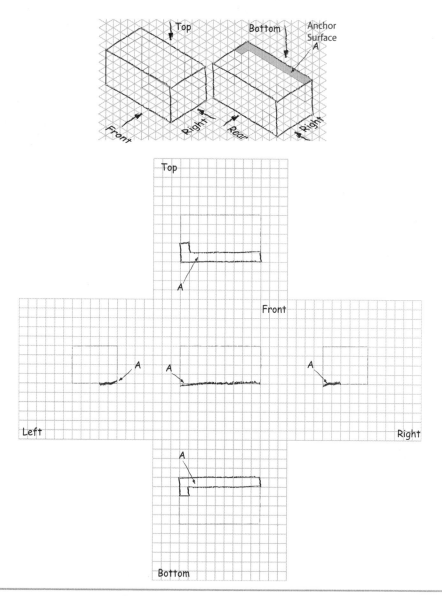

FIGURE 10.45. Create the foundation space, the viewing directions, and an anchor surface. The selected anchor surface must be identifiable with confidence in all views.

Next, select a surface that is adjacent to the anchor (step 4). Call this surface B, locate and orient this surface relative to the anchor surface, and create surface B in each of the orthogonal views. Keep in mind that object surfaces that are parallel to a viewing plane will appear as their true shape when viewed through that plane. If an object surface is perpendicular to a viewing plane, that surface will appear as a single edge when viewed through that plane. Surface B on the object is parallel to the front plane; so in the front view, that surface appears in its entirety. All of its lines will appear as their true length in the front view, and all of its angles will be appear as their true values. Surface B, however, is orthogonal to the top, bottom, and both side views.

In those four views, surface B will appear as an edge, which would be drawn as a line. Creating surface B by surface tracking is shown in Figure 10.46.

Locating each of the object's other surfaces on the orthogonal views is continued until all surfaces have been selected and the drawing is complete (step 5). Be aware that each surface that is created may partially or completely obscure surfaces that have been completed. The edges that have been obscured must be converted to hidden lines (step 6).

Step 7 and step 8 for surface tracking are the same steps used in the point tracking and edge tracking methods. The hidden lines are identified or additional views are created so that hidden lines are not necessary. The completed drawing is shown in Figure 10.47.

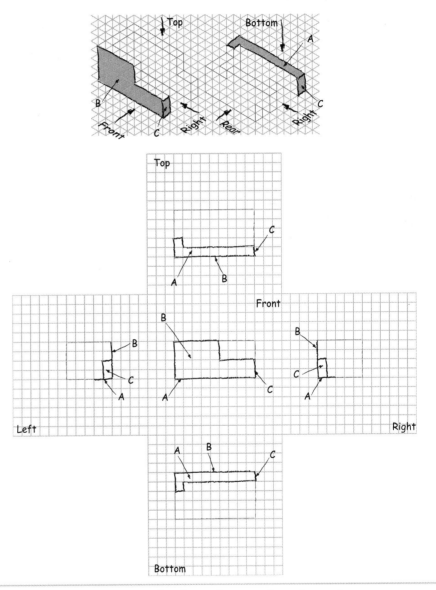

FIGURE 10.46. Locating additional surfaces adjacent to the anchor surface.

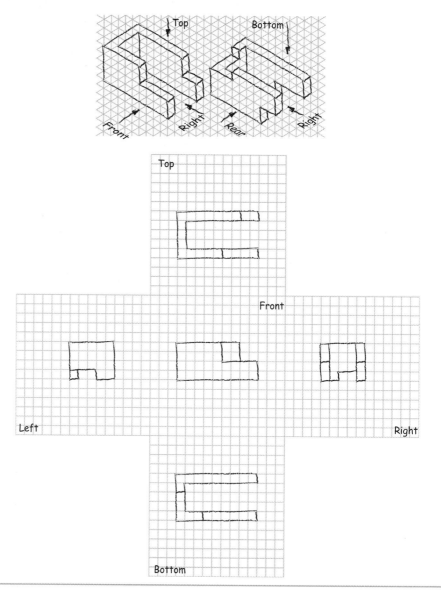

FIGURE 10.47. Continue tracking surfaces until all surfaces are accounted for.

In Figure 10.48, an alternative presentation method is shown. The rear view eliminates the need for a bottom view and a right-side view. The rear view also provides a better description of the rear of the object, which is partially obscured in the front view.

Using hidden lines (step 6), as shown in Figure 10.49, can further reduce the number of views and present the object in the preferred format of the front view, top view, and right-side view.

Whichever presentation method is used, your final step is to assure that each vertex in every view has at least three edges connected to it (step 8). Any vertex not having three edges connected to it means a line is missing. But you need to keep in mind that an edge may be oriented into the page, which means it will appear as a point coincident with the vertex.

In the preceding examples, the problems were simple because all of the surfaces on the object were parallel or perpendicular to each other and, thus, either parallel or perpendicular to the orthogonal views. These orientations are common for many but not all engineered parts.

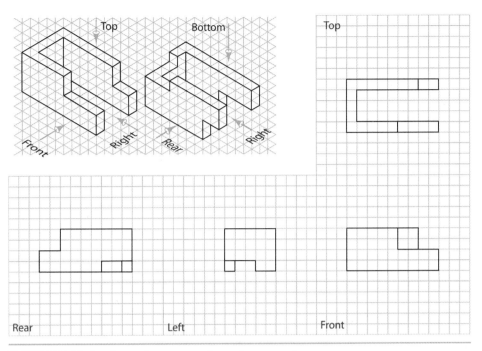

FIGURE 10.48. An alternative presentation using a rear view.

Next, you need to consider more complex objects, starting with an object that has surfaces inclined with respect to one another. That means you have to learn how to represent those surfaces in the orthogonal views of the object. Figure 10.50 shows an object with normal and inclined surfaces. For an object with inclined surfaces, the edges of the surfaces will appear to be inclined in one or more orthogonal views.

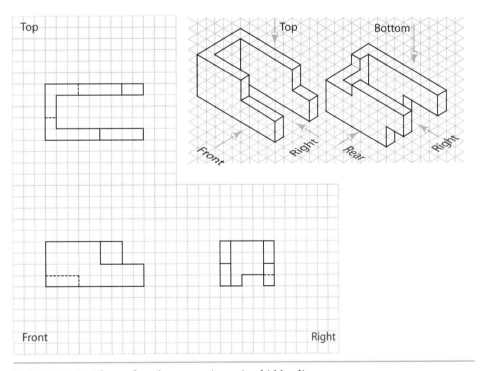

FIGURE 10.49. The preferred presentation using hidden lines.

FIGURE 10.50. Considering the existence of inclined surfaces, how would you create a multi-view drawing of this object?

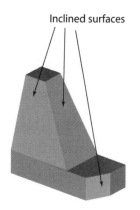

Inclined surfaces

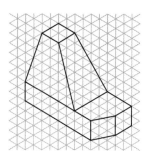

The initial steps to solving this problem are the same as with the preceding problems. Decide how many orthogonal views you think you will need to represent the object completely; then define the space and directions occupied by the object in each of those views, as shown in Figure 10.51. Point tracking, edge tracking, or surface tracking can be used. Assume you have a little experience now and surface tracking can be used for a quicker solution. An anchor surface is necessary. This time, for convenience, surface A will be used, as shown in Figure 10.51.

One way to approach a problem with inclined surfaces is to create the surfaces that are not inclined (i.e., the normal surfaces—parallel and perpendicular surfaces—as was done in the earlier examples). This is done in Figure 10.52. When only one inclined surface is on the object, such as when one edge of the object has been beveled, or chamfered, there is no need to consciously discover the location of the object's edges. Because the other surfaces completely surround the one inclined surface, the edges of the inclined surface are formed by the edges of the other surfaces. The same would be true if there were multiple inclined surfaces on the object, unless the inclined surfaces share a common edge.

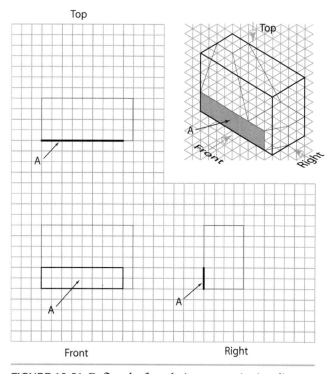

FIGURE 10.51. Define the foundation space, viewing directions, and anchor surface.

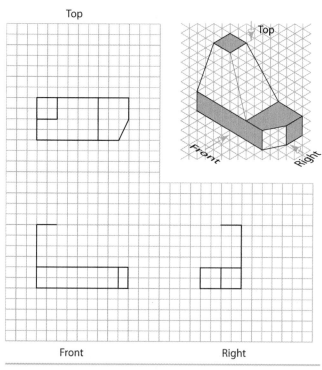

FIGURE 10.52. Continue the process of surface location for the noninclined surfaces.

FIGURE 10.53. By point tracking or edge tracking, add the intersection of the inclined surfaces.

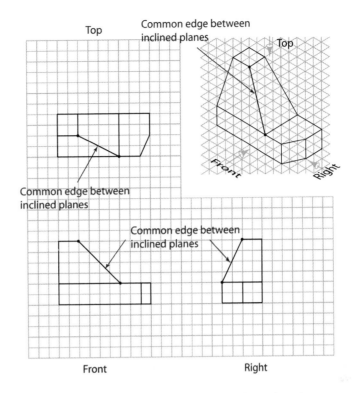

On this object, there are, indeed, two inclined surfaces that share a common edge. Once the parallel and perpendicular surfaces have been created, the shared edge of the inclined surfaces must be located. You can do this by either point tracking or edge tracking. The result is shown in Figure 10.53.

For more complicated objects, the hidden lines are identified or additional views are created so that hidden lines are not necessary.

For any object, no matter which method of tracking you use to create orthogonal views, your final step is to assure that each vertex in every view has at least three edges connected to it and to be aware that one of the edges may be oriented into the page and thus appear as a point coincident with the vertex. When this is not the case, a line is missing.

In the previous example, the inclined surfaces were inclined in a single direction only; that is, each was still perpendicular to one of the three preferred viewing planes. In this case, the entire inclined surface can be seen as an edge from two of the six standard views.

The next example is slightly more complicated. The object in Figure 10.54 has surfaces that are inclined in two directions (i.e., oblique surfaces). Neither of the two oblique surfaces is perpendicular to any of the six standard views; therefore, neither surface appears as an edge view in any of those views. Although creating the multiview drawing of this object may seem daunting, the procedure is the same as that used for creating surfaces inclined in only one direction.

FIGURE 10.54. Considering the existence of oblique surfaces, how would you create a multiview drawing of this object?

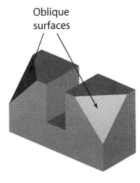

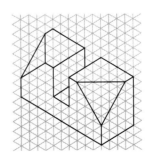

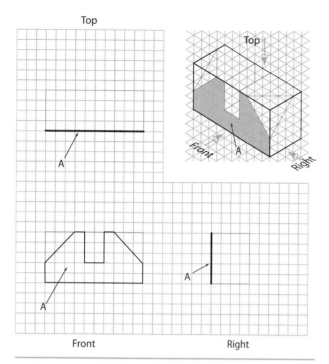

FIGURE 10.55. Define the foundation space, viewing directions, and anchor surface.

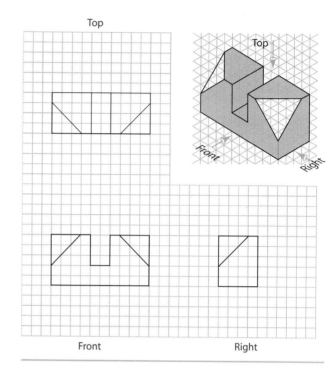

FIGURE 10.56. Continue the process of surface location for the noninclined surfaces. Since the oblique surfaces do no intersect, their boundaries are automatically formed by the normal surfaces.

Create the views for the noninclined surfaces by temporarily ignoring the oblique surfaces and using the surface tracking procedure, which is shown in Figure 10.55.

For the object in this example, the inclined surfaces do not intersect; so their boundaries are formed by the edges of the noninclined surfaces and the drawing is complete, as shown in Figure 10.56.

Next, consider how to represent in orthogonal views an object that has curved surfaces. Although there are an infinite number of types of curved surfaces, the most common are surfaces that are either cylindrical or conical; the most common curved surface is a simple round hole. Drawing a curved surface is unusual because in addition to an edge being shown where it intersects another surface, an artificial edge is drawn where there is an optical limit to the object. Examining Figure 10.57, make sure you understand that the indicated edge is not an intersection of any of the surfaces. This particular edge is the visible limit between the object and the surrounding air when the object is seen in that particular orientation. The location of this limit on the object changes when the orientation of the object changes.

When creating a multiview drawing of an object such as this, you must include one of these limits in each view of the drawing. For the object shown in Figure 10.57, the process of creating the four curved surfaces is made easier by the fact that each surface is orthogonal to one of the standard viewing planes. Therefore, the curved edges will appear in the orthogonal views as their true shape or as an edge view. When viewed as

FIGURE 10.57. Considering the existence of curved surfaces, how would you create a multi-view drawing of this object?

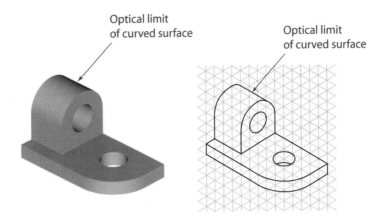

its true shape, a circle will appear as a true circle, with its correct geometry, size, and location. In an edge view, the circle will appear as a straight line. Selecting the necessary number of views, creating the foundation space, defining their directions, and selecting an anchor surface are done as before, which is shown in Figure 10.58.

Holes and rounds appear distorted as ellipses or parts of ellipses in the pictorial. In the process of surface tracking, when a surface contains a circle or a part of a circle, that edge can be drawn as a circle by locating its center point and tangent points to the other edges on the surface. This process is shown in Figure 10.59. In this example, the two holes are internal features; thus, step 7 in the eight-step drawing creation process cannot be dismissed when the views are completed.

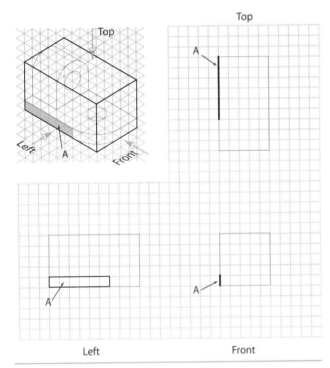

FIGURE 10.58. Define the foundation space, viewing directions, and anchor surface.

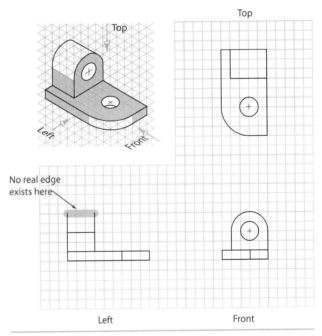

FIGURE 10.59. Locate the remaining planar surfaces of the object in all views.

FIGURE 10.60. Add the optical limits of the curved surface, add hidden lines to show hole depths, remove tangent edges, and add centerlines to the centers of the holes.

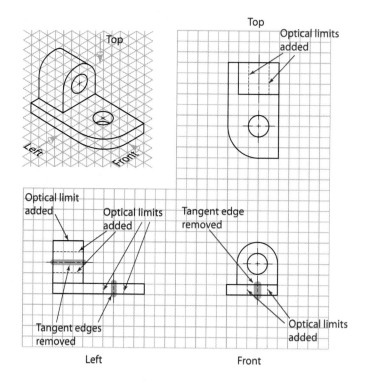

FIGURE 10.60. Add the optical limits of the curved surface, add hidden lines to show hole depths, remove tangent edges, and add centerlines to the centers of the holes.

When the orthogonal views are completed, as with the pictorial, additional line segments must be added to delineate the physical limits of the object, as shown in Figure 10.60. Even though an actual edge may not exist there, it is nevertheless what would be seen if the object were real.

The hidden lines are identified or additional views are added to eliminate the need for hidden lines. For this example, it is convenient to use hidden lines to show the depth of the holes. These hidden lines do not represent true edges; rather, the hidden lines delineate the optical limits of curved surfaces internal to the object (i.e., as would be seen if the object were partially transparent).

During the final check, which involves ensuring that each vertex on the object has at least three edges connected to it, it is important to remember that an edge is formed where a curved surface is tangent to a plane. This type of edge is called a **tangent edge** and customarily is not shown on either the pictorial or its multiview drawing, except for objects where not showing the tangent edges deletes key features that may lead to misinterpretation of the drawing.

When an internal feature such as a hole or a round is located on an inclined plane on the object, as shown in Figure 10.61, creating the multiview drawing becomes more difficult. For this problem, the views of the basic object will be created first; then the

FIGURE 10.61. Considering the existence of cutouts on an inclined surface, how would you create a multiview drawing of this object?

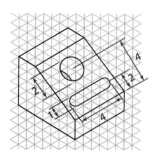

circular features (in this case, a hole and a circular slot) will be added. Because the hole and slot are located on the inclined plane, it is difficult to ascertain their true sizes even with an isometric grid. For convenience, the sizes and locations of these features are given. The center of the hole and slot are otherwise assumed to be symmetrical around the center of the inclined surface.

Determining the necessary number of views, creating the foundation space, defining their directions, and selecting an anchor surface are done as before. The multiview drawing, less the hole and slot, are shown in Figure 10.62.

Because inclined planes are not parallel to any of the six standard orthogonal views, they are not shown in their true shape in any of these six views. This means a circle on an inclined plane will appear not as a circle but as an ellipse and a circular edge will appear as a portion of an ellipse. A circle on an inclined plane will appear as a circle only in an auxiliary viewing plane created to be parallel to the inclined surface, but this is the topic of Chapter 14. The true location of the hole center, as given by the measurements on the pictorial, can be measured only in the front view, where the inclined plane is shown on its edge. The centers of the holes can be found in the other views by point tracking, as shown in Figure 10.63. The fact that points in adjacent views must be aligned vertically or horizontally greatly aids in locating the circle centers on all of the views.

Because the plane containing the circle in Figure 10.63 is inclined in one direction only (i.e., it can be seen as an edge in the front view), you can create the ellipses representing the circle in the other views by realizing that the major axis of the ellipse on the inclined surface will be the same size as the diameter of the circle.

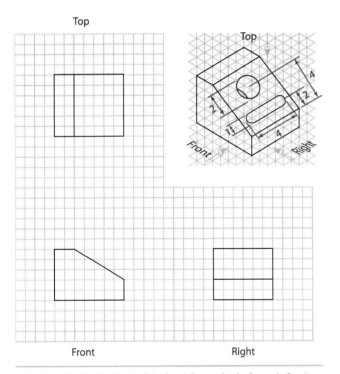

FIGURE 10.62. The basic block without the hole and slot is created.

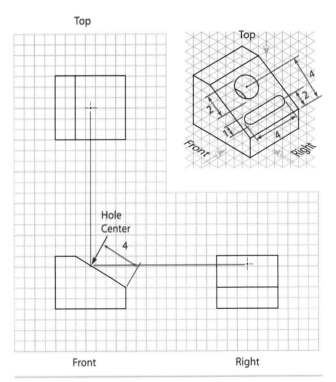

FIGURE 10.63. Locating the hole center by feature alignment in each view.

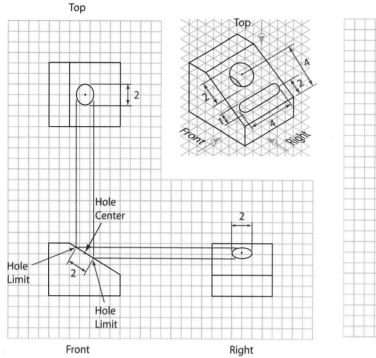

FIGURE 10.64. Construction of the major and minor axes of the ellipse in each view.

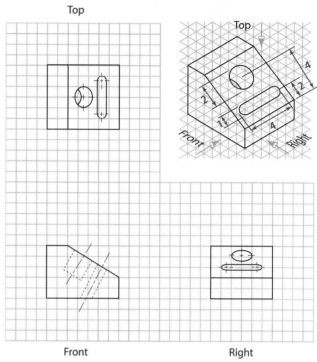

FIGURE 10.65. The addition of the slot by converting the circular edges to elliptical shapes, addition of hidden lines to indicate depth, and addition of centerlines. Note the addition of the hole bottom in the top view.

The measurements of the major and minor axes of the ellipse can be deduced graphically. You do this by marking the limits of the circle on the inclined surface in the front view, as shown in Figure 10.64, and projecting these limits into the right side and top views. Mathematically, the size of the minor axis of the ellipse will be the circle diameter multiplied by the cosine of the inclination angle of the plane from a horizontal plane.

The slot is added to the right-side view, as shown in Figure 10.65, by converting its circular edges to elliptical edges. The depth of the hole and slot are specified using hidden lines in the front view.

10.07 Breaking the Rules—and Why It Is Good to Break Them Sometimes

Creating an engineering drawing using orthogonal views is sometimes a balance between how accurately the drawing can be interpreted and how easily the drawing can be created. Strictly following some of the guidelines presented so far may lead to problems. To avoid those problems, you should consider some generally accepted exceptions to the guidelines, which are usually graphical shortcuts or approximations. These exceptions can reduce the time it takes to create a drawing and/or minimize possible misinterpretation of a drawing. With all of the exceptions that follow, the main question you need to ask yourself before using any of them is whether the approximation or shortcut could lead to misinterpretation of the drawing. If the answer is yes, the exception should not be used.

10.07.01 Threaded Parts

The first shortcut is in the representation of a threaded part, such as the bolt shown in Figure 10.66. A thread is essentially a helical mating surface for a fastener. The thread may be external, such as on the outside of a bolt or screw, as shown in Figure 10.66, or internal, such as on the inside of a nut. An accurate drawing of all surfaces on such an object would result in a very complicated drawing, especially if the drawing had to be created with manual instruments or 2-D CAD software. A much simpler representation of the external thread is shown as the schematic representation in Figure 10.66. For internal threads, the schematic representation is shown in Figure 10.67. These schematic representations are much simpler to construct with very little loss of information, especially since thread sizes are, for the most part, standardized based on the diameter of the part. A note (and arrow) is required to specify the precise thread sizes. Methods for the complete specification of thread sizes are found in Chapter 17 of this book. You can also find thread specifications in most machinists' or engineers' handbooks.

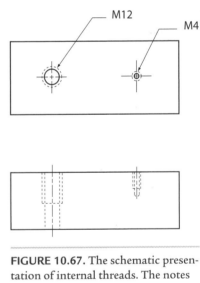

FIGURE 10.67. The schematic presentation of internal threads. The notes specify the metric sizes of the threads.

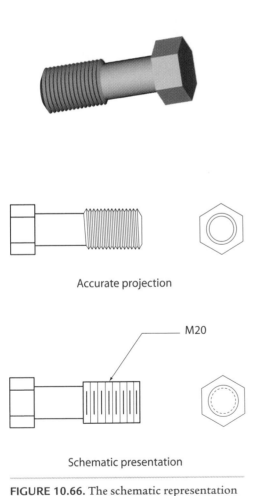

FIGURE 10.66. The schematic representation of an externally threaded part. The note specifies the metric size of the thread.

10.07.02 Features with Small Radii

An exception to the guidelines is in the representation of edges with small radii. Consider the object shown in Figure 10.68, which has small rounds on some of its edges. Based on the guidelines established in this chapter, a multiview drawing of the object should look like the drawing in Figure 10.68. Recall that cylindrical surfaces have no defined edges and that the tangent lines between curved and planar surfaces are not shown. Following the established guidelines, the top view should look like a featureless plane. Such a presentation, however, would likely cause confusion because upon initial inspection, the front view contains features that are absent in the top view.

A better, albeit not accurate, representation would be a presentation where the small rounds are represented as if they were true edges. The rounded edges are still shown in the front view, where their measurements can be specified. However, the approximation of the small rounds as edges enables the reader of the drawing to grasp the larger shape of the object more quickly. But what exactly is a "small" radius, and when should a small round be approximated as an edge on a drawing? The purpose of the approximation is to clarify the drawing. When the approximation clarifies the drawing, it should be used. As a rule of thumb, when the radius is less than about 5 percent of the overall size of the object, consider using the approximation.

10.07.03 Small Cutouts on Curved Surfaces

An approximation also is allowed when there is a small hole or another cutout on a curved surface. Figure 10.69, for example, shows a small hole and slot on a tube as compared to larger cutouts.

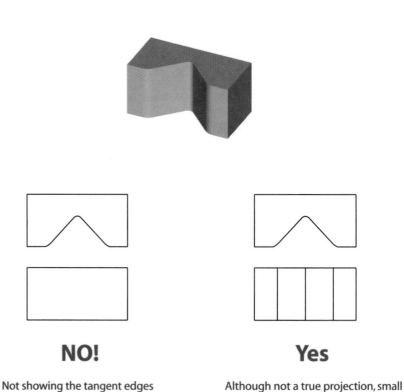

NO!

Not showing the tangent edges on small radii is an accurate projection but creates a deceiving presentation

Yes

Although not a true projection, small radii shown as edges present a clearer representation of the object geometry

FIGURE 10.68. The representation of small radii on a part.

If a true projection were made of these features, the orthogonal views would show a curved depression on the surface of the tube. The shape of this curve is complex and would take time to create. In most applications, the size of the depression on the surface is unimportant; so the depression is not shown on the orthogonal views. The true projection of these features and the accepted shortcut are shown in Figure 10.69. This approximation makes the drawing easier to create, with very little loss of information. However, when the cutouts are large or the size of the depression cannot be ignored in the function of the object, the true projection should be used. Within these guidelines, what is considered "small" is up to whoever is creating the drawing. The question that must be asked is this: Will this approximation possibly lead to misinterpretation of the drawing? If the answer is yes, the shortcut should not be used.

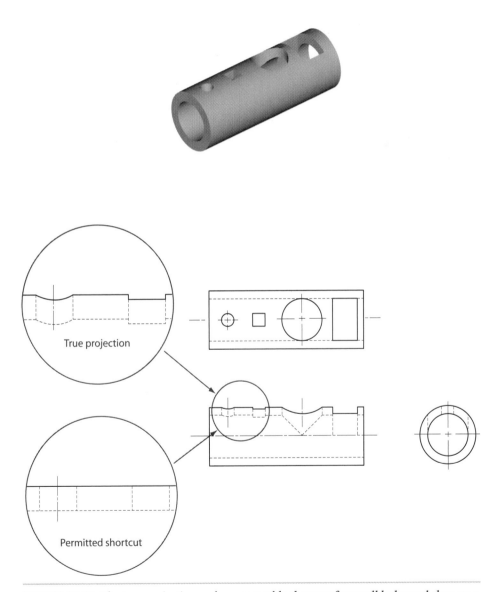

FIGURE 10.69. The true projection and an acceptable shortcut for small holes and slots on a curved surface. The shortcuts should not be used for large holes and slots because the geometric inaccuracies would be too obvious.

10.07.04 Small Intersections with Curved Surfaces

A similar approximation is allowed for small protrusions that extend from a curved surface, as shown in Figure 10.70. As with small cutouts on a curved surface, the appropriate use of this approximation is subjective. When the protrusions are small relative to the arc of the surface, their intersections on the curved surface can be shown as lines without affecting the intended representation of those features. When the protrusions are large relative to the arc of the surface, the approximation cannot be made. Again, the question that must be asked is whether this approximation could lead to misinterpretation of the drawing. If the answer is yes, the shortcut should not be used.

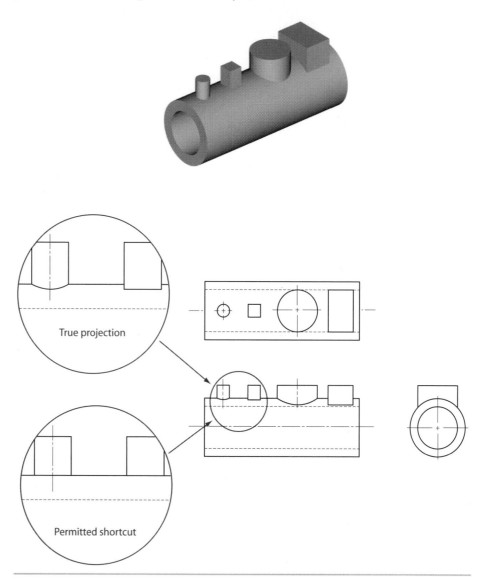

FIGURE 10.70. The true projection and an acceptable shortcut for small protrusions from a curved surface. The shortcuts should not be used for large protrusions because the geometric inaccuracies would be too obvious.

10.07.05 Symmetrical Features

An interesting exception to the rules of true projection occurs in the representation of objects with symmetry, as shown in Figure 10.71. This object has one-third rotational symmetry, which means the object can be divided into three identical sections about its axis of rotation, with three support ribs about the center tube.

An accurate multiview drawing would be the true projection drawing shown in Figure 10.71 using a front and top view. However, using a true projection for the front view in this case has two problems. One problem is that when instruments or 2-D CAD is used, an accurate projection is difficult to create. The other problem is that the true projection of the side view may be incorrectly interpreted as representing a nonsymmetrical object.

A preferred presentation for this drawing is shown in Figure 10.71. This drawing is easier to create and gives the impression that the object is symmetrical. The top view clarifies any possible misinterpretation about the number and locations of the support ribs. This may seem strange, but if the object had one-quarter rotational symmetry, for example, with four equally spaced support ribs instead of three, the front view would be the same as the view for the three support ribs.

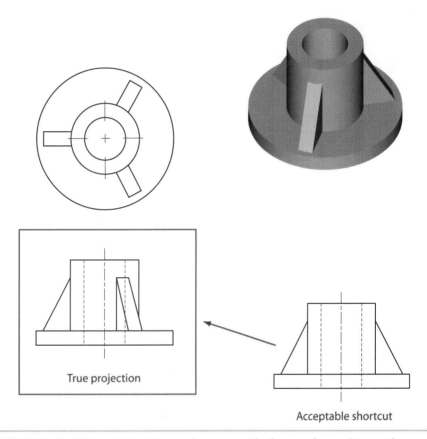

FIGURE 10.71. The true projection and an acceptable shortcut for an object with prominent symmetry. This property is emphasized by the use of a projected view that is modified to appear symmetrical.

10.07.06 Representation of Welds

Objects that contain welds, which are very common in civil engineering and some mechanical engineering applications, use special notation to specify the geometry of the weld. The use of this notation increases the speed of drawing creation with little loss of information. A simple object made from individual pieces that are welded together is shown in Figure 10.72. Even though a welded object is composed of two or more smaller pieces, it is common that such an object be fabricated at a single shop and delivered as a single unit. Thus, a single drawing showing the final welded configuration is often desirable.

Drawing the geometry of the welds on the multiview drawing takes time and effort, especially when the object contains many welds. So instead of the weld being drawn, a shorthand symbol is used. The notation specifies the geometry and locations of the weld, as well as any necessary modifications to the individual pieces in preparation for welding.

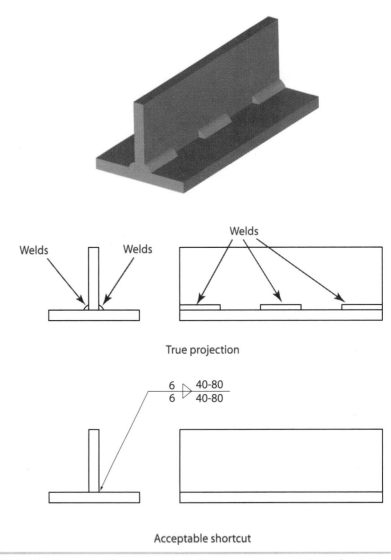

FIGURE 10.72. The acceptable presentation of two parts that are welded together to make a single part. The note specifies the size and location of the welds.

CAUTION   Inexperienced engineers, designers, and drafters can unwittingly introduce errors to their drawings. Despite the errors, the person reading the drawing probably will interpret it as intended because the necessary information is contained on the views not having an error. Nevertheless, errors can cause confusion and slow down interpretation of the drawing. A more serious case of errors can result with an ambiguity that makes the drawing impossible to interpret correctly. In a worst-case scenario, the errors may cause the object to be interpreted as an entirely different object than what was desired. The following sections are a compilation of the most common beginners' errors and ways to fix them.

Missing Lines

A common problem with hand-created or 2D CAD-created drawings is that one or more line segments may be missing from one or more of the orthogonal views. This error is especially difficult to correct when someone else made the drawing. As an example, examine the drawing shown in Figure 10.73, which shows the top, front, and right-side views of an object. Two lines are missing from the side view, and one line is missing from the front view.

The general procedure for locating a missing line is to examine the vertices in the adjacent views, as shown in Figure 10.74. Vertices are formed when surfaces or edges intersect as features on the object. A vertex in one view means there must be a corresponding vertex or edge in its adjacent views. Also, vertices representing the same point or edge on the object must be aligned horizontally or vertically in adjacent views. To discover any missing features, you can start with any view; but eventually you have to examine all of the views. From each vertex in a view, create horizontal or vertical alignment lines into the adjacent view. In the adjacent views along each alignment line, you should see the meeting of two surfaces to form an edge or the meeting of multiple surfaces to form another vertex.

Two vertices in the front view are missing some corresponding feature in the side view. The top view reveals that these vertices are the intersections of perpendicular edges. A horizontal line representing an edge must be added to the side view to keep the

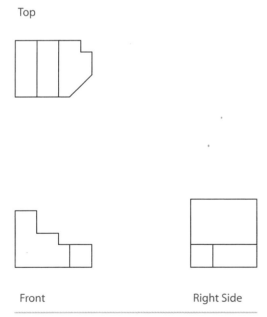

FIGURE 10.73. Are any lines missing from this multiview drawing? If so, insert them into the views at their correct locations with their correct visibilities.

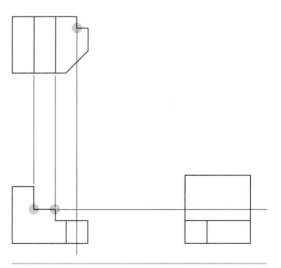

FIGURE 10.74. These vertices do not have corresponding features (i.e., another vertex or edge) in all views.

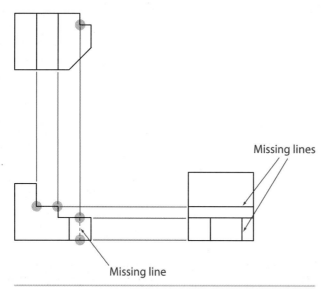

Missing lines

Missing line

FIGURE 10.75. The missing lines are shown here. The vertex in the top view produces a hidden line in the front view, which, in turn, shows that another line is missing in the side view.

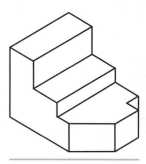

FIGURE 10.76. An isometric presentation of the object shown in the previous figure.

features consistent between the front and top views. Keep in mind that when a line appears to be missing, the next step is to determine whether that line should be visible; that is, the missing line might actually be a hidden line. Because the front view is uncluttered, it would be best to include the hidden line because it would reinforce the presence of the rectangular cutout on the back of the object. This hidden line produces two new vertices, which are missing some corresponding feature in the side view. A vertical line representing an edge must be added to the side view to maintain feature consistency between the front and side views. Figure 10.75 shows the drawing with the missing lines added. Figure 10.76 shows an isometric presentation of the complete object.

As another example, the drawing in Figure 10.77 has two lines missing from the front view. You can find the missing lines by examining the vertices in each view to ensure that a vertex in one view leads to some corresponding feature in an adjacent view, as shown in Figure 10.78. Note that hidden lines are used to show the depth of the

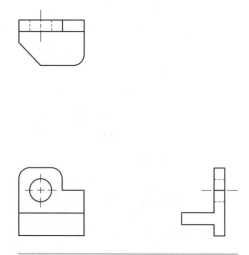

FIGURE 10.77. Are any lines missing from this multiview drawing? If so, insert them into the views at their correct locations with their correct visibilities.

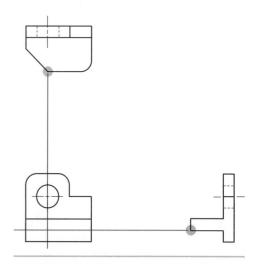

FIGURE 10.78. These vertices do not have corresponding features in all views.

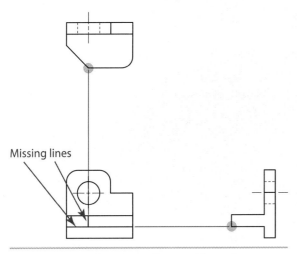

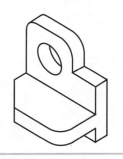

FIGURE 10.80. An isometric presentation of the object in the previous figure.

Missing lines

FIGURE 10.79. The missing lines are shown here. Tangent edges are not shown.

hole. These hidden lines are optical limits, not true edges; therefore, they do not form vertices or intersections as with true edges. Also observe that tangent edges are not shown even though they form intersections and vertices. Figure 10.79 shows the drawing with the missing lines added. Figure 10.80 shows an isometric presentation of the complete object.

Solving problems of missing lines is an excellent way to develop your skills with multiview projection.

Missing Views

When an entire view is not shown, consider it an opportunity to challenge your ability to find missing lines. Figure 10.81 is the drawing of an object where the front view is not shown. Although a missing view of this type rarely occurs in real-world engineering, this is the kind of problem for homework and exams. These types of problems are a test of your ability to recognize and extract 3-D data from 2-D views.

The procedure for finding the missing view in Figure 10.81 is to locate identical vertices in the given views and then transfer the locations of these vertices into the missing view. One way to proceed in this example is to select, one at a time, vertices that

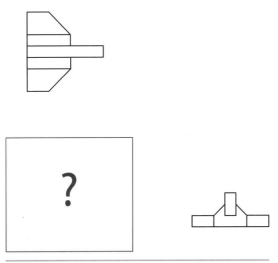

FIGURE 10.81. Create the front view of this object from the top and side views.

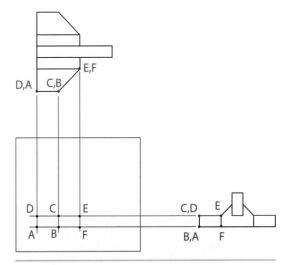

FIGURE 10.82. Locate corresponding vertices by alignment in the given views.

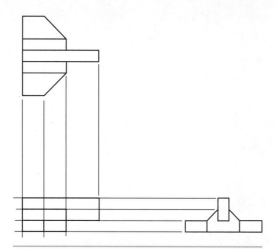

FIGURE 10.83. Continue locating vertices, adding edges in the front view when they exist in either of the given views.

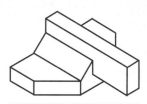

FIGURE 10.84. An isometric presentation of the object in the previous figure.

are closest to the front view and then proceed toward the back of the object. Edges between the vertices in the front view are produced when the existence of the edge is evident for one of the given views. This process is shown in Figure 10.82.

Figure 10.83 shows the drawing with the missing view added. Figure 10.84 shows an isometric presentation of the complete object.

Incorrect Visibility

Sometimes all of the lines are there, but the visibility of one or more lines is incorrect. This means lines that are suppose to be shown dashed (representing hidden lines) are erroneously shown as solid (representing visible lines) or vice versa. Figure 10.85 shows an example of a drawing with an incorrect line visibility in the front view. One of the hidden lines is erroneously shown as a visible edge. Even though a person reading

FIGURE 10.85. Care must be taken to ensure that the visibility of edges is correct.

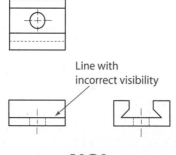

Line with incorrect visibility

NO!

A hidden edge is incorrectly displayed as a solid line

Yes

Hidden edges displayed as dashed lines, visible edges displayed as solid lines

FIGURE 10.86. Overuse of hidden lines causes confusion.

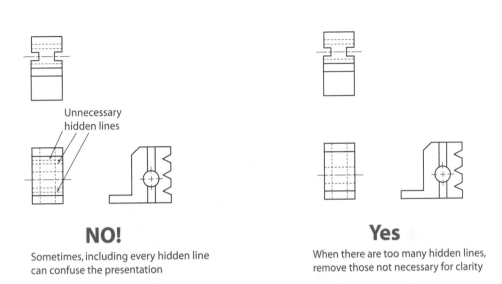

Unnecessary hidden lines

NO!
Sometimes, including every hidden line can confuse the presentation

Yes
When there are too many hidden lines, remove those not necessary for clarity

the drawing would probably figure out the error when it is realized that features between the views are not consistent, the error does create some confusion.

Too Many Hidden Lines

Although hidden lines usually aid in the interpretation of a drawing, using more hidden lines than are necessary can lead to confusion. For example, in Figure 10.86, the original front view shows the hidden lines representing the internal features (the hole and slots), as well as the V-grooves on the back of the object, resulting in a large number of hidden lines in that view. There should be no confusion about which feature a hidden line represents. For such cases, consider using hidden lines to emphasize only the most important features or use additional views to characterize the features fully. In this case, limiting the hidden lines in the front view clarifies the presentation. Hidden lines are used for the hole and the two slots in the front view to confirm that these features extend straight and all the way through the object. The fact that the three V-grooves also extend straight and all the way through the object can be confirmed from the hidden lines used in the top view.

Too Few Hidden Lines

Anyone reading a drawing not having any hidden lines, as in Figure 10.87, may have to guess the geometry of features. In this figure, without hidden lines or additional views for clarification, the drawing has two possible interpretations, as shown; the reader will have to guess which interpretation is corect. Never make the reader guess because that guess may be wrong. And if you made the drawing, the wrong guess would be your fault, not the reader's. Legally, a drawing's creator is responsible for ensuring that accepted guidelines for geometry presentation are followed so the drawing's contents cannot be misinterpreted. Just because something is obvious to you does not mean it will be obvious to someone else. Figure 10.88 shows the correct drawing for the desired object, using hidden lines.

FIGURE 10.87. Underuse of hidden lines may delete critical information.

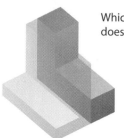

Which one of these objects does the drawing represent

?

FIGURE 10.88. Use hidden lines as often as practical to define and reinforce features.

Squared surfaces

Squared surfaces

Inclined surface

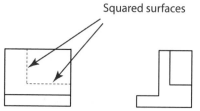

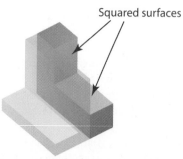

This one

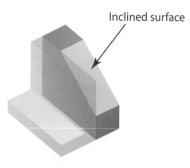

Not this one

FIGURE 10.89. Centerlines and centermarks should be used whenever possible to help define and locate the centers of holes and other axes of rotational symmetry.

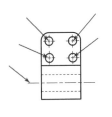

Added centerlines and centermarks

NO!

Centerlines and centermarks are missing from cylindrical surfaces

Yes

Centerlines and centermarks are present on cylindrical surfaces

No Centerlines and/or No Centermarks

To aid in the interpretation of a drawing, centerlines and centermarks mark the location of an axis of rotational symmetry. A centerline on a feature alerts the reader that the edges seen next to the centerline may be optical limits of a surface, not true edges. Without these marks, a drawing cannot be interpreted as quickly, as shown in Figure 10.89. With centermarks and centerlines added, the hidden lines and circles are quickly identified as having been created by holes.

Showing Tangent Edges

A tangent edge is formed when two curved surfaces or a curved surface and a plane are tangent to each other on a line. Tangent edges are normally not shown on drawings because they cannot be seen on a real object. Showing tangent edges, as in Figure 10.90, gives the false impression of the existence of a visible edge. Ideally, a tangent edge on a real object is smooth, without any abrupt changes in surface direction; and the drawing is made to reflect this attribute of real surfaces.

Not Showing Tangent Edges

Some exceptions exist as to when tangent edges should be shown to aid in interpreting the drawing. There are cases, for example, where the precise locations of tangent edges are important for the proper function of the object; and those locations must be emphasized for clarity, as shown in Figure 10.91. In this case, the tangent edges show precisely where the curved surfaces and the flat surfaces intersect. Also, when pictorials of objects that contain many rounded edges are created, the absence of tangent edges can produce relatively featureless presentations. In these cases, it is better to make the tangent edges visible.

FIGURE 10.90. On a real part, tangent edges cannot be seen and thus, in most cases, are not shown on a drawing.

Tangent edges deleted

Don't show these tangent edges

NO!

Tangent edges have incorrectly been included

Yes

Tangent edges generally should not be shown

FIGURE 10.91. In a some cases, tangent edges may be shown to emphasize surface geometry; otherwise, views may appear to be featureless.

Missing tangent edges

Show tangent edges

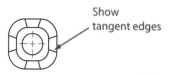

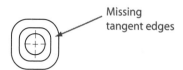

NO!

Removal of tangent edges results in deceptively featureless views

Yes

Including the tangent edges reinforces the existence of curved surface features

FIGURE 10.92. Small radii between surfaces should be shown as edges; otherwise, views may appear featureless.

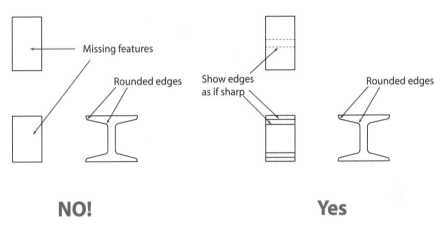

Not Showing Small Radii

The intersection of two surfaces is not usually a sharp edge, but rather a smooth transition with a small radius between the surfaces. The general purpose of this transition is to reduce the number of external sharp edges for safety during use and handling of the object and to eliminate breakage by reducing stress concentrations that exist at sharp internal corners. When the tangent edges of these transitions are removed, the result is a drawing devoid of features in certain views, especially when the object has inclined surfaces, such as the object shown in Figure 10.92. When the radius of a transition is very small relative to the remainder of the object, instead of the object's tangent edges being shown, it is acceptable to show the transition as a single edge, as if the radius is a sharp edge.

Mismatched View Scales

When the scale, or object magnification, in each view of a drawing is different, as shown in Figure 10.93, it becomes very difficult to align features between views. Consequently, when an object has many features, it becomes difficult to identify and characterize those features correctly. All of the orthogonal views on a drawing must have the same scale.

Unaligned Views

When the views are not aligned, as shown in Figure 10.94, it is difficult to align the same features in each view so that each feature can be uniquely identified. The rules of orthogonal projection Orthogonal multiview presentation mandate that orthogonal views be aligned.

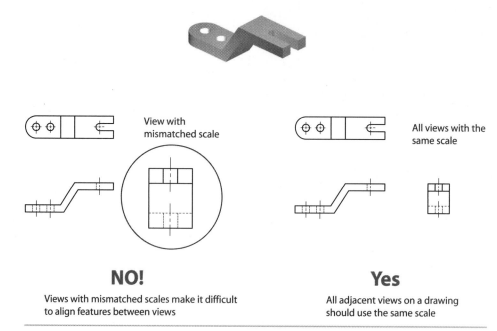

FIGURE 10.93. Orthogonal views must have the same scale.

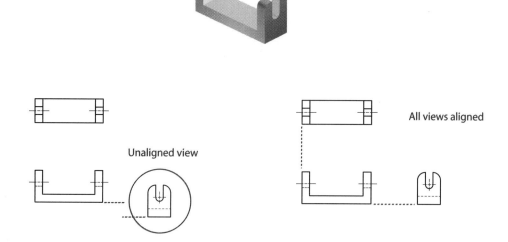

FIGURE 10.94. Orthogonal views must be aligned.

Views in Incorrect Relative Locations

The rules of first-angle or third-angle projection dictate that different views on a drawing must be located in certain positions with respect to each other. Consequently, people who read drawings have learned to expect certain views to appear in certain locations, such as a top view located above a front view (using third-angle projection). When the locations of the views are different from what is expected, as shown in Figure 10.95, the reader may become confused because the same features on the object are no longer properly aligned horizontally and vertically between these views.

Poor Choice of Object's Original Orientation

A poor choice in the original orientation of the object leads to a drawing with many hidden lines and/or inclined surfaces, as shown in Figure 10.96. The choice of object orientation should be such that the use of hidden lines and/or inclined surfaces is minimized.

Incorrect Rotational Orientation within a View

Inexperienced drafters may rotate a view by 90 or 180 degrees from its correct orientation with respect to the other views, as shown in Figure 10.97. An indication that this has happened is when the outer edges of the object are not aligned horizontally or vertically in adjacent views or when features on the object do not align. Such a rotation would confuse the person trying to read the drawing. Care should be taken to ensure that the rotational orientation of every view is correct with respect to first-angle or third-angle projection.

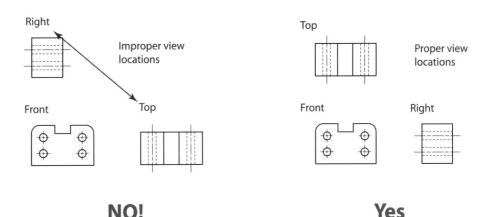

FIGURE 10.95. Orthogonal views must be in their proper locations with respect to one another.

FIGURE 10.96. The part should be oriented to show as many visible lines as possible in their true length.

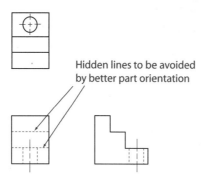

Hidden lines to be avoided by better part orientation

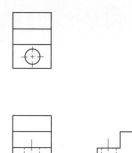

NO!

This object orientation generates many hidden lines which can be avoided by using a differnt orientation

Yes

This object orientation minimizes the number of hidden lines that are generated

FIGURE 10.97. The rotational orientation within each view must be consistent with proper orthogonal projection, as seen in the glass box.

Incorrect rotational orientation of view

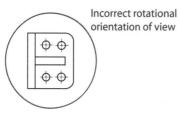

NO!

Views in incorrect rotational orientations make it difficult to align features between views

Yes

All adjacent views on a drawing should be in their correct rotational orientation

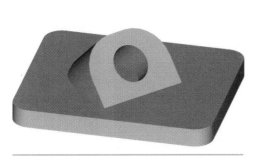

FIGURE 10.98. An object such as this one cannot be fully described by the six standard views.

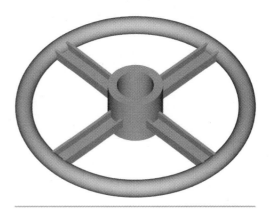

FIGURE 10.99. An object with internal features such as this one cannot be fully described by the six standard views.

10.08 When Six Views Are Not Enough

It would seem that the six orthogonal views provided by the glass box would be sufficient to specify the geometry of any object. But the views are not sufficient for every object.

10.08.01 Features at Odd Angles

An example of an object requiring more than six views or nonstandard views is shown in Figure 10.98, where features are located on surfaces that are inclined or oblique. For this object, none of the six standard orthogonal views would show these features in their true shape. A supplementary view, known as an auxiliary view, must be created before measurements can be specified for the feature represented in that view. Auxiliary views are covered in detail in Chapter 14 of this book.

10.08.02 Internal Features

Certain internal features, such as holes, bores, or cutouts with an irregular wall profile and details that are hidden from view, cannot be seen in any of the six standard views. An example of an object with internal features is the wheel shown in Figure 10.99. For this object, the geometry of spokes cannot be seen because the rim of the wheel obscures it. Although hidden lines can sometimes be used to show such features, those features will appear more clearly in a cutaway, or section view. Section views of all sorts are covered in detail in Chapter 13 of this book.

10.09 Considerations for 3-D Modeling

The proliferation of 3-D solids modeling software, especially in mechanical engineering applications, has made the process of creating drawings much easier than in the past. Typically, with solids modeling software, objects are initially modeled as a series of protrusions and cuts to create their 3-D graphical representation. The solids modeling software creates a mathematical model of the geometry from which the projections of the object are used to create drawings. The model can be scaled and rotated for viewing from any orientation direction. Once the solids model is created, it usually is simple to specify the viewing directions needed to for the software to create isometric and other pictorial views. It also is easy to extract a front view, side view, or any of the other orthogonal views from a solids model.

The ease with which pictorials and multiview drawings can be created from a solids model has many advantages, but also some disadvantages. The greatest advantage is the speed and accuracy with which orthogonal views can be created. With most software, additional views can be created by specifying the location of the viewing plane and then picking a location on the drawing where the additional view is to appear. Usually this is done by striking a few keys on a keyboard or making a few clicks with a mouse or another pointing device. The time required to produce the additional view is usually only a few seconds. Hidden lines can be added or removed for individual features or for an entire view. Also, accurate orthogonal projections of features that were previously represented by shortcut practices, such as small cutouts in curved surfaces or thin symmetric features, are easily created. In fact, with most software, it would be difficult to create a view that is *not* an accurate projection.

But there is a disadvantage to having so much ease in creating drawings. Remember, the original process of manually creating projected views from pictorials and mental images and pictorials from projected views depended on the drawer's developed skills of spatial reasoning and mental imaging. When software makes the process of creating drawings too automatic, a person may not be able to apply these skills in the absence of the software because she did not develop adequate drawing skills. In other words, the person may have become too dependent on the software. That person, when faced with a multiview drawing in the shop, may not be able to create a mental image of the object or may not develop the skills necessary to interpret standard drawings. Eventually, the person will develop these skills, but it may require experience with many solids models and their drawings. Whether you are working with instruments, 2-D CAD, or solids modelers, the key to successful development of mental imaging skills is simply to practice—a lot.

10.10 Chapter Summary

Orthogonal projection and the use of the standard views of an object are accepted nationally and internationally as the formal means of creating and presenting images for the purpose of producing the original object. Constructed correctly, these views are used to re-create the same 3-D object, no matter who is viewing the images. Care must be taken to ensure that the rules for view creation, orientation, scale, and alignment are followed. Hidden lines are used for completing the description or for additional emphasis of certain features on the object. Extra views are used as necessary for completing the description of these features. From these formal views, the original 3-D object can be re-created. When done successfully, whether you are the person making the drawing or the person reading the drawing, you will find that the interpretation of the views and the object they represent are the same.

10.11 glossary of key terms

adjacent views: Orthogonal views presented on a single plane that are created immediately next to each other.

anchor edge: The same edge that can be easily and confidently located on multiple views and on a pictorial for an object.

anchor point: The same point, usually a vertex, that can be easily and confidently located on multiple views and on a pictorial for an object.

anchor surface: The same surface that can be easily and confidently located on multiple views and on a pictorial for an object.

centerline: A series of alternating long and short dashed lines used to identify an axis of rotational symmetry.

centermark: A small right-angle cross that is used to identify the end view of an axis of rotational symmetry.

edge tracking: A procedure by which successive edges on an object are simultaneously located on a pictorial image and on a multiview image of that object.

first-angle projection: The process of creating a view of an object by imprinting its image, using orthogonal projection, on an opaque surface behind that object.

foundation space: The rectilinear volume that represents the limits of the volume occupied by an object.

glass box: A visualization aid for understanding the locations and orientations of images of an object produced by third-angle projection on a drawing. The images of an object are projected, using orthogonal projection, on the sides of a hypothetical transparent box that is then unfolded into a single plane.

hidden lines: The representation, using dashed lines, on a drawing of an object of the edges that cannot be seen because the object is opaque.

multiple views: The presentation of an object using more than one image on the same drawing, each image representing a different orientation of the object.

multiview: Refers to a drawing that contains more than one image of an object and whose adjacent images are generated from orthogonal viewing planes.

orthogonal projection: The process by which the image of an object is created on a viewing plane by rays from the object that are perpendicular to that plane.

point tracking: A procedure by which successive vertices on an object are simultaneously located on a pictorial image and a multiview image of that object.

preferred configuration: The drawing presentation of an object using its top, front, and right-side views.

six standard views (or six principal views): The drawing presentation of an object using the views produced by the glass box (i.e., the top, front, bottom, rear, left-side, and right-side views).

surface tracking: A procedure by which successive surfaces on an object are simultaneously located on a pictorial image and a multiview image of that object.

tangent edge: The intersection line between two surfaces that are tangent to each other.

third-angle projection: The process of creating a view of an object by imprinting its image, using orthogonal projection, on translucent surface in front of that object.

viewing plane: A hypothetical plane between an object and its viewer onto which the image of the object, as seen by the viewer, is imprinted.

10.12 questions for review

1. What is orthogonal projection?
2. What are the advantages and disadvantages of using pictorial images, such as isometric images, for the graphical representation of an object?
3. What is a multiview presentation?
4. What are the advantages and disadvantages of using a multiview presentation for the graphical representation of an object?
5. How are different views located with respect to each other on the same drawing?
6. Why should features be aligned between views in a multiview presentation?
7. Why is it important that different views have the same scale?
8. What are the advantages of having features of an object aligned between views?
9. What are the standard (or principal) views?
10. What is the preferred configuration?
11. When should extra orthogonal views be used?
12. When should hidden lines be used?

10.12 questions for review (continued)

13. When should hidden lines not be shown?

14. When should tangent edges be shown?

15. When should tangent edges not be shown?

16. What is the difference between first-angle projection and third-angle projection?

17. When can the rules of orthogonal projection be bent? What are the advantages of doing so?

10.13 problems

The following exercises may be done with instruments, with CAD, or on square and isometric grids. Use third-angle or first-angle projection as specified by your instructor.

1. From the isometric pictorials shown in Figure P10.1, create accurate multiview drawings with a sufficient number of views to specify all details of the object completely. Do not use hidden lines.

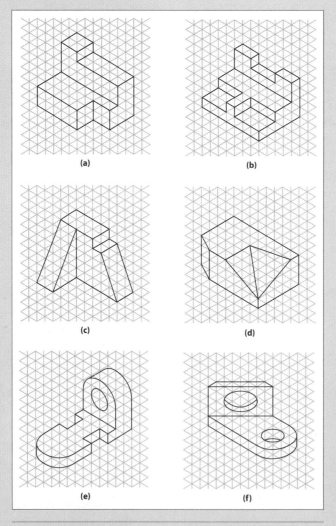

(a)

(b)

(c)

(d)

(e)

(f)

FIGURE P10.1.

10.12 questions for review (continued)

2. From the isometric pictorials shown in Figure P10.2, create accurate multiview drawings in the preferred format of front view, top view, and right-side view. Use hidden lines as necessary to specify all details of the object completely.

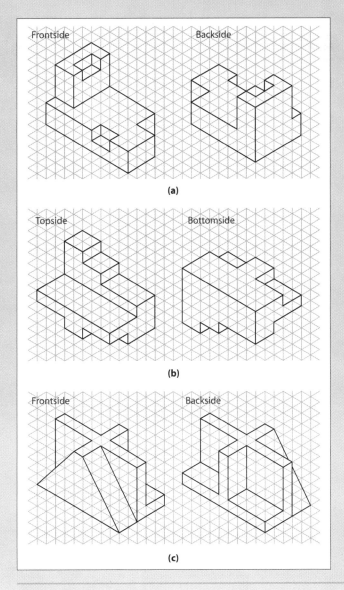

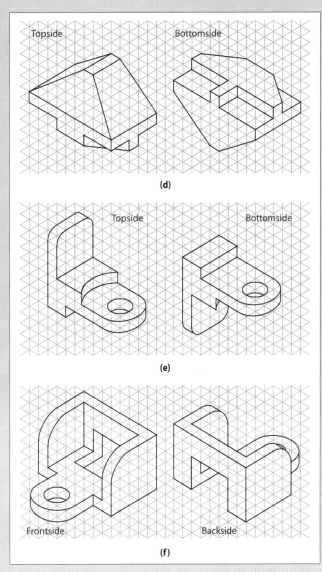

FIGURE P10.2.

10.13 problems (continued)

3. Each set of multiview drawings shown in Figure P10.3 may have visible or hidden lines missing. Add the missing lines to the drawing. An isometric pictorial has been included for clarity.

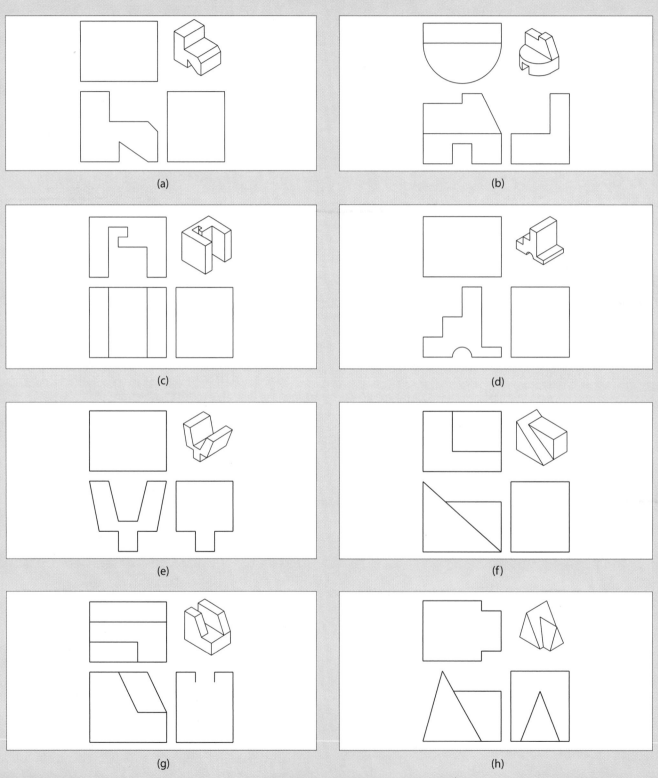

(a)

(b)

(c)

(d)

(e)

(f)

(g)

(h)

FIGURE P10.3.

10.13 problems (continued)

4. For each front view shown in Figure P10.4, draw the top view (in the correct scale, location, and orientation) that corresponds to each of the possible side views that are shown.

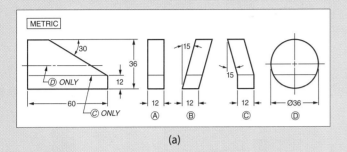

(a)

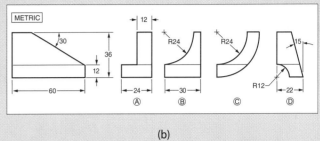

(b)

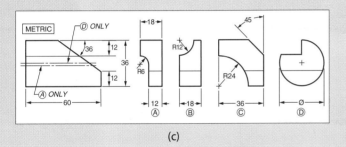

(c)

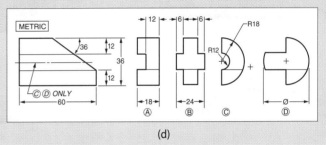

(d)

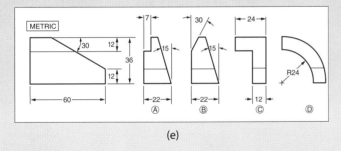

(e)

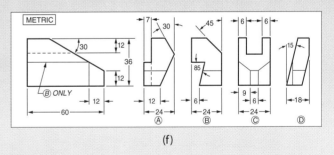

(f)

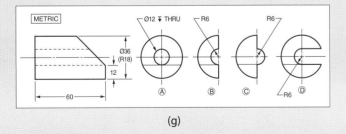

(g)

FIGURE P10.4.

10.13 problems (continued)

5. For each set of multiview drawings shown in Figure P10.5, add the missing view to the drawing in the indicated location. An isometric pictorial has been included for clarity.

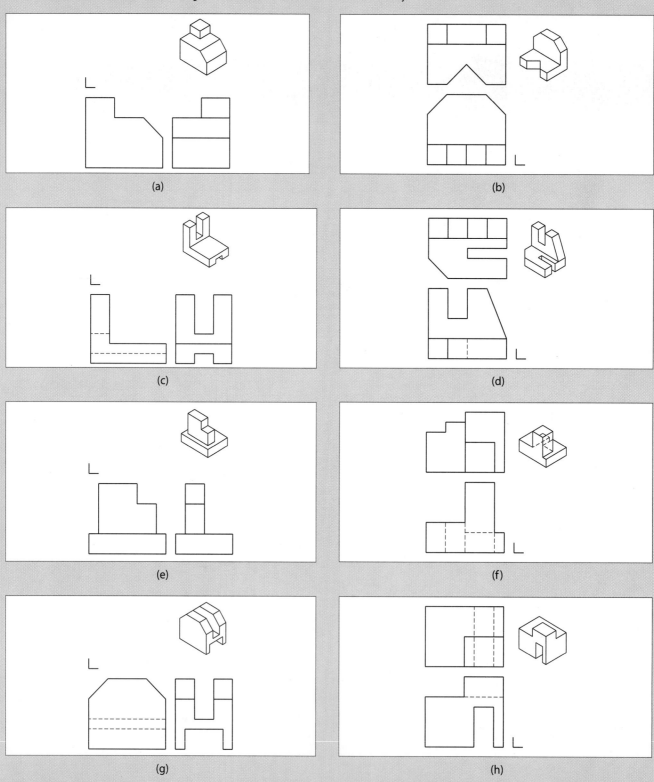

(a)   (b)

(c)   (d)

(e)   (f)

(g)   (h)

FIGURE P10.5.

10.13 problems (continued)

6. Create correctly scaled multiview orthogonal drawings of the objects shown in Figure P10.6. Show at least the front, top, and right-side views. Include hidden lines. Recommend when additional views would be useful to clarify the presentation and add these views to the drawing.

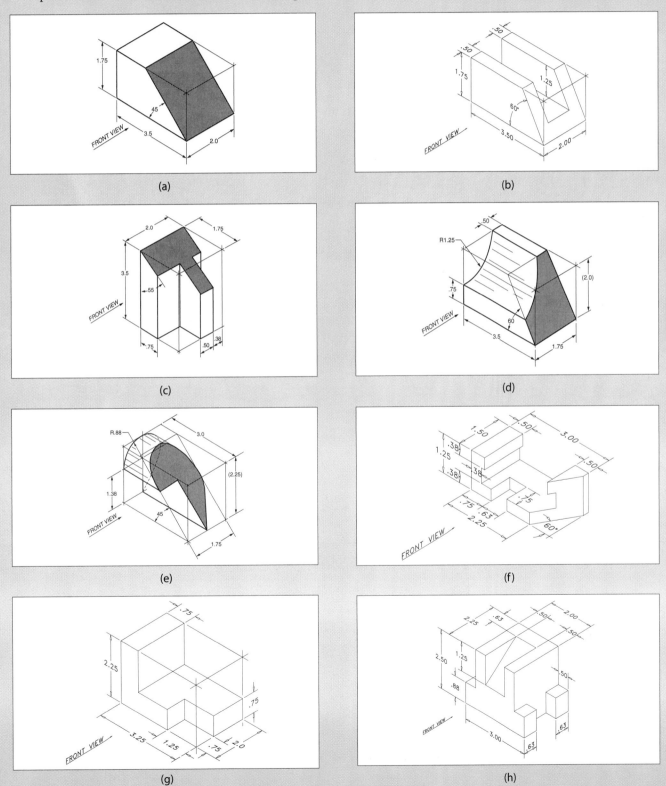

10.13 problems (continued)

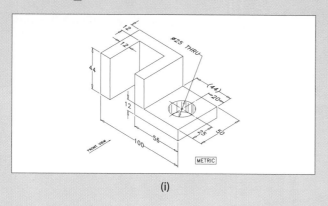

(i)

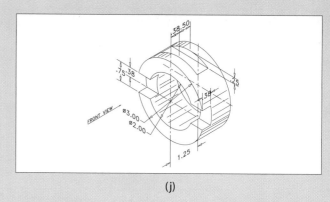

(j)

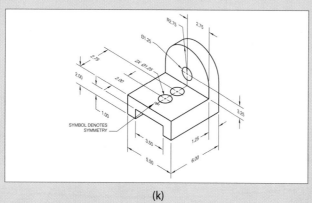

(k)

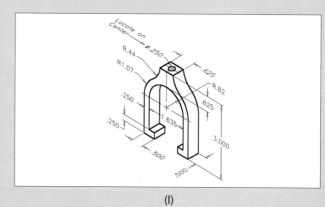

(l)

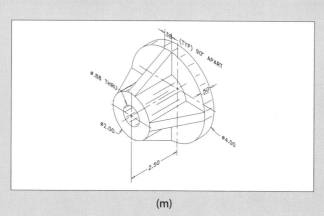

(m)

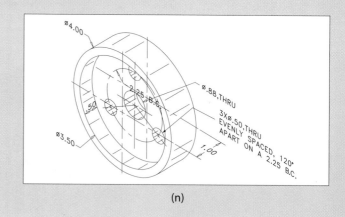

(n)

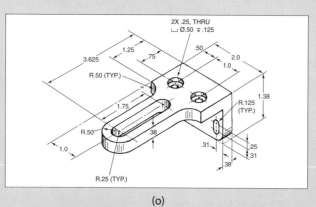

(o)

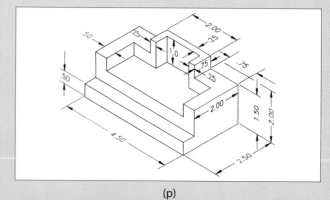

(p)

10.13 problems (continued)

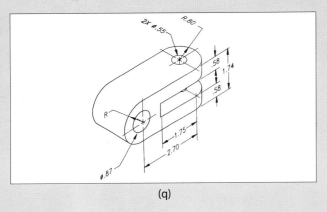

(q)

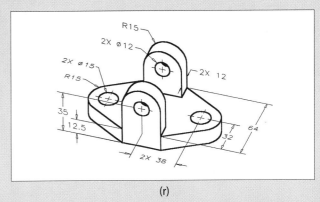

(r)

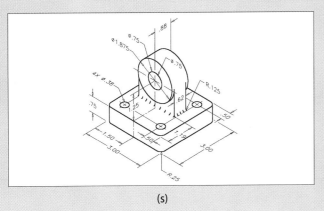

(s)

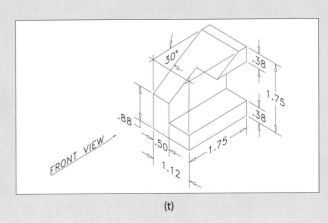

(t)

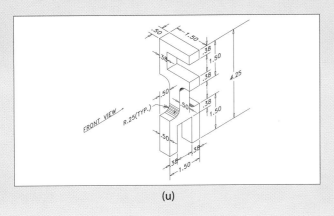

(u)

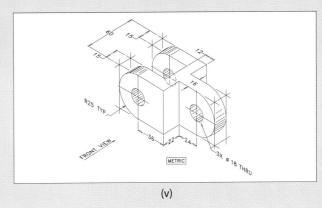

(v)

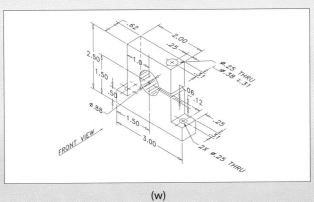

(w)

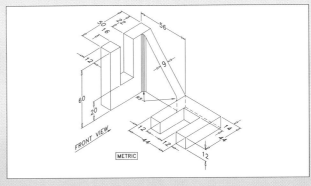

(x)

10.13 problems (continued)

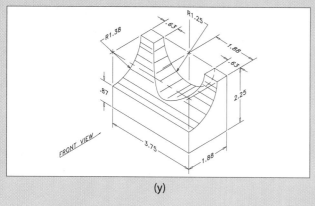

(y)

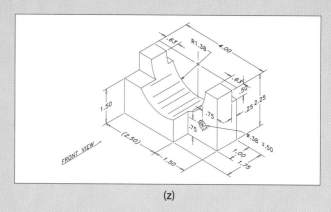

(z)

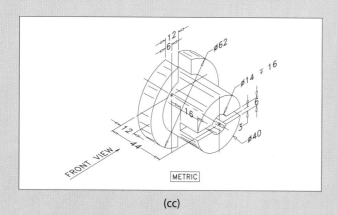

(aa)

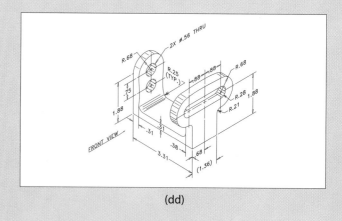

(bb)

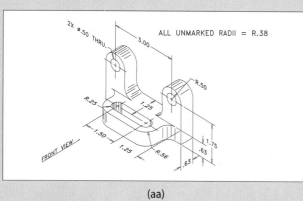

(cc)

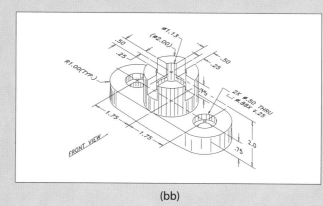

(dd)

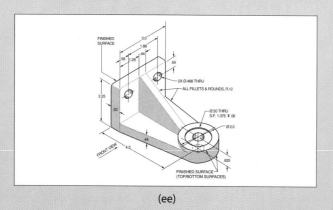

(ee)

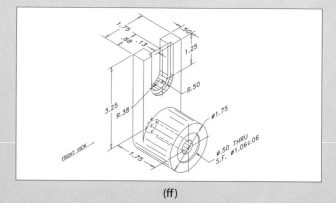

(ff)

10.13 problems (continued)

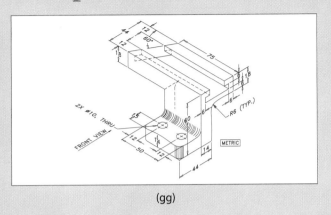

(gg)

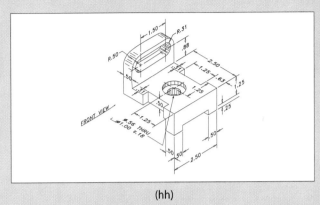

(hh)

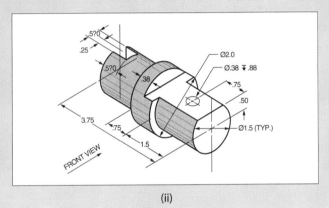

(ii)

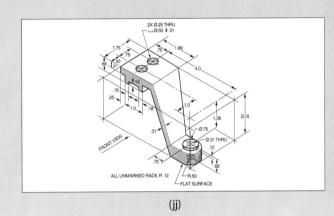

(jj)

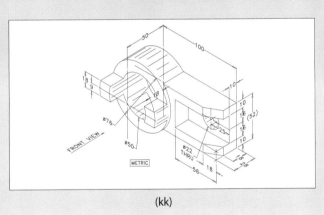

(kk)

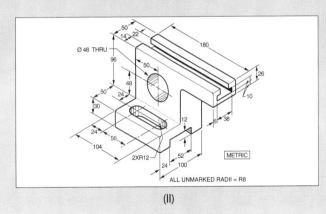

(ll)

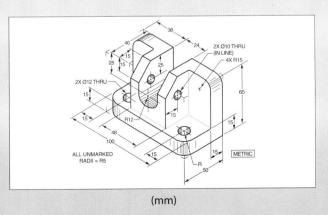

(mm)

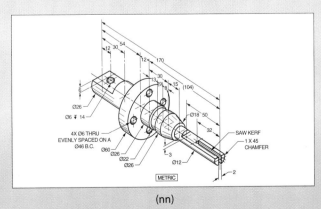

(nn)

10.13 problems (continued)

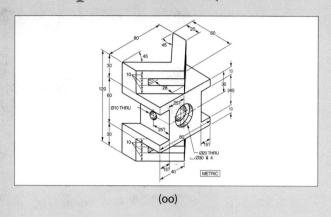

(oo)

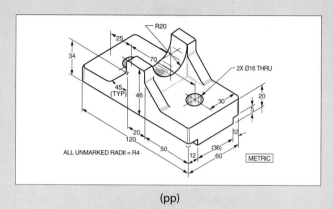

(pp)

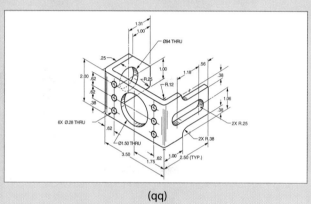

(qq)

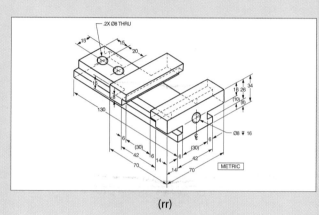

(rr)

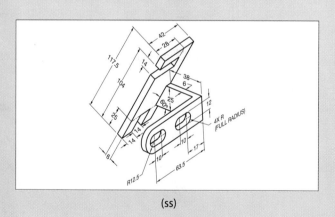

(ss)

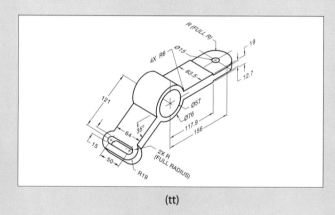

(tt)

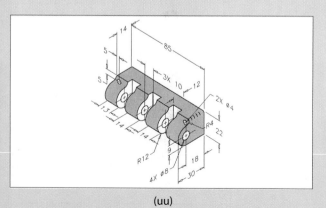

(uu)

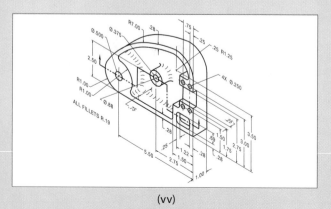

(vv)

10.13 problems (continued)

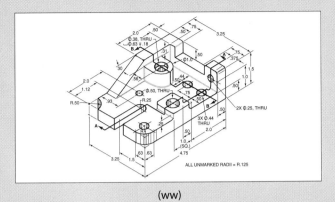

(ww)

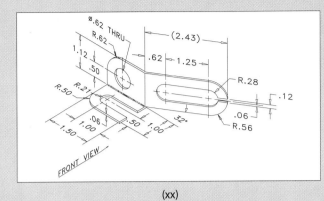

(xx)

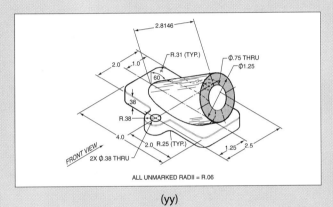

(yy)

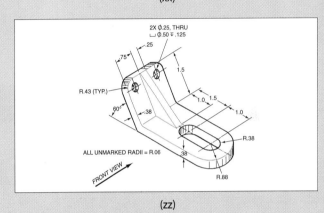

(zz)

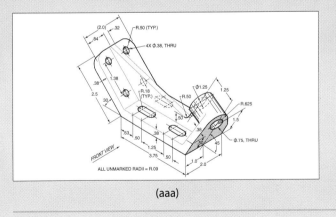

(aaa)

FIGURE P10.6.

13

Section Views

objectives

After completing this chapter, you should be able to

- Use cutaway, or section, views as a method for showing the features of a part that are normally hidden when presented on a multiview drawing

- Decide when a section view is necessary

- Decide what category of section view should be used for particular circumstances

- Create a desired section view such that it adheres to accepted engineering drawing practices

13-1

13.01 introduction

The precisely aligned images in a multiview drawing offer an excellent start in defining the exact geometry needed for a part that you want to build. However, this description alone may not be adequate to define all of the features in many types of parts. Some features may be partially or fully obscured in the standard views. The use of hidden lines can alleviate the problem, but too many hidden lines may cause confusion. In these cases, it is useful to have a means of revealing proposed interior detail. This is done by showing cross sections, or section views, at important locations. As with multiview drawings, to minimize ambiguity, you must follow certain guidelines when you want to present a section view.

13.02 A Look Inside

Pick up an everyday object (for example, a coffee mug) and look at it from all directions. If you cannot find a coffee mug, some images have been provided for your convenience in Figure 13.01. You will notice that you cannot view the mug from a direction where the inside depth of the cup or the thickness of the bottom can be directly measured (unless it is made of a clear material). If the mug has a handle on it, look at that as well. Are the edges of the handle rounded? Can you look at the handle from a direction where you get an undistorted view of the radius of the edge? These features are simple examples of measurements that cannot be made from looking at an object in a multiview drawing. Yet there must be some means of showing these types of features so a fabricator will know what to make and what sizes are required. A coffee mug is a very simple example.

Here is an industrial example. Consider the Hoyt AeroTec bow handle again. Its image and multiview engineering drawing are shown in Figure 13.02, with its cross brace highlighted. Note that the edges of the cross brace are rounded. Can these rounded edges be seen on the drawing? Assume the edges of the cross brace are not rounded, (i.e., the surfaces meet at a 90° angle). How would the drawing change? The answer is that in its current state, with all of the complexity and exquisite detail, the drawing cannot show the existence of rounded edges. Clearly, something must be added to the drawing to show that these edges are rounded and to what size they are rounded.

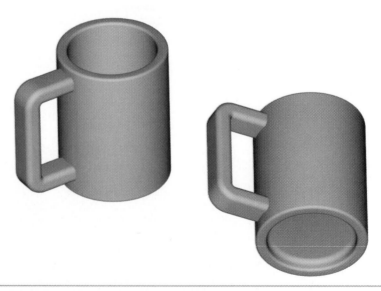

FIGURE 13.01. Two views of an object (a coffee mug) with interior detail.

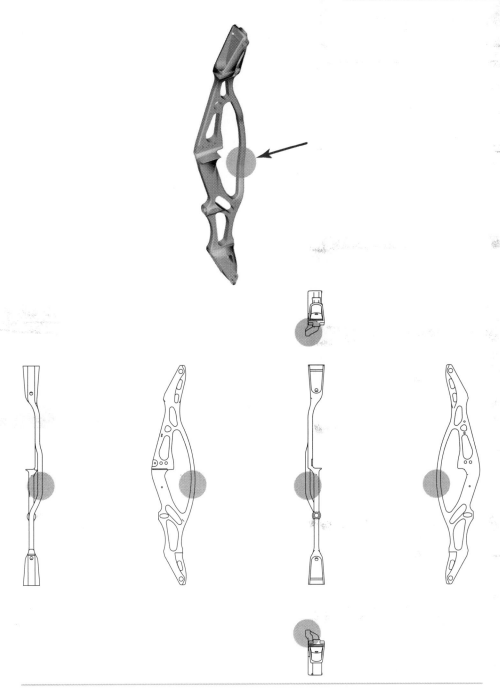

FIGURE 13.02. The geometry of the cross brace on the AeroTec riser cannot be seen in the multiview drawing.

Backing up a bit, look at the mug again to find out what is causing the problem. Figure 13.03 shows the multiview engineering drawing of the mug. Note that the depth of the mug and the radius of the edges of the handle cannot be seen on this drawing. The reason is because the object gets in the way of itself. Portions of the object obscure other portions of the same object. The outside of the mug hides the inside.

A possible solution to this problem is to use hidden lines, as shown in Figure 13.04. The hidden lines show the depth and geometry of the inside of the mug, as well as the geometry of the edges on the handle. However, the use of hidden lines is not always an ideal solution. As objects become more complicated, too many hidden lines make the views confusing, particularly when the images of different features start to fall atop one another.

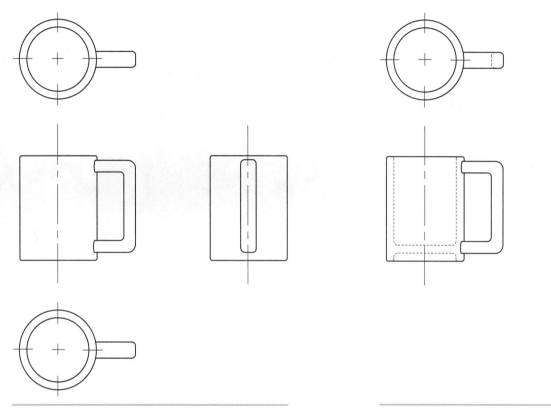

FIGURE 13.03. Orthographic views of the coffee mug fail to define interior detail.

FIGURE 13.04. A multiview drawing of the coffee mug using hidden lines to show interior detail.

In Chapter 3, you learned about cross sections of 3-D objects. If there were a way to cut the mug open, as shown in Figure 13.05, you could take the sliced part and turn it around until you were able to see the desired geometry. This hypothetical slicing is the essence of creating a cross section of the object, to create what is called a **section view**. The slicing, however, must be done following certain rules to ensure that the person who sees a section view on a drawing knows exactly where the slicing has occurred and how it was performed.

A drawing of the mug with three orthogonal views and two types of sections views is shown in Figure 13.06. Do not worry if you have difficulty understanding the extra views in this figure. The following sections discuss in detail how various types of section views are made and how they should be interpreted.

FIGURE 13.05. Hypothetical cutting of the object to reveal interior detail.

FIGURE 13.06. A multiview drawing of the coffee mug using section views to show interior detail.

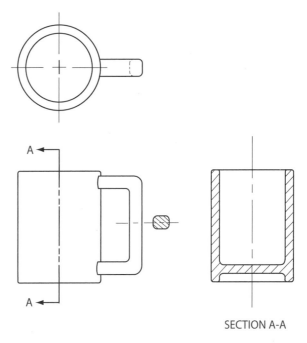

SECTION A-A

13.03 Full Sections

The simplest section view is the **full section**. In a full section, the object is cut completely apart by a **cutting plane** that is perpendicular to one of the standard viewing planes, such as the front, top, or side views. The image of the original whole object is made on the viewing plane using orthogonal projection, and the cutting plane is seen in edge view. A good way to think of a cutting plane is as a very thin knife with the blade held perpendicular to the viewing plane, which hypothetically splits the part into two pieces. This process is shown in Figure 13.07. Note that the cutting plane has an associated **viewing direction**, identified by a set of arrows pointing in the direction of the freshly cut surface that is to be viewed. To create the section view, the image of the split part is imprinted on the cutting plane. The cutting plane and the image are then rotated away from the split part until it is coplanar with the viewing plane. The hinge for this rotation of the cutting plane is its intersection with the viewing plane. With this definition of a section view and its location on the viewing plane, the alignment and orientation of the section view is the same as that used to create an orthogonal view. The section view is the image of the cut object as seen through the cutting plane, and this image is then placed on the viewing plane. In essence, a full section view is just another orthogonal view, but one that reveals the interior of the object.

On an engineering drawing, the original images of the object are not cut apart, as shown in Figure 13.08. A heavy line that extends across the entire part, with alternating short-short-long dashes, represents the edge view of the cutting plane. This line is called a **cutting plane line**. The orientation of the section view relative to the original view of the object is the same as if the viewing plane and the cutting plane were orthogonal viewing plans that had been unfolded. **Section lines**, which are a form of shading, are used to identify areas on the section view that are solid on the original whole object.

There are some important things to note in a full section on an engineering drawing. First, the cutting of the part is imaginary. The part is not to be split into separate pieces. The use of a full section is similar to saying, "If we imagine that the part was cut here, this is what we would see." The cutting plane is flat and goes all the way through the object. Notice the pairs of large, bold capital letters on the cutting plane line next to the arrows. These are used for unique identification of cutting plane lines and their associated section views on a drawing. If the letter *A* is used beside both arrows on a cutting plane line, there must be a note immediately below the corresponding section view that identifies it as "SECTION A-A." The arrows on the cutting plane line point in

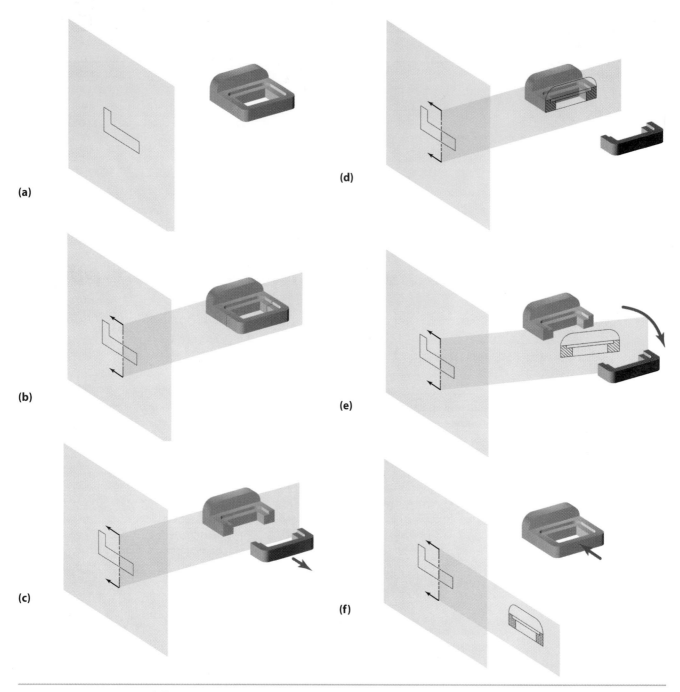

(a)

(b)

(c)

(d)

(e)

(f)

FIGURE 13.07. Creating a full section. An object is projected onto a viewing plane in (a). A cutting plane orthogonal to the viewing plane slices the object in (b). The piece to be viewed remains, while the other piece is removed in (c). The projection of the sliced object is made on the cutting plane in (d). The cutting plane and image are rotated about the section line in (e). The section view is coplanar with the viewing plane in (e).

the direction of viewing. This last point is important because the viewing direction and the orientation of the section view are not arbitrary. An error in either may cause confusion for the reader. Try to visualize the cutting process by comparing Figure 13.07 with Figure 13.08. Correlate the 3-D cutting process in Figure 13.07 with what is shown on the 2-D representation in Figure 13.08. The arrows on the cutting plane point are in the same direction as the arrows on the cutting plane line.

If the arrows on the cutting plane and its corresponding cutting plane line were reversed, as shown in Figure 13.09, the section view would be slightly different. Although the surface that is created by the cutting operation would be the same, the background image of the part would be different. This change is due to the fact that you would be retaining and looking at the other piece that was created when the part was hypothetically split compared to the case in Figure 13.08. When working with multiview drawings, you can remember the proper orientation of the section view by noting that it has the same orientation as the orthogonal view opposite to which the cutting plane line arrows point. For example, if the cutting plane line was located on the front view (and its arrows pointed away from the right-side view), the associated section view would have the same orientation and alignment as the right side view.

FIGURE 13.08. An engineering drawing with a section view to reveal interior detail.

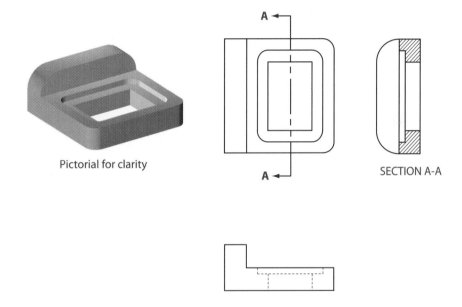

Pictorial for clarity

A

A

SECTION A-A

FIGURE 13.09. An engineering drawing with a section view to reveal interior detail.

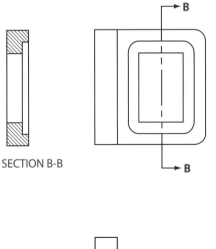

B

B

SECTION B-B

The drawing in Figure 13.10 shows a part with multiple section views. If a drawing has multiple section views, a pair of letters must uniquely identify each set of cutting plane lines and corresponding section views. So if there is a second cutting plane line and corresponding section view on the drawing, it may be identified as "SECTION B-B" if "SECTION A-A" already exists. The third set may be called "SECTION C-C," and so on. These identification labels are customarily used even when a drawing has only one section view. The hypothetical interpretation of the multiple sections on the object in Figure 13.10 is shown in Figure 13.11.

One way section views differ from conventional orthogonal views is that, in practice, section views are not required to remain aligned with their adjacent orthogonal views. Although breaking this alignment may violate the rules of orthogonal projection used to create a section view, it is allowed for convenience. Figure 13.12, for example, shows multiple section views of the part. One section is aligned with the view in which it was created. The other section views are nonaligned, but this is permitted in engineering drawing. However, note that even when the section views are nonaligned, they still are required to maintain the same rotational orientation as if they were aligned.

FIGURE 13.10. Multiple section views on a single object.

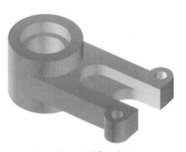

Pictorial for clarity

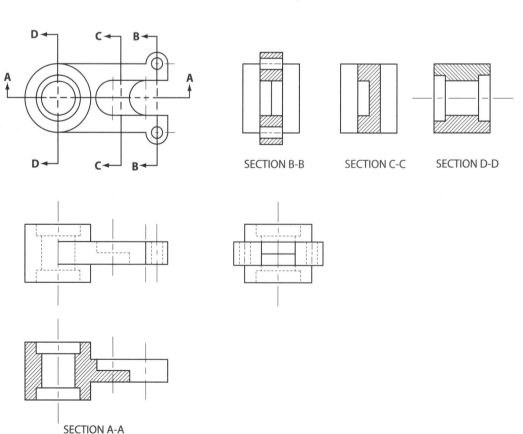

FIGURE 13.11. A hypothetical interpretation of the cutting planes for the previous figure.

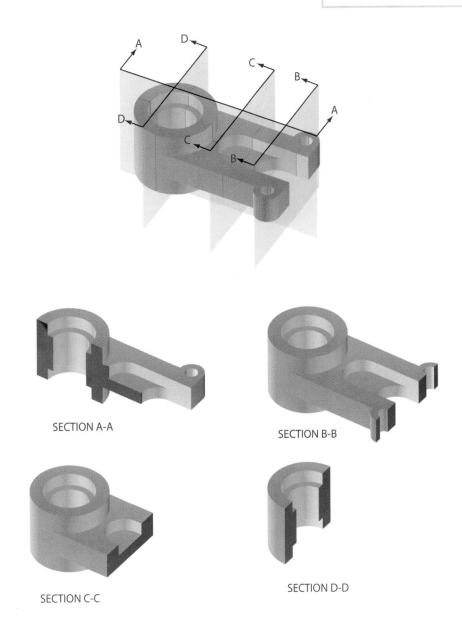

SECTION A-A

SECTION B-B

SECTION C-C

SECTION D-D

Another difference between a section view and a conventional orthogonal view is that a section view is permitted to have a different scale, or magnification, than the view in which it was created. An example of this property is shown in Figure 13.12, where three of the section views are magnified to reveal detail inside the part that would otherwise be difficult to see. When a section view uses a scale that is different from that of the principal views, the new scale must be clearly marked below the note used to identify the section view, as shown in Figure 13.12.

When a section view is created, even though the cutting plane is perpendicular to the viewing plane, there is no requirement that the cutting plane be parallel or perpendicular to any of the other orthogonal views. This property of section views makes it convenient to view features that may be placed at odd angles with respect to the principal views, as with the part shown in Figure 13.13.

FIGURE 13.12. Multiple sections with nonaligned section views and different scales.

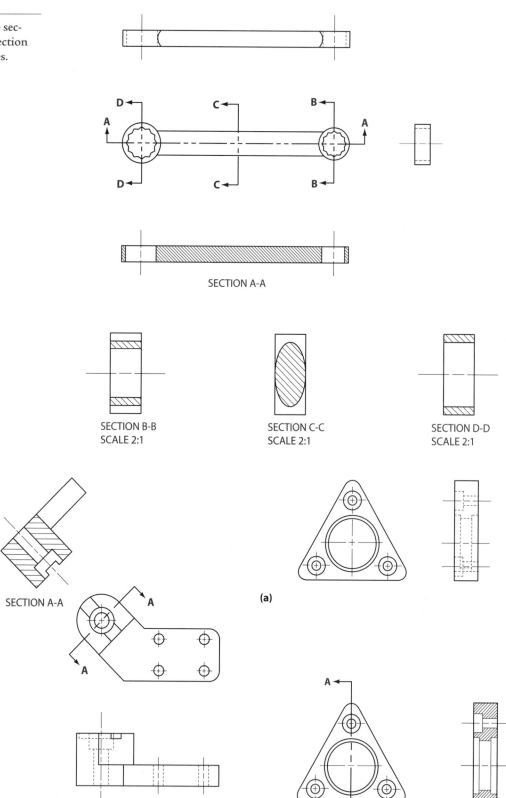

SECTION A-A

SECTION B-B
SCALE 2:1

SECTION C-C
SCALE 2:1

SECTION D-D
SCALE 2:1

SECTION A-A

A

A

(a)

(b)

SECTION A-A

FIGURE 13.13. A full section through a feature placed at an angle.

FIGURE 13.14. The need for many hidden lines in the original drawing (a) is reduced by the use of a section view (b).

13.04 What Happens to the Hidden Lines?

One of the main incentives for using section views is to reduce the use of hidden lines, which until now has been the only method available for revealing the interior and hidden features of many types of objects. When there are too many hidden lines on the view of an object, the drawing becomes confusing. Replacing those hidden lines with one or more section views greatly clarifies the drawing. When section views are used in this manner, there is no longer any need to retain the hidden lines; and they can be removed from the drawing. Hidden lines are typically not shown on the section-line-filled portions of a section view except to indicate the presence of screw threads. Figure 13.14 compares an example of a drawing that originally contained many hidden lines with a revised drawing that replaces one of the orthogonal views with a section view. The improvement in clarity is substantial.

13.05 The Finer Points of Section Lines

Section lines are used to improve the clarity of a section view by indicating the portions of the part that had been solid at the location it was hypothetically cut. However, indiscriminate section line patterns may cause more confusion than clarification. The most basic pattern is a set of lines with a common inclination angle, thickness, and spacing, as shown in Figure 13.15. The line thickness for the pattern is usually no thicker than that used for the part edges. Even with this simple set of variables, the pattern requires some thought. The pattern must be discernible as being section lines when the drawing is read, and the pattern must be reproducible without significant distortion occurring when the drawing is copied. For example, optical copiers, scanners, and fax machines can greatly distort a high-density pattern. A low-density pattern may not appear as section line patterns at all, and the section lines may be misinterpreted as edges on the part.

The pattern should not be parallel or perpendicular to any of the major feature edges of the part; otherwise, there may be some confusion about which lines are part edges and which are section lines. Vertical and horizontal lines are rarely used for section lines.

Different section line patterns can be used to represent different materials. Sample patterns are shown in Figure 13.16. For some materials used in construction, such as concrete or earth, section line patterns are more of a texture than a simple geometric pattern.

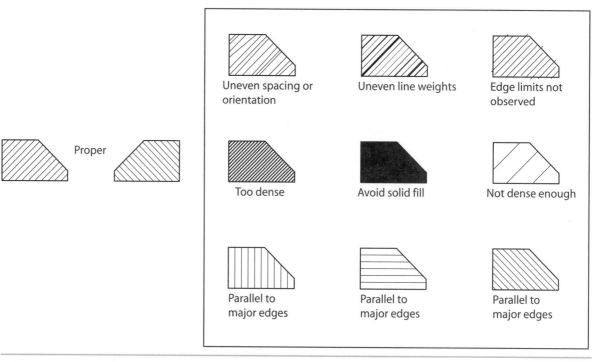

POOR!

Proper

Uneven spacing or orientation

Uneven line weights

Edge limits not observed

Too dense

Avoid solid fill

Not dense enough

Parallel to major edges

Parallel to major edges

Parallel to major edges

FIGURE 13.15. Examples of proper and poor cross-hatching techniques.

FIGURE 13.16. ANSI standard cross-hatch patterns for various materials.

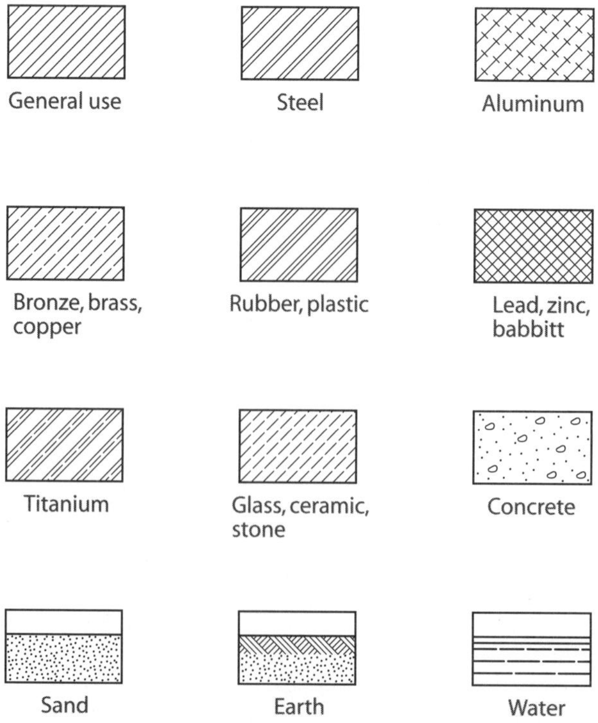

General use

Steel

Aluminum

Bronze, brass, copper

Rubber, plastic

Lead, zinc, babbitt

Titanium

Glass, ceramic, stone

Concrete

Sand

Earth

Water

13.06 Offset Sections

Offset sections can be considered modifications of full sections. An offset section allows multiple features, which normally require multiple section views, to be captured on a single view. As with a full section, an external surface hypothetically cuts through an entire part. However, instead of the part being divided with a single flat cutting plane, the cutting surface is stepped. The size and location of each step is chosen to best capture the features to be displayed. Also, as with a full section, an offset section has its viewing direction indicated by arrows that point at the cut surface to be seen. When the offset cutting surface is rotated onto the viewing plane, the cross sections of multiple features, which could not be shown otherwise with a single cutting plane, can be displayed on a single view. This process is shown in Figure 13.17.

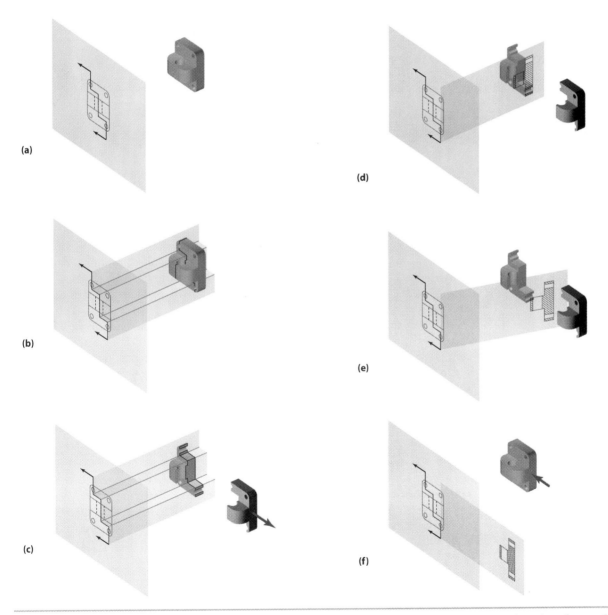

(a)

(b)

(c)

(d)

(e)

(f)

FIGURE 13.17. Creating an offset section. An object is projected onto a viewing plane in (a). A stepped cutting plane orthogonal to the viewing plane slices the object in (b). The piece to be viewed remains, while the other piece is removed in (c). The projection of the sliced part is made on the outermost segment of the stepped cutting plane in (d). The cutting plane and image are rotated about the section line in (e). The section view is coplanar with the viewing plane in (f).

FIGURE 13.18. An engineering drawing using an offset section view to reveal multiple interior detail.

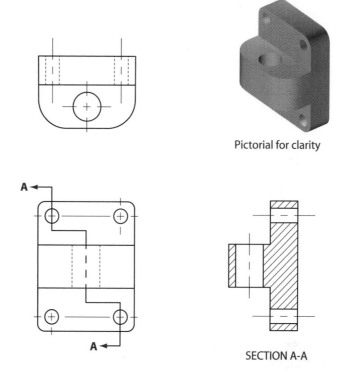

Pictorial for clarity

SECTION A-A

On an engineering drawing such as the one shown in Figure 13.18, the edge view of the stepped cutting surface is represented by a heavy stepped line with alternating short-short-long dashes. This is still called a cutting plane line, although technically it is no longer a straight line. The arrows point in the direction of viewing, and the cutting plane line and its associated offset section view are uniquely identified in each drawing with a pair of capital letters, as before.

As with full sections, the rotation orientation of an offset section view must be consistent with the creation of an orthogonal view; but the location and scale of the view is left to the discretion of the person creating the drawing. Note that in an offset section view, it is customary not to show the locations of the steps on the view. The reason is because this information is already available by inspecting the cutting plane line and because adding step lines may cause confusion by showing edges that do not actually exist on the part.

13.07 Half Sections

Half sections are used to save space and labor on an engineering drawing, especially for symmetrical parts. Recall what you learned about symmetry in Chapter 3. When an object is symmetrical about a plane or an axis, it is acceptable to present the object partially in its original state and partially in a sectioned state on the same orthogonal view. The plane of symmetry separates the two states. Another way of visualizing a half section is to imagine a part that is cut such that one-quarter of it is removed to reveal the interior detail. This hypothetical process is shown in Figure 13.19.

In the engineering drawing for this half section, the cutting plane line extends across the object only to the plane of symmetry. The cutting plane line extends partway across the object. A single arrow on the cutting plane line points in the direction of viewing. The absence of a second arrow is an indication that the cutting plane line is for a half section. There is no separate section view. Instead, the orthogonal view and the section view are combined such that the exterior of the part is shown on one half and the interior of the part is shown on the other half. In Figure 13.20, the view types change at the plane of symmetry, which is shown as a centerline. Note that hidden lines are not shown on the unsectioned half of the part.

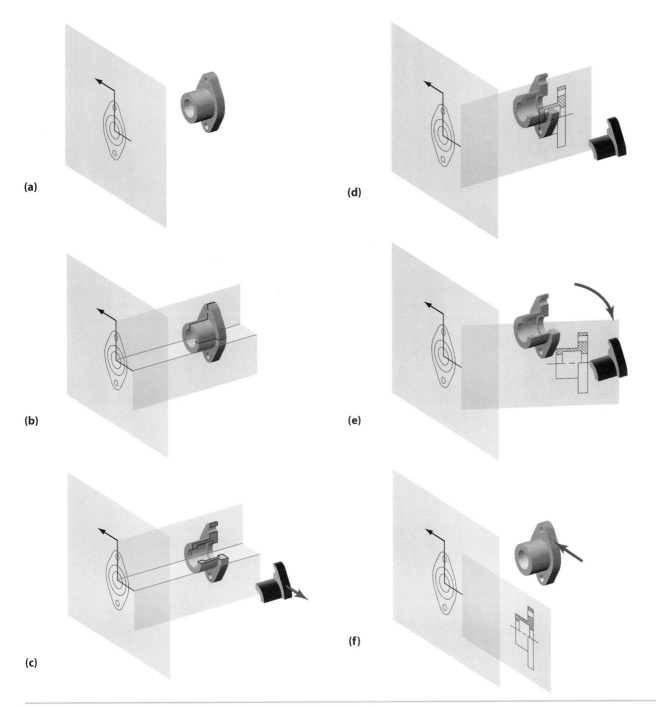

(a)

(b)

(c)

(d)

(e)

(f)

FIGURE 13.19. Creating a half section. An object is projected onto a viewing plane in (a). A stepped cutting plane slices through the object to the plane of symmetry in (b). The piece to be viewed remains, while the other piece is removed in (c). The image of the sliced object is projected onto an orthogonal viewing plane in (d). The viewing plane and image are rotated about the intersection line in (e). The section view is coplanar with the original viewing plane in (f).

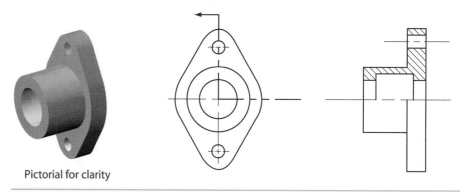

Pictorial for clarity

FIGURE 13.20. An engineering drawing shows the use of a half section to reveal interior as well as exterior detail.

13.08 Procedures for the Creation of Section Views

Later in this chapter, you will learn about some special types of section views; but for now, you will focus on creating the three types you have learned about so far: the full, offset, and half section views. A problem that many new engineers have when they are creating an engineering drawing is deciding whether to include section views. The basic question that must be answered when making this decision is this: Will the section view improve the clarity of the presentation? When the answer is clearly "yes," include section views. When the answer is "probably not," section views may not be necessary. Since section views are used to show interior or hidden details, objects that do not have such features usually fall into the latter category. Objects with such details must reveal them with hidden lines or section views. The question then becomes, which technique is better?

13.08.01 Deciding When to use Section Views

The decision to use section views is somewhat subjective. If the hidden features are relatively few and simple in geometry, such as a few simple holes or slots that go all the way through the part, the use of hidden lines would probably be best. Such features are so common that standard orthogonal views with hidden lines are quickly interpreted, and the addition of section views may actually contribute to unnecessary clutter on the drawing. However, as the hidden features become more numerous or complex in geometry, section views should be used to clearly define their geometries. As a guide, consider using section views when the answer to any of the following questions is yes if only hidden lines will be used.

■ Are any hidden lines composed of multiple segments?

■ Do any hidden lines of a feature intrude into the area occupied by another hidden feature?

■ Do any hidden lines of a feature share or come close to sharing any hidden lines with another feature unless the lines are exactly common?

Examples of these types of features are shown in Figure 13.21. An overall rule of thumb is that whenever the shear number or the geometric complexity of hidden lines makes the presentation of the object confusing, consider using section views.

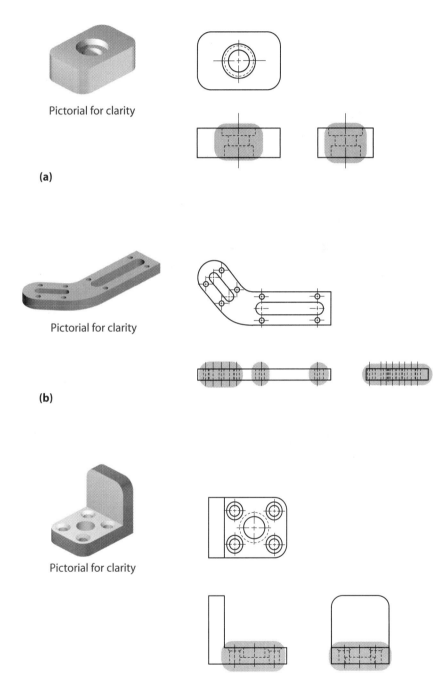

FIGURE 13.21. Internal features with hidden lines that have multiple segments (a) or overlap (b and c) are good candidates for using section views.

Pictorial for clarity

(a)

Pictorial for clarity

(b)

Pictorial for clarity

(c)

13.08.02 Creating a Full Section View

When the decision has been made to add section views to a drawing, the next step is to create them. When you are the original designer of the part, this task may be simple since you probably already visualize the internal geometry you want to feature. If the part is someone else's design, the process is trickier because you may need to interpret a rather messy drawing that needs the section views to improve the drawing's presentation. If this is the case, you will need to correctly align, identify, and visualize internal features that have been outlined with hidden lines in adjacent views. This task becomes difficult when some hidden lines are missing or have been removed for clarity. The steps to creating a full section view are outlined below and then explained in more detail using an example.

Step 1: Identify the feature(s) to be revealed and the desired viewing direction.

Step 2: Draw the cutting plane line that represents the edge of the cutting plane.

Step 3: Outline the modified part in an adjacent orthogonal view.

Step 4: Identify the intersection points of the part's exterior and interior edges with the cutting plane.

Step 5: Outline the internal features associated with the intersection points on the cutting plane.

Step 6: Find the boundaries between solid and empty space and fill the solid areas with section lines.

Step 7: Add or remove background edges in space and remove edges in solid areas.

When the section view is completed, it may be moved to a more convenient location on the drawing as long as its rotational orientation remains the same.

Consider the object shown in Figure 13.22, which has a pair of grooves inside its main bore. When the geometry of this feature is defined using hidden lines, these lines are composed of multiple segments. Thus, a section view would probably present this feature more clearly.

First (step 1), the bore with its grooves is identified as the feature to be shown in a section view. This feature can be presented best by using a cutting plane that contains the axis of the bore. Slicing the part in this manner would reveal the width and depth of the grooves. In this case, as in most cases, choosing a cutting plane that is parallel to one of the preferred principal views will make section view creation simpler. A cutting plane line (step 2) is drawn in the top view to represent the edge of the cutting plane, as shown in Figure 13.23. The cutting plane is a vertical plane seen as an edge in the top view. Because the cutting plane line is horizontal on the top view of the drawing, the cutting plane also is parallel to the front view; and outlining the part for the next step becomes easier.

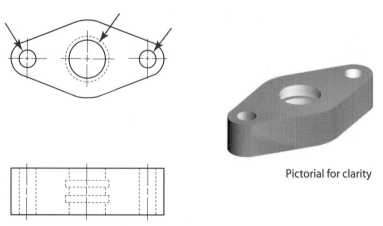

Pictorial for clarity

FIGURE 13.22. Construct a full section view of this part. It is desired to reveal the indicated features (step 1).

FIGURE 13.23. Step 2: Draw the cutting plane and the desired viewing direction.

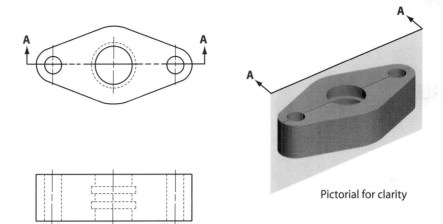

Pictorial for clarity

The direction of the arrows on the cutting plane line shows that the direction of viewing is from front to back. Since the cutting plane is parallel to the front viewing plane, the outline of the part in the section view is likely to be a significant portion of the outline as seen in the front view. This outline (step 3) is shown in Figure 13.24. Note that the size of the outline and its orientation are the same as in the front view from which it was derived. This outline is temporarily placed below the front view for convenience in feature alignment.

Next (step 4), examine the intersections of the cutting plane line with each visible and hidden edge inside the part, as shown in Figure 13.25. Note that some hidden edges may be obscured by visible edges. At every such intersection, a corresponding point will exist in the section view where the edge direction of an internal feature will change. The edges of the internal features appear as hidden lines in the front view but become visible edges in the section view. By tracking the internal edges, the outline of each sectioned internal feature on the cutting plane can be created.

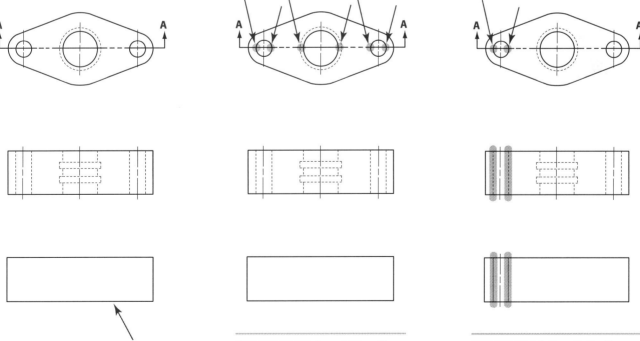

FIGURE 13.24. Step 3: Outline the sectioned part based on the adjacent view.

FIGURE 13.25. Step 4: Identify the intersection points with the cutting plane and see what is happening on the adjacent view.

FIGURE 13.26. Step 5: Outline the internal features associated with the intersection points on the cutting plane.

One way to proceed (step 5) is to examine sets of intersections on the cutting plane line and try to associate and visualize the internal features that created those intersections on the adjacent view. For example, from left to right on the cutting plane line in the top view, the first feature crossed is the visible edge of a circle. When the two intersection points of the cutting plane line on the circle are aligned with their corresponding features on the adjacent view, as shown in Figure 13.26, a pair of hidden lines is seen. The internal feature capable of generating such 2-D geometries on adjacent views is a simple hole that extends all the way through the part. In the section view, the optical limits (or "sides") of the hole become visible edges when the part is hypothetically split at the cutting plane.

The next feature crossed by the cutting plane line is a bit more complicated. It is composed of a visible circular edge inside a hidden circular edge. When these elements are aligned with their corresponding elements in the adjacent view, as shown in Figure 13.27, the feature described is a hole with two internal grooves. In the section view, the hidden edges of this feature seen in the front view become visible edges in the split part.

The final feature crossed by the cutting plane line is another hole. The section view showing all of the edges of the interior features revealed by the cutting plane is shown in Figure 13.28.

The next question that must be asked is, which of the interior areas of the section view were formerly solid, and which were formerly space? The ability to visualize the interior features is important here. The insides of holes, slots, and grooves, for example, contain space. Their edges in the section view separate space from former solid. In Figure 13.29, the portions of the section that are solid have been filled with section lines for easier visualization (step 6). Since the sectioned part also reveals the edges of the slots in the interior surface of the bore, these must be added to the section view (step 7), as shown in Figure 13.30. Note that in the final presentation, the original front

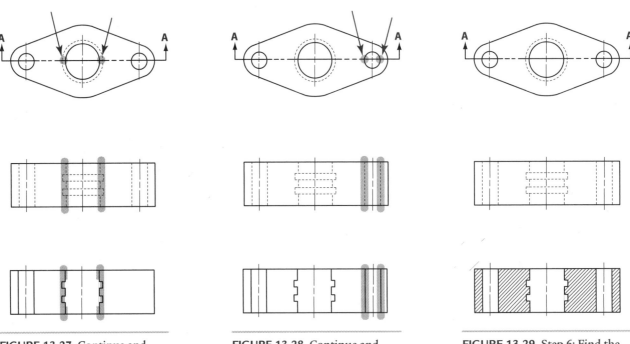

FIGURE 13.27. Continue and outline the next internal feature associated with the intersection points on the cutting plane.

FIGURE 13.28. Continue and outline the last internal feature associated with the intersection points on the cutting plane.

FIGURE 13.29. Step 6: Find the boundaries of air and solid and cross-hatch the solid areas.

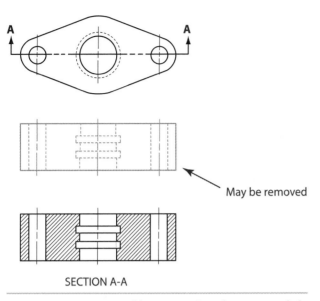

May be removed

SECTION A-A

FIGURE 13.30. Step 7: Add any new edges that are revealed. Label the view. Note that the former front view may be removed since it adds no additional information.

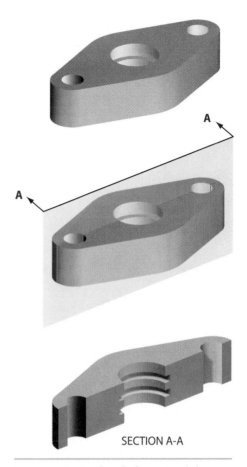

SECTION A-A

FIGURE 13.31. The whole part and the sectioned part.

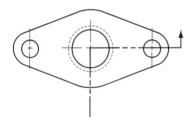

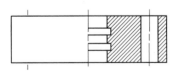

FIGURE 13.32. Presentation as a half section view.

view may be removed because it adds no additional information after the completed section view has been added. A pictorial of the part before and after sectioning is shown in Figure 13.31.

13.08.03 Creating a Half Section

The steps for creating a half section view are identical to those for creating a full section view except that only half the interior of the object needs to be revealed. A drawing with a half section view of the object in Figure 13.31 is shown in Figure 13.32. Note that this object is symmetrical about the centerline of the bore on its left and right sides.

In this case, the cutting plane line is created on the top view and extends only to the plane of symmetry (located at the axis of the bore). The single arrow on the cutting plane line points in the direction that the object is to be viewed. The half section view completely replaces the front view and shows the object in its unsectioned state without hidden lines on one side of the symmetry axis and the interior of the object on the other side of the axis.

13.08.04 Multiple Section Views

When an object is particularly complex, multiple section views should be used to reveal all of its internal details. The object shown in Figure 13.33, for example, has multiple holes and slots that extend from different directions and that intersect. The plethora of hidden lines that result from the internal features make the multiview drawing difficult to interpret.

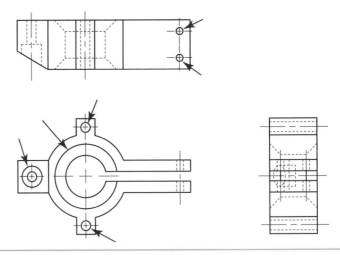

FIGURE 13.33. A complex object requiring multiple sections. It is desired to reveal the interior of the indicated features (step 1).

To reveal the interior details of the part (step 1) and remove the necessity of the hidden lines, three section views are needed. The cutting plane lines are labeled as A-A, B-B, and C-C on Figure 13.34. Note that each section has been chosen to reveal something unique about the interior detail (step 2), although different sections may share the same details. The seven-step process will be used to create Section A-A. The creation of Section B-B and Section C-C are left as a reader exercise, and only the results are shown.

Cutting plane line A-A extends across the length of the part at the keyhole-shaped slot in the front view. Since the arrows of the cutting plane line point away from the top view, an outline of the section view can be begun with a copy of the outline of the top view (step 3), as shown in Figure 13.35. Note that if the arrows of the cutting plane line had been pointing in the other direction (i.e., in the direction away from the (nonexistent) bottom view), the section view would need to have the same alignment and rotational orientation as the bottom view.

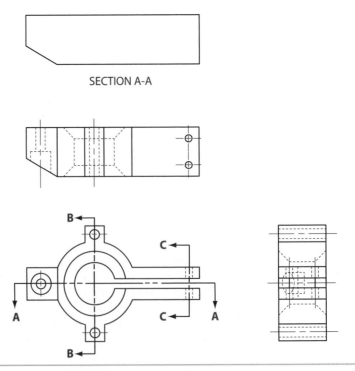

FIGURE 13.34. Step 2: Draw the cutting planes with the desired viewing directions.

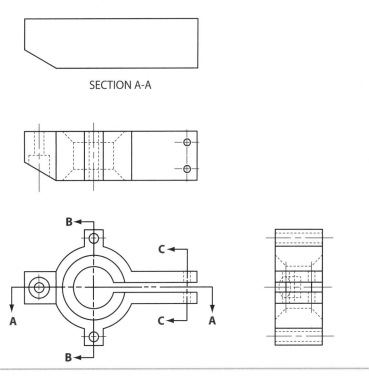

FIGURE 13.35. Step 3: Outline the sectioned part based on the adjacent view.

From left to right, the cutting plane line enters the part; crosses a set of concentric circles, then a set of concentric partial circles; and exits the part. The top view shows that the interior line is created by the edge of the inclined surface. When the intersection between the cutting plane line and concentric circles is aligned to their corresponding hidden edges in the adjacent views (step 4), as shown in Figure 13.36, it can be seen

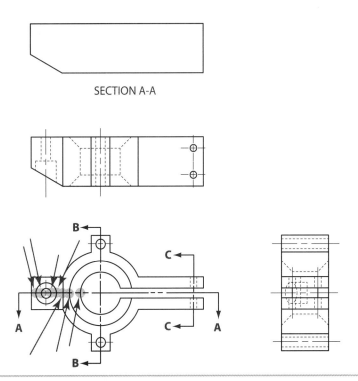

FIGURE 13.36. Step 4: Identify the intersection points with the cutting plane and see what is happening on the adjacent view.

FIGURE 13.37. Step 5: Outline the first internal feature associated with the intersection points on the cutting plane.

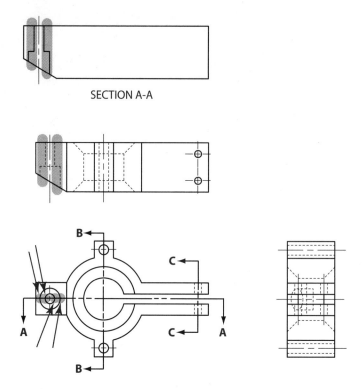

SECTION A-A

that the concentric circles represent the edges of a counterbored hole. On the section view, the hidden edges of the hole become visible (step 5), as shown in Figure 13.37.

By aligning the intersection between the cutting plane line and circles to their corresponding hidden edges in the adjacent views, it can be seen that the semicircles represent the edges of a countersunk-keyhole-shaped slot. On the section view, the hidden edges of the slot become visible (more of step 5), as shown in Figure 13.38.

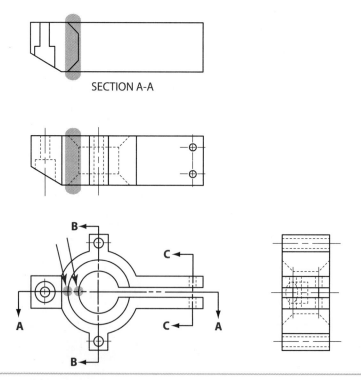

SECTION A-A

FIGURE 13.38. Step 5 cont: Outline the next internal feature associated with the intersection points on the cutting plane.

FIGURE 13.39. Step 6: Find the boundaries of air and solid and cross-hatch the solid areas.

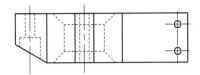

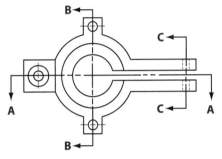

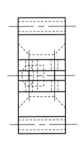

Notice that as you continue to move from left to right along the cutting plane line, it does not intersect any other object feature. This means that the object behind the cutting plane is still visible, but there will not be any section lines to worry about because the cutting plane is not "cutting" through any more solid areas. The insides of the hole, slot, and counterbores contain space. Their edges in the section view separate space from former solid. In Figure 13.39, the portions of the section that were formerly solid have been filled with section lines for visualization (step 6). Note that in this case, the section view reveals the back "uncut" part of the object along with two edges in the keyhole slot that were previously hidden in the regular orthogonal view (step 7), as shown in Figure 13.40.

FIGURE 13.40. Step 7: Add background edges in the air. Label the view.

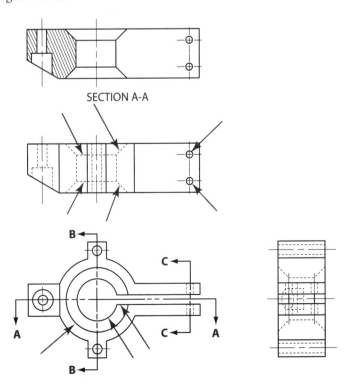

FIGURE 13.41. Add the other two sections using the same method of construction. Note that many of the hidden lines can be removed.

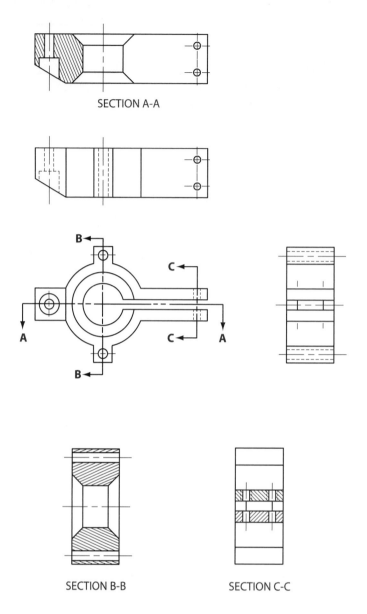

The completed Sections B-B and C-C are shown in Figure 13.41. The addition of Section B-B reveals the interior detail of the two holes beside the countersunk hole, which eliminates the confusion of the multiplicity of hidden lines in the multiview drawing. The addition of Section C-C reveals the interior detail of the cross hole that goes through the keyhole-shaped slot. Note that this view gives the appearance of two disjointed pieces because of the direction in which the section is viewed. A pictorial of the part before and after sectioning is shown in Figure 13.42.

FIGURE 13.42. The whole part and the part split at three different locations.

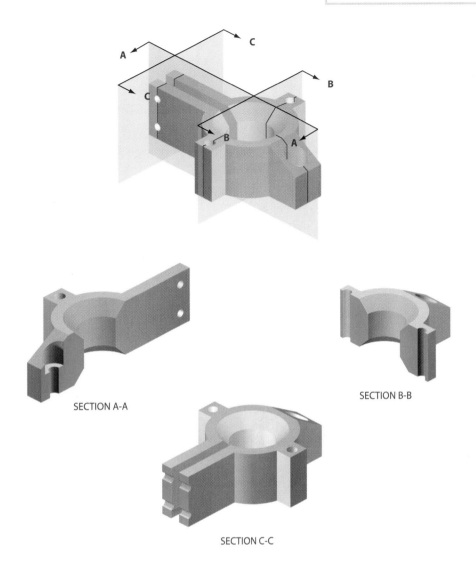

SECTION A-A

SECTION B-B

SECTION C-C

13.08.05 Creating an Offset Section

As mentioned previously, when the multiple internal features do not line up along a single cutting plane, it may be possible to capture most or all of them with an offset cutting plane, which is not a true plane but rather a stepped planar surface. The procedure for creating an offset section is similar to creating a full section, with a few modifications to step 2.

Step 1: Identify the features to be revealed and the desired viewing direction.

Step 2: Draw the stepped cutting plane line to reveal the desired features.

Step 3: Outline the modified part in an adjacent orthogonal view.

Step 4: Identify the intersection points of the part's exterior and interior edges with each segment of the cutting plane.

Step 5: Outline the internal features associated with the intersection points on the cutting plane.

Step 6: Find the boundaries between solid and empty space and fill solid areas with section lines.

Step 7: Add or remove background edges in space and remove edges in solid areas.

In particular, for step 2, it is desired to create a stepped cutting surface that reveals the true dimensions of the features to be revealed with no overlap of these features in the section view.

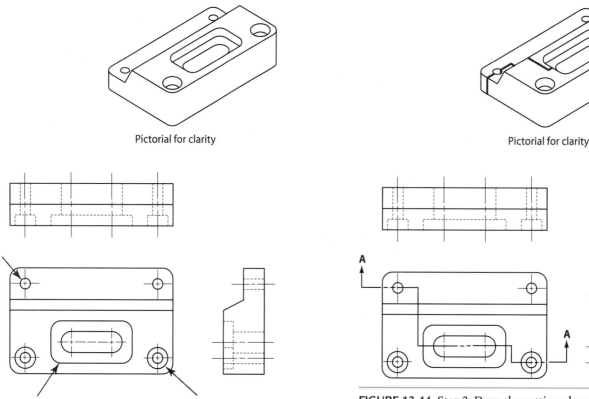

Pictorial for clarity

Pictorial for clarity

FIGURE 13.43. The indicated features (step 1) of this part can be revealed with an offset section.

FIGURE 13.44. Step 2: Draw the cutting plane and select the desired viewing direction.

Consider, for example, the part shown in Figure 13.43, which contains two counterbored holes, a stepped slot, and two simple holes. It is desired to reveal the interior detail of the slot and each type of hole (step 1).

When creating the cutting plane line for an offset, it is important to select a good viewing direction as well as a good line configuration. The hidden lines in the right-side view show that the projections of these features overlap in this view. In the top view, however, the hidden lines show that the projection of these features do not overlap in this view. An offset cutting plane line can be imagined as being composed of two types of segments. The **cutting segments** are the portions that cut through the internal features to be viewed. Each of these segments should pass through entire features if they are to be revealed in their entirety. The **step segments** are transitions between the various cutting segments and are perpendicular to them. The step segments should not pass through any features on the object. A section view that shows all of the desired internal features without interference is desirable; so in this case, the cutting segments are chosen to be parallel to the top view. The precise lengths of the cutting segments are not important as long as they pass through the entire feature. A good offset cutting plane line (step 2) is shown in Figure 13.44.

Since the arrows of the cutting plane line point away from the (nonexistent) bottom view, an outline of the section view can be begun with the outline of the bottom view (step 3). Since a bottom view does not exist, this view or its outline needs to be created with the proper alignment and orientation of a regular orthogonal view, as shown in Figure 13.45. If only the outline of this view is created, the projections of the internal features must then be inferred from the top view.

In this example, each cutting sample passes through only one feature, although in general, a cutting segment can pass through multiple features. From left to right on the cutting plane line in Figure 13.45, the first feature crossed is a circle that represents the edge of a simple hole. The next cutting segment passes through the stepped

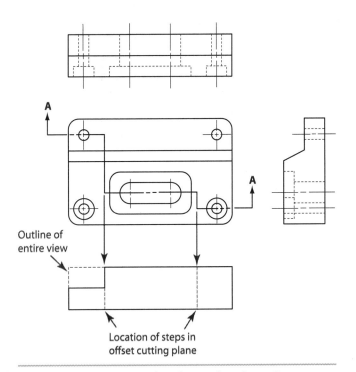

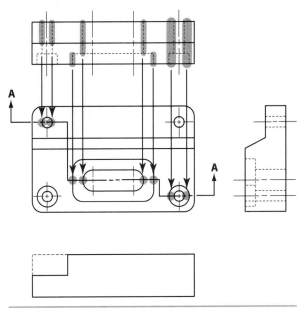

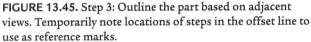

FIGURE 13.45. Step 3: Outline the part based on adjacent views. Temporarily note locations of steps in the offset line to use as reference marks.

FIGURE 13.46. Step 4: Identify the intersection points with the cutting plane and see what is happening on the adjacent view.

slot, and the final cutting segment passes through a set of concentric circles that represent the edges of a counterbored hole. The intersections of the cutting plane line with the edges of these features (step 4), shown in Figure 13.46, indicate the aligned locations on the section view where something should be happening (namely, a change in depth of the feature) to create those edges.

When the part is hypothetically cut, the edges of the counterbored hole, the slot, and the simple hole would be exposed (step 5), as shown in Figure 13.47. Note that if

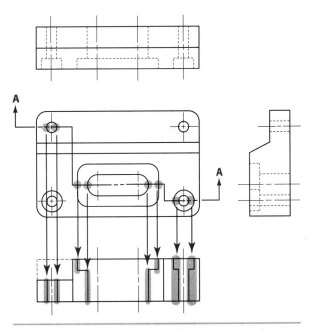

FIGURE 13.47. Step 5: Transfer the features into the section view and form the feature edges.

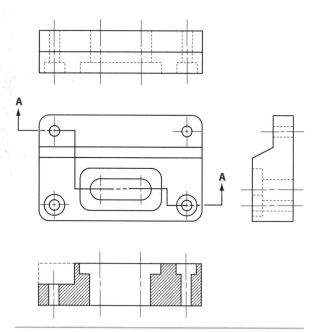

FIGURE 13.48. Step 6: Find the boundaries of air and solid and cross-hatch the solid areas.

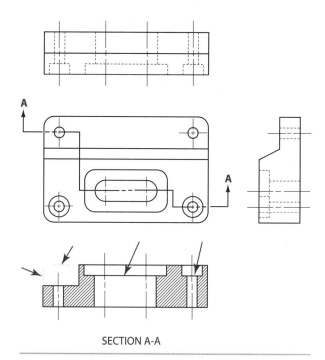

SECTION A-A

FIGURE 13.49. Step 7: Add newly revealed background edges and remove the step edges of the cutting plane. Label the section view.

the cutting implement had actually been a stepped plane, new edges also would have been created at the locations of the step segments. These edges are temporarily shown in Figure 13.47 merely to illustrate the location of the steps. In engineering drawing practice, these edges are removed.

The inside of the hole, slot, and counterbores contain space. Their edges in the section view separate space from solid. In Figure 13.48, the portions of the section that are supposed to be solid have been filled with section lines for visualization (step 6). Note that in this case, the section view reveals edges in the counterbored hole and slot that were previously hidden in the regular orthogonal view (step 7), as shown in Figure 13.49. The boundary edges in the upper left corner of the section view must be deleted because those edges were formed by a portion of the object that would not be seen on the sectioned object. Finally, you must delete any edges formed by the stepped cutting plane that you may have included for reference.

13.08.06 Creating a Sectioned Pictorial

An excellent aid for visualizing sectioned objects is to present pictorials of them. Creating this type of view is also an excellent academic exercise for the development of visualization skills. The process involves removing the portion of the object that is not viewed, creating a multiview drawing of the remaining portion, and creating a pictorial of the remaining portion from the modified drawing. Constructing such a pictorial continues the previous example. The construction of a section pictorial should not be done on the original drawing; rather, it should be done on a copy of the drawing on a separate worksheet to avoid confusion between the real part that is to be built and the model that is for visualization purposes only.

In the drawing in Figure 13.49, the cutting plane line arrows in the front view point toward the portion of the object to be retained and viewed, while the other portion is to be discarded. The modified front view is shown in Figure 13.50.

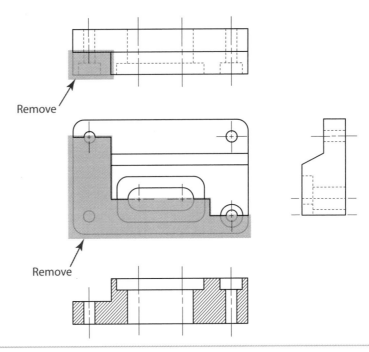

FIGURE 13.50. To visualize the sectioned part, remove the portion that is not seen from the existing orthogonal views.

Once a portion of the part has been removed in the front view, the remaining views also must be modified to be consistent with the modified part. In this case, there will be no changes to the top view. The right-side view must be modified to show that material has been removed. The section view can be used for the bottom view if the section lines are removed and the edges formed by the step segments are once again included. Note that if a left-side view was created, that view also would need to include the new edges formed by the stepped cutting plane. These modified views are shown in Figure 13.51.

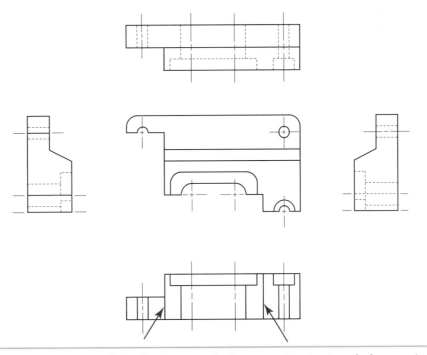

FIGURE 13.51. For ease of visualization, turn the former section view into the bottom view by removing cross-hatching and adding a section step line. Add a left view.

FIGURE 13.52. Create the pictorial using the sectioned part instead of the whole part.

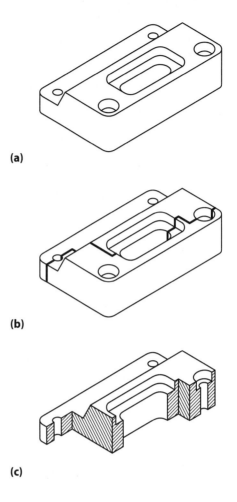

(a)

(b)

(c)

With the completed modified views of the object actually cut, the pictorial can be created by using the point, edge, or surface tracking techniques detailed in Chapter 11. The complete pictorial of the sectioned object is shown in Figure 13.52. Note that the freshly created surfaces from the cutting operation should be shaded or filled with section lines to show that these surfaces were artificially created and do not exist on the real part.

13.09 Removed Sections

In certain cases, it is convenient to use a removed section instead of a full section. A **removed section** offers the convenience of showing only the new surfaces created by a cutting plane, without the complexity of showing the remaining surfaces on an object. A hypothetical procedure for creating a removed section image is shown in Figure 13.53.

In this figure, a cutting plane intersects the object in the area of interest in (a). The cutting plane should be parallel to one of the principal views or perpendicular to the major surfaces of the part where the cut is made in order to reveal its true sizes. In (b), the cutting plane is removed from the part with the image of the intersection imprinted on the plane. The cutting plane and image are then rotated by 90 degrees in (c) such that the arrows point into the page on a drawing (d). The complete removed section view, as would be seen in an engineering drawing, is shown in Figure 13.54.

There is no need for view alignment for the removed section, although its orientation must still follow the rules of multiview presentation and the section view should be located near the cutting plane line. If the scale of the section view is different from that used on the multiview projections, the new scale must be included with the labeling of the section view.

For views where the surfaces created by a hypothetical cut are relatively small compared to the remaining surfaces of the view or where full sections may create unnecessarily large or confusing views, removed sections are a good option for improving clarity while reducing effort and complexity in a drawing. Figure 13.55 shows how removed sections were used for defining various parts of the Hoyt AeroTec bow handle. In this case, full sections or offset sections would have created unnecessary complexity in the drawing.

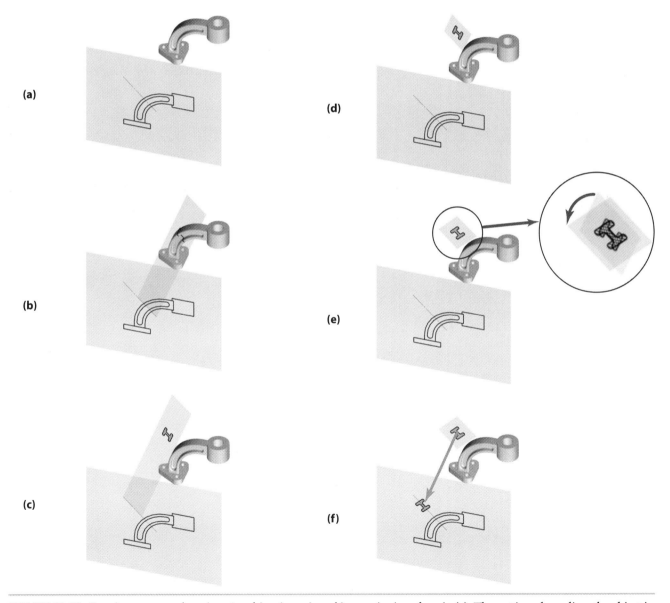

FIGURE 13.53. Creating a removed section. An object is projected into a viewing plane in (a). The cutting plane slices the object in (b). The image of the intersection is removed from the object in (c). The removed image is initially perpendicular to the viewing plane in (d) but is then rotated to be parallel to the viewing plane in (e). The removed image is finally projected onto the viewing plane in (f).

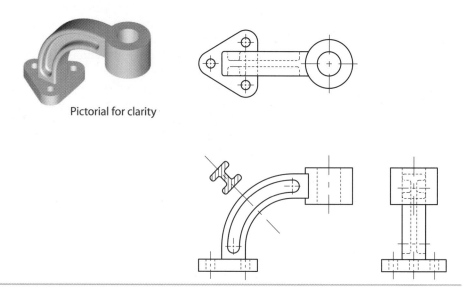

Pictorial for clarity

FIGURE 13.54. A removed section as it would be placed on an engineering drawing.

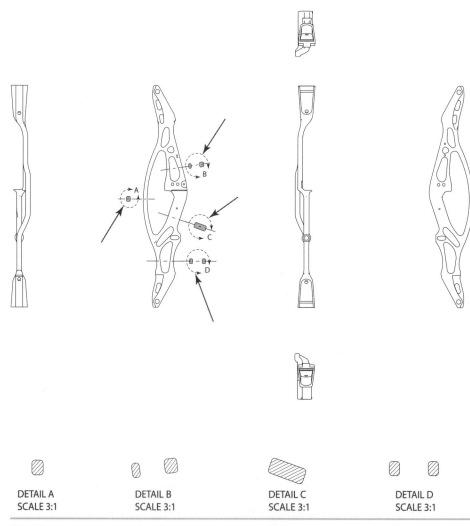

DETAIL A
SCALE 3:1

DETAIL B
SCALE 3:1

DETAIL C
SCALE 3:1

DETAIL D
SCALE 3:1

FIGURE 13.55. Use of removed sections on the Hoyt AeroTec bow example.

13.10 Revolved Sections

Revolved sections are created in a manner similar to that of removed sections. A hypothetical procedure for creating a revolved section image is shown in Figure 13.56.

In this figure, a cutting plane intersects the object in the area of interest and the image of the intersection is imprinted on the plane. The cutting plane should be parallel to one of the principal views or perpendicular to the major surfaces of the part where the cut is made in order to reveal its true sizes. The cutting plane is rotated by 90 degrees such that the arrows point into the page on a drawing. The axis of rotation of the intersection image is on the cutting plane, parallel to the cutting plane line, and through the geometric center of the image. Unlike the removed section, the cutting

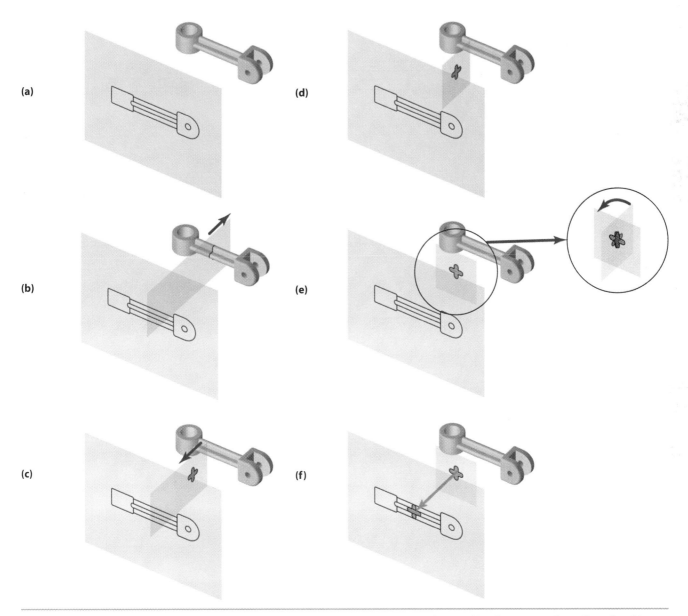

(a)

(b)

(c)

(d)

(e)

(f)

FIGURE 13.56. Creating a revolved section. An object is projected onto a viewing plane in (a). The cutting plane slices the object in (b). An image of the intersection is removed in (c). The intersection image is initially perpendicular to the viewing plane in (d) and then rotated to be parallel to the viewing plane in (e). The image is projected onto the viewing plane in (f).

plane is not removed from the object. Thus, the image of the intersection is superimposed on the orthogonal view. The complete revolved section view, as would be seen in an engineering drawing, is shown in Figure 13.57. Since a revolved section view is constructed at the location of the cutting plane line, there is no need to label the view.

The scale of the revolved section must be the same as for the principal views, and its orientation must follow the rules of multiview presentation. For views where the surfaces created by a hypothetical cut are relatively small compared to the remaining surfaces of the view, revolved sections are another good option for improving clarity while reducing effort and complexity in a drawing. Revolved sections should not be used when the section image interferes significantly with other features in the principal view. Figure 13.58 shows another example where the use of revolved sections is convenient.

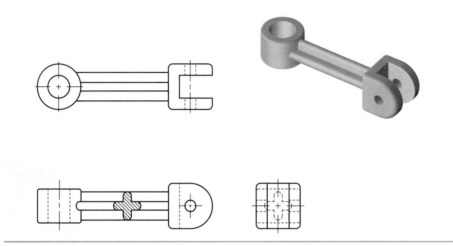

FIGURE 13.57. A revolved section as it would be placed on an engineering drawing.

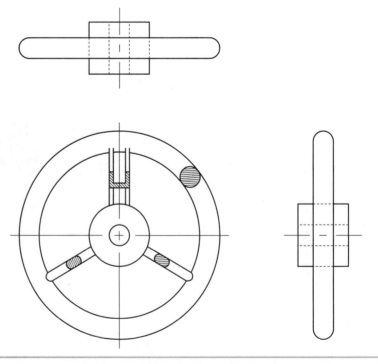

FIGURE 13.58. An example of a part with multiple revolved sections.

13.11 Broken-Out Sections

A **broken-out section** can be used when the internal feature to be revealed is a small portion of the entire object and a full section would not reveal additional details of interest. Use of a broken-out section in this manner would decrease the size and complexity of a drawing, as well as reduce the effort required to make it.

A broken-out section, as with the revolved and removed sections, offers the convenience of slicing only a fraction of the entire object when only a small slice is needed to define an internal geometry. However, a broken-out section offers the added convenience of not requiring the cutting plane to go all the way through the part. With all of the other sections you have studied so far, cutting plane lines start in space, go through the part, and end in space. With a broken-out section, the ends of the cutting plane line can be wholly or partially embedded in the part, as shown in Figure 13.59, where a cutting plane that has its extent limited to the area immediately surrounding a feature is

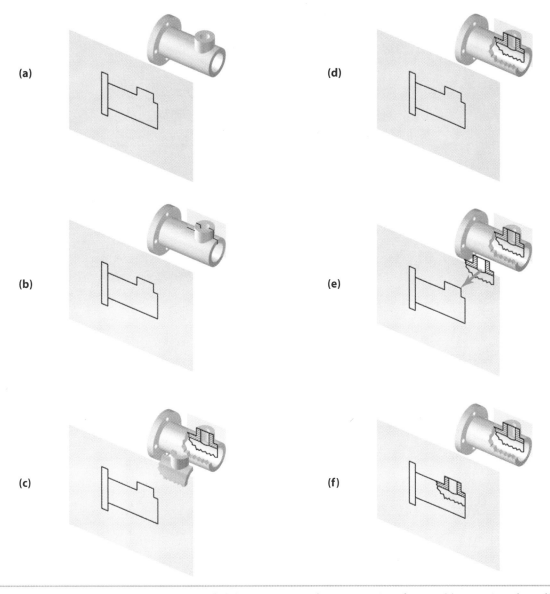

FIGURE 13.59. Creating a broken-out section. The object is projected onto a viewing plane on (a). A cutting plane slices through the feature of interest (but not the entire part) in (b). The portion in front of the cutting is broken out and removed in (c). The interior details of the feature are shown in (d). The image of these features is projected forward in (e) and placed directly on the part image in (f).

imbedded into the part. A piece of the object that is opposite the viewing direction is then hypothetically broken off to reveal the interior details of the feature.

The portion of the cutting plane that is embedded in the part is shown on the section view as an irregular edge to emphasize that the part would hypothetically be broken to reveal the interior details shown at that location. The broken-out-section view may be shown on the corresponding orthogonal view, as shown in Figure 13.60, or in a separate detail view, as shown in another example in Figure 13.61.

FIGURE 13.60. A broken-out section as it would be placed on an engineering drawing.

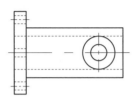
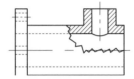

FIGURE 13.61. A broken-out section used to reveal some pocket details of the Hoyt AeroTec bow.

E

DETAIL E
SCALE 2:1

FIGURE 13.62. The method for showing the assembly of many parts.

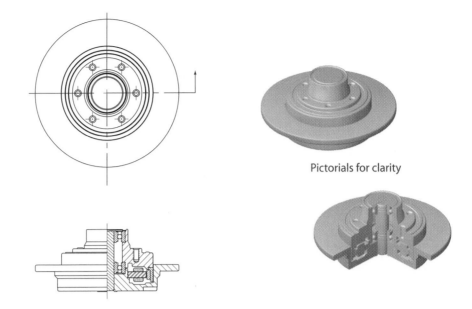

Pictorials for clarity

13.12 Sections of Assemblies

Section views are commonly used in drawings that show multiple parts in their intended mating configuration to illustrate proper alignment of different features between the parts. When multiple parts are sectioned, as in Figure 13.62, it is advisable to use a different section line pattern for each part in order to distinguish the different parts easily. In everyday practice, assemblies that include pins, keys, shafts, or bolts usually do not show these items sectioned even though the cutting plane line may pass through them. These items usually have standardized geometries and sizes; thus, their sections add little information to a drawing and may even detract from the information presented by parts of greater interest.

13.13 A Few Shortcuts to Simplify Your Life

As with many other engineering drawing practices, acceptable shortcuts for creating section views can be used to reduce the time it takes to create a drawing and/or to minimize possible misinterpretation of a drawing. With all of the shortcuts presented next, the main question you need to ask yourself before using any of them is, "Will this approximation or shortcut increase or decrease the speed and accuracy of interpretation of the drawing?" If the speed or accuracy of interpretation decreases, the shortcuts should not be used.

13.13.01 Small Cutouts on Curved Surfaces

A shortcut is allowed when there is a small hole or another cutout on a curved surface. Figure 13.63, for example, shows a small hole and slot on a tube compared to larger cutouts. If a true projection of these features were made, the orthogonal views would show a curved depression on the surface of the tube. The shape of this curve is complex and would take some time to create. Since in most applications the size of the depression on the surface is unimportant, the depression is not shown on the orthogonal views. The true projection of these features and the accepted shortcut are shown in Figure 13.63. This approximation makes the drawing easier to create, with very little loss of information. However, when the cutouts are large or the size of the depression cannot be ignored in the function of the part, the true projection should be used. What is considered "small" is rather subjective.

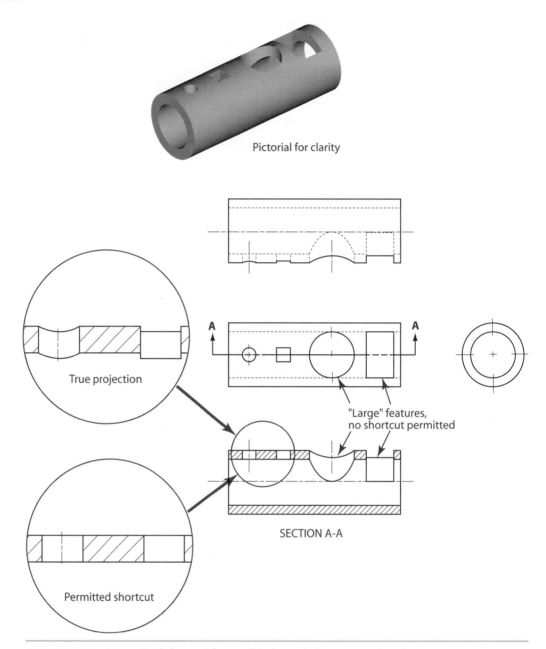

FIGURE 13.63. A permitted shortcut for small holes and slots in curved surfaces.

13.13.02 Threaded Parts

Another shortcut is in the representation of a threaded part, such as the pneumatic fitting shown in Figure 13.64. A thread on the outside of a bolt or screw or the inside of a nut has many complex curved surfaces that would result in a very complicated drawing, especially if it were created with manual instruments or 2-D CAD. Much simpler representations of internal and external threads are included in Figure 13.62. These schematic representations are easier to construct, with very little loss of information, especially since thread sizes are mostly standardized based on the diameter of the part. A note and arrow are required to specify the precise thread sizes. Methods for the complete specification of thread sizes can be found in most machinists' or engineers' handbooks.

FIGURE 13.64. A section of a threaded part.

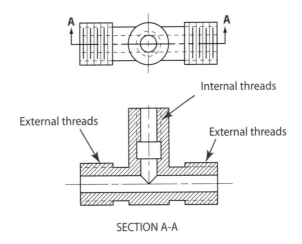

SECTION A-A

13.13.03 Thin Features

For sectioned features that have relatively small thickness when compared to the remainder of a sectioned part, it is acceptable not to fill these features with section lines even when cutting plane lines pass directly through them. As an example, consider the objects in Figure 13.65. These two objects are composed of the same main body but

FIGURE 13.65. The conventional section (a) and recommended variation for a thin feature (b).

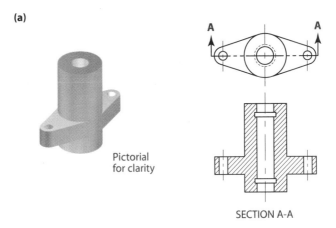

(a)

Pictorial for clarity

SECTION A-A

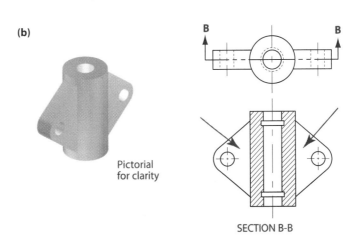

(b)

Pictorial for clarity

SECTION B-B

FIGURE 13.66. The recommended presentation of thin webs.

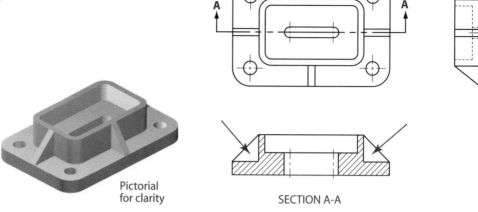

Pictorial
for clarity

SECTION A-A

with mounting flanges turned differently. In both cases, the cutting plane line goes through both the main body and the flanges. For the part in (a), the thickness of the two flanges in the section view is about the same as the depth of the main body. In this case, the flanges are filled with section lines, as normal. For the part in (b), the thickness of the two flanges in the section view is a fraction of the depth of the main body. In this latter case, it is acceptable not to fill the flanges with section lines because doing so may give an immediate false impression that the flanges are about the same thickness as the main body. As an alternative to not filling thin features with section lines, it is permissible to use a different section line pattern for spokes and vanes than is used for the main body of the object. Note that for this shortcut, an extra edge must exist to separate the thin feature from the main body in the section view. Webs and fins, such as those shown in Figure 13.66, are generally treated in this manner.

13.13.04 Vanes, Fins, Spokes, and the Like

Objects with axially symmetric features such as vanes and spokes, as shown in the two parts in Figure 13.67, also are not filled with section lines even when cutting plane lines pass directly through them. Filling such features with section lines may give the false impression that the features are solid throughout the part. It also is permissible to use a different section line pattern for spokes and vanes than is used for the main body of the object. Note that for this shortcut, an extra edge must exist to separate spokes and vanes from the main body in the section view.

13.13.05 Symmetry

An interesting exception to the rules of true projection occurs when parts with rotational symmetry, which means that the part can be divided into identical wedges along an axis, are sectioned. Note that rotational symmetry is different from the planar symmetry discussed in Chapter 3, where the image of an entire object can be created by reflecting a portion of it on a plane. For example, examine the part shown in Figure 13.68. This part has one-third rotational symmetry, with three thin support ribs and three holes about the center tube.

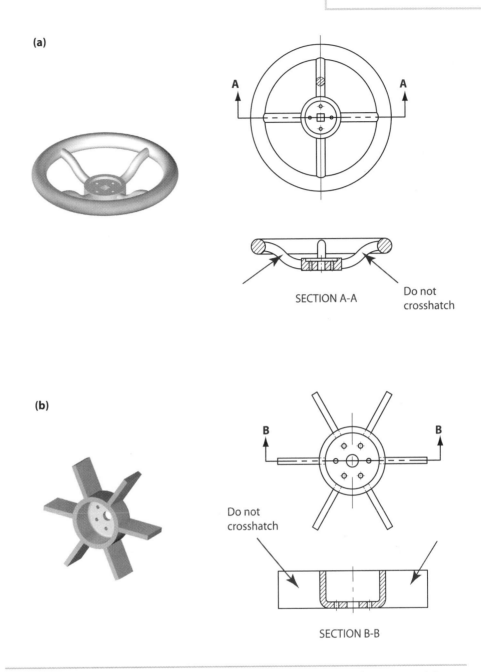

(a)

(b)

FIGURE 13.67. Two examples of the recommended presentation of spoke, vanes, and fins.

A multiview drawing created using true projection would be like that shown in Figure 13.68. Using a true projection for the front view in this case has some problems. First, using instruments or 2-D CAD, the projection is rather difficult to create. Also, the true projection of the side view may have the negative effect of representing the part as being nonsymmetrical.

An acceptable shortcut for this drawing also is included in Figure 13.68. This drawing is easier to create and gives the impression that the part is symmetrical. The top view clarifies any possible misinterpretation about the number and locations of the support ribs. Interestingly, if the part had one-quarter (or higher) symmetry, for example, four (or more) support ribs instead of three, the front view would be exactly the same as the part with one-third symmetry.

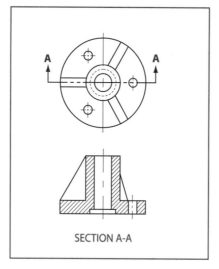

SECTION A-A

True projection

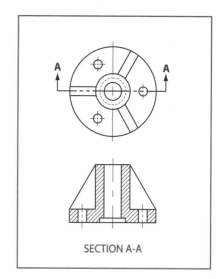

SECTION A-A

Preferred presentation

FIGURE 13.68. The preferred presentation of symmetrical features.

CAUTION

Creating section views is still part science and part art. Even though the rules of orthographic projection generally must be followed (except for the shortcuts mentioned), engineers, designers, and drafters are allowed considerable freedom in choosing when and where section views should be used, what type of section to use, and what presentation method to use. However, experienced people who are required to read and interpret drawings expect certain rules to be followed when the drawings are created; and deviation from these rules may cause confusion. Beginners are sometimes prone to poor choices and errors. In the best case, the person reading the drawing can interpret it because the necessary information is still contained on the remaining views. Still, errors can cause confusion and slow down the process of interpreting the drawing. In a more serious case, errors cause ambiguity that makes the drawing impossible to interpret correctly. In a worst-case scenario, the errors may cause the part to be interpreted as an entirely different part than originally desired. The following sections of this text are a compilation of the most common beginners' errors and ways to avoid them.

Cutting Through Only a Piece of an Internal Feature

Section views should be constructed to reveal true sizes. For example, consider the object shown in Figure 13.67. The full section cuts through the center of the large bore, revealing the true measurable sizes of the diameters inside. The cutting plane line goes through two holes, but not at their centers. The resulting section shows the two holes not at their true diameters. This section may be easily misinterpreted as having hole diameters that are smaller than they really are. A better way to section the object is to use an offset section in which the cutting plane line goes through the center of all of the internal features revealed, also shown in Figure 13.69.

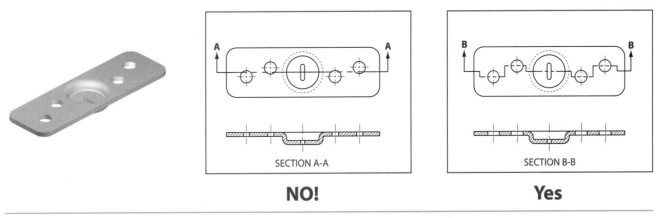

FIGURE 13.69. A common error: Cutting through a feature such that its true size is not shown.

Forgetting the Rest of the Object

A proper full or offset section shows the object as if it had been cut, including any background edges that still may appear outside the cut surfaces. Sometimes it is easy to forget these background edges because the cut surfaces are usually of prime importance. Nevertheless, for a full or offset section to be correct, the background edges must be included, mostly for use as reference locations for the cut surfaces, as shown in Figure 13.70.

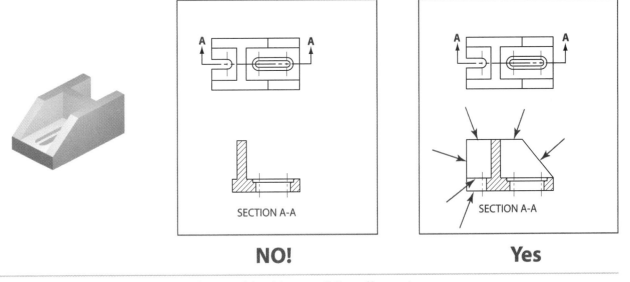

FIGURE 13.70. A common error: Forgetting the rest of the object on a full or offset section.

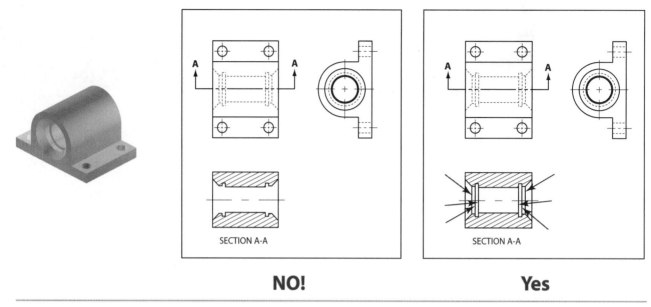

FIGURE 13.71. Forgetting internal edges made visible.

Forgetting Back Edges That Are Made Visible

Newly revealed internal edges also are often carelessly omitted. Edges of grooves, counterbores, cross holes, and other similar features have edges that become visible once the object is cut, as shown in Figure 13.71. Neglecting to include these edges may cause confusion about the true geometry of the features.

Incorrect Rotation Orientation

Sometimes in a hastily created section view, the rotational orientation of the view is incorrect, as shown in Figure 13.72. Section views are created and presented using the rules of orthogonal projection and multiview presentation. Even though a section view is forgiven the requirement of proper position alignment with the other orthogonal views (for purposes of drawing convenience), the requirement for proper rotational orientation still exists. Recall that a cutting plane line on an orthogonal view is the edge view of a cutting plane that is perpendicular to that view. Incorrect rotational orientation of the section view may cause confusion with its interpretation.

Viewing the Object from the Wrong Side

The arrows of a cutting plane line point in the viewing direction. A common error, as shown in Figure 13.73, is to show the section view looking at the piece of the object that should have been removed, rather than the piece that is to remain. The areas that have been cut (i.e., the areas that are filled with section lines) are the same for both pieces. However, the background edges and the rotational orientation of the object may be incorrect.

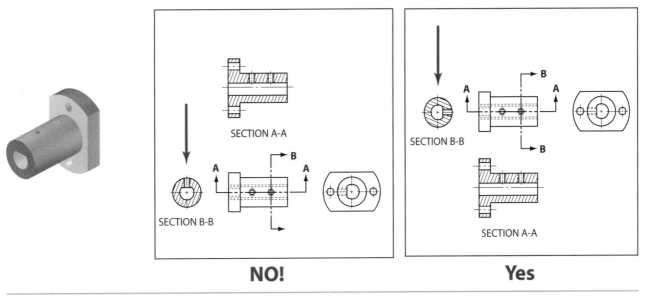

FIGURE 13.72. A common error: Rotational orientation of the section view is incorrect.

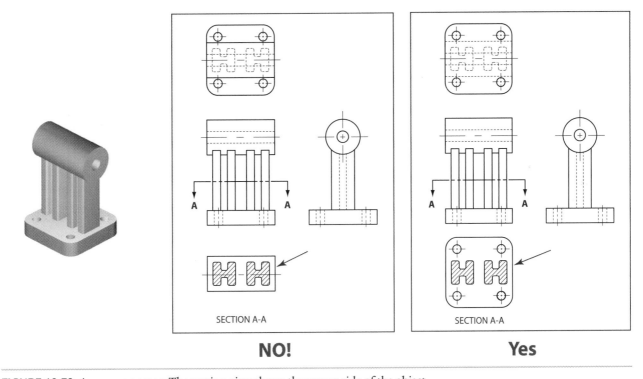

FIGURE 13.73. A common error: The section view shows the wrong side of the object.

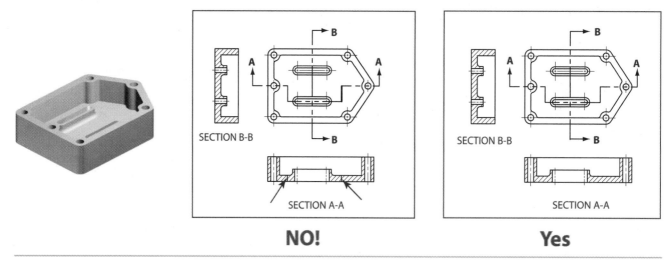

FIGURE 13.74. A common error: Step lines are not removed from the offset section.

Including Step Lines on an Offset Section

The steps in an offset section, as shown in Figure 13.74, create edges; but leaving these edges on a section view is considered improper. Therefore, they should be removed. Actually, if you were to follow the rules of orthogonal projection strictly, the edges created by the changes in direction of the cutting plane should be shown. However, someone in the past thought a nicer-looking drawing would result from their removal; thus, the practice remains today. Until this practice is formally changed, the edges in an offset section should be removed.

No View Label or View Scale

To avoid confusion with parts that have multiple section views, every full or offset section view must be labeled with the same letters used to identify their respective cutting plane line, as shown in Figure 13.75. This labeling is practiced even when only one section view is on the drawing. Half, revolved, and broken-out section views have the same scale as the view on which it was created. Full, offset, and removed section views are allowed to be a different scale than the view on which they were created. However, whenever there is a change in scale, the new scale must be clearly labeled on the view.

Section Lines with Poor Spacing or Angle

Section lines should be created in such a manner that they are easily recognizable as section lines. Section lines should be easily distinguishable from edges on the part. If the section line density is too low or if the angle of the section lines matches the angle of some of the edges of the part, as shown in Figure 13.76, there may be confusion between the section lines and the edges of the part. On the other hand, too dense a section line pattern is difficult to reproduce cleanly when the drawing is printed, copied, or transmitted.

FIGURE 13.75. A common error: No scale or view is missing labels.

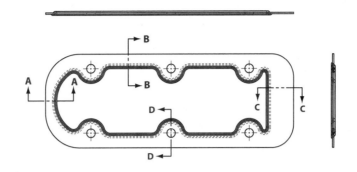

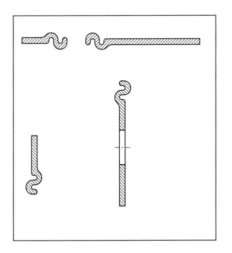

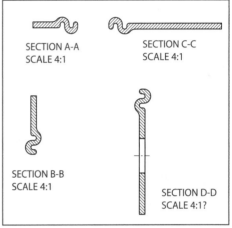

SECTION A-A
SCALE 4:1

SECTION C-C
SCALE 4:1

SECTION B-B
SCALE 4:1

SECTION D-D
SCALE 4:1?

NO!   **Yes**

FIGURE 13.76. A common error: Poor choice of cross-hatching.

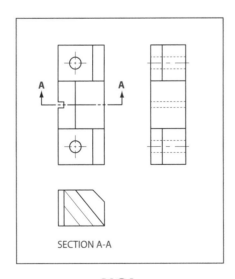

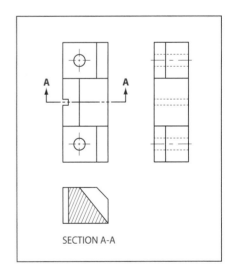

SECTION A-A

SECTION A-A

NO!   **Yes**

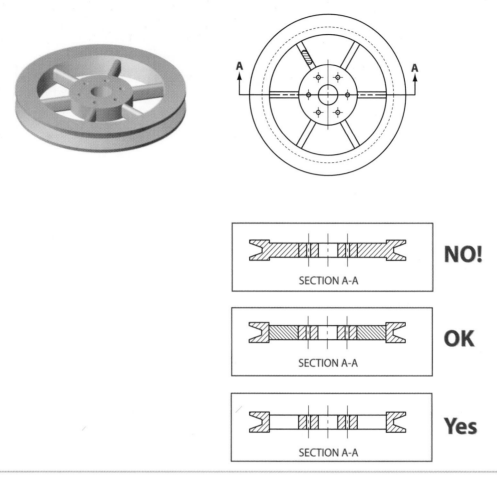

FIGURE 13.77. A common error: Cross-hatching in vanes or spokes.

Filling Vanes or Spokes with Section Lines

Filling spokes or vanes with section lines, as shown in Figure 13.77, gives an immediate but false impression that the object is solid throughout the spoke or vane area. Spokes and vanes should not be filled at all or should be filled with a different section line pattern than is used for the rest of the sectioned object.

Common Section Line Pattern on Different Parts in an Assembly

A common section line pattern used for different parts in a sectioned assembly, as shown in Figure 13.78, gives the immediate but false impression that the separate parts are a single part. Different parts in a sectioned assembly, even when they are made of the same material, should be filled with section lines that are of different patterns.

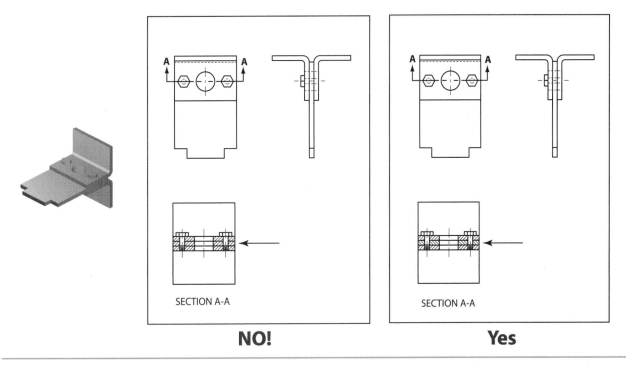

FIGURE 13.78. A common error: The same cross-hatch pattern for different parts in an assembly.

13.14 Considerations for 3-D Modeling

With solids modeling software, parts are initially modeled as a series of protrusions and cuts to create a 3-D graphical model of a part. The solids modeling software creates a mathematical model of the geometry from which the projections of the object are used to create drawings. Once the solids model is created, it is usually a simple matter to extract a front view, side view, or any of the other orthogonal views from the model. A section view is created merely as another orthogonal view, but with a portion of the object removed. The ease with which section views can be created from a solids model has many advantages, but also some disadvantages. The greatest advantage is the speed and accuracy with which section views can be created. With most software, creating additional views is simply a matter of specifying the cutting plane and viewing direction and then picking a location on the drawing where the new view is to appear. Cutting planes can be specified as existing or newly created reference planes. Creating stepped cutting plane lines in the views of interest usually specifies offset cutting planes. The process is often a matter of a few strokes on a keyboard or a few clicks with a mouse or another pointing device. The time required is usually only a few seconds. Also, accurate orthogonal projection of features that were previously represented by shortcut practices, such as small cutouts in curved surfaces or thin symmetrical features, are very easy to create. In fact, with most software, it would be difficult to create a view that is *not* an accurate projection. Using section lines to fill areas that were formerly solid is also a rather simple matter. The software identifies the newly cut surfaces and automatically fills them. All the software user needs to do is specify the section line pattern to be used and modify it if necessary.

The selection of where to section an object to view its interior or the type of section to use is still up to the person making the drawing. One disadvantage of the nearly automatic section creation offered by 3-D modeling is that in some cases, the modeling becomes too accurate. Many of the shortcuts and clarification practices used in traditional drafting are no longer available in some software. For example, a section through a spoke or vane used in a 3-D model would show the spoke or vane filled with section lines, not blank as would be preferred. Also, all projections would be true projections. With an object of odd rotational symmetry, there would be no opportunity to modify the projection to create a symmetrical presentation, as would be preferred. With some software, the step edges of an offset section may be visible in the section view, and not removed as is practiced.

Another disadvantage of 3-D modeling is that manual creation of section views has been a traditional method of developing spatial reasoning and mental imaging skills. When the process is too automatic with software, a person may not adequately develop these skills in the absence of the software and may become too dependent on the software. When faced with multiple section views in a shop drawing, that person may not be able to create a mental image of the part or may not develop the skills necessary to interpret the drawings. Eventually, the person will develop these skills, but it may require exposure to many solids models and their drawings.

13.15 Chapter Summary

With many complex objects, looking only at the exterior may not fully reveal all of their features. The use of section views is a method of looking at the internal details of such objects. The section process involves using a hypothetical cutting plane to hypothetically cut an object into pieces so the interior details one or more features. These features can then be examined more closely, specified in such a manner that the details can be fabricated and inspected to ensure that they meet the desired specifications. On an engineering drawing, the cutting plane appears in an edge view called a cutting plane line. Several types of section views are available for use at the discretion of the drafter, depending on the desired presentation. Whichever type is used, certain rules and practices must be followed to ensure that these views can be interpreted easily and quickly without ambiguity. Of primary importance is that the rules of orthogonal projection and multiview presentation be used.

13.16 glossary of key terms

broken-out section: The section view produced when the cutting plane is partially imbedded into the object, requiring an irregular portion of the object to be removed before the hypothetically cut surface can be seen.

cutting plane: A theoretical plane used to hypothetically cut and remove a portion of an object to reveal its interior details.

cutting plane line: On an orthographic view of an object, the presentation of the edge view of a cutting plane used to hypothetically cut and remove a portion of that object for viewing.

cutting segment: On a stepped cutting plane for an offset section view, that portion of the plane that hypothetically cuts and reveals the interior detail of a feature of interest.

full section: The section view produced when a single cutting plane is used to hypothetically cut an object completely into two pieces.

half section: The section view produced when a single cutting plane is used to hypothetically cut an object up to a plane or axis of symmetry, leaving that portion beyond the plane or axis intact.

offset section: The section view produced by a stepped cutting plane that is used to hypothetically cut an object completely into two pieces. Different portions of the plane are used to reveal the interior details of different features of interest.

removed section: The section view produced when a cutting plane is used to hypothetically remove an infinitesimally thin slice of an object for viewing.

13.16 glossary of key terms

revolved section: The section view produced when a cutting plane is used to hypothetically create an infinitesimally thin slice, which is rotated 90 degrees for viewing, on an object.

section lines: Shading used to indicate newly formed or cut surfaces that result when an object is hypothetically cut.

section view: A general term for any view that presents an object that has been hypothetically cut to reveal the interior details of its features, with the cut surfaces

perpendicular to the viewing direction and filled with section lines for improved presentation.

step segment: On a stepped cutting plane for an offset section view, that portion of the plane that connects the cutting segments and is usually perpendicular to them but does not intersect any interior features.

viewing direction: The direction indicated by arrows on the cutting plane line from the eye to the object of interest that corresponds to the tail and point of the arrow, respectively.

13.17 questions for review

1. When should a section view be used?

2. What does a cutting plane line represent?

3. What does the area filled with section lines on a section view represent?

4. What are some guidelines concerning good drafting practice in creating section line patterns?

5. What is the significance of the direction of the arrow on a cutting plane line?

6. Why is it important that the rotational orientation of a section view, even if it is moved, be maintained as if it were an orthogonal view?

7. When should an offset section be used instead of a full section?

8. When should revolved or removed sections be used instead of full or offset sections?

9. Under what conditions should certain areas on a section view not be filled with section lines even though the cut is through solid material?

13.18 problems

1. In the problem shown in Figure P13.1, the views indicated by the balloons are to be changed to full section views taken along the centerline in the direction indicated by the arrows in the remaining view. For each set of views, select the correct section view from the twenty-four proposed views shown at the right. A section view choice may be used more than once. A correct answer may not be available as a choice.

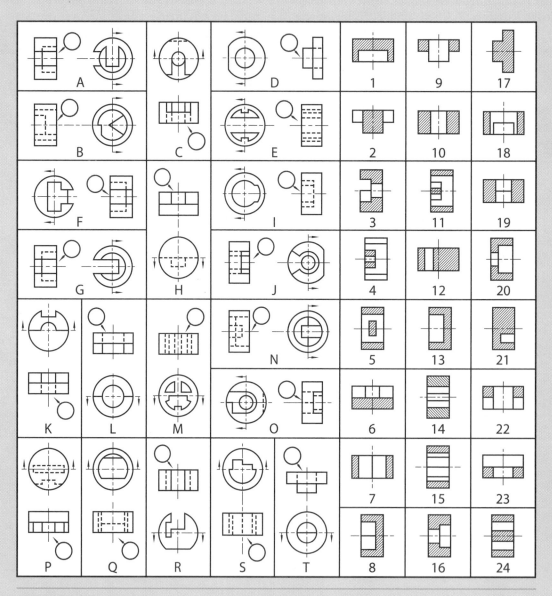

FIGURE P13.1.

13.18 problems (continued)

2. In the problem shown in Figure P13.2, the views indicated by the balloons are to be changed to half section views as indicated by the letters A-A taken along the centerline in the direction in the remaining view. For each set of views, select the correct section view from the twenty-four proposed views shown at the right. A section view choice may be used more than once. A correct answer may not be available as a choice.

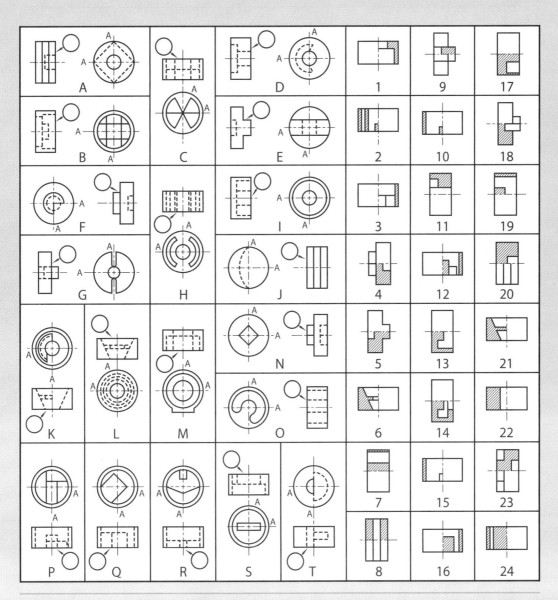

FIGURE P13.2.

13.18 problems (continued)

3. In the problem shown in Figure P13.3, the views indicated by the circles are to be the location of section views. Select the correct section view to complete each problem from the thirty proposed views shown. A section view choice may be used more than once. A correct answer may not be available as a choice.

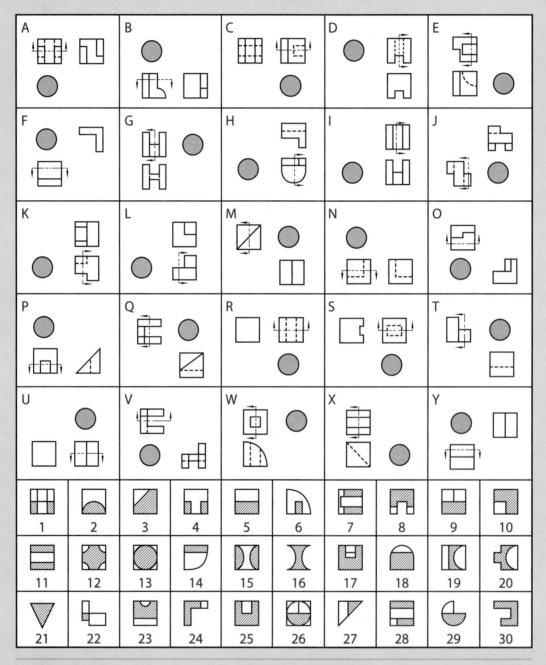

FIGURE P13.3.

13.18 problems (continued)

4. In the problem shown in Figure P13.4, the views indicated by the circles are to be the location of offset section views. Select the correct section view to complete each problem from the thirty proposed views shown. A section view choice may be used more than once. A correct answer may not be available as a choice.

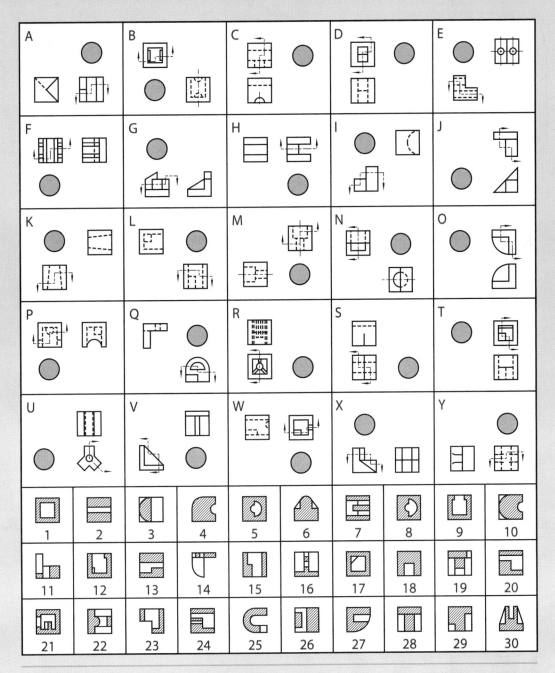

FIGURE P13.4.

13.18 problems (continued)

5. For each object represented in Figure P13.5, create a multiview drawing to fully describe the object, including the indicated full section views to reveal interior detail. When the precise location of the cutting plane line for the full section is not specified, choose the location to best reveal the interior detail.

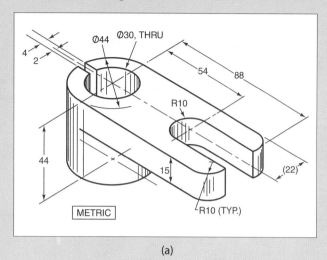

(a)

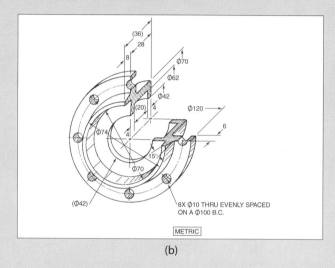

(b)

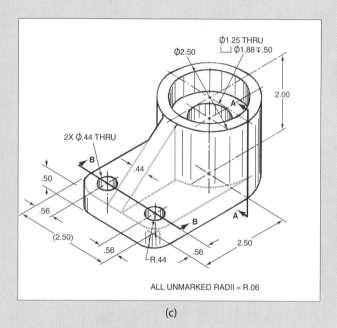

(c)

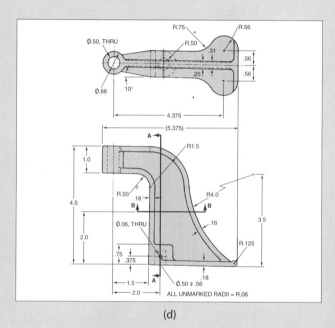

(d)

13.18 problems (continued)

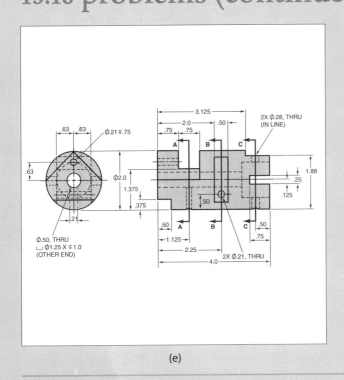

(e)

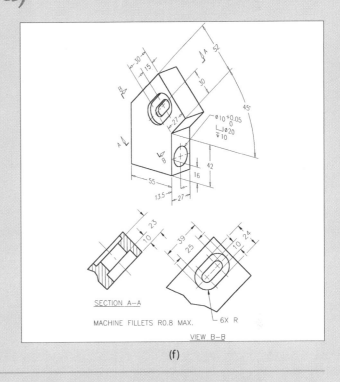

(f)

FIGURE P13.5.

6. For each object represented in Figure P13.6, create a multiview drawing to fully describe the object, including the indicated half section views to reveal interior detail. When the precise location of the cutting plane line for the half section is not specified, choose the location to best reveal the interior detail.

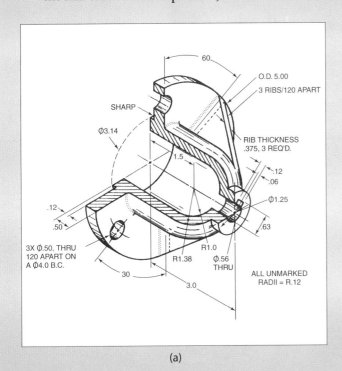

(a)

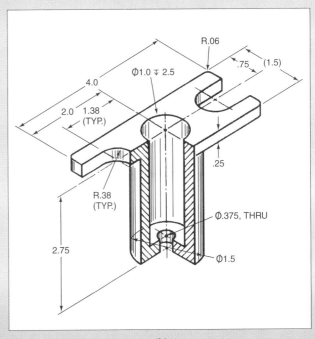

(b)

13.18 problems (continued)

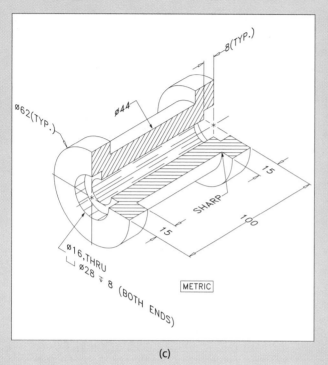

(c)

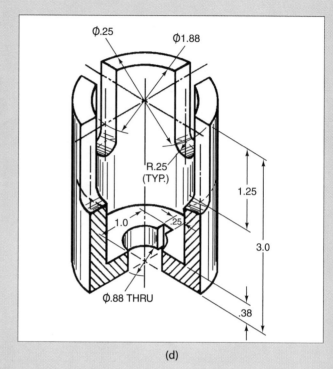

(d)

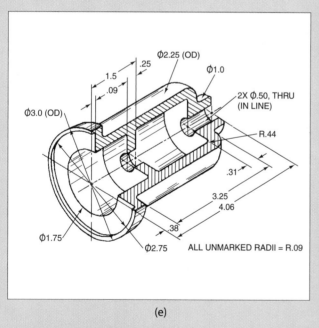

(e)

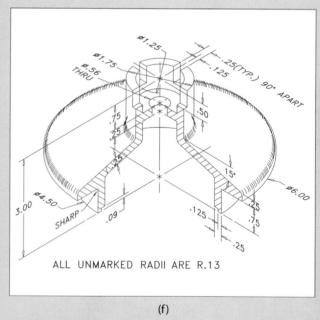

(f)

FIGURE P13.6.

13.18 problems (continued)

7. For each object represented in Figure P13.7, create a multiview drawing to fully describe the object, including the indicated offset section views to reveal interior detail. When the precise location of the cutting plane lines for the offset sections are not specified, choose the locations to best reveal the interior detail.

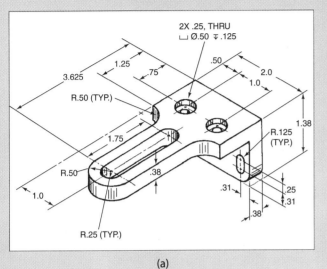

(a)

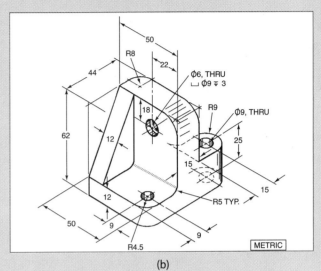

(b)

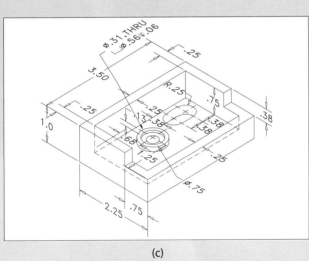

(c)

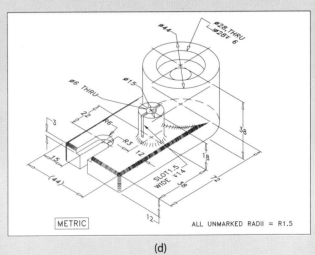

(d)

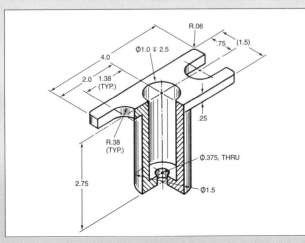

(e)

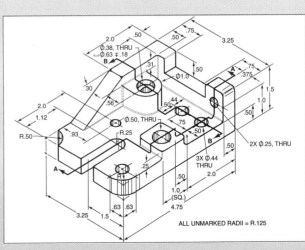

(f)

13.18 problems (continued)

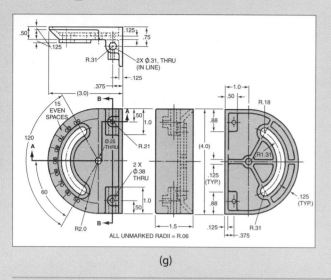

(g)

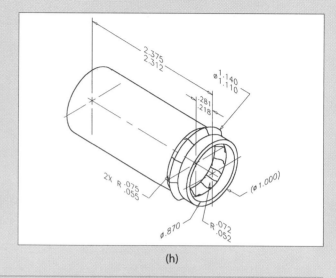

(h)

FIGURE P13.7.

8. For each object represented in Figure P13.8, create a multiview drawing to fully describe the object, including the indicated removed or revolved section views to reveal interior detail. When the precise location of the cutting plane line for the removed or revolved section is not specified, choose the location to best reveal the interior detail.

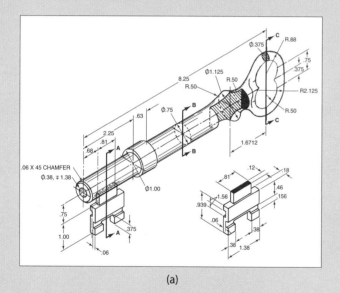

(a)

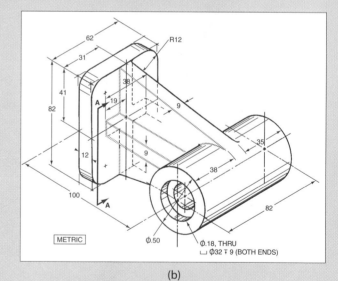

(b)

13.18 problems (continued)

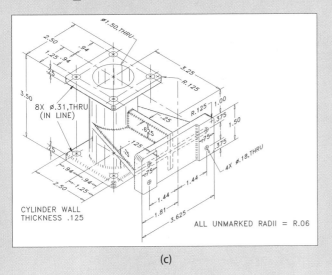

(c)

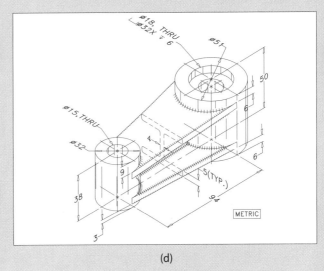

(d)

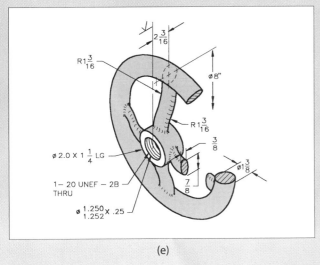

(e)

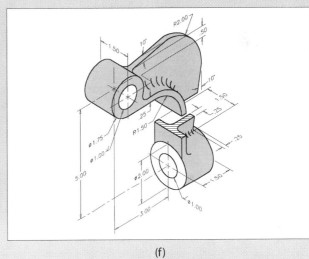

(f)

FIGURE P13.8.

13.18 problems (continued)

9. For each object represented in Figure P13.9, create a multiview drawing to fully describe the object, including the indicated broken-out-section view to reveal interior detail. When the precise location of the broken-out section is not specified, choose the location to best reveal the interior detail.

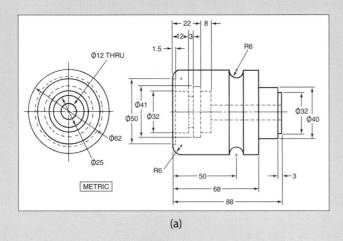

(a)

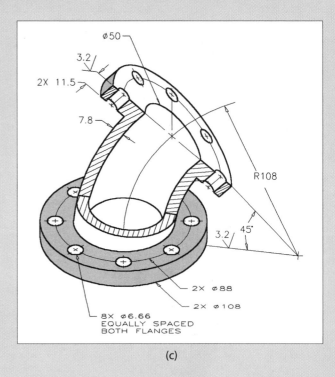

(c)

FIGURE P13.9.

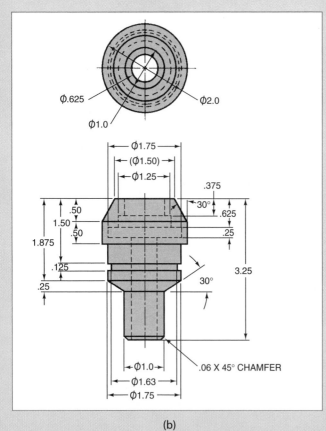

(b)

13.18 problems (continued)

10. For the three objects represented in Figure P13.10, create a multiview drawing to fully describe objects in their assembled state, including a removed section view to reveal the interior detail of how the separate parts are mated.

11. For each object presented in a multiview format in Figures P13.1–P13.10, create an isometric pictorial of the remaining object after it has been sectioned.

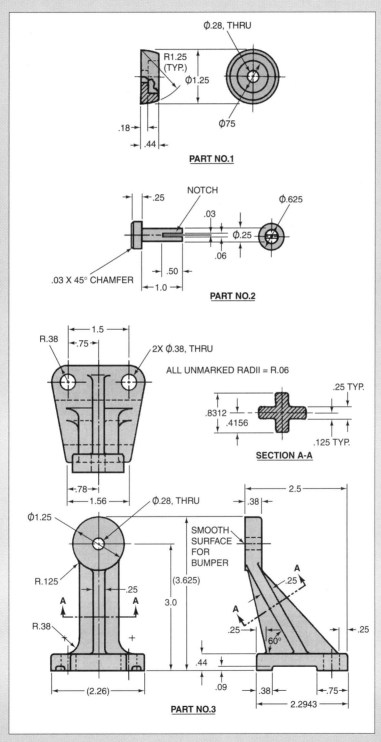

FIGURE P13.10.

15

Dimensioning

objectives

After completing this chapter, you should be able to

- Use the concept of dimensioning
- Explain the idea of tolerance in dimensioning
- Recall the fundamental rules and apply the techniques for dimensioning
- Select appropriate dimensions for a moderately complex part and correctly apply them to a drawing of that part

15.01
introduction

In the previous chapters, you learned how to represent the shape of objects in various ways. You learned about standard ways of representing objects with orthogonal projection techniques, pictorials, sectional views, and auxiliary views. You learned about different techniques for creating solid models and the way parametric, feature-based modeling is used to create 3-D representations of objects. All of this information is great for representing the shape of objects; but at some point, you will want to communicate size information to someone who will construct or manufacture your design. Until your designs are built, you will not be making any money. As with orthogonal projection, there are standard ways of displaying this size information, or dimensions, on drawings. In this chapter, you will examine some of these standards as well as look at some reasons for dimensioning objects in certain ways.

To begin, it is critical that you understand something about how dimensions are formally presented in a design. As you learned in your work with 3-D solid modeling, objects are a combination of features such as rectangular prisms, cylinders, holes, fillets, and chamfers. Recall from solid modeling that most of these features require that they be defined by their **sizes** and their **locations**. For example, the hole in the object shown in Figure 15.01 is considered a feature. The size (.500 diameter) must be given so the person manufacturing the part can select the correct drill bit or cutting tool to machine the hole to the proper size. For engineering drawings, diameters (such as the .500 for this hole) are preceded with the Ø symbol. Location dimensions (1.250 from the right and .750 from the top) are given from the sides of the part to the center of the hole so the machinist can accurately locate the center of the drill bit on that point.

Similarly, the slot in the top of the object shown in Figure 15.02 must also be defined by its size and location. The size of the slot feature is defined by its width (.500) and its height (.250). A location dimension is given from the left side (1.000).

Dimensioning is much like creating constraint-based solid models—you define the size and location of the features within the software, and the part is created "virtually" to your size and location specifications. Figure 15.03 illustrates how the size and location dimensions for a rectangle are used to define an extruded cut in a constraint-based solid modeling program for the object shown in Figure 15.02.

One of the key points you should learn from this chapter is a strategy for determining the types of dimensions required to define a part. You already have a head start through your experiences with 3-D solid modeling software. Following the correct standards for representing dimensions on a drawing is important, but being able to apply the best dimensions to a drawing will impress your boss more than your knowing the standards and applying bad dimensions. For example, imagine you work for a company that manufactures hardware for household doors. Your current project involves the deadbolt lock assembly shown in Figure 15.04. Your boss asks you to design a cover plate where the door meets the doorjamb. You are familiar with the standard ways to represent the shape of the part. One or two views will be enough to describe the shape of the plate, but what are the dimensions needed to manufacture the plate? What are the critical dimensions that must be given? What are some of the standard dimensions that exist on other parts or previous parts? Think about the assembly and these questions because you will return to this example later in the chapter.

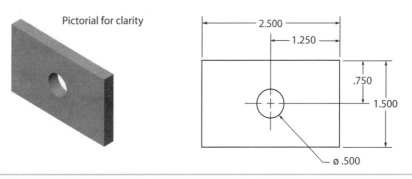

FIGURE 15.01. The size and location of a hole feature.

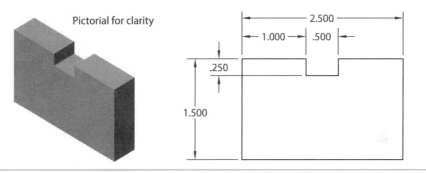

FIGURE 15.02. The size and location of a slot feature.

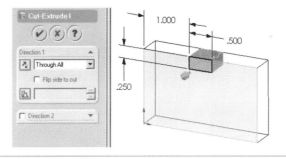

FIGURE 15.03. Defining features in a constraint-based modeling program.

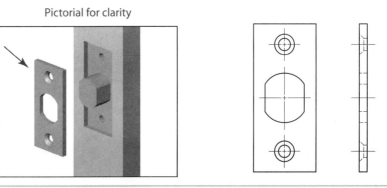

FIGURE 15.04. A deadbolt lock plate.

15.02 Is the Dimension I See on a Drawing Exact?

People are not perfect. When they fabricate metal objects, mold plastic parts, and build houses, some room must be made to account for their imperfection. Even when robots are used to machine parts, there may be some slight imperfection in the resulting object. For machined parts, the amount of variation, or **tolerance**, might be relatively small. There are various ways of including allowable tolerances for a part on a drawing. An example of a note appearing on an engineering drawing might be this:

ALL LINEAR DIMENSIONS ± .010 UNLESS OTHERWISE SPECIFIED.

In the construction industry, tolerances for laying brick or pouring a concrete foundation are typically larger than tolerances on hand-held sized machined parts.

Tolerance dimensions also help with effective size control of finished parts. Examine the assembly of parts in Figure 15.05. For this design, the BUSHING is not supposed to spin inside the WHEEL, but the SHAFT is designed to spin inside the BUSHING. Therefore, the largest diameter of the SHAFT must be just a little smaller than the diameter of the hole in the BUSHING, and the outside diameter of the BUSHING must be just a little larger than the hole in the WHEEL. Dimensioning the hole in the BUSHING and the diameter of the SHAFT as .750 would not communicate the intended type of fit between the two parts. The person putting the parts together would not know whether you wanted the parts to spin freely or be jammed together.

Detail drawings of the BUSHING and the SHAFT are shown in Figure 15.06 and Figure 15.07, respectively. Notice that tolerance dimensions (specifically, limit dimensions) are given to ensure effective size control between the parts. The hole in the BUSHING is dimensioned as .7500–.7512, and the diameter of the SHAFT is given as .7484–.7492. If the parts are manufactured within these specifications, the SHAFT will spin freely within the BUSHING.

FIGURE 15.05. Parts requiring effective size control.

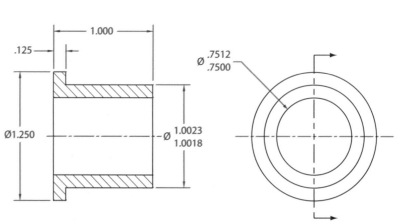

ASSEMBLED

FIGURE 15.06. The detail drawing of the BUSHING.

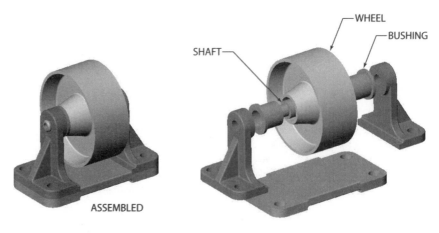

FIGURE 15.07. The detail drawing of the SHAFT.

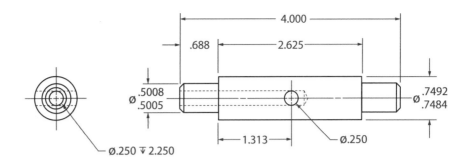

15.03 What Are the Rules for Dimensioning?

As with most topics in engineering graphics, dimensions conform to national, international, and individual company standards. The accepted national standard in the United States for Dimensioning and Tolerancing is **ANSI Y14.5** (currently referenced as *ASME Y14.5M-1994*), which is published by the American Society of Mechanical Engineers (ASME). This standard outlines uniform practices for displaying and interpreting dimensions and related information on drawings and other forms of engineering documentation. The information in *ASME Y14.5M-1994* is important, but do not be too concerned with it right now. Remember, keep trying to figure out what the critical dimensions are, and you will worry about standard dimensioning technique later.

15.03.01 Millimeters, Inches, or Angstroms?

"The 200 meter dash." "First down and 10 yards to go." "Hand me that 2 × 4." These are all examples of length measurements that are familiar to most people. For most track and field events, lengths are defined in meters. In baseball and football, lengths are measured in feet and yards. In the construction industry, decimal or fractional inch measurements are the standard way lengths are defined. Engineering drawings also have standard units of measure. Most drawings conform to the International System of Units (SI), which is metric and uses the millimeter as the standard unit; or they conform to U.S. customary units with a standard unit of the decimal inch. Throughout this chapter, you will see examples using both millimeter and inch dimensions. The next section will discuss how to recognize the differences between the two. Since both standards are used thoughout the United States, it is important that you be able to work with each type. You should be familiar with both standards by the end of the chapter.

15.03.02 Types of Dimensioning

At this point in your class, you may have noticed that your instructor or professor is fairly picky about the way things look on sketches or drawings, mostly because, as was mentioned earlier, engineering drawings do follow standards. Well, here is the first really picky thing about dimensioning that will help you recognize the differences between metric- and inch-based drawings. For metric drawings where millimeters are the standard unit (see Figure 15.08), the following rules apply (*ASME Y14.5M-1994*, p. 5):

1. Where the dimension is less than one millimeter, a zero precedes the decimal point.
2. Where the dimension is a whole number, neither the decimal point nor the zero is shown.
3. Where the dimension exceeds a whole number by a decimal fraction of one millimeter, the last digit to the right of the decimal point is not followed by a zero.
4. Neither commas nor spaces shall be used to separate digits into groups in specifying millimeter dimensions on drawings (e.g., 1000 not 1,000).

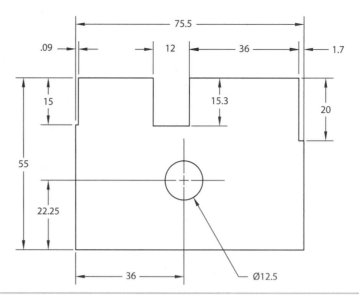

FIGURE 15.08. Millimeter dimensions.

To help distinguish between the two systems, the following rules have been established for decimal inches (*ASME Y14.5M-1994*, pp. 5–6) (see Figure 15.09):

1. A zero is not used before the decimal point for values less than one inch.
2. A dimension is expressed to the same number of decimal places as its tolerance. Zeros are added to the right of the decimal point where necessary.

What does this mean? When dimensioning in millimeters, show leading zeros for values less than 1, but do not show trailing zeros. When using inches, do not show leading zeros for values less than 1, but do show trailing zeros equal to the precision on the drawing.

15.03.03 Fundamental Rules for Dimensioning

As you can imagine, making sure that a drawing created by a designer in Raleigh, North Carolina, can be read by a manufacturer in Detroit, Michigan, or Taipei, Taiwan, requires that some standards be established. The main reason for having standards is

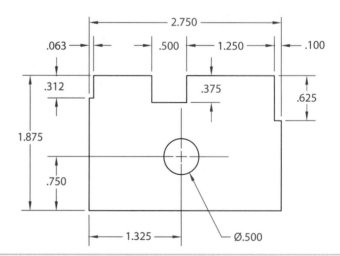

FIGURE 15.09. Dimensioning in inches.

to ensure consistency in the way things are done. Over the last 100 years, individuals in the automotive, aircraft, and military industries and in other industries have refined the standards for dimensioning objects. As mentioned previously, fundamental rules and standards for dimensioning and tolerancing are published in *ASME Y14.5M*. These rules define engineering and design intent clearly. Some of the rules are listed here. (A complete list of the fundamental rules is given at the end of the chapter.)

1. *Each dimension shall have a tolerance.* As was mentioned earlier in the chapter, tolerance dimensioning is necessary to account for human imperfection and to allow for effective size control. If a dimension does not appear as a limit dimension, the tolerance is usually covered by a general note on the drawing or in the title block.

2. *Dimensioning and tolerancing shall be complete so there is full understanding of the characteristic of each feature.* Drawings need to be dimensioned so the manufacturer or construction worker does not have to guess at anything. It is your responsibility to provide all necessary information to produce, manufacture, or build the design.

3. *Each necessary dimension of an end product shall be shown. No more dimensions than those necessary for complete definition shall be given.* As you will see later in the chapter, you do not want to give more dimensions than necessary to describe your design. Show only the dimensions that the person producing the design will need. Taking rule 3 together with rule 2 means you need "just enough" dimensions to define the part—not too many and not too few.

4. *The drawing should define a part <u>without</u> specifying manufacturing methods.* Do not specify that a hole is to be drilled, reamed, punched, or made by any other operation. The person manufacturing your design is responsible for determining the best method for producing the hole.

5. *Dimensions should be arranged to provide required information for optimum readability. Dimensions should be shown in true profile views and refer to visible outlines.* Show the size and location of a hole in the view where the hole shows up as a circle. When the hole is created in the part, it will be located and drilled from that same view. This ensures consistency between the design and the manufacturing of the part. Also, do not dimension hidden features on a part. Find a view where the feature is visible, and dimension in that view.

15.04 Definitions

The following terms are used in the remainder of this chapter. Studying them now will help you better understand the dimensioning concepts that follow. (*Definitions are from *ASME Y14.5M-1994*.)

- **Dimension**—*A numerical value expressed in appropriate units of measure and used to define the size, location, geometric characteristic, or surface texture of a part or part feature.

- **Arrowhead**—A small triangle at the end of dimension lines and leaders to indicate the direction and extent of a dimension (see Figure 15.10).

- **Dimension Line**—A thin, dark, solid line that terminates at each end with arrowheads. The value of a dimension typically is shown in the center of the dimension line. *A dimension line, along with its arrowheads, shows the direction and extent of a dimension (see Figure 15.10).

- **Extension Line**—A thin, dark, solid line extending from a point on an object, perpendicular to a dimension line. *Extension lines are used to indicate the extension of a surface or point to a location preferably outside the part outline (see Figure 15.10). There should be a visible gap between extension lines and

FIGURE 15.10. Dimensioning terminology.

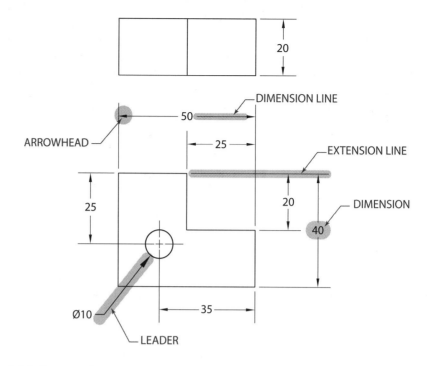

visible lines so the person reading the drawing can distinguish between the part and the dimensions describing the part.

- **Leader**—A thin, dark, solid line terminating with an arrowhead at one end and a dimension, note, or symbol at the other end. *Leaders are used to direct a dimension, note, or symbol to the intended place on a drawing.

15.05 Redundancy is Dumb

As you learn more about dimensioning parts, you will discover that clarity is very important and that a certain amount of economy goes a long way. The machinist is not going to be too happy if you dimension every point in every view on a drawing. He or she is expecting to see only the dimensions that are necessary to manufacture the part. Dimensions should appear only once on a drawing. In addition, each dimension should be placed in the view where the contour shape is best shown. This is known as the **contour rule** or **contour dimensioning**. Examine the part and dimensions shown in Figure 15.11. In (a), too many dimensions are given. It is not necessary to give dimensions to every point in each view. Notice the dimensions in (b). Each dimension is shown only once in the view where the contour or shape for that particular dimension shows up the best. For example, the hole shows up the best in the top view; therefore, it is best to show the size and location of the hole in that view rather than in the front view.

Another example of redundancy that should be avoided is shown in Figure 15.12. This is a very simple example, but notice that one of the horizontal dimensions can be omitted since 20 + 15 + 20 = 55. The same is true for the vertical dimensions since 10 + 20 = 30. The task here is to determine which dimensions are needed most and include just those.

To help you determine which dimensions are most critical, imagine a similar part in a couple of situations. In Figure 15.13(a), notice that the spacer must fit correctly with respect to a couple of different features within the larger part. The tab in the larger part fits into the slot, and the left side of the spacer fits against the right side of the larger part. For the drawing in (b), there is no need to include the dimension of 23 on

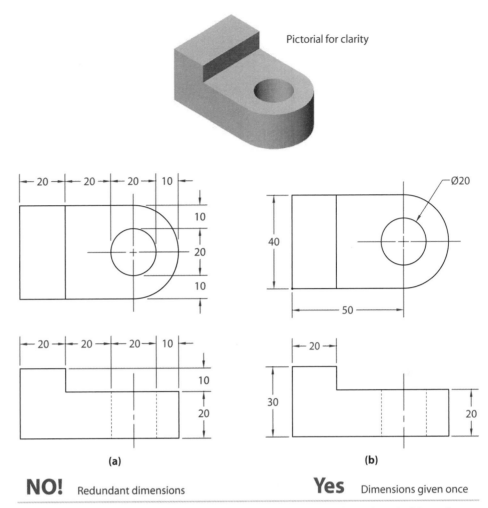

Pictorial for clarity

(a)

NO! Redundant dimensions

(b)

Yes Dimensions given once

FIGURE 15.11. Redundant dimensions in (a) are poor practice. Dimensions in (b) are shown once in the view best suited for viewing.

the right of the part since it is not really critical. The overall dimension is more important in this context. Overall dimensions help to define outer boundaries of parts quickly. Figure 15.13(c) is not appropriate in this situation. The critical dimension of 20 is omitted, and the noncritical dimension of 23 is included. It is being left to chance

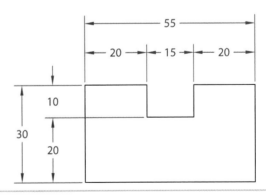

FIGURE 15.12. Redundant dimensions.

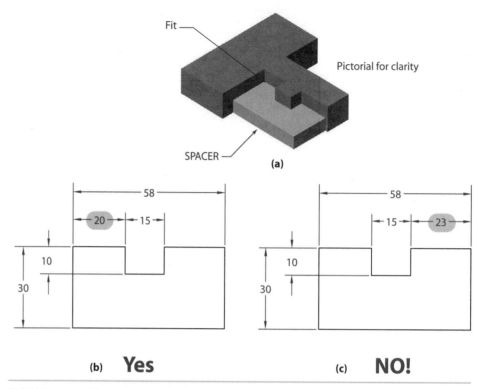

FIGURE 15.13. Dimensions applied, considering the fit and function of the part named SPACER.

that the feature whose size is 20 will be correct based on the other three dimensions being manufactured to their exact correct sizes.

When the "inside" dimensions are more important or more critical than the overall dimension, the overall dimension should be identified as a reference dimension. In Figure 15.14 (a), the two tabs on the spacer fit into two holes in the larger part. In this case, the sizes of the tabs *and* the space between them are critical for the parts to fit together. In this case, the overall dimension is given as a reference dimension so the person making the part does not have to add the three dimensions to figure out the overall size. Reference dimensions, like the overall dimension in (b), are identified by enclosing them in parentheses. Here the person inspecting the parts can use the overall dimension as a quick check.

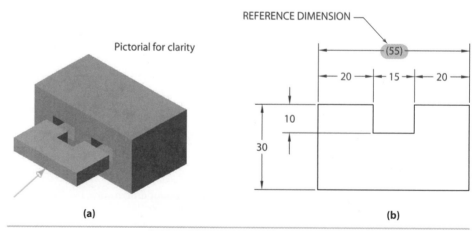

FIGURE 15.14. Reference dimensions.

15.06 Geometrically Correct, but Still Wrong!

Why does it matter what dimensions are given if all of the geometry is defined? It may not matter if you are converting 3-D CAD data *directly* to produce molds for plastic parts, STL (stereolithography) file data for rapid prototyping, or tool paths for CNC machining. However, when drawings are being used to document parts for manufacture, accepted rules and practices must be followed to ensure acceptable results.

15.06.01 Different Ways of Specifying the Same Geometry

One of the first things to recognize when dimensioning objects is that there are standards for specifying particular types of geometry. For example, circles are typically dimensioned as diameters (∅), and arcs are dimensioned as radii (see Figure 15.15). Circles are dimensioned with diameters since they typically represent machined holes, and machined holes are produced with standard tools that are defined by diameter dimensions. If the part in Figure 15.15 is a gasket, the three holes must line up with three holes on mating parts. Therefore, the 35 and the 70 dimensions are important dimensions to include since they identify the centers of the holes. Although the 94 dimension might be of interest to someone knowing the overall width of the object, it is not critical for defining the geometry. For the part shown in (a), the overall width can be determined by adding the 70 to the radii on the ends if necessary.

15.06.02 Identifying and Specifying the Critical Dimensions for Part Function

As you get more experience in engineering and design, one skill you will acquire is the ability to identify the critical dimensions on parts. In fact, by carefully planning the way a part is dimensioned, you may be able to eliminate potential errors in assembly. Examine the SPACER shown in Figure 15.16. The purpose of this part is to make sure the vise assembly stays together when the vise is opened to its maximum width. What are the critical dimensions on the SPACER? Are the overall height and width dimensions critical? To some extent yes, but the most important dimensions are the size of the machined holes and the distance between the two holes. The size of the holes is critical because the cylindrical bars must fit correctly in the holes. The location dimension between the holes is important because it ensures that both bars line up with both holes. For this example, you are going to concentrate on dimensioning the location of the holes.

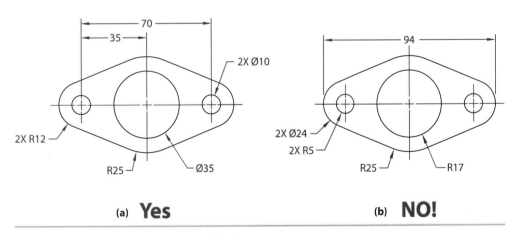

(a) **Yes**   (b) **NO!**

FIGURE 15.15. Proper dimensioning of circles and arcs.

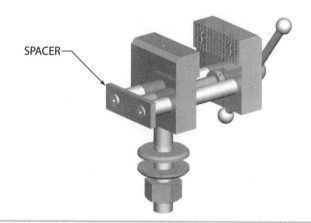

FIGURE 15.16. The vise assembly SPACER.

Figure 15.17 includes two examples of dimensioning the location of the holes on the spacer from the assembly shown in Figure 15.16. You might be asking yourself, why does it matter whether you dimension the holes from the ends of the part (b) or give the dimension between the centers (a)?

Imagine the parts are manufactured according to the fixture shown in Figure 15.18. A jig has been set up such that the SPACER stock material is slid into the jig, held down, and then cut to its overall length of 70 mm. Next, a machinist uses the dimensions on the drawing you prepared to locate and drill the two holes. What happens if during the day of manufacturing parts, the jig begins to slip? By the end of the day, the overall length of the parts are coming out to be 72 mm instead of 70 mm. If the machinist used

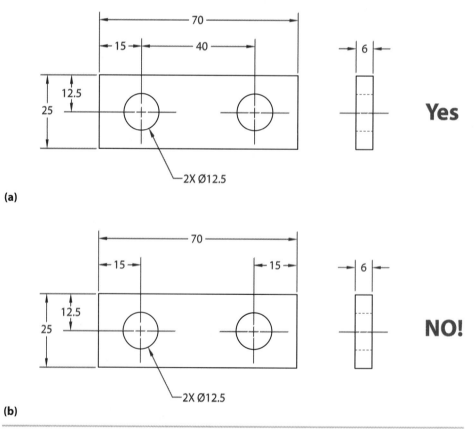

FIGURE 15.17. Two possible dimensioned drawings of the SPACER.

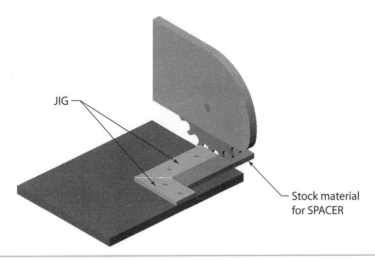

FIGURE 15.18. Cutting the SPACER.

the drawing in Figure 15.17(a) to locate and drill the holes, the parts would not function since the distance between the holes is probably 42 mm instead of 40 mm (72 − 30 = 42). If the drawing in Figure 15.17(b) was used to machine the parts, the overall length would still be incorrect, but the distance between the holes would be right. The SPACER would still function, and the additional material could be removed if necessary.

15.06.03 Baseline versus Chain Dimensioning

There are many different ways to locate features. As mentioned already, starting with an examination of how the part will function within the assembly is the best way to begin determining which dimensions are most important. Two of the main types of dimensioning techniques are baseline and chain.

Baseline dimensioning is illustrated in Figure 15.19. Notice how all of the dimensions in a given direction originate from a base or datum. This type of dimensioning is frequently used for CNC machines that work from a rectangular coordinate system.

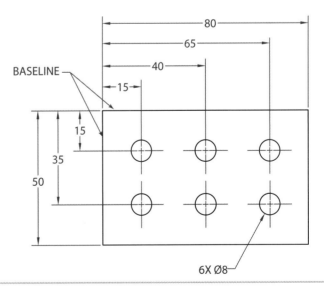

FIGURE 15.19. Baseline dimensioning.

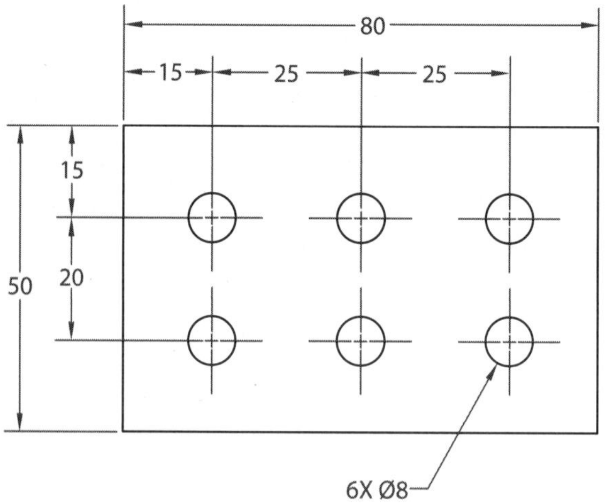

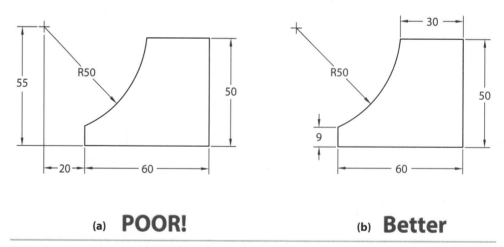

FIGURE 15.20. Chain dimensioning.

Chain dimensioning is shown in Figure 15.20. In this system, features are dimensioned relative to one another. This is appropriate when part function requires that features be related to one another, as discussed previously for the part in Figure 15.17(b). As you will see in the next chapter, chain dimensioning can cause problems with tolerance accumulation; so baseline dimensioning is often preferred, However, there are times when chain dimensioning is appropriate.

15.06.04 What Types of Dimensions Can Be Measured and Checked?

As was discussed earlier, it is important that you give dimensions that make sense to the person who is manufacturing or constructing the object you are designing. When dimensioning holes, you dimension to their centers because the machinist will locate the same points and center the drill bit at that location. When dimensioning parts, you also should select dimensions that can be measured. The object in Figure 15.21(a) is dimensioned to locate the center of the R50 arc. It would be very difficult for the person inspecting the part to locate the center of the arc since it is not on the object. In Figure 15.21(b), the ends of the arc are dimensioned, as well as the radius. This is better practice because the linear dimensions on the final part can be easily checked with standard measuring tools.

(a) POOR!

(b) Better

FIGURE 15.21. Checking the location of an arc center.

15.07 Guidelines to Guide Your Lines

As you dimension more parts, you will get a better idea about where to place particular dimensions. As mentioned earlier in the chapter, showing dimensions in the view where the contour or shape of the object shows up the best is a good global rule to follow. There are some exceptions; but for most parts, following this contour rule is good practice. Figure 15.22(a) shows an example of poor dimensioning. Notice that the contour of the slot shows up the best in the right-side view; but the depth dimension of 16 is given in the top view, and the height dimension of 5 is given in the front. The size and location dimensions for the hole also are not clear in Figure 15.22(a). The diameter of 8 and the location dimension of 30 from the left side should both be in the top view, not the front view. Figure (b) shows the hole correctly dimensioned in the view where its size, location, and shape show up the best (top view).

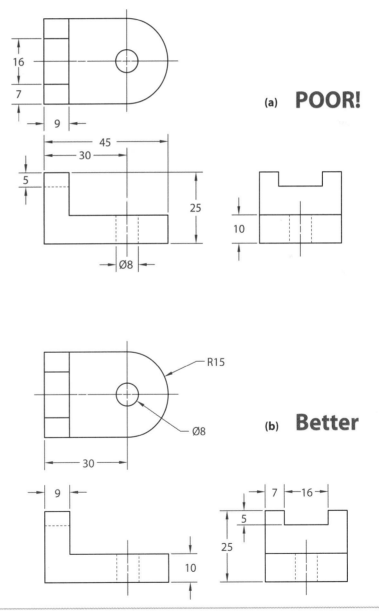

FIGURE 15.22. Contour dimensioning.

As an illustration of the process used in picking the correct view for dimensions, this example can be broken down into smaller steps. Figure 15.23 illustrates a step-by-step feature breakdown of the CONTOUR BLOCK. A solid model of the first feature is shown in Figure 15.23(a). This feature is defined by three dimensions shown in (b): the radius of the arc (R15), the distance from the left side of the part to the center of the arc (30), and the height of the feature (10). Based on following contour dimensioning, the

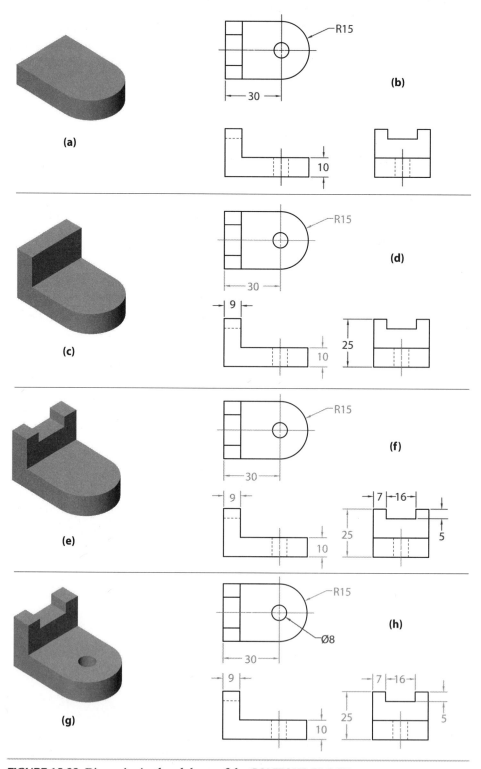

FIGURE 15.23. Dimensioning breakdown of the CONTOUR BLOCK.

R15 and 30 dimensions show up best in the top view; but the 10 dimension is best placed in the front view. The next feature is the extruded piece on the left side of the part shown in Figure 15.22(c). This feature is defined by the two dimensions in (d): the height of the feature from the bottom of the part (25) and the width of the part (9). The front view is the only view where the 9 dimension clearly shows the width of the extrusion. The height of the extrusion (25) can be shown in either the front or right-side views; but since you will be putting other dimensions in the right-side view, it is better to group them. The rectangular cut feature is shown in Figure 15.23(e). This feature is defined by three dimensions in (f): the height of the cut (5), the depth of the cut (16), and a location dimension for the cut (7). The contour of this feature is best seen in the side view, so that is where these three dimensions should be located. The last feature of this part is the hole shown in Figure 15.23(g). Since the hole has the same center as the arc, there is no need for a location dimension. The only dimension necessary for the hole feature is the diameter. Figure 15.23(h) illustrates how this dimension shows up best in the top view, where the hole's contour is most clearly seen.

15.07.01 Solid Lines Only

Another good rule of thumb to follow when dimensioning is to dimension only to visible or solid lines. This is related to the contour rule. In Figure 15.24(a), notice how the extension line of the 10 dimension is related to the hidden line. The dimension is much clearer in figure (b) where the extension line extends from a visible or solid line. Also notice the illustration of this rule on the drawing shown in Figure 15.22.

15.07.02 Placement and Spacing

As you place dimensions on drawings, you should follow established guidelines for the distance that dimensions should be located from views, gaps between extension lines and visible lines, lengths of arrowheads, etc. Figure 15.25 shows the standard practice related to dimension placement and spacing. When someone is looking at your drawing, the first thing that will be noticed will be the object itself. Several conventions and standards help distinguish dimensions from object geometry. As mentioned earlier in the book, visible lines are thick and dark to make the outline and visible edges of the object stand out. Dimension lines, extension lines, and leader lines should be thin and dark. Dimension lines also should be at least 10 mm (.375 inches) from any view, helping to avoid clutter. When dimensions are placed outside other dimensions, there should be at least 6 mm (.25 inches) between dimension lines. The standards for dimensioning also require a visible gap between extension lines and object geometry. Typically, 1 mm (.0625 inches) is a good rule of thumb. Also, extension lines should extend just past their corresponding dimension line (2–3 mm or .125 inches).

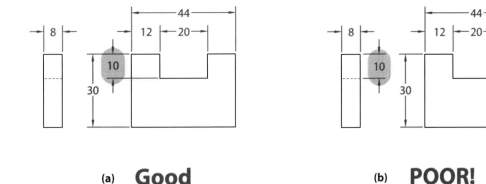

(a) **Good**   (b) **POOR!**

FIGURE 15.24. Dimensioning to solid lines.

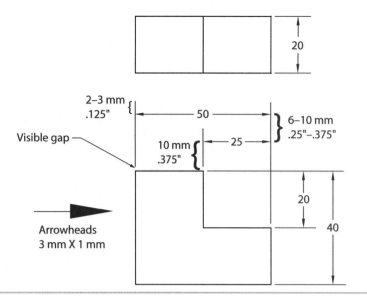

FIGURE 15.25. Dimension placement and spacing.

FIGURE 15.26. Fonts for dimensioning.

15.07.03 Font

Engineering drawings require the use of single-stroke gothic lettering. In addition, letters should be uppercase since few languages worldwide have an upper- and a lowercase. Typical fonts used in CAD software are Century Gothic and Romans.shx (see Figure 15.26).

15.08 Shortcuts

The last 20 years have seen a shift toward the use of symbols to define features on drawings rather than notes written in English. Since many companies have adopted international standards for design and production and they must be able to communicate in a universal language that everyone understands, symbols often lend themselves to clarity of design intent. Some of these symbols are used in the shortcuts representing dimensions for diameters, radii, chamfers, machined holes, threads, and standard features as described in the following sections.

15.08.01 Diameters and Radii

As shown earlier in the chapter in Figure 15.15, circles are dimensioned as diameters using the Ø symbol and arcs are dimensioned as radii using the R symbol. Both symbols are shown preceding the dimension value. For holes, diameter dimensions are usually shown in the view where the hole appears as a circle since that is the view of the part a machinist will see when the hole is being produced. When the diameter of a cylinder is dimensioned, however, the dimension should be placed in the rectangular view of the feature (see Figure 15.27). This helps distinguish holes from positive space cylinders.

Figure 15.28 illustrates several options for dimensioning arcs. When the arc is large enough, as in (a), the leader line and text can be placed on the inside of the arc. In (b), the arc is not large enough to place the text on the inside. In this case, the leader line should extend through the arc with the text on the outside. With small arcs such as (c) and (d), the leader line and the text should be placed on the outside.

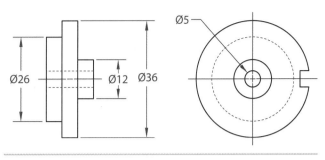

FIGURE 15.27. Dimensioning cylinders and holes.

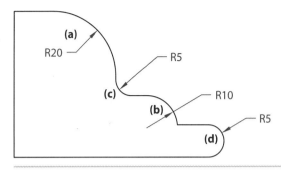

FIGURE 15.28. Dimensioning arcs.

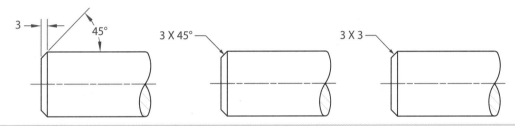

FIGURE 15.29. Dimensioning chamfers.

15.08.02 Chamfers

Chamfers are beveled or angled edges that typically appear on the ends of shafts or fasteners to aid in assembling parts or to smooth out rough edges. They are dimensioned by giving a length from the end of the part and an angle or by specifying two distances. Figure 15.29 illustrates the different options for dimensioning a chamfer.

15.08.03 Standard Machined Holes: Countersinks and Counterbores

The use of symbols also is very important when you are dimensioning the sizes of machined holes such as counterbores, countersinks, spotfaced holes, and blind holes. Take a look at Figure 15.30. Symbols used in the top view represent the different types of machined holes. In these examples, ⊔ represents a counterbore, ∨ represents a countersink, and ▽ is the symbol used for specifying depth. Note that according to standard practice, no manufacturing processes are specified (e.g., drill, ream, or bore).

- Figure 15.30(a) illustrates a standard *drill* hole with a diameter of 8 mm.
- Figure 15.30(b) illustrates a *blind* hole with the same diameter. The depth of 15 is measured from the top surface to the horizontal line at the bottom of the cylindrical portion of the hole, not the point.
- A *counterbore* hole is shown in (c). The 8 diameter indicates the original drill size, the 15 diameter is the size of the counterbore, and the 7 is the depth of the counterbore. Counterbore holes are used to accept fillister head and hex socket head screws.
- Figure 15.30(d) illustrates a *countersink*. The 8 indicates the original drill diameter, the 14 is the diameter of the countersink, and the 82° is the angle of the countersink bit. Countersunk holes are used for applications with flat head and oval head screws.

FIGURE 15.30. Dimensioning the sizes of machined holes.

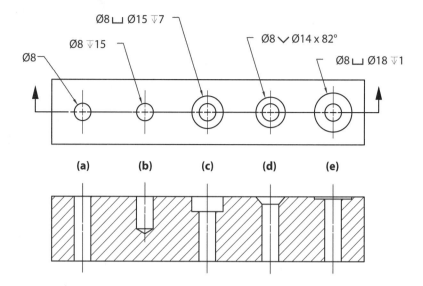

(a) (b) (c) (d) (e)

■ A *spotface* hole is shown in (e). Spotfacing is used to clean off the rough surface of a cast part typically to accept a hexagon head type screw. The format of the dimension is the same as the counterbore; however, the depth dimension may be left off if a company uses a standard spotface depth.

It should be noted that you string the symbols together in the order that a machinist would perform the operations. For example, in Figure 15.30(c), the diameter of the through hole is given first, followed by the diameter and depth of the counterbore. These symbols are included in that order because a machinist would first drill the hole and then make the counterbore at that location.

When multiple holes with the same size are present, only dimension one of the holes. The X symbol is used to indicate how many times that particular hole is machined. In Figure 15.31, 4X is placed before the counterbored hole dimension to indicate that four holes require that size dimension.

15.08.04 Slots

Slots are produced with standard tools such as milling bits. Since these tools are specified by their diameters, slots also should be dimensioned by their diameters. Figure 15.32 shows several acceptable ways that slots can be dimensioned. Notice that in each case, the end radii are indicated but not dimensioned.

FIGURE 15.31. Dimensioning multiple holes.

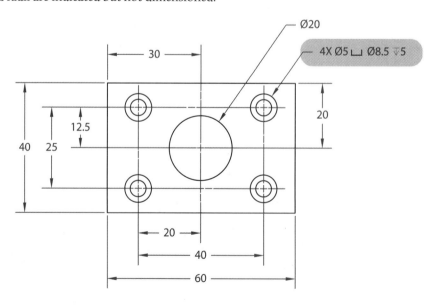

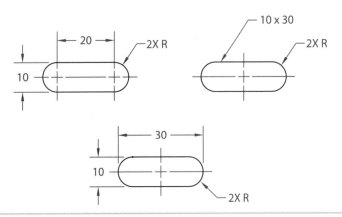

FIGURE 15.32. Dimensioning slots.

15.09 Notes

Most drawings require some type of note or notes in addition to the dimensions on the drawing in order to fully define the part. Since the purpose of your drawing is to give all of the information necessary to manufacture the part, some pieces of information cannot easily be shown in typical dimensions. No matter what type of notes are being shown, all of them should be placed so they are read from the bottom of the sheet of paper.

15.09.01 General Notes

General notes typically appear in the lower right-hand corner of a drawing and apply to the whole drawing. Some may be located in the titleblock. Examples of general notes are as follows:

> **MATERIAL: CAST IRON**
> **FAO** (*finish all over*)
> **ALL DIMENSIONS ARE IN MILLIMETERS**
> **ALL DIMENSIONS `0.1 UNLESS OTHERWISE SPECIFIED**
> **BREAK ALL SHARP EDGES**

15.09.02 Local Notes

Local notes appear on the drawing views and are usually specified with a leader line. Like general notes, local notes are used to specify information that cannot be shown with regular dimensions. Figure 15.33 includes examples of local notes.

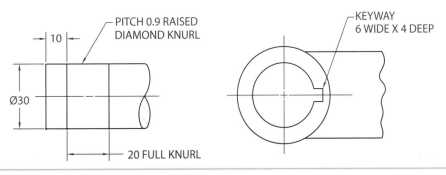

FIGURE 15.33. Using local notes.

15.10 Considerations for 3-D Modeling

Now that you have covered all of the rules and guidelines for dimensioning, take some time to think about what all of this means as you are creating parts using a 3-D modeler. If you have already been creating solid models, you probably noticed that drawings sometimes require more dimensions than what you would use when modeling. This happens because you can imbed certain geometric relations or constraints within a 3-D model that must be explicitly pointed out on a drawing. Figure 15.34 illustrates this idea. Notice that the drawing includes dimensions from the center of the hole to the ends of the part, but the 3-D model sketch does not. A machinist would need to know this information to locate the hole in the center of the part. The sketch incorporates symmetric constraints between the outside lines and their corresponding center line.

Since these differences between the dimensions are required in 3-D models and the drawings are required for documenting the parts, drawings with dimensions for manufacturing are typically done at the end of the design process instead of at the beginning. As you model parts, you want to add geometric and dimensional constraints that capture the design intent for each part. Documentation drawings can then be completed with dimensions for manufacture when the design is complete.

One of the nice features of constraint-based modelers is the ability of the software to let you know when geometry has been underdimensioned or overdimensioned. Your goal should be to fully define the geometry with geometric and dimensional constraints. If a constraint or constraints are missing, the software usually has some type of indicator that the geometry is underdefined. When geometry is underdefined, you should be able to grab entities and move them. When too many dimensions or geometric constraints are present, the software lets you know that the geometry is overdefined or overconstrained. To correct this problem, you must delete a dimension or geometric constraint that is in conflict with other constraints.

15.11 Dimensions for the Plate Example

Return to the senario where you work for the company that manufactures hardware for household doors. You were asked to think about several questions. What are the dimensions needed to manufacture the plate in Figure 15.35? What are the critical dimensions that must be given? What are some of the standard dimensions that exist on other parts or previous parts?

Figure 15.36 shows an example of how the part might be dimensioned. The critical dimensions on the plate are the distances between the countersunk holes and the center hole, the sizes of the holes, and the overall size of the plate (since it must fit in the door properly).

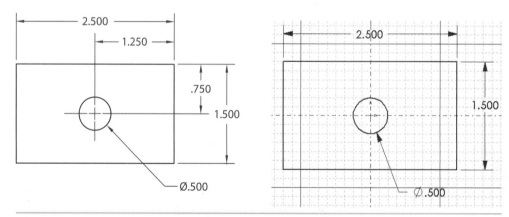

FIGURE 15.34. Differences between dimensioning drawings and 3-D models.

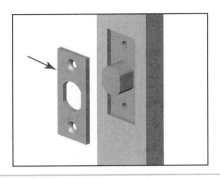
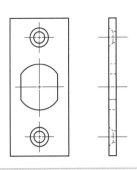

FIGURE 15.35. A deadbolt lock plate.

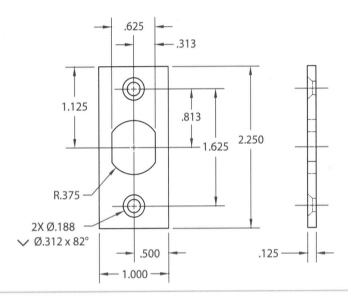

FIGURE 15.36. Plate dimensions.

The plate drawing includes dimensions that may not be present in the constraint-based solid model. Since symmetric geometric constraints may have been incorporated into the model, the highlighted dimensions may not exist in the 3-D solid model database. These dimensions will need to be specified on the drawing to ensure that the part is manufactured properly.

15.12 Fundamental Rules for Dimensioning

This chapter contains best practice suggestions for dimensioning a part; however, as stated previously, *ASME Y14.5M-1994* is the accepted standard for dimensioning practice. The following fundamental rules are quoted from the *ASME Y14.5M-1994* standards for Dimensioning and Tolerancing. For a complete listing of the standards, see *ASME Y14.5M-1994*.

a. Each dimension shall have a tolerance, except for those dimensions specifically identified as reference, maximum, minimum, or stock (commercial stock size). The tolerance may be applied directly to a dimension (or indirectly in the case of basic dimensions), indicated by a general note, or located in a supplementary block of the drawing format.

b. Dimensioning and tolerancing shall be complete so there is full understanding of the characteristic of each feature. Neither scaling (measuring the size of a feature directly from an engineering drawing) nor assumption of a distance of size is permitted, except as follows: Undimensioned drawings, such as loft, printed wiring, templates, and master layouts prepared on stable material, are excluded provided the necessary control dimensions are specified.

c. Each necessary dimension of an end product shall be shown. No more dimensions than those necessary for complete definition shall be given. The use of reference dimensions on a drawing should be minimized.

d. Dimensions shall be selected and arranged to suit the function and mating relationship of a part and shall not be subject to more than one interpretation.

e. The drawing should define a part <u>without</u> specifying manufacturing methods. Thus, only the diameter of a hole is given without indicating whether it is to be drilled, reamed, punched, or made by any other operation. However, in those instances where manufacturing, processing, quality assurance, or environmental information is essential to the definition of engineering requirements, it shall be specified on the drawing or in a document referenced on the drawing.

f. It is permissible to identify as nonmandatory certain processing dimensions that provide for finish allowance, shrink allowance, and other requirements, provided the final dimensions are given on the drawing. Nonmandatory processing dimensions shall be identified by an appropriate note, such as NON-MANDATORY (MFG DATA).

g. Dimensions should be arranged to provide required information for optimum readability. Dimensions should be shown in true profile views and refer to visible outlines.

h. Wires, cables, sheets, rods, and other materials manufactured to gage or code numbers shall be specified by linear dimensions indicating the diameter or thickness. Gage or code numbers may be shown in parentheses following the dimension.

i. A 90° angle applies where center lines and lines depicting features are shown on a drawing at right angles and no angle is specified.

j. A 90° basic angle applies where centerlines of features in a pattern or surfaces shown at right angles on the drawing are located or defined by basic dimensions and no angle is specified.

k. Unless otherwise specified, all dimensions are applicable at 20°C (68°F). Compensation may be made for measurements made at other temperatures.

l. All dimensions and tolerances apply in a free state condition. This principle does not apply to non-rigid parts.

m. Unless otherwise specified, all geometric tolerances apply for full depth, length, and width of the feature.

n. Dimensions and tolerances apply only at the drawing level where they are specified. A dimension specified for a given feature on one level of drawing (for example, a detail drawing) is not mandatory for that feature at any other level (for example, an assembly drawing).

15.13 Chapter Summary

This chapter provided an introduction to dimensioning. The chapter discussed how all dimensions have a tolerance and how tolerances are important for the function of designs. Dimensioning, like other drawing topics, follows fairly specific standards or rules. Whether dimensioning in inches or millimeters, you must follow these standards. This chapter also covered techniques for dimensioning different features, such as standard parts, machined holes, and notes.

The next chapter will discuss tolerance dimensioning in more detail, as well as introduce the topic of geometric dimensioning and tolerancing. These topics are key to the production of parts that are based on the specific intent of the designer.

15.14 glossary of key terms

ANSI Y14.5 (ASME Y14.5M-1994): Industry standard document that outlines uniform practices for displaying and interpreting dimensions and related information on drawings and other forms of engineering documentation.

arrowhead: A small triangle at the end of dimension lines and leaders to indicate the direction and extent of a dimension.

baseline dimensioning: A system of dimensioning where each feature is dimensioned from the same origin.

chain dimensioning: A system of dimensioning where features are dimensioned from one another instead of from an origin.

contour dimensioning: Placing each dimension in the view where the contour or shape of the feature shows up best.

contour rule: A drawing practice where each dimension should be placed in the view where the contour shape is best shown.

dimension: A numerical value expressed in appropriate units of measure and used to define the size, location, geometric characteristic, or surface texture of a part or part feature.

dimension line: A thin, dark, solid line that terminates at each end with arrowheads. The value of a dimension typically is shown in the center of the dimension line.

extension line: A thin, dark, solid line extending from a point on an object, perpendicular to a dimension line used to indicate the extension of a surface or point to a location preferably outside the part outline.

leader: A thin, dark, solid line terminating with an arrowhead at one end and a dimension, note, or symbol at the other end.

location: A dimension associated with the position of a feature on a part.

size: The general term for the size of a feature, such as a hole, cylinder, or set of opposed parallel surfaces.

tolerance: The total amount a specific dimension is permitted to vary. It is the difference between the upper and lower limits of the dimension.

15.15 questions for review

1. What is the current standard for dimensioning and tolerancing in the United States?

2. Explain the difference between dimensioning standards for inches and the standards for millimeters.

3. List at least four fundamental rules for dimensioning.

4. What are the correct line types and darkness for dimension lines, extension lines, and leaders?

5. When a two-view drawing of a simple rectangular block is given, what dimensions are necessary?

6. Explain the difference between baseline and chain dimensioning.

7. What is contour dimensioning?

8. What are the standard symbols for diameter, radius, counterbore, countersink, and depth?

9. Explain why the dimensions for a constraint-based solid model of a design may be different from the dimensions that appear on a detail drawing of the part.

15.16 problems

1. Sketch the necessary dimensions to fully define each object shown in Figure P15.1. Do not use redundant or reference dimensions.

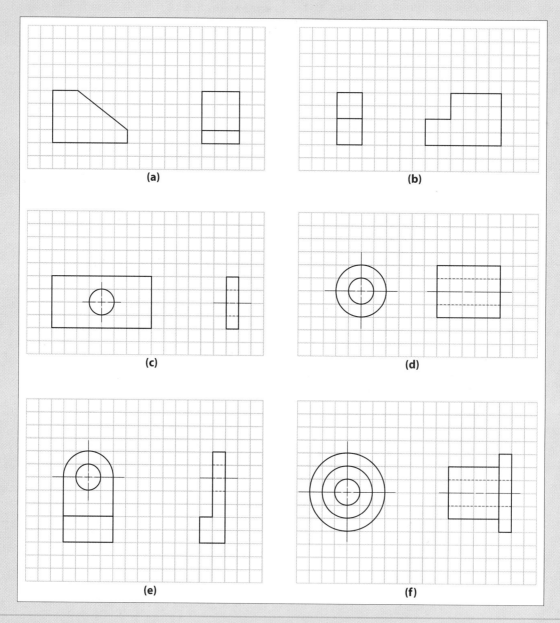

FIGURE P15.1.

15.16 problems (continued)

2. Scale and copy the drawings shown in Figure P15.2, leaving sufficient space between the views to add dimensions. Add the necessary dimensions to fully define each object. Add additional views as necessary to conform to the dimensioning guidelines in this chapter. Do not use redundant or reference dimensions.

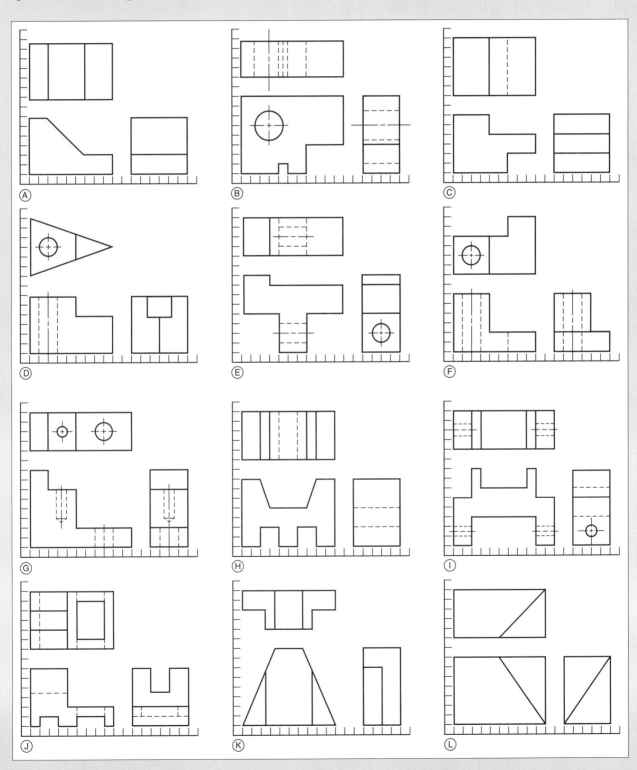

15.16 problems (continued)

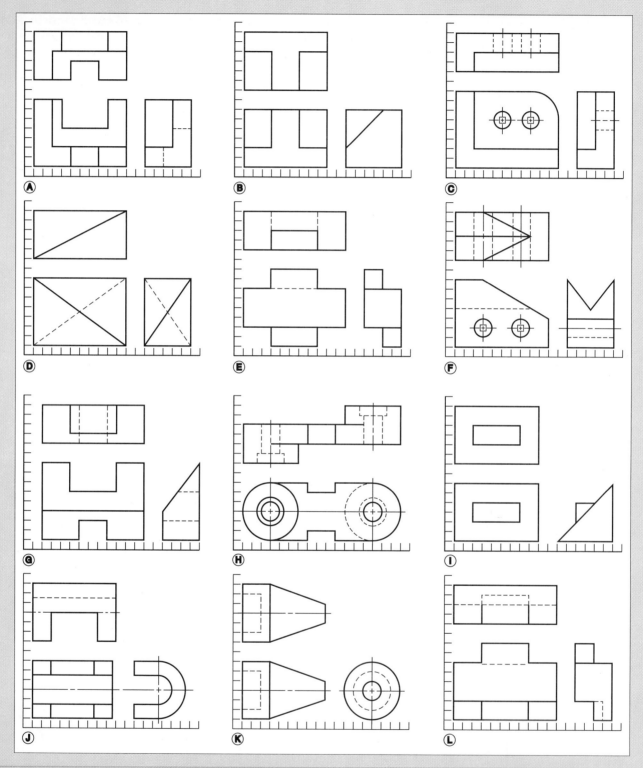

FIGURE P15.2.

15.16 problems (continued)

3. Scale and copy the drawings shown in Figure P15.3, leaving sufficient space between the views to add dimensions. Add the necessary dimensions to fully define each object. Add additional views and section views as necessary to conform to the dimensioning guidelines in this chapter. Whenever possible, apply accepted shortcut practices to describe appropriate features. Do not use redundant or reference dimensions.

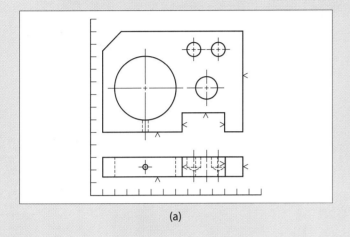

(a)

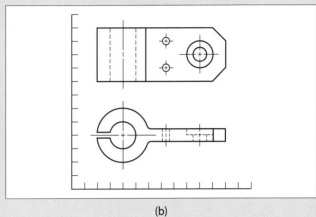

(b)

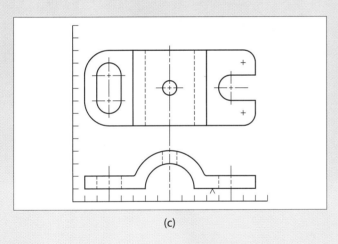

(c)

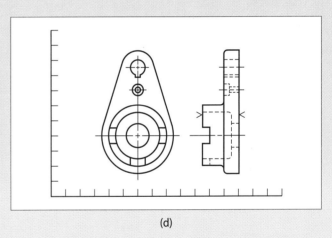

(d)

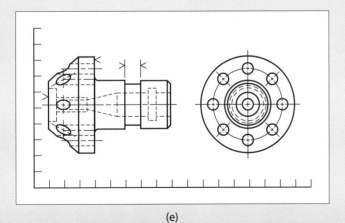

(e)

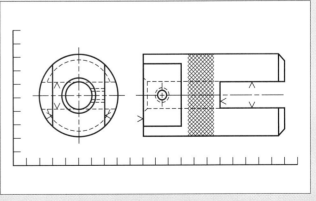

(f)

15.16 problems (continued)

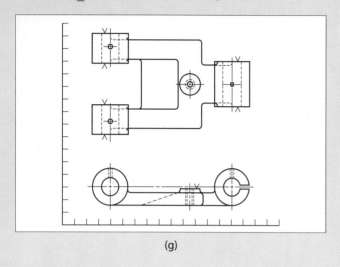

(g)

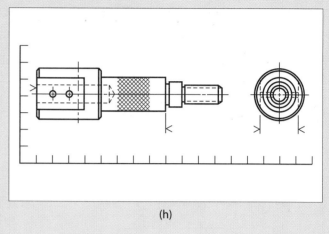

(h)

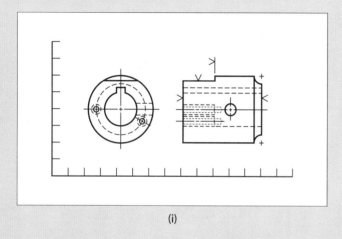

(i)

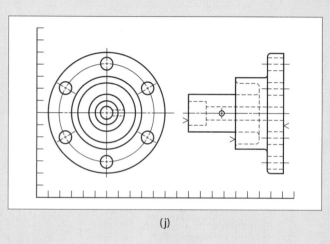

(j)

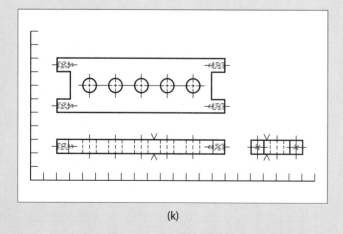

(k)

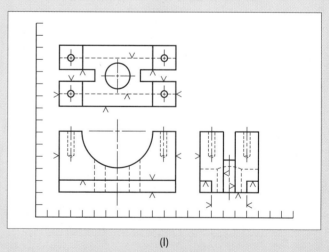

(l)

15.16 problems (continued)

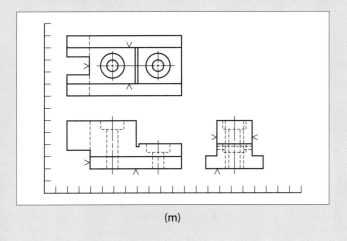

(m)

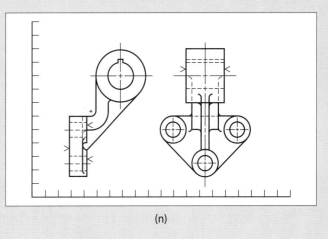

(n)

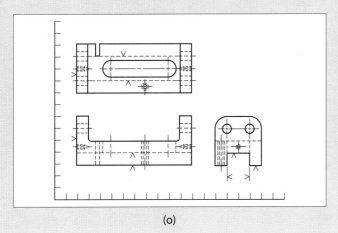

(o)

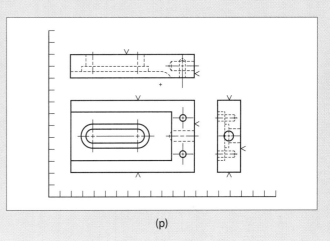

(p)

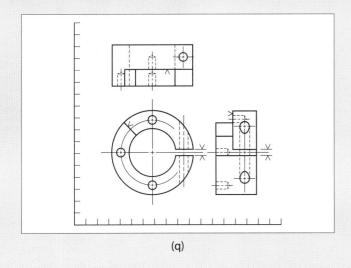

(q)

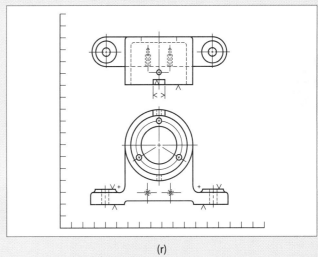

(r)

15.16 problems (continued)

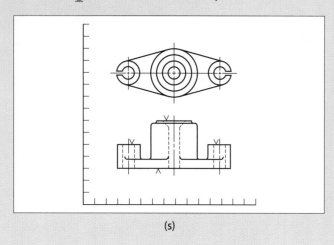

(s)

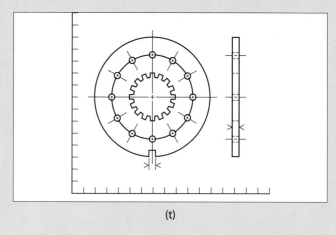

(t)

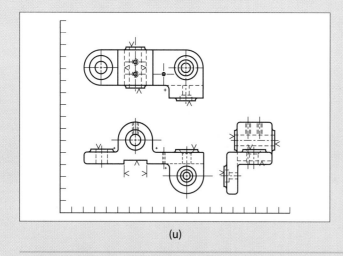

(u)

FIGURE P15.3.

15.16 problems (continued)

4. In Figure P15.4, consider the function of the indicated parts shown in their intended assemblies. For each drawing, add the necessary dimensions to fully define the object, giving consideration to the critical dimensions necessary for each part to fit and function in its intended assembly.

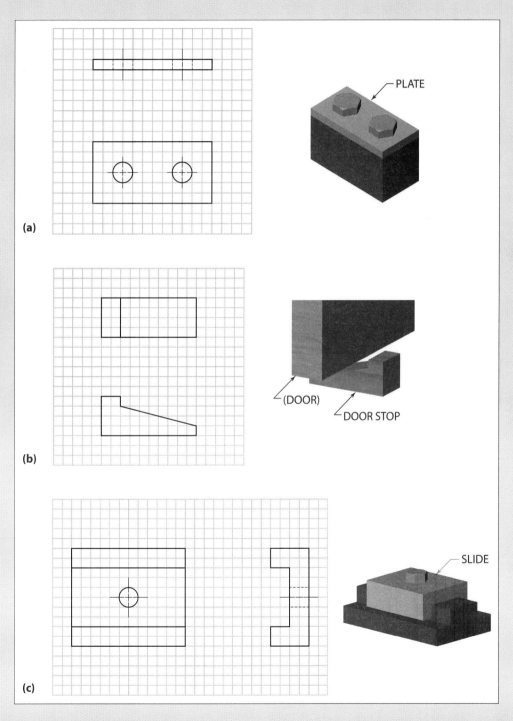

15.16 problems (continued)

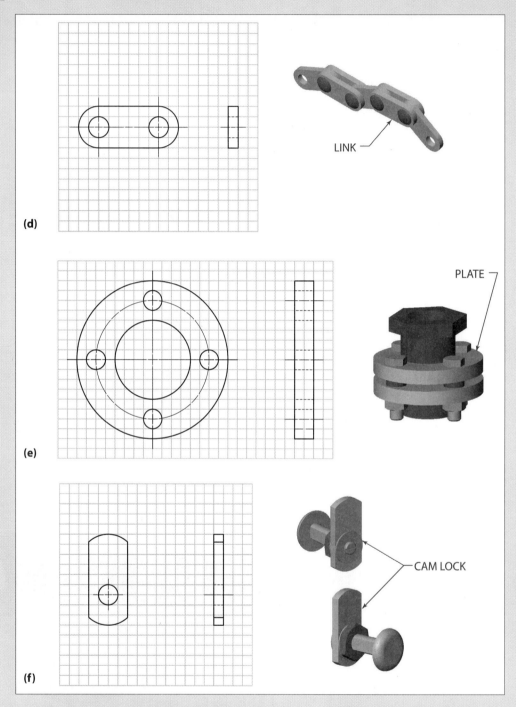

(d)

(e)

(f)

LINK

PLATE

CAM LOCK

15.16 problems (continued)

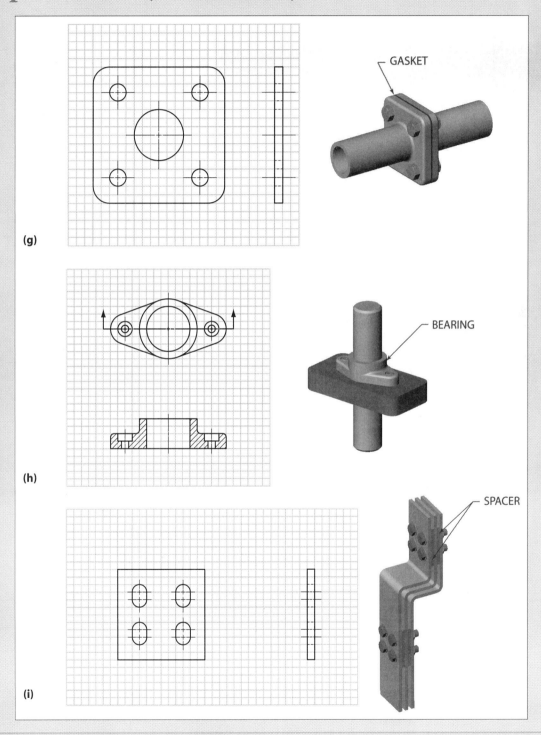

(g)

(h)

(i)

GASKET

BEARING

SPACER

FIGURE P15.4.

18

Working Drawings

objectives

After completing this chapter, you should be able to

- Specify the contents, formatting, and organization of engineering drawings

- Correctly prepare and interpret formal, professional engineering drawings

- Discuss the primary differences between drawings used in manufacturing projects and those used in construction projects

- Effectively use scales to measure the length of lines on a drawing

18.01
introduction

In this chapter, you will learn about conventions and practices used in real-world engineering drawings. You will learn about two primary types of drawings—manufacturing and construction. **Manufacturing drawings** are used by engineers other than just mechanical engineers, and **construction drawings** are used by engineers other than just civil engineers; however, for the sake of simplicity in terminology, this chapter will sometimes refer to working drawings as "mechanical engineering drawings" or as "civil engineering drawings" since those two disciplines are concerned primarily with manufacturing and construction drawings, respectively. As a further simplification, the term *object* or *part* will refer to the mechanical parts that have been designed as well as a civil infrastructure project. Manufacturing drawings are used for products such as bicycles and toasters. Construction drawings are used for roads and bridges. Mechanical drawings depict products that are mass-produced; civil drawings represent unique projects that are known as **one-offs**. (A one-off is a system for which only one such system is constructed.) Although there are similarities between manufacturing and construction drawings, there are also significant differences. In the following sections, you will learn about manufacturing working drawings and construction working drawings. In particular, in the discussion of construction drawings, you will learn about the characteristics that set them apart from typical manufacturing drawings.

When parts and assemblies are ready for fabrication or when structures are ready for construction, the drawings must be presented in a format that is considered formal and professional. There are several reasons for this formality. First and foremost, the drawings must be able to stand on their own without any vagueness or ambiguity. They must be interpreted the same way when viewed by different people. In fact, for complex projects (in particular, for construction projects), many people will view the drawings. Also, the engineer responsible for the design may not be available to answer questions that arise during manufacturing or construction. Formal drawings need to be formatted in such a way that relevant information concerning the specifications, records, and identification of the part is easy to locate and is included with the drawing.

Next, an engineering drawing is considered a legal document and, as such, must contain a certain amount of information concerning the history of and responsibilities for the design. In the case of a set of construction drawings, the seal and signature of a registered **professional engineer (PE)** is typically a requirement. Finally, since engineering drawings are usually presented to third parties for cost estimation or fabrication, the presentation of the drawing is a reflection of the quality of the originator. Drawings that are presented well reflect favorably on the person or company that made the drawings.

When fabricated parts and assemblies are later used in the field or when infrastructure projects are constructed in the field, additional people may need to see the design drawings. These people sometimes include technicians and assemblers who install the parts in the final working environment; salespeople who ensure that the parts are compatible with other products produced by different companies; subcontractors who construct specific systems in the project, such as the wiring or plumbing; maintenance people who repair or replace the parts in the field; government inspectors who monitor the progress of a civil works project; and for certain types of systems, engineers or technicians who are responsible for the removal, recycling, or disposal of the parts at their end of life.

18.02 Making It Formal

If you have decided that you would like someone else to make your parts or device for you, you must produce a set of formal documents known as **working drawings** to send to the fabricator. In civil engineering projects, contractors bid on projects based on the working drawings and specifications. Working drawings show each part or structure in all of the views necessary to fully define their features, their sizes and tolerances, and the way they are to be assembled into the completed product. Consequently, much of what you have learned in the previous chapters concerning orthogonal projection, pictorial views, dimensioning, and tolerancing is used extensively in working drawings. In the ideal case, once you have produced a set of working drawings and they are delivered to the fabricator or contractor, your systems should be able to be fabricated correctly without any further intervention from you. No one should need to call you with questions concerning any feature of the part or the way the part is to be made. In large construction projects, this is rarely the case and the engineer who designed the structure is often extensively involved in overseeing final construction of the project.

Once a drawing leaves your hands as the responsible engineer, it is likely to be reproduced many times and viewed many times by different people. You must have confidence that the information contained on the drawing will be interpreted correctly by every person who views it. In a complex manufacturing project, for example, the first person who will likely see the drawing is a buyer who must evaluate the operations required to fabricate the system and the degree of difficulty of fabrication. Thus, a fabricator with the capability to produce the part will be selected. For construction projects, the first people to see the drawings are usually the contractors who bid on the project. Contractors estimate project costs based on the drawings and specifications; the person with the lowest estimate, or bid, is typically awarded the project. The selected fabricator or contractor must then produce the part or **assembly** as specified on the drawings. Inspectors measure and test the part or materials to ensure that they meet the criteria defined in the drawings and specifications. The engineers and technicians who are responsible for installing the part in the final product must know the sizes of the part's features and their allowable variation so that any special tooling required for the installation can be built. The subcontractors who install various systems on a construction project must know how their portion fits in with the overall structure. This process of design and specification, fabrication, inspection, and installation is shown in Figure 18.01 for the prototype production of a computer disk drive spindle, a typical manufacturing project. Not shown is the special tooling required to ensure the proper alignment of the parts when they are assembled.

When you finish making a working drawing, you have created part of a legal document. Engineering drawings are, in fact, legally binding documents. Once an agreement between you and the fabricator or contractor has been reached for the manufacture or construction of a part or system, the engineering drawing becomes the focal point of the agreement. A working drawing is part of a contract in which a fabricator or contractor agrees to make the specified part in accordance with all of the requirements indicated on the drawing in exchange for an agreed amount of money, products, or services. For manufactured products, an additional agreement usually outlines what information, if any, can be shared with others besides the fabricator. If any information required to make the part is missing on the working drawing, the contract may not be able to be completed. In the worst-case scenario, if any information on the working drawing can be easily misinterpreted, an error in the part may result. In either case, as the originator of the drawing, the fault would lie with you and you may be required to compensate the fabricator or contractor for whatever time and effort was expended in the attempt to make the part.

Manufactured parts that meet all of the requirements specified on the drawing must be purchased for the agreed-upon volume, delivery schedule, and price.

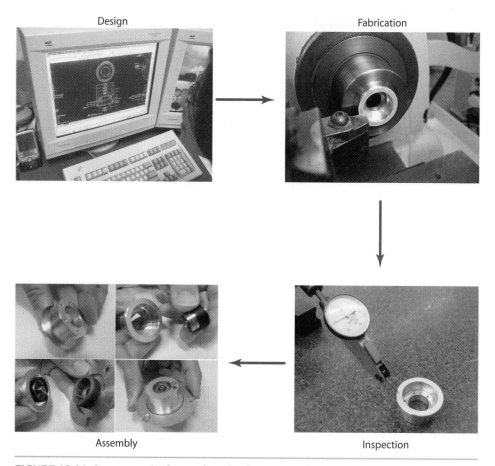

FIGURE 18.01. Some steps in the product development cycle that require the use of working drawings.

Contractors must be paid the agreed-upon amount when the structure is completed. On the other hand, for manufactured products, you can reject delivered parts that fail to meet any specification of the drawing. For construction projects, contractors must typically redo the portion of the structure that is not in keeping with the drawings and specifications—eating into their profit margin for the project. If there is an error on the drawing, the buyer must still purchase the manufactured parts if they have been made according to the drawing given to the fabricator. For construction engineering projects, the design firm may have to pay for cost overruns due to incorrect design information on the drawings. Information that is missing on a drawing (and then misinterpreted by the fabricator) is most often considered the fault of the designer. For example, if the numerical dimensions for a part to be manufactured are meant to be in centimeters, this information is missing on the drawing, and the numerical dimensions are interpreted as inches, the error is considered the buyer's fault. Still, these parts must be purchased. Since construction projects are one-off designs, missing dimensions or missing information is a relatively frequent occurrence. Contractors and engineers typically remain in close contact during the construction phase so that these issues can be easily resolved in the field.

Working drawings can usually be distinguished from less formal drawings by their formatting. Just as courts require all submitted legal documents to adhere to a required format and colleges and universities require graduate theses to have a uniform appearance, engineering working drawings also have a prescribed presentation form. Informal drawings, such as those shown in Figure 18.02, have no required formatting and can appear on any size paper; multiview presentations are not required, and dimensions

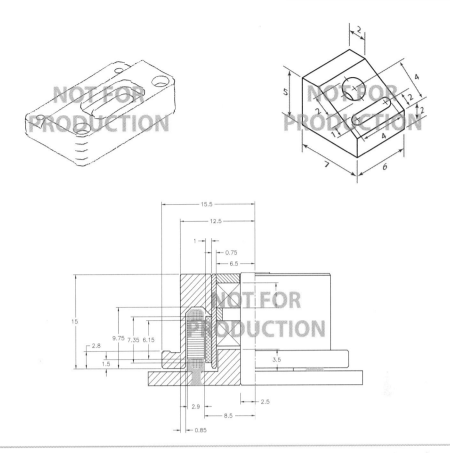

FIGURE 18.02. Sketches, pictorials, and layouts are helpful for visualization and initial sizing but are usually not considered complete, formal drawings.

frequently appear on pictorials. Informal drawings can be sketches, can be made with mechanical instruments or CAD, and can include many parts on a single page. Working drawings, on the other hand, are to be of specific sizes and include borders and headers containing specific information. Specific views and presentation techniques are expected. Most of all, working drawings must be complete in providing the information required to make the parts they describe. This is not to say, however, that only working drawings can be legal documents. In civil engineering practice, written specifications usually accompany the drawings and are considered part of the project's legal documentation.

Under certain conditions, informal drawings (even sketches) can be considered legal documents. If, for example, you or your buyer gives an informal drawing to a fabricator with instructions to make the part, even the informal drawing becomes part of the legal contract. The drawing just will not look very nice—or professional. Another example involves patent disputes. The courts may consider the notes and sketches you make in your engineering notebook to be legal documents for establishing the date of conception of an idea. For this purpose, you should have a witness sign and date any notes, sketches, or drawings that you produce that may lead to a patent.

In the engineering and business worlds, appearances are important. The progression from informal drawings to formal drawings, as shown in Figure 18.03, is in many ways a transition in appearance and presentation. Many people consider a formal engineering drawing to be not only a means of information transfer but also a work of art. The presentation of this document can reflect well or poorly on its originator. For that reason, the formal drawings you submit should be well organized, neat, and polished—a part of engineering professionalism.

FIGURE 18.03. The typical progression of the design of a part from a conceptual hand sketch to a computer 3-D model to a formal working drawing extracted from the model.

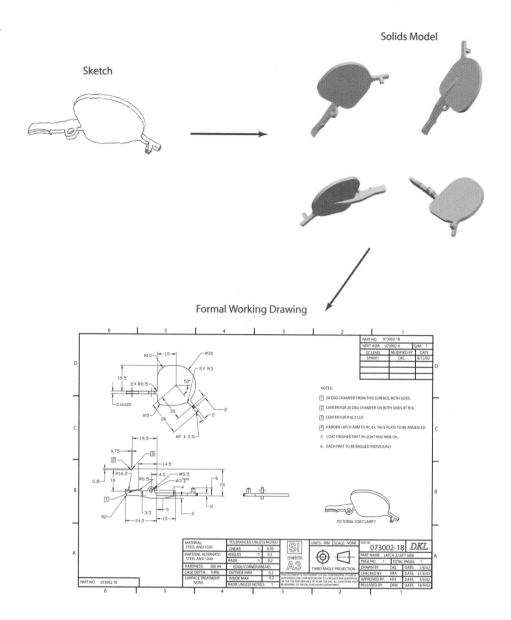

Sketch

Solids Model

Formal Working Drawing

18.03 Sheet Sizes

The first step in making a formal working drawing is to choose an appropriate sheet size. This statement might sound strange today, when computers can generate a drawing of almost any size with the part views shown in any scale. However, most working drawings need to be printed for easy viewing, perhaps by a machinist trying to make the parts in a shop, a contractor examining the drawing in the preparation of a bid, or a group of engineers sitting around a conference table reviewing the design. When a working drawing is printed to its intended size, it must be readable.

Most of the world, with the exception of the United States, uses **international sheet sizes**. The most common international sizes are A4, A3, A2, A1, and A0. Size A4 is 297 mm × 210 mm. (For anyone not well-versed in metric sizes, this is approximately the size of the paper used in a computer printer.) If the horizontal dimension size is larger than the vertical size, the paper orientation is known as **landscape**; otherwise, the orientation is called **portrait**. Landscape paper orientation is used almost exclusively in engineering working drawings. The next largest paper size, A3, is generated by

FIGURE 18.04. Some relative standard sheet sizes, international and US, used for formal drawings.

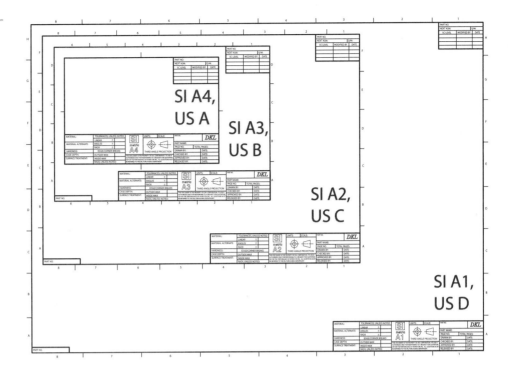

attaching two A4 "sheets" along their lengths, producing a sheet that is twice the area of an A4 sheet, or 420 mm × 297 mm. The A2 sheet (594 mm × 420 mm) is similarly produced by putting together two A3 sheets. The A1 (840 mm × 594 mm) and A0 (1188 mm × 840 mm) sizes are generated similarly. The A0 size is generally accepted as the largest size that will fit, without rolling or folding, inside available cabinets made for drawing storage.

US sheet sizes, which are designated A, B, C, D, and E, are close to the international sheet sizes. Size A paper is 11″ × 8.5″ and is commonly called letter size. As with the international paper sizes, each increasing US sheet size is generated by attaching its two smaller sizes along their lengths. Thus, a B size sheet is 17″ × 11″, a C size sheet is 22″ × 17″, etc. An E size sheet, which is 44″ × 34″, is the largest drawing size that will fit easily inside a common filing cabinet for drawings. Civil engineering drawings are usually drawn on E size paper unless a bound book of B size drawings is created for a project. The common International and US sheet sizes are shown in Figure 18.04.

Some caution is necessary when you are printing a drawing less than its full size, which provides convenience in printing, copying, and handling. In large construction projects, printing a drawing to less than full size is a necessity. The font size used for the dimensions and notes on a working drawing is usually 3 mm to 6 mm in height and is independent of the size of the drawing; that is, the font size on an A4 drawing is the same as that on an A0 drawing. If you want to see the notes and dimensions printed to their full size, the drawing needs to be printed to its full size. If, for example, an A1 or A0 size drawing is reduced to an A4 size, the notes and dimensions may be reduced to the point where they are no longer legible. This effect is demonstrated in Figure 18.05 as larger drawings are reduced to a smaller sheet size. Fortunately, a larger printer, such as the one shown in Figure 18.06, is fairly easy to find, and drawings can be easily printed to a size that is legible and convenient for handling.

The previous discussion covered working drawings in a generic way. The similarities and some differences between manufacturing and construction drawings were discussed. In the following sections, the discussion of manufacturing and construction drawings will diverge. You will first learn about manufacturing drawings and then about construction drawings.

FIGURE 18.05. Geometry and letter font size reduction when larger drawings are printed to smaller sheets.

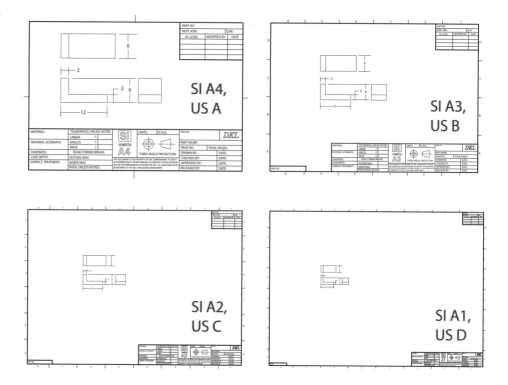

FIGURE 18.06. An ink-jet printer capable of creating a full size International A0 or US size E drawing.

18.04 The Formal Drawing Header in Manufacturing Drawings

In addition to the information about the geometries of the parts or assemblies, working drawings need to contain other information. There must be information, for example, on how each part can be uniquely identified; otherwise, it may be difficult to locate specific parts and drawings among the vast numbers of parts being manufactured or assembled at any given time. Also, there must be some information about the history of a part or an assembly; otherwise, it may be difficult to distinguish modified new parts from original old parts as the design progresses. If the design for a part does change with time, there must be a way of recording those changes so that everyone working with the part knows what it looks like, how it fits into other parts, and how it performs in the completed device. Is it a new style part or an old style part? If it is an old style part, how old is it? How many changes has it undergone? Can the old style be used instead of the new style?

There also must be a sense of accountability for the design of a part. Who made the drawing? Which engineer was responsible for the part's proper function? Who approved the release of the drawing outside the company? When were those things done? Is the information contained on a drawing considered confidential to the originator? Most of those questions can be answered by examining the drawing header, which is described next.

A **header** is a printed frame or outline on which a drawing is created. Drawing headers are usually unique to the company that produces the drawing, but they follow a similar format and contain the same type of information. A typical header for a manufacturing drawing is shown in Figure 18.07. A heavy line **border** defines the limit of the formal drawing area. Any added markings that are to be a part of the drawing must be inside this border. On some headers, evenly spaced **location grid** marks appear in the horizontal and vertical directions outside the border. The location grid on a drawing, similar to the location grid on a street map, helps readers of the drawing locate areas on the sheet where specific features can be found. For large drawings with many features, the location grid is particularly useful. If, for example, you were told to look for a specific feature at location C5 on the drawing, you would immediately begin looking at the double highlighted area shown in Figure 18.07. A major part of the header is the **main title block**. The main title block contains most of the information required to identify the part on the drawing as well as to track its progress in the design cycle. The main title block provides space for specifying the material and the material processing required to fabricate the part. Some companies provide a **secondary title block** for additional information a company would like to see included on its manufacturing drawings.

The main title block contains information on how to interpret what is seen on the drawing, as highlighted in the magnified portion shown in Figure 18.08. The definition of the units for the dimensions is specified there. Usually the units are specified as MM (millimeters), CM (centimeters), M (meters), IN (inches), or FT (feet). In addition, words and/or graphics specify whether the orthogonal views on the drawing are produced using first-angle projection, which is popular internationally, or using third-angle projection, which is used in the United States. The scale of the drawing is defined as "the ratio of the size of the actual part to the size of the image of the part shown on the drawing when the drawing is printed to its full sheet size."

FIGURE 18.07. A typical header for a formal engineering drawing.

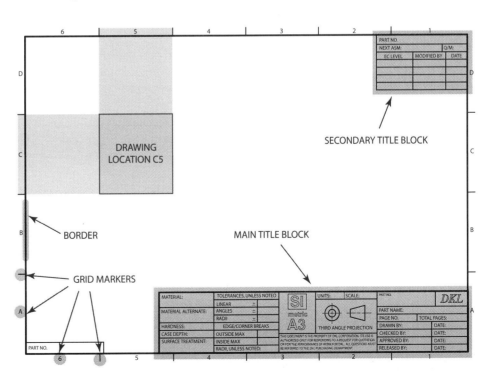

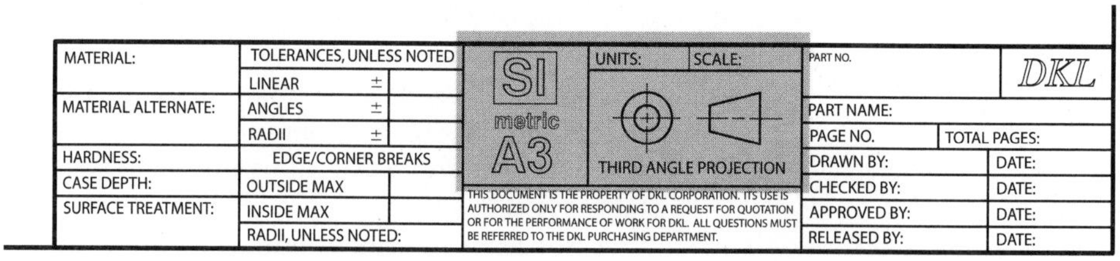

FIGURE 18.08. Inside the main title block, the definitions of the units, scale, and projection angle help the reader to correctly interpret the placement and orientation of the views and the dimensions that are shown on them.

The main title block also contains information about who owns the drawing and the information it contains, as indicated in Figure 18.09. A manufacturing drawing and any of its copies are usually considered the property of the company for which the part is made. Usually the name, initial, or logo of the company (in this case, DKL Corporation) is displayed and some sort of message expresses how the information contained in the drawing can be used and distributed. If this information is considered confidential, or proprietary, it is clearly marked as such. The purpose of these statements is to ensure that the information contained in the drawings is not freely distributed, especially to the company's competitors.

The main means of identification of a part is through its **part number**, as highlighted in Figure 18.10. Every individual part that is fabricated according to the same drawing (or a copy of it) carries the same part number. Ideally, all parts with the same part number should be interchangeable. When it is important to identify each part fabricated from the same drawing, those parts can be assigned unique serial numbers. Since assemblies and subassemblies are often handled and transported as complete units, they also are assigned part numbers. Every company has its own method of assigning part numbers. Some are alphanumeric strings, some include information on the date the number was assigned, and some include coded information on the project type or the location of the engineering facility. Whether an individual part, a subassembly, or a full assembly is defined, part numbers must be unique within a company. A firm usually has an internal accounting system for assigning and tracking part numbers to ensure that no two unique parts are given the same number. In addition to the part number, a part, subassembly, or full assembly is usually given a **part name**. A part name is given for convenience and is usually based on a part's function or appearance, such as L-bracket, or Base Plate, or Pillow Block A. Part names do not have to be unique since they are meant to provide temporary convenience for identifying parts while they are in fabrication or use. A company could have several L-brackets defined for use in various assemblies; however, each unique L-bracket is defined by a unique number.

If a part is modified during its life, the drawing is given an **EC Level** number. EC is an acronym for Engineering Change; it also may be called Revision Level or something similar depending on the terminology a company uses. The existence of an EC Level

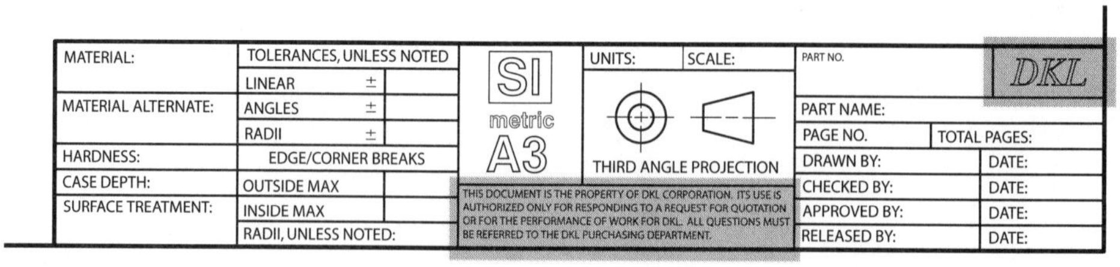

FIGURE 18.09. The name of the company, a statement of ownership of the drawing contents, and conditions of use are permanently printed in the title block.

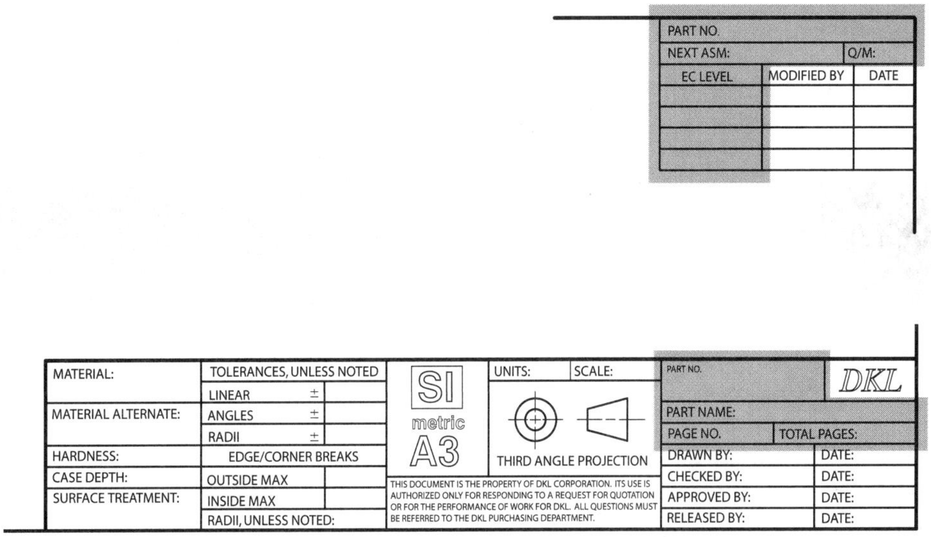

FIGURE 18.10. The part name, part number, and revision (or EC) number uniquely distinguishes this part from different parts or earlier versions of the same part.

number is an indication that the original design has been updated in some way (e.g., changes in the material or in one or more dimensions or tolerances). In Figure 18.10, the EC Level appears on the secondary title block. Different parts and assemblies can have the same EC Level number if they are from the same product and were updated at the same time. As with part numbers, EC Level numbers can be an alphanumeric string and cannot be reused on the same part or assembly after they have been assigned. If the design of a part has changed significantly to the point where it is no longer interchangeable with the older versions of the part, that part should be assigned a new part number rather than a new EC Level number.

Drawings with large numbers of detail views and notes may require more than one sheet. In this case, each sheet must have a page number and specify the total pages in the entire drawing. Some companies require that each part specifies its next assembly, which is the part number of the assembly or subassembly into which the part is to be immediately installed. If the next assembly requires more than one of a particular part, that quantity is specified as the **quantity per machine (Q/M)**.

A chain of responsibility is required for all manufacturing drawings. The people responsible for the creation of a drawing must be identifiable should any questions arise about the drawing's contents. Every formal drawing has areas for **approval signatures** in the main title block, as shown in Figure 18.11, where the appropriate people can initial

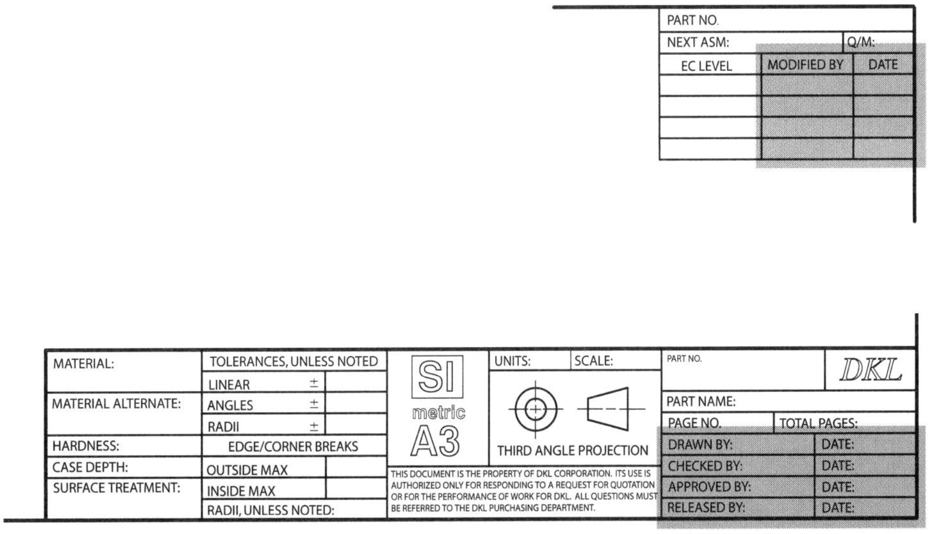

FIGURE 18.11. Signatures and dates help establish the history of development and leave a trail of accountability.

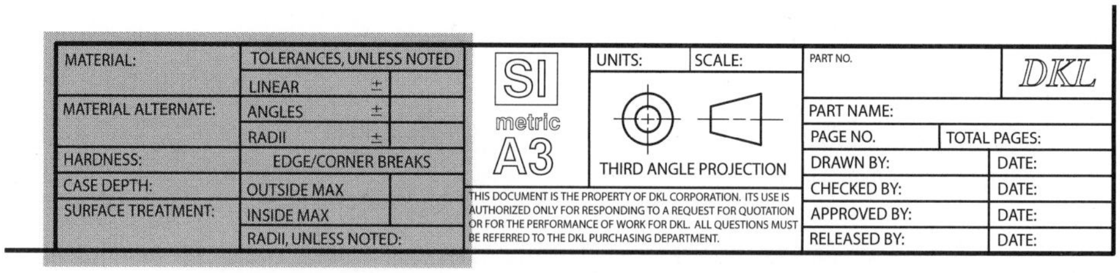

FIGURE 18.12. Areas for entry of information about material, hardening, surface treatment, and tolerances ensure that this information is not neglected.

and date the drawing. (However, with most CAD drawings, the initials are no longer handwritten; rather, they are inserted as a drawing note.) The required signatures usually include those of the drafter who made the drawing (drawn by . . .), the person who reviewed the drawing to make sure it was free from errors (checked by . . .), the designer or engineer who checked to make sure the fabricated part would fit and function in its intended manner (approved by . . .), and a manager who checked that the formal drawing would meet all accounting and security requirements when delivered to a fabricator outside the company (released by . . .). In smaller companies, it is common to see two or more of these functions performed by the same person.

The main title block usually includes spaces where additional information required for the fabrication of the part is contained, as shown in Figure 18.12. The reason for these spaces is to prompt the entry of additional information; usually the information required for the fabrication of the parts is included on the drawing. Typical additional information might include the material from which the part is made and any special heat treatment or surface treatments that are required. Other important information includes the **default tolerances**, which are the dimensional tolerances that may be assumed when no tolerance appears with the dimension. Using default tolerance in this manner saves effort in assigning a tolerance to every dimension when the tolerances are the same and generally gives the drawing a neater appearance. Default tolerances can be specified to be different according to the number of decimal places shown on the dimension. Dimensions that have one, two, or three decimal places can be assigned different default tolerances, usually with stricter tolerances used as the number of decimal places increases.

If the drawing extends to multiple pages, the header blocks on the subsequent pages can be simplified, as shown in Figure 18.13. These simplified blocks are called **continuation blocks** and usually contain information that identifies the sheets as being part of a larger drawing. This information includes the part number, EC number, and sheet number of the drawing. The size of the sheet is also included in case the sheets of the drawing are of different sizes.

If the company has no preferred standard title blocks for its drawings, ANSI has recommended the use of some generic title blocks, which are shown in Figure 18.14.

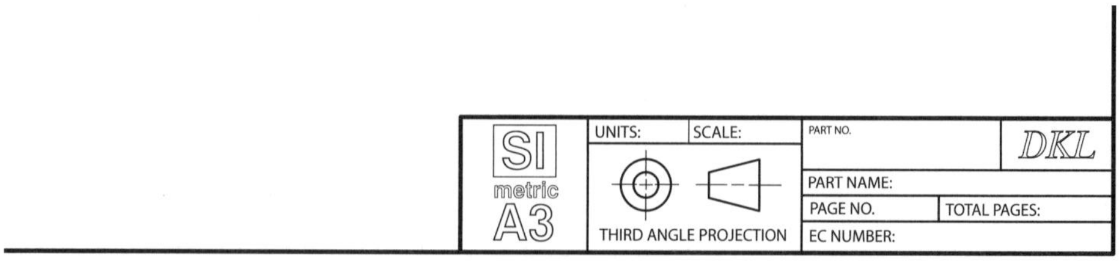

FIGURE 18.13. When a drawing is composed of multiple pages, the title block on the second and subsequent pages may be simplified.

FIGURE 18.14. An ANSI standard title block and continuation sheet block for US sheet sizes A, B, and C (above) and for sizes D and larger (below). Dimensions shown are in inches.

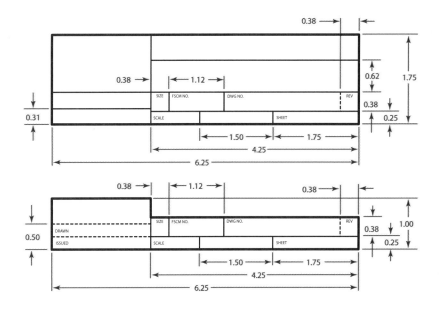

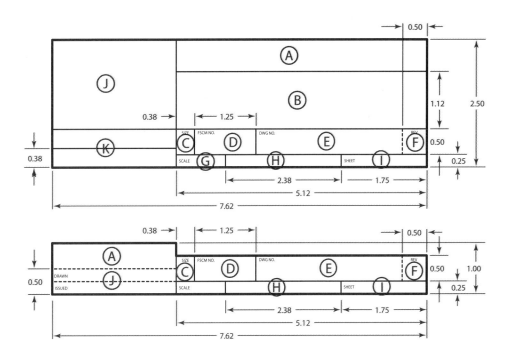

The information contained in the generic ANSI title blocks is representative of that expected to be contained in most formal drawing title blocks. This information is entered in the proper areas of the ANSI title block as indicated in Figure 18.14 and as listed here:

A. A statement of origin or ownership of the drawing

B. The title of the part or drawing

C. The size of the sheet when the drawing is printed to its full size

D. The Federal Supply Code for Manufacturers (FSCM) number if the work is being done for the federal government

E. The drawing number or part number

F. The revision, or EC, number

G. The ratio of the item size shown on the drawing versus that of the actual item

H. The approximate weight of the item if it is heavy

I. The page number (for drawings with multiple pages)

J. Names of the drafter and checker, with dates

K. Names of any additional people needed to approve the drawing, with dates

18.05 The Drawing Area for Manufactured Parts

The drawing area is defined as the area inside the border of the drawing. It is informally subdivided in an area reserved for showing geometry and an area for the **notes**, as shown in Figure 18.15. Notes are usually listed in one corner of the drawing, and the rest of the drawing area is dedicated to showing the views of the part.

18.05.01 Geometry Presentation

The size of the sheet and the scale of the object should be selected so that the area reserved for showing the object's geometry is uncluttered, even after the dimensions are added. These choices are rather subjective, and looking at how other (good) formal drawings have been prepared gives you some clues about how to make these choices. Simple objects with few geometric features and dimensions generally require smaller sheets. Complicated objects with many features and dimensions require larger sheets or perhaps multiple sheets. Some consideration, however, should be given toward handling convenience. Smaller sheets are easier to store and carry, whereas larger sheets are more difficult to store but are better for showing to a group of people.

FIGURE 18.15. For clarity, text notes are kept in a separate area on a formal drawing so a reader can look in a single location to find all of them.

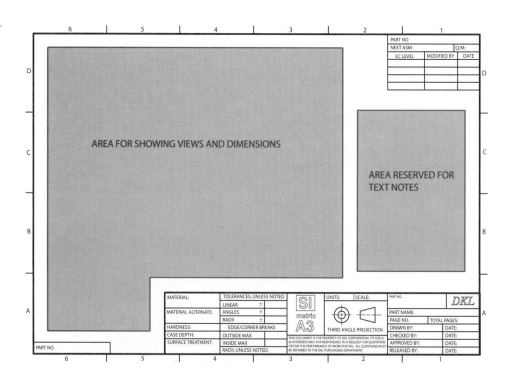

FIGURE 18.16. A formal drawing of a tooling block presented in the preferred multiview configuration showing all hidden lines. All of its features can be shown using the top, front, and right-side views.

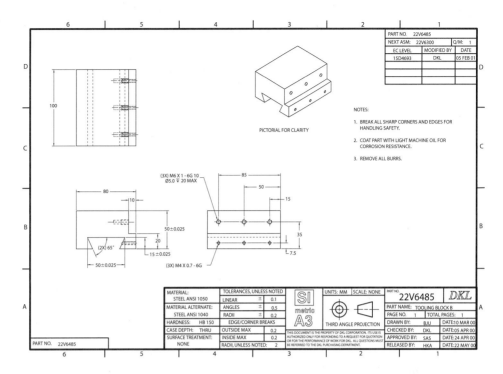

18.05.02 Object Views

Whether the object is a part or an assembly, its geometry must be presented using the rule of orthogonal projection and multiview representation. Further, unless there is a good reason not to do so, the views to be shown are those of the preferred configuration (i.e., the front, top, and right-side views, as shown in Figure 18.16). Cases where more or fewer than three orthographic views should be used are shown in the chapter on orthogonal projection and multiview drawings. A more complex part requiring more views is shown in Figure 18.17. For this part, a left-side view has been added to

FIGURE 18.17. This modified tooling block requires an additional left-side view in order to show the features on that side.

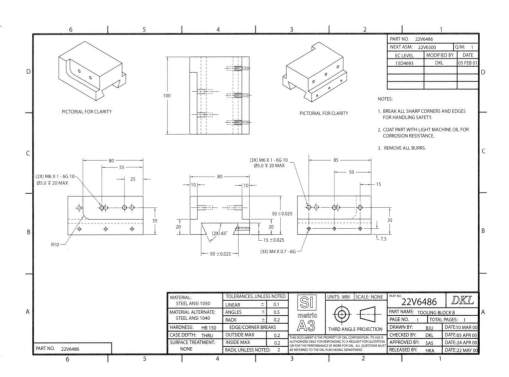

show a cutout and threaded holes on that side of the object. Using the preferred configuration and hidden lines alone to show those features would have required that dimensions be applied to the hidden lines, which produces views that are more complex and difficult to interpret.

The orientation of the object must be such that these three views show as many visible edges in their true length as possible. The guidelines for adding additional drawing details and additional views are as follows:

1. Start by showing the object in the preferred configuration (i.e., the top, front, and right-side views). Orient the object such that as many edges as possible are shown in their true length in these views. If a view adds no additional information to the presentation, it may be removed.

2. Add more of the standard orthogonal views (e.g., left-side, bottom, and/or back view) as necessary so that dimensioning can be applied to visible edges or features only.

3. Add all hidden lines from the exterior edges and interior detail that are not visible.

4. If there are too many hidden lines and the views are confusing, remove the hidden lines that are not necessary for fully defining the geometry or features of the object.

5. If there are still too many hidden lines and the views are still confusing, add more of the standard orthogonal views as necessary to reduce the number of hidden lines and to maintain full definition of the object's geometry.

6. Use shorthand notation to define screw threads and the size and depth of counterbored and countersunk holes and slots. Otherwise, add section views to clarify the interior details.

7. If the hidden lines from different interior details cross or overlap, add section views to clarify the interior details.

8. If any edges cannot be seen in their true lengths in the standard orthogonal views, add auxiliary views so these true lengths can be seen.

9. If features cannot be seen clearly and cannot be defined because they are small, add detail views with a magnified scale.

10. Add the appropriate dimensions and tolerance specifications for the object. If the drawing starts to look crowded, transfer everything to a larger-sized sheet.

For people with a great deal of drawing experience, most of those steps can be done mentally. Then the general rule for presenting the object becomes simply, "Start with the preferred configuration; then add or subtract whatever views are necessary to best show all of the geometry."

18.05.03 Notes

The notes on a formal drawing refer to special processing, handling, or assembly procedures that are required on a part or an assembly that cannot be specified by the dimensions and tolerances on the part or by the materials specifications in the title block. The notes are usually numbered according to each specific requirement and listed together in the same area of the drawing. Notes on a drawing might include "This surface to be free of plating" or "Part to be cleaned and degreased when completed" or "All internal edges to be free of burrs." Generally speaking, a note is added whenever you want something done to a part and you do not know how else to specify it.

18.06 Parts, Subassemblies, and Assemblies

An engineered device is composed of one or more pieces, and one of the purposes of manufacturing drawings is to document how those pieces should be made and how the pieces should be put together to make the device. A set of drawings must contain

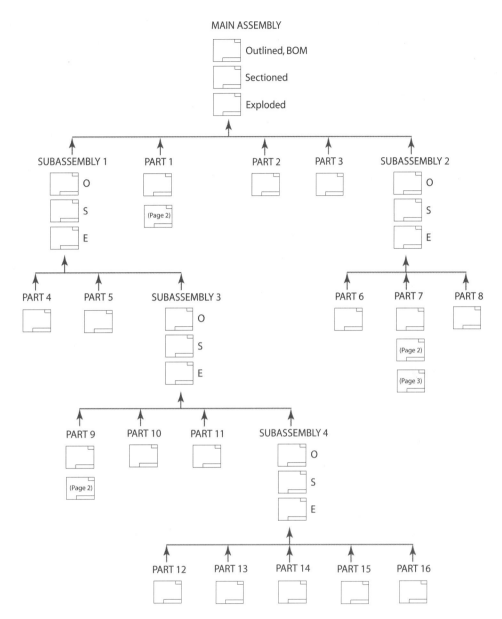

FIGURE 18.18. A set of drawings for a project is organized like the roots of a tree. Individual parts fit into subassemblies or the main assembly. Subassemblies fit into higher subassemblies or the main assembly.

enough information so that any manufacturer with the proper fabrication tools and skills can make all of the pieces and put them together properly. This fabrication must be possible from the information available on the drawings, without consultation with the engineers, designers, or drafters who made the drawings. A set of manufacturing drawings is structured like the roots of a tree, as shown in Figure 18.18.

At the very top of the root structure is the **main assembly** for the device. Assembly drawings are required to show how to put the main assembly together and how all of the pieces look and fit when this is done. The main assembly is composed of smaller individual parts that can be made especially for the device or purchased as commercially available parts. Examples of common commercial parts include screws, bolts, washers, nuts, and rivets.

Assembly drawings contain information that identifies the parts or subassemblies in the assembly. This is done with **balloons** and arrows pointing to each part. Balloons are closed geometric shapes, not necessarily circular, that contain a number. Depending on individual company practices, the number inside the balloon can be the part number or an **item number** that is referenced to the part number and listed with the drawing's notes. Some companies like to include the quantity of each part inside the balloon along with the item or part number.

The main assembly also can be composed of smaller **subassemblies**, which are collections of custom-made and/or commercially available parts that have already been put together and installed in the main assembly as a single piece. A large project may have several levels of subassemblies in the main assembly. Each subassembly needs its own layout drawing and assembly drawing for the various sub-subassemblies, or parts, that go into it. Finally, each custom-made part requires a **detail drawing** that shows the geometry, dimensions, tolerances, materials, and all other information needed to fabricate the part.

At this time, a more precise definition of a part is needed. The most common interpretation of a **part** is that it is a single object made from a single, contiguous material. Most metal, plastic, or wooden objects, for example, fall under this definition. Up until the twentieth century, this definition was correct. Since that time, products have become increasingly complex in their construction and use of different materials. Is an electric motor a single part; or is it a collection of parts, otherwise known as an assembly? What about the headlight module on a car? Imagine an electric circuit board with various electronic components installed on it. If you were the user of the board, you would probably consider it to be a single part. However, if you were its manufacturer, you would probably consider it to be an assembly. Therefore, the definition of a part depends on how you expect to receive it from the manufacturer making it for you. You can generally refer to an object as a single part, even though it may be composed of many different pieces and be made of many different materials, when you expect the fabricator to deliver it to you as a single unit with only its external dimensions and functional requirements specified.

Consider the drawings that would be necessary for the product shown in Figure 18.19, which shows a vise clamp used for holding work pieces during machining operations. All of the drawings necessary to fabricate this device will be discussed, with more detail on the type and method of presentation of information for each type of drawing.

FIGURE 18.19. A 3-D computer-generated model of a machine vise.

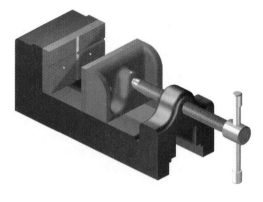

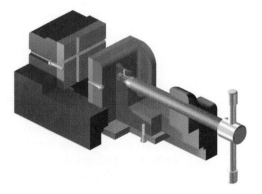

FIGURE 18.20. An exploded assembly drawing including a bill of materials for a machine vise.

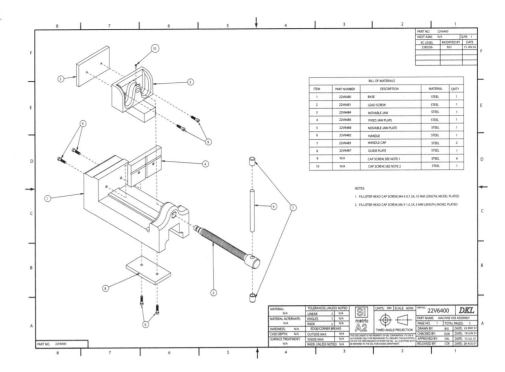

18.06.01 Exploded Assembly Drawings

Exploded assembly drawings show how various parts and pieces that compose an assembly or subassembly are put together. Rather than showing everything in their final position, as with a layout drawing, an assembly drawing shows the parts of a device in a disassembled state. The assembly drawing for the vise clamp is shown in Figure 18.20. The various parts are shown in their final resting orientation, but not necessarily in their final location. Instead, the parts are located such that they are removed from their final location in the opposite direction of manufacturing insertion. The path of insertion for each part is then shown using a dashed path called a **trail**. Therefore, the trail of each part shows the fabricator how that part is to be placed in the device to create the final configuration.

Since assembly drawings are used to show a process rather than precise geometry, using a pictorial presentation is preferred to using a multiview presentation. Neither part nor assembly dimensions are shown, except for occasional reference dimensions for convenience only. As with a layout drawing, assembly drawings use numbered balloons and arrows pointing to each piece to identify their parts or subassemblies. The item number in each balloon must correspond to the same item number in the layout drawing and is then listed with its corresponding part number and part name in the assembly drawing's notes.

18.06.02 Outline Assembly Drawings

Outline assembly drawings, sometimes called **layout drawings**, are used to show the fit and function of all of the various pieces that go into a completed assembly or subassembly. The main outline assembly drawing for the vise clamp is shown in Figure 18.21. An outline assembly drawing shows the final product in its final configuration using the multiview format required for all working drawings. Sometimes isometric or other pictorial views are included for additional clarity. Section views are added to reveal parts that cannot be seen externally, and magnified detail views are used to show parts that are too small to recognize. Note that the dimensions for the individual parts are not shown in

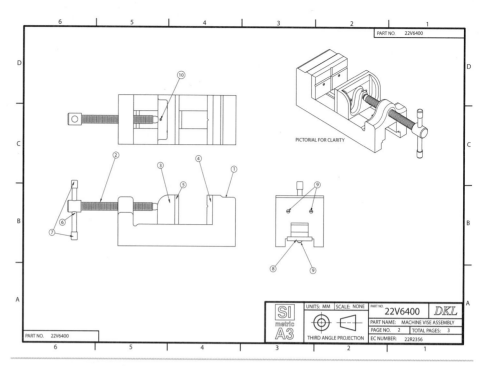

FIGURE 18.21. An outline assembly drawing of the machine vise.

any assembly drawing. That information is contained in the detail drawings. Information pertaining to tolerances and materials on the drawing header are left blank since that information is contained in the detail drawing for the individual part and does not need to be repeated for the assembled device.

If any **assembly dimensions** are required, they must be shown with their tolerances on the layout drawing. Assembly dimensions show where parts must be placed relative to other parts when the device is being put together (e.g., when a special alignment between parts is required and no features on the individual parts provide for this alignment). An example of when assembly dimensions are required is when a smaller block is to be welded or bonded to a larger plate. Unless there are features on the plate for locating the block, assembly dimensions must be supplied. If the parts are to be welded together, specification for the welds must be placed on the layout drawing.

Reference dimensions, if used at all, should be used sparingly and must be clearly identified and placed inside parentheses. These dimensions already exist on or can be extracted from other drawings. They are shown mostly for the convenience of the reader and are usually used to show gross sizes, such as the overall width, height, and length of a device. The reason reference dimensions are used sparingly is because errors sometimes occur when the dimension on a part changes and the change is forgotten on the reference dimension.

The notes on a layout drawing are used to specify any special procedures or processes needed to put the device together and any tests that are necessary to ensure that the device will work in its intended manner. The notes also list the definitions of the item numbers referenced in the multiview presentation.

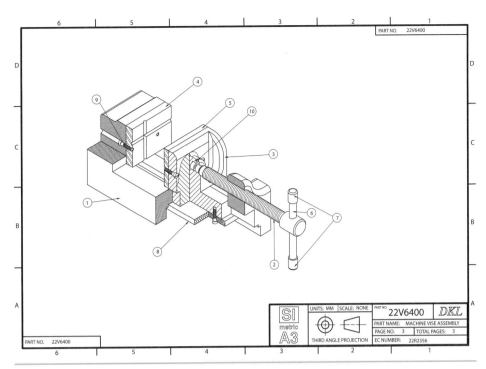

FIGURE 18.22. A sectioned assembly drawing of the machine vise.

18.06.03 Sectioned Assembly Drawings

A **sectioned assembly drawing** is a pictorial or orthogonal view(s) that shows all of the various pieces of an assembly or a subassembly in their final resting position. For purposes of revealing otherwise hidden parts, some parts have been cut away. The cut surfaces are indicated by the use of section lines. A section line pattern is usually used for each part to aid in its distinction. The various pieces within the assembly are identified using numbered balloons with the same item numbers used in the other assembly drawings. A sectioned assembly drawing for the vise clamp is shown in Figure 18.22. Although sectioned assembly drawings are difficult to create, especially without the use of 3-D modeling, such drawings offer unparalleled clarity for showing how various parts fit together to make a complete device. Whenever possible, a sectioned assembly drawing should be included in a drawing set.

18.06.04 The Bill of Materials

The **bill of materials (BOM)** for a device is not an actual drawing, but rather a text list of its parts, subassemblies, and subassembly parts. The BOM, which can appear on any one of the assembly drawings or as a separate drawing or document, is used mainly by a fabricator to check that all of the drawings and materials needed to make the device are available. Commercial parts are also included on this list. Although not a drawing, a BOM is usually printed as a table on an assembly drawing to emphasize that this list is considered a member of the set of drawings for the device. The BOM is often included as part of the layout or assembly drawing.

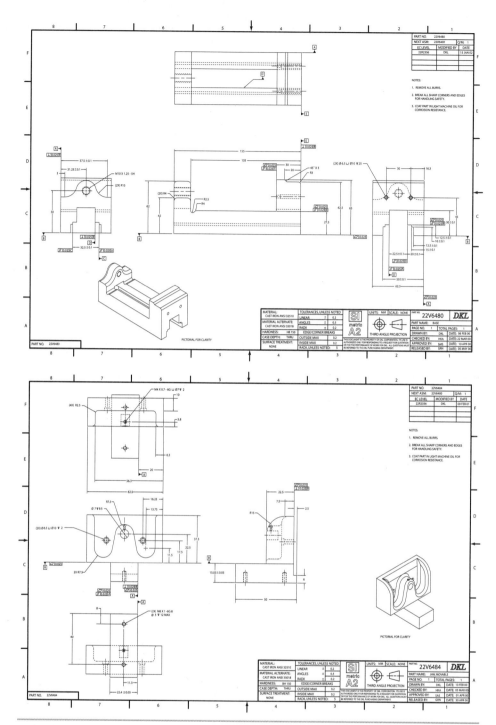

FIGURE 18.23. Detail drawings for the machine vise.

The typical information included on a BOM of an assembly includes the item number (if the bill is included as part of the layout or assembly drawing), the corresponding part number, its part name, the material from which the part is made, and the number of times the part is used in the assembly. Subassemblies have their own BOMs. When the main assembly contains subassemblies, the part numbers and names for those subassemblies are listed on the main BOM. The various parts and sub-subassemblies are listed on the BOM for each respective subassembly. If commercial parts are used, their

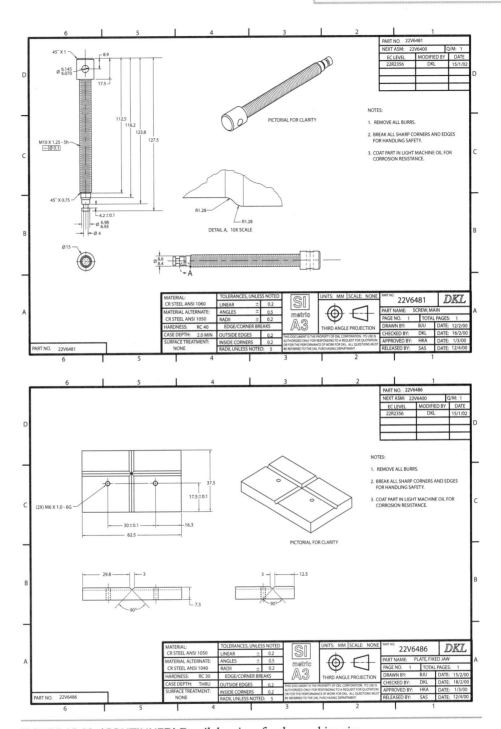

FIGURE 18.23. (CONTINUED) Detail drawings for the machine vise.

descriptions must be included on the BOM. These descriptions must contain enough information for the parts to be acquired without subsequent explanation.

18.06.05 Manufacturing Detail Drawings

A detail drawing shows all of the geometry, dimensions, tolerances, material, and processes needed to fabricate a single part. Each custom-made part must have its own detail drawing. Some companies even require that commercially available parts have

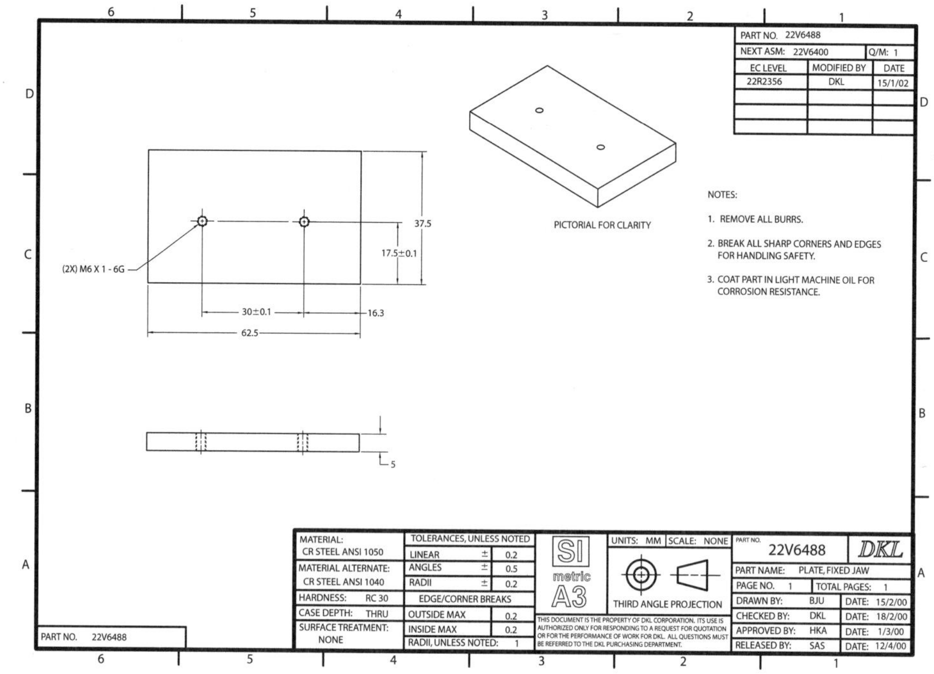

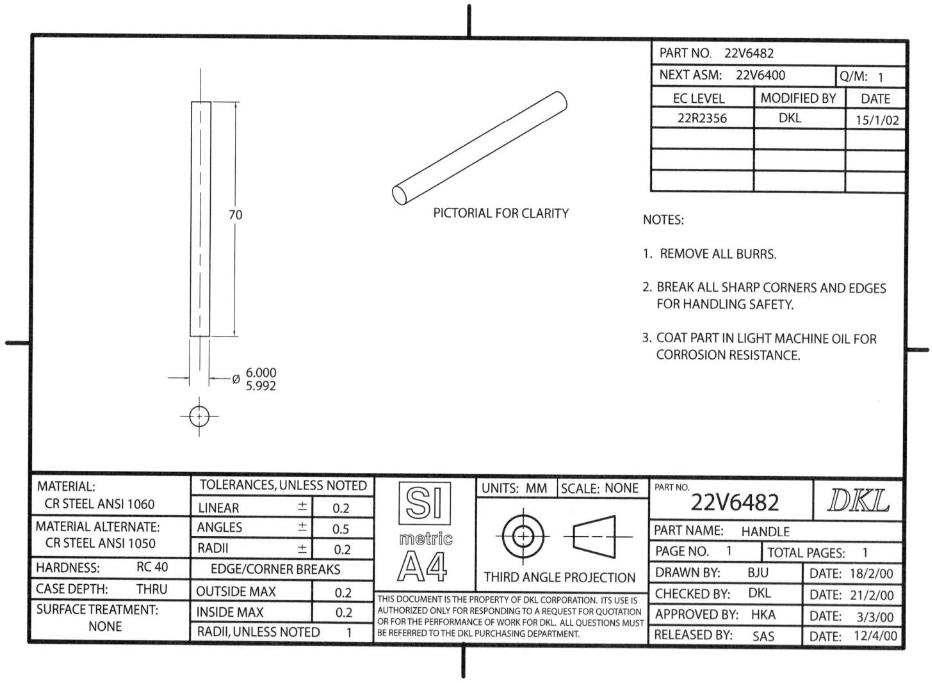

FIGURE 18.23. (CONTINUED) Detail drawings for the machine vise.

their own detail drawings placed on that company's header to ensure that these parts will fit and function properly with the custom-made parts. The detail drawings for the parts of the vise clamp are shown in Figure 18.23. The drawings shown in Figure 18.16 and Figure 18.17 are also classified as detail drawings.

The detail drawing for each part shows it using the multiview format required for all manufacturing drawings. Sometimes isometric or other pictorial views are included for additional clarity. Section views are added as necessary to reveal interior features. Magnified detail views are added as necessary to show features that would otherwise be too small to dimension. All of the dimensions for each part must be shown.

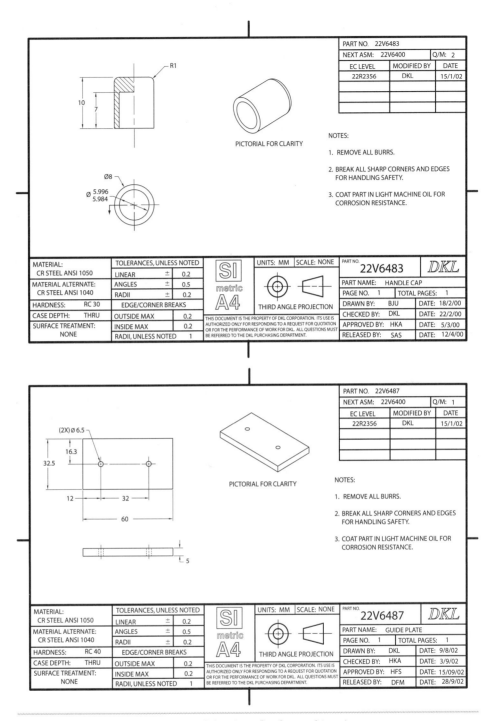

FIGURE 18.23. (CONTINUED) Detail drawings for the machine vise.

Information pertaining to tolerances and materials on the drawing header is also included.

The notes on a detail drawing are used to specify any special procedures or processes needed to fabricate or finish the part that are not evident from the dimensions and tolerances and any tests that are necessary to ensure that the part works in its intended manner. Putting a closed geometric shape, usually a box, around the note number highlights a note that refers to a particular feature on the part. A leader arrow then points to that feature and is annotated "See note X," which tells the reader of the drawing that a special instruction in the notes is associated with that feature.

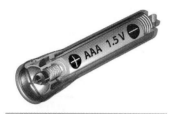

FIGURE 18.24. Three-dimensional computer-generated models of a disposable one-cell flashlight.

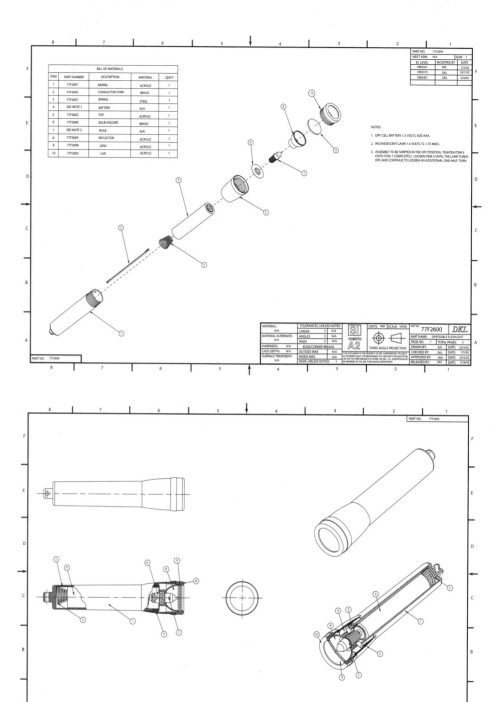

FIGURE 18.25. Working drawings for the disposable flashlight.

18.06.06 More Examples of Manufacturing Drawings

The 3-D model of a small, inexpensive flashlight is shown in a complete state and in a sectioned state in Figure 18.24. The working drawings for this product are shown in Figure 18.25. The assembly drawings show how the individual pieces fit together, and the detail drawings show the required sizes of the custom parts. The complete assembly drawing is three pages long and includes exploded, outline, and sectioned views as well

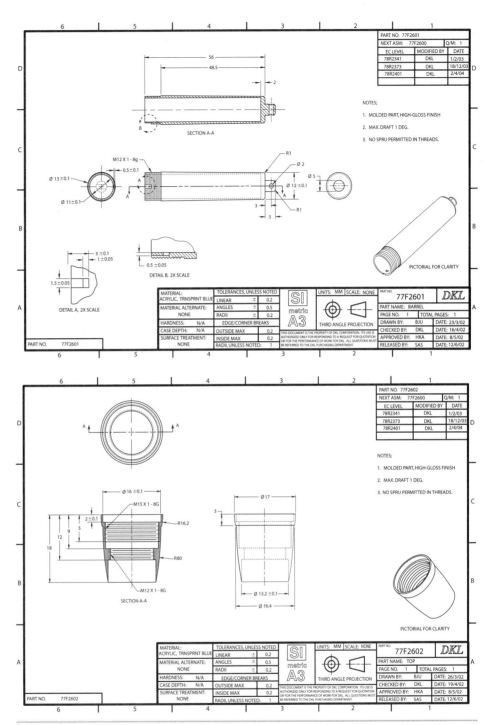

FIGURE 18.25. (CONTINUED) Working drawings for the disposable flashlight.

as a BOM. For this intended low-cost, high-volume product (more than 100,000 per month), many of the pieces will be molded from plastic. The product has been designed such that stringent tolerances on the dimensions are not required for the parts to fit together and function. Two of the parts, the battery and the light bulb, are commercially available; thus, detail drawings are not needed for them. The assembly drawings, however, show all of the parts, including the battery and bulb. The BOM, located on the first page of the assembly drawing, specifies enough information about these two parts so that they may be purchased.

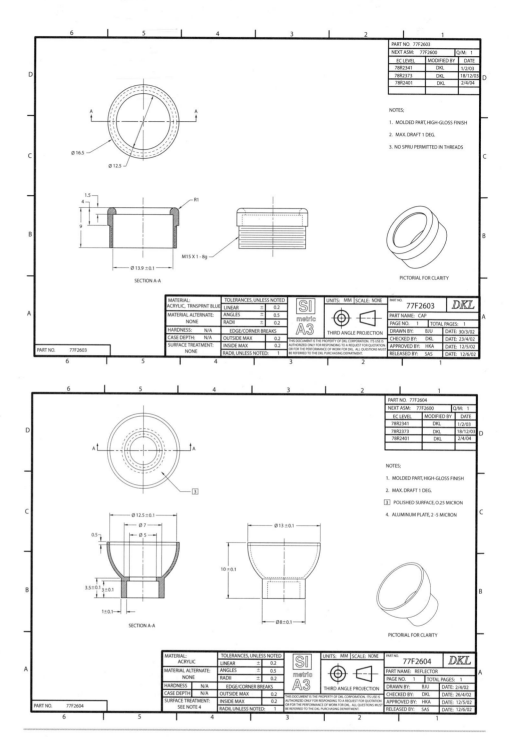

FIGURE 18.25. (CONTINUED) Working drawings for the disposable flashlight.

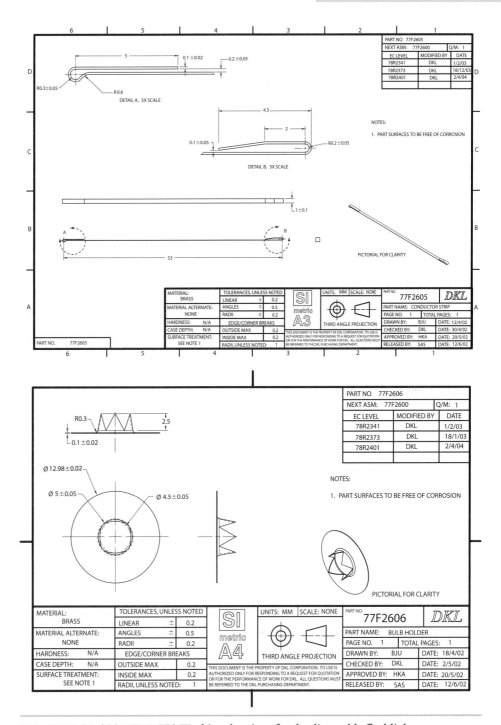

FIGURE 18.25. (CONTINUED) Working drawings for the disposable flashlight.

Part drawing 77F2607 (SPRING)

PART NO. 77F2607		
NEXT ASM: 77F2600		Q/M: 1
EC LEVEL	MODIFIED BY	DATE
78R2341	DKL	1/2/03
78R2373	DKL	18/1/03
78R2401	DKL	2/4/04

PICTORIAL FOR CLARITY

Ø 5
Ø0.5±0.05
Ø 9
10

MATERIAL: CD STEEL ANSI 1040	TOLERANCES, UNLESS NOTED			SI metric A4	UNITS: MM	SCALE: NONE	PART NO. 77F2607	DKL
	LINEAR	±	0.2					
MATERIAL ALTERNATE: CD STEEL ANSI 1050	ANGLES	±	0.5		THIRD ANGLE PROJECTION		PART NAME: SPRING	
	RADII	±	0.2				PAGE NO. 1	TOTAL PAGES: 1
HARDNESS: N/A	EDGE/CORNER BREAKS						DRAWN BY: BJU	DATE: 20/4/02
CASE DEPTH: N/A	OUTSIDE MAX		0.2				CHECKED BY: DKL	DATE: 4/5/02
SURFACE TREATMENT: ZINC PLATE, 2-5 MICRON	INSIDE MAX		0.2				APPROVED BY: HKA	DATE: 21/5/02
	RADII, UNLESS NOTED:		1				RELEASED BY: SAS	DATE: 12/6/02

THIS DOCUMENT IS THE PROPERTY OF DKL CORPORATION. ITS USE IS AUTHORIZED ONLY FOR RESPONDING TO A REQUEST FOR QUOTATION OR FOR THE PERFORMANCE OF WORK FOR DKL. ALL QUESTIONS MUST BE REFERRED TO THE DKL PURCHASING DEPARTMENT.

Part drawing 77F2608 (LENS)

PART NO. 77F2608		
NEXT ASM: 77F2600		Q/M: 1
EC LEVEL	MODIFIED BY	DATE
78R2341	DKL	1/2/03
78R2373	DKL	18/1/03
78R2401	DKL	2/4/04

NOTES:

1. PART TO BE OPTICALLY CLEAR.

Ø 13.5±0.1
1±0.05

PICTORIAL FOR CLARITY

MATERIAL: ACRYLIC	TOLERANCES, UNLESS NOTED			SI metric A4	UNITS: MM	SCALE: NONE	PART NO. 77F2608	DKL
	LINEAR	±	0.2					
MATERIAL ALTERNATE: NONE	ANGLES	±	0.5		THIRD ANGLE PROJECTION		PART NAME: LENS	
	RADII	±	0.2				PAGE NO. 1	TOTAL PAGES: 1
HARDNESS: N/A	EDGE/CORNER BREAKS						DRAWN BY: BJU	DATE: 21/4/02
CASE DEPTH: N/A	OUTSIDE MAX		0.2				CHECKED BY: DKL	DATE: 6/5/02
SURFACE TREATMENT: SEE NOTE 1	INSIDE MAX		0.2				APPROVED BY: HKA	DATE: 21/5/02
	RADII, UNLESS NOTED:		1				RELEASED BY: SAS	DATE: 12/6/02

THIS DOCUMENT IS THE PROPERTY OF DKL CORPORATION. ITS USE IS AUTHORIZED ONLY FOR RESPONDING TO A REQUEST FOR QUOTATION OR FOR THE PERFORMANCE OF WORK FOR DKL. ALL QUESTIONS MUST BE REFERRED TO THE DKL PURCHASING DEPARTMENT.

FIGURE 18.25. (CONTINUED) Working drawings for the disposable flashlight.

The 3-D model of a computer disk drive spindle is shown in Figure 18.26. The working drawings for this spindle are shown in Figure 18.27. The anticipated production volume of this product (more than 250,000 per month) is very high; however, performance requirements for its application demand very strict tolerance control on many of its part dimensions. Close attention needs to be paid to fabrication techniques to ensure that the required tolerances can be met with a minimum of manufacturing

FIGURE 18.26. A 3-D computer-generated model of a computer disk drive spindle.

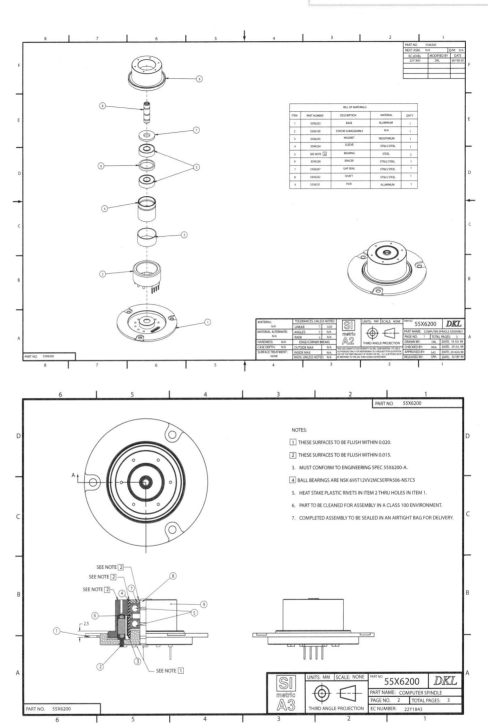

FIGURE 18.27. Working drawings for the computer disk drive spindle.

cost. The computer spindle uses two commercially available ball bearings; detail drawings are not necessary, but they are shown and specified in the assembly drawing and BOM. Note also that one of the parts, the stator, in the main assembly is actually a subassembly. The stator is composed of custom laminations that are stacked, insulated, wound, and insert-molded with connector pins. The part is then delivered as a single piece, ready to be installed into the spindle main assembly.

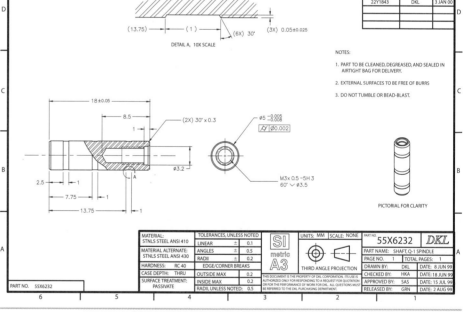

FIGURE 18.27. (CONTINUED) Working drawings for the computer disk drive spindle.

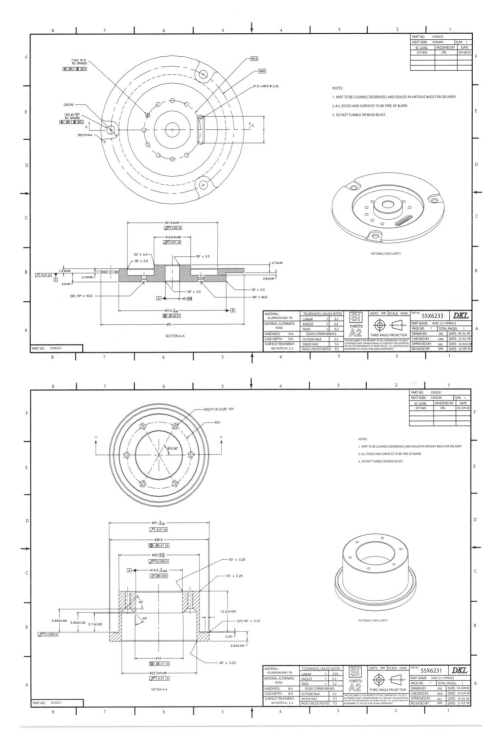

FIGURE 18.27. (CONTINUED) Working drawings for the computer disk drive spindle.

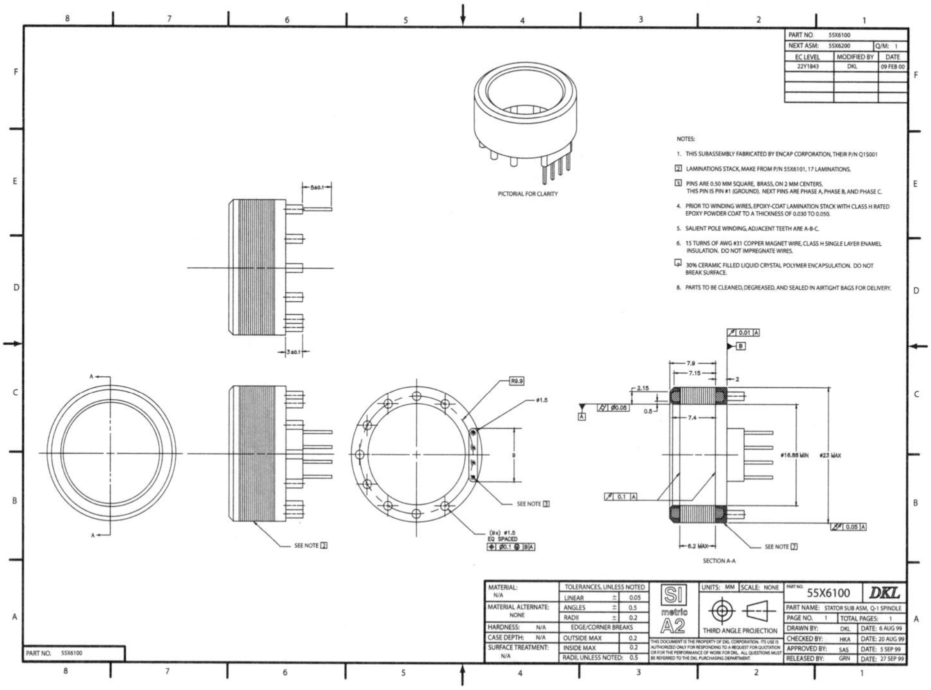

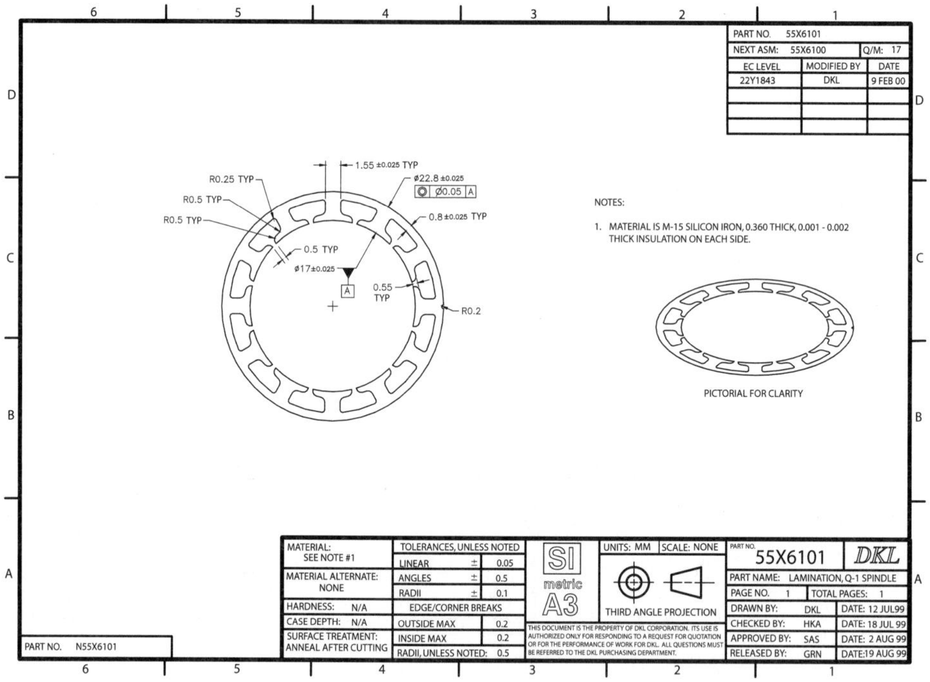

FIGURE 18.27. (CONTINUED) Working drawings for the computer disk drive spindle.

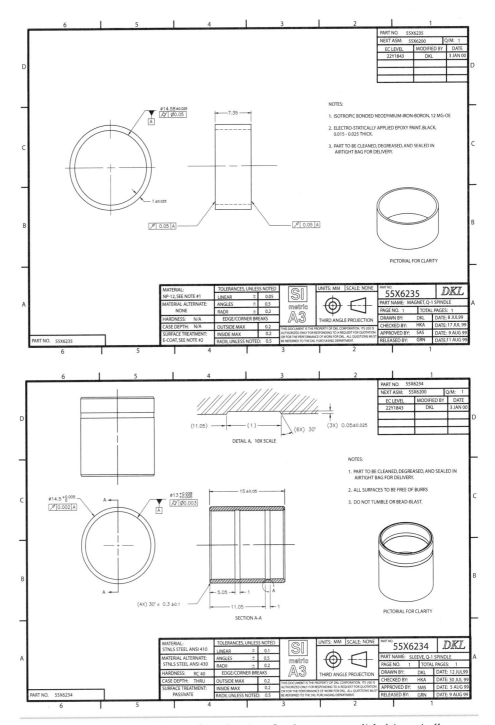

FIGURE 18.27. (CONTINUED) Working drawings for the computer disk drive spindle.

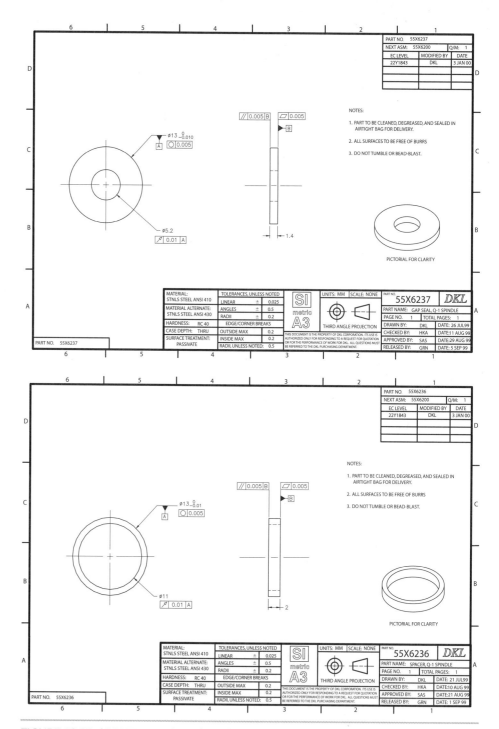

FIGURE 18.27. (CONTINUED) Working drawings for the computer disk drive spindle.

18.07 Construction Drawings

In the previous sections, you learned about working drawings in general and about manufacturing drawings specifically. In the following sections, you will learn about a different type of drawings—those used primarily in the construction of large civil engineering structures. In these sections, the term *structure* refers to any type of large infrastructure project, such as roads, bridges, buildings, and dams.

18.07.01 Why Construction Drawings Are Different from Manufacturing Drawings

Earlier in this chapter you learned that one of the primary differences between manufacturing and construction engineering projects is that mechanical designs are developed for mass production, whereas civil designs represent a single, one-off system. Another significant difference between the two types of engineering projects is that construction projects are typically site-specific and manufacturing projects typically are not. Bridges are constructed at specific locations. Water treatment facilities are located on specific property. Mechanical products are manufactured and shipped to various locations throughout the world—it does not matter where they are manufactured or where they are used.

Another difference between construction and manufacturing projects is their relative size. Construction projects are typically large-scale. Bridges can be several miles in length; buildings can be several stories high; dams can be massively large; sewage treatment plants can cover several acres. Manufactured products are typically shipped from one location to another for eventual use, and their size is relatively small when compared to construction projects.

Yet another difference between construction and manufacturing projects is that in the United States, construction projects are often designed in the English system of units. Although the government has encouraged the construction industry to adopt the metric system of measurement (and in some cases has required that civil designs include metric dimensions), the metric system is generally not used for this type of project. In fact, in many cases where engineers working on infrastructure projects were required to include metric dimensions, they merely converted the dimensions from English to metric and did not actually *design* the system in metric. Thus, a dimension might be given on a construction drawing as 25.4 cm, having been converted from something originally designed to be 10 inches. In contrast, manufacturing projects are often designed from the start in the metric system; so dimensions will appear as whole numbers such as 25 cm or 30 cm.

Infrastructure projects are often designed and constructed for the members of society. In fact, the name *civil engineering* comes from the profession's origins in France where citizens demanded roads, water, and sanitary systems for the *civilians*—these facilities were already in place for the armed forces. Because construction projects are designed for use by the general public, they are usually required to be approved by a registered PE. A PE must pass two tests that assess his or her level of proficiency in solving engineering problems. In addition, an engineer must work for several years under the supervision of a PE before being eligible to attempt the second day-long test. After passing the exam, the new PE is legally and ethically responsible for the integrity of the designs developed under his or her supervision and can be sued if a structure fails. In contrast, manufacturing projects rarely have PEs working on them, although the senior engineer on a project usually has several years of experience and would not have been trusted to verify the integrity of the design without the demonstrated ability to perform this function.

Although 3-D computer modeling predominates in manufactured systems, its use in civil engineering design practice is still fairly limited; this trend will likely continue for the foreseeable future. In some of the larger civil engineering firms, 3-D models of projects are created, but these computer models are typically specialized for civil applications and cannot be used to generate 2-D drawings directly from the models. The 2-D drawings are still created independently from the 3-D models. For manufactured products, drawings are becoming less important, especially as modern software enhances the ability to send 3-D computer models electronically to CNC lathes for production. This is not the case for civil and architectural applications. In civil engineering practice, design and construction are still accomplished primarily through drawings. Construction projects are not built in climate-controlled, clean environments. Projects are constructed outside with exposure to the elements, often far away from electric power sources or network connections. Physical drawings are still far more practical in this environment than are 3-D computer models.

Finally, construction projects are like large-scale assembly projects that are always built from the ground up. With a construction project, the contractor performs the site excavation first; then the foundation is poured. The first floor of a structure must be built before the second floor can be built, and the second floor must be constructed before the third floor can be constructed. All of the floors must be complete before the roof can be added. Also, wiring, plumbing, and ductwork must be in place before the walls and ceilings can be completed. Further, each subsystem on the project, like the wiring and plumbing, is typically put in place by a subcontractor who is hired by the general contractor on the project. Thus, there is a specific order and timing in which the various parts of the project are completed; and significant communication and coordination are required between the client, engineer, contractor, and subcontractors. Scheduling is a significant part of a construction project. Manufacturing projects typically do not require this complex level of communication, scheduling, or coordination and do not typically have a rigid order for assembly. (Although, of course, some subassemblies must be put together before other subassemblies.)

18.07.02 How Construction Drawings Are Different from Manufacturing Drawings

Due to the some of the differences between construction and manufacturing practices described in the previous paragraphs, several differences in the development of working drawings have evolved over time. In the following paragraphs, these differences will be described and illustrated.

Terminology

Drawings used in the design and construction of civil or architectural projects are frequently referred to as **blueprints**. The name *blueprint* is derived from an earlier era when construction drawings were reproduced by a method that resulted in a blue background with white lines. The original drawings were made using ink on large sheets of paper; but there was no such thing as copiers or printers, especially of this size. Special blueprint machines were developed so that multiple copies of the handmade ink drawings could be produced. Although modern-day computer hardware with large printers has enabled the creation of construction drawings with black lines on a white background, they are still often referred to as blueprints. Figure 18.28 shows a blueprint of a hand-drawn sketch of a mixer plate design. Note that the title block shows the date that this blueprint was drawn.

In construction applications, **plan views** are views made from a vantage point above the "object." Thus, plan views can be thought of as top views. You are probably familiar with the term **floor plan**; in fact, you may have seen a floor plan in a newspaper or magazine. A floor plan is a drawing made from a vantage point above a building that shows the layout of all of the rooms on a particular floor. Similarly, a **foundation plan** shows the building foundation from above, the **electrical plan** shows the wiring diagram from above, and the **heating and ventilation plan** shows the location of ducts and equipment from above. **Profile views** show the building or project from the front or the side. In other words, they are views where the top of the structure is seen as an edge. **Elevation views** are drawings that show differences in elevations on a structure. Since changes in elevation can be seen in any view where the top is an edge, elevation views are essentially the same as profile views.

In the design and construction of large infrastructure projects, several drawings are necessary to describe the facility completely so that it can be built. The entire set of drawings is called the **set of construction plans**, or "the plans," even though not all of the drawings represent plan (top) views of the structure. The **specifications**, or **specs**,

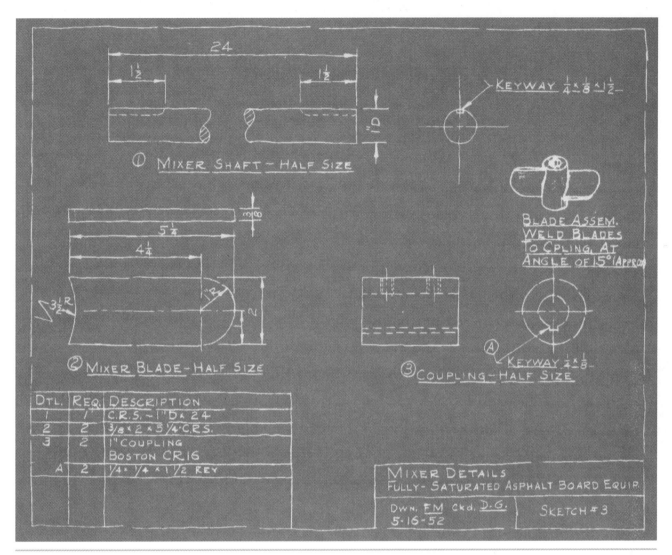

FIGURE 18.28. Hand-drawn blueprint of a mixer plate.

consist of written instructions regarding the construction of the facility. Together the plans and specs make up the entire construction documentation. In this text, you will focus on understanding the drawings—specifications are beyond its scope.

Size Considerations

Construction drawings are almost always created or printed on E size sheets. Recall that E size sheets are 34″ × 44″; however, smaller sheets may be used for drawings that are brought into the field. Large sheets are used for construction drawings due to the relative large size of the projects. For a bridge that is three miles long, it would be difficult to show the entire structure on an 11″ × 17″ sheet of paper (B size) or to show it in sufficient detail for understanding. Construction drawings are always made to scale, with 1 inch sometimes equaling hundreds of feet. It would be impossible (and impractical) to draw a large structure true size—imagine the size of the sheet of paper that would be required.

The relative large size of construction projects also makes strict tolerancing relatively meaningless. When a slab of concrete is specified as 10'-6" × 40'-9", no one expects the slab to be *exactly* that size; plus or minus a few tenths of an inch is probably acceptable. For concrete slabs, making sure that the surface is level is far more important than its overall surface area. Smaller tolerances may be needed when bolt holes are located on a steel structural member; however, once again, the tolerances are nowhere near the precision found in manufacturing projects where tolerances as small as 0.001" are acceptable and routine. A contractor would likely laugh out loud if a tolerance of 0.001" were ever specified on the design drawings for an infrastructure project.

Another difference in the working drawings that results due to the large size of construction projects is that views typically do not project orthogonally from one view to the next. Often the plan view (or top view) is on one sheet with the elevation view (or front view) located several sheets away. Sometimes even the scale used to draw the plan view differs from the scale used to draw the elevation view, meaning you could not separate the sheets and try to line them up if you wanted to see how features projected from one view to the next. In this respect, the need for well-developed 3-D spatial skills may be even more important for engineers working on construction projects. You often must remember what the plan view looks like as you search for the elevation view on a separate sheet.

Site-Specific Considerations

In the construction industry, the orientation and location of a project with respect to its surroundings are extremely important. Imagine the problems that would develop if a building were constructed on someone else's property. Several methods used on drawings help the contractor locate the structure properly. **Bearings** of lines may be shown on a drawing. The bearing of a line is the angle that the line makes with a North-South line, as illustrated in Figure 18.29. Bearings of lines are seen only in plan views (i.e., from above). On the construction site, bearings of lines can be obtained by any of several surveying techniques and the building can then be accurately located on the property. Alternatively, a North line may be placed on the drawing to show the relative orientation of the structure.

Control points are often provided on construction drawings to help locate features of the project accurately. With this method, an "origin" for the construction site is designated and all points are referenced north, south, east, or west from it. Thus, a point on a drawing might have coordinates N13750 and E7895, for example. Similar to bearings, the coordinates of the control points are seen only in plan views. The origin for the coordinate system is usually referred to as a **benchmark**. Benchmarks have been established across the United States by the U.S. Geological Survey (USGS) and typically consist of a concrete cylinder with a brass, circular medal on top imbedded in the earth. The location of each benchmark was determined with a high degree of accuracy. Many times job benchmarks are established on construction sites when a USGS benchmark is not located within the vicinity of the project.

Benchmarks are also used to determine the elevation of points on a construction site. Elevations are used to establish vertical distances between points on a building. For example, the top of a floor slab might be specified as having an elevation of 556 feet. Elevations are seen only in profile views (or elevation views) and are usually referenced to true elevations (i.e., the height of the point above sea level) or to job elevations. With job elevations, a benchmark is established and given an arbitrary elevation of, for example, 100 feet. All other elevations for the project are then specified relative to that point. A benchmark elevation of 0 is usually not specified to ensure that job elevations are never negative.

One of the first steps in the design of a structure is to send a crew out to do a **site survey**. Usually there are existing structures or features that must be noted on the plans before the design can proceed. Modern survey equipment is computerized such that the survey data is automatically stored and later easily converted to a drawing.

FIGURE 18.29. Illustration of the definition of a bearing of a line. Bearings are only seen in the plan views.

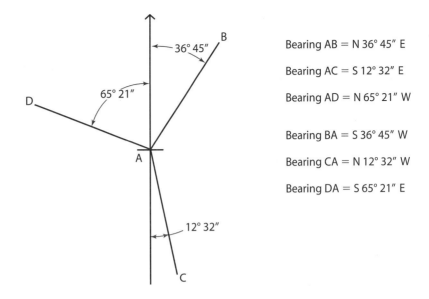

Bearing AB = N 36° 45″ E

Bearing AC = S 12° 32″ E

Bearing AD = N 65° 21″ W

Bearing BA = S 36° 45″ W

Bearing CA = N 12° 32″ W

Bearing DA = S 65° 21″ E

Figure 18.30 shows the survey data for a site taken in the field; Figure 18.31 shows the survey data after it has been converted to a site plan drawing.

One-of-a-Kind Considerations

In manufacturing projects, prototypes of products are created and tested for their integrity and functionality. The prototypes can be virtual or actual physical models. Construction projects are too large and expensive to warrant the building of prototypes; however, sometimes small-scale models are developed to allow clients and others to visualize what a structure will look like when completed. The models built in construction practice have little value in analyzing the structure—they are merely used for display purposes, especially when dealing with a client who may not be able to visualize a project based on the plans. Virtual computer models may also be available for analysis, especially in larger engineering firms. Because large structures are one-offs, unforeseen problems are likely to occur during construction. Ductwork may interfere with

FIGURE 18.30. Data from site survey showing existing structures and other entities.

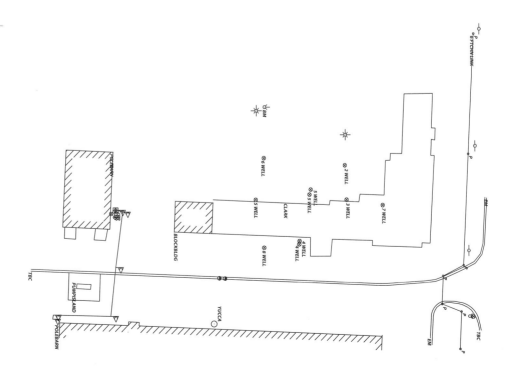

FIGURE 18.31. Survey data converted to site drawing.

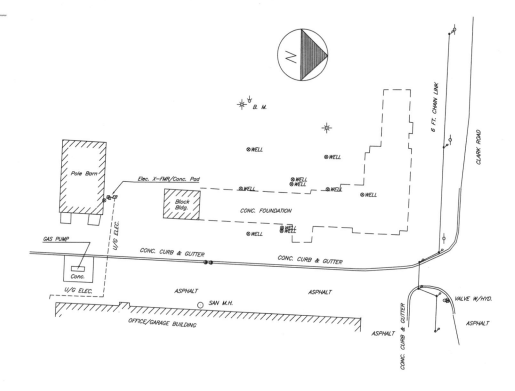

plumbing pipes and need to be rerouted. Dimensions may have inadvertently been left off the drawing. The engineer may discover that walls or doorways need to be moved. Because changes to the original design may need to be made during construction, the contractor keeps track of them on a set of **as-built plans**. As-built drawings graphically show any changes from the original design and are important for future maintenance and operation of the facility.

18.08 Construction Plans

A set of construction plans usually consists of a large number of drawings. The drawings in the plans usually include the cover sheet, site plan, elevation views, foundation plan, floor plans, electrical plans, roofing plans, sections, detail drawings, and any other drawings needed to describe the project completely. The drawings are included in the set of plans in the order in which they are needed for the construction of the project. This means that the foundation plan appears before the first-floor plan, the floor plans appear before the roofing plan, etc.

For a complete set of plans, several sheets are often required for each type of drawing. In addition to the drawings, **schedules of materials**, which list, for example, the types of doors and windows to be used in the construction of the facility, are included on the drawings. In this case, a schedule of materials is much like a BOM for manufacturing projects. Most public projects require the seal and signature of a PE, which often appears on the cover sheet of the drawing set. The PE is legally responsible for the design and construction of the facility even if he or she did not complete all of the analysis for the project. A PE will usually meticulously check the calculations and analysis before signing off on the plans. The name of the PE appears in the title block of each drawing in the set of plans. The title block also typically includes the name of the drafter who made the drawings and others involved with the design; however, title blocks on construction drawings do not typically contain all of the information found on the title block for manufacturing drawings.

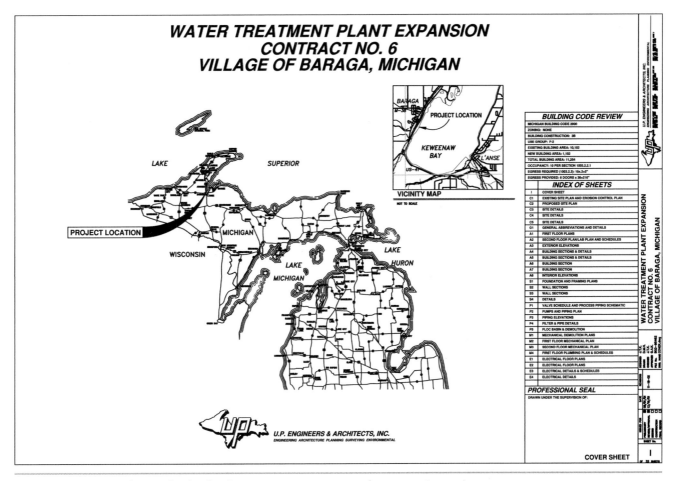

FIGURE 18.32. Cover sheet and index for the Baraga water treatment plant expansion project.

18.08.01 Cover Sheet

The **cover sheet** for the plans typically contains a map of the area surrounding the project site. The map is not overly detailed, but shows the general location of the project. Since the set of drawings for a project usually consists of several sheets, an **index** of all drawings in the set is included on the cover sheet or on the first page following the cover. Figure 18.32 shows the cover sheet from a set of plans drawn for an expansion project for a water treatment plant in the village of Baraga in the state of Michigan. Note the map showing part of the state with the portion of the state near the project site enlarged to show the area in greater detail. Also note the index listing all of the drawings in the set of plans and the area reserved on the cover sheet for the seal of the PE.

18.08.02 Site Plan

One of the first drawings in the set of construction plans is a site map or a **site plan**. Figure 18.33 shows the proposed site plan for the Baraga water treatment facility. Note that this plan shows the highway as well as an arrow indicating north. Since this project constitutes an addition to an existing structure, the outline of that building is shown on the site plan as well. The scale for the drawing is shown in the upper-left corner both graphically and numerically (1 inch = 20 feet). Contour lines showing changes in existing ground elevation are also shown. You will learn more about contour lines and topographic maps in a later chapter.

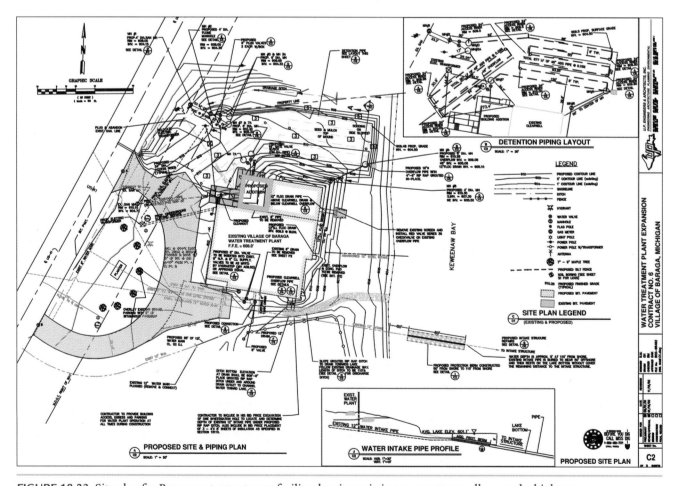

FIGURE 18.33. Site plan for Baraga water treatment facility showing existing structure as well as nearby highway.

18.08.03 Elevation Views

As stated previously, elevation views show the structure from a vantage point where changes in elevation are visible. Elevation views can be thought of as front or side views; but for a large structure, the terms *front* and *side* are fairly meaningless. Elevation views are defined by their orientation with respect to the compass points of North, South, East, and West. A North Elevation shows what the structure would like if you stood to the north of it and looked back, a South Elevation shows what it would look like from the south, etc. Although elevation views do not contain a great deal of detail or many dimensions about the actual construction of the facility, they do help contractors and owners visualize the resulting project. Figure 18.34 shows the South Elevation view for the overflow and drain portion of the lagoon for the Baraga water treatment facility. Note that there are no dimensions on this drawing, but elevations of some features are included—the existing ground profile has an elevation specified of 811.5′ ±, and the proposed ground profile shows an elevation of 814′. The symbol for elevation on the drawing is a circle with a cross through it with the horizontal "crosshair" on the surface whose elevation is being specified.

18.08.04 Foundation and Floor Plans

Because a building is constructed from the foundation up, the foundation plans are among the first drawings in the set of plans. A building foundation is usually constructed out of concrete that has been reinforced with steel bars, or **rebars** (<u>re</u>inforcing <u>bars</u>). Concrete footings support the walls and columns in a building, and the foundation walls are often made of reinforced concrete. Details about the size of the footings and the size and location of rebars are usually included in a wall section drawing. Sometimes a reinforced concrete slab is constructed for the building and included as part of the foundation plan or in a wall section view. Concrete slabs typically contain reinforcing bars or a steel mesh for controlling the thermal expansion and contraction of the slab.

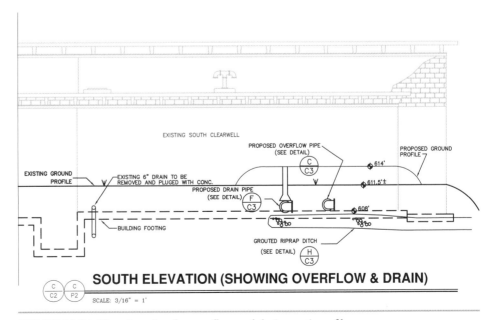

FIGURE 18.34. Elevation view for overflow and drain portion of lagoon.

FIGURE 18.35. Foundation plan for portion of the Baraga water treatment facility.

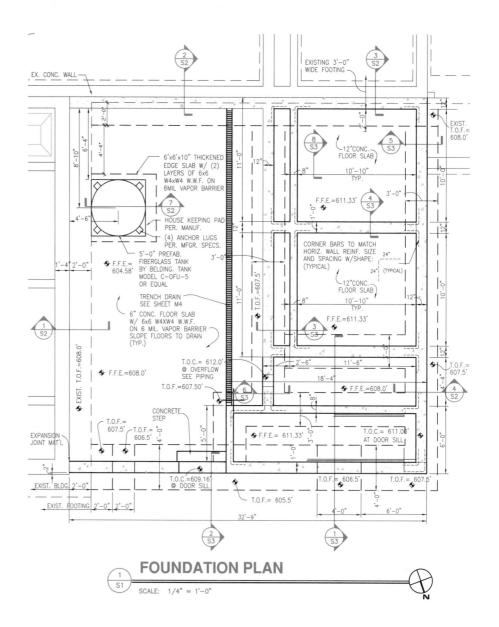

FOUNDATION PLAN

SCALE: 1/4" = 1'-0"

Figure 18.35 shows the foundation plan for a portion of the Baraga water treatment facility. In this drawing, the right portion of the foundation includes a 12″ slab and the left portion includes a 6″ slab. The reinforcing for the 6″ slab is specified on the foundation plan as 6X6 W4XW4 W.W.F. This specification means that the spacing of the bars is 6″ × 6″ and that the diameter of the steel wire is a gage of 4 (approximately two-tenths of an inch). The WWF in this specification refers to welded wire fabric. The dashed lines around both sides of the outer walls of the structure define the footings. Since this project is an addition to an existing structure, the existing footing sizes are given—3'-0″ along one wall and 2'-0″ along another wall. The new footings to be constructed are 4'-0″ and 3'-0″ on each of the remaining two walls, respectively. Note the specification of the elevation of the T.O.F. (top of footing) in various locations on the plan. Also notice the various cutting plane lines for sectional views through the walls. The sectional views will be found on various sheets that are labeled in this view. For example, for the wall located nearest the top of the page, two section lines are shown and both section views will be located on S2 (section sheet 2); they will be drawing 2 and drawing 3, respectively.

FIGURE 18.36. First floor plan for the Baraga water treatment facility.

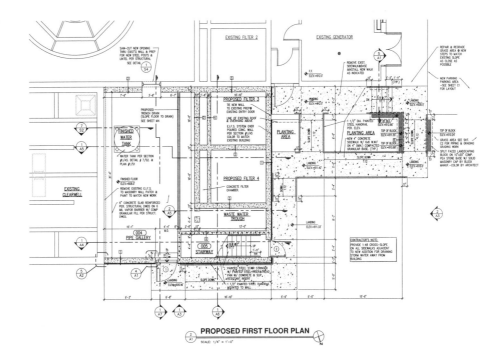

PROPOSED FIRST FLOOR PLAN
SCALE: 1/4" = 1'-0"

The type of construction drawing with which you are probably most familiar is the floor plan. A floor plan shows the layout of the rooms in a building. Doors between rooms are shown, as is the location of windows, closets, plumbing fixtures, and any other pertinent information about the drawings. The dimensions of the rooms as well as the thickness of walls are usually shown on the floor plans. Figure 18.36 shows the first-floor plan for the Baraga water treatment facility. Notice how the new construction fits within the existing structures on two sides. For this floor, the new walls will be constructed from concrete. (Dotted cross-hatching is used to show this graphically.) A concrete landing also surrounds the new construction, connecting to the existing generator; and spaces for planting in the landing are included to avoid the "concrete jungle" look. Two doors will be installed in the new construction. (Several are shown on the existing structure.) One of the doors leads to the stairway; the other door leads directly into the pipe gallery. Notice that the way the doors swing is also shown on the plan.

Figure 18.37 shows a different type of floor plan for the first floor—the electrical plan. According to the legend provided with this electrical plan, seven types of electrical devices are to be installed on this floor—duplex convenience receptacles, ground fault interrupt duplex convenience receptacles, single pole wall switches, three-way wall switches, electric control valves, motors, and disconnect switches. Notice that the exact locations of these devices are not shown—just approximations. Their locations are not critical to the integrity of the building, so the electrical subcontractor is free to put them wherever it makes the most sense in the field.

18.08.05 Sections

Sections in construction drawings can be organized into two types: **general sections**, which show room or floor layouts for buildings, or **detail sections**, which show cross sections with enough detail for construction purposes. In fact, a floor plan also can be thought of as a horizontal section through a building. Figure 18.38 shows a vertical section through a house. Note that with this type of general section, not enough detail is included for construction purposes; but the detail that is given is helpful because it provides a general idea about the layout of the rooms and the floors within the house.

FIGURE 18.37. Electrical plan for the first floor of the Baraga water treatment facility.

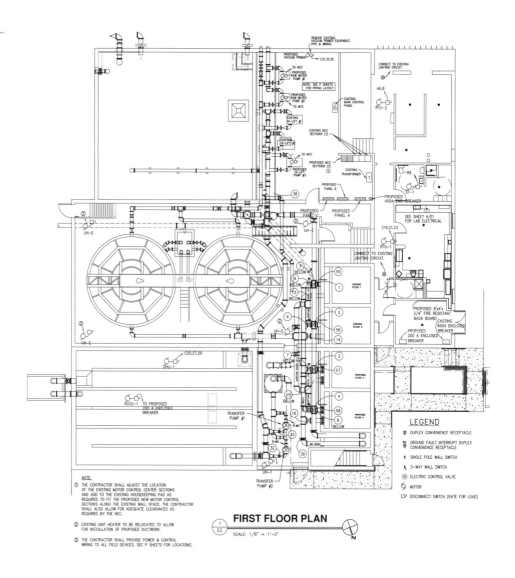

FIRST FLOOR PLAN

SCALE: 1/8" = 1'-0"

LEGEND

⊕	DUPLEX CONVENIENCE RECEPTACLE
⊕	GROUND FAULT INTERRUPT DUPLEX CONVENIENCE RECEPTACLE
⌐	SINGLE POLE WALL SWITCH
⌐	3-WAY WALL SWITCH
Ⓜ	ELECTRIC CONTROL VALVE
Ⓜ	MOTOR
☐	DISCONNECT SWITCH (RATE FOR LOAD)

NOTE:
① THE CONTRACTOR SHALL ADJUST THE LOCATION OF THE EXISTING MOTOR CONTROL CENTER SECTIONS AND ADD TO THE EXISTING HOUSEKEEPING PAD AS REQUIRED TO FIT THE PROPOSED NEW MOTOR CONTROL SECTIONS ALONG THE EXISTING WALL SPACE. THE CONTRACTOR SHALL ALSO ALLOW FOR ADEQUATE CLEARANCES AS REQUIRED BY THE NEC.

② EXISTING UNIT HEATER TO BE RELOCATED TO ALLOW FOR INSTALLATION OF PROPOSED DUCTWORK.

③ THE CONTRACTOR SHALL PROVIDE POWER & CONTROL WIRING TO ALL FIELD DEVICES. SEE P SHEETS FOR LOCATIONS.

FIGURE 18.38. General section through a house showing room layouts.

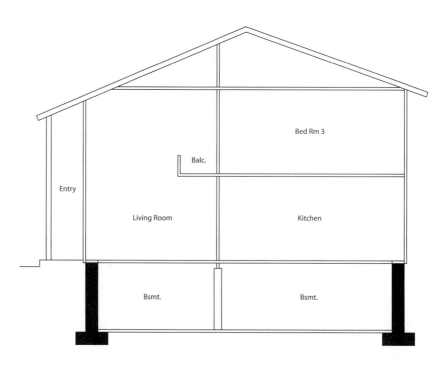

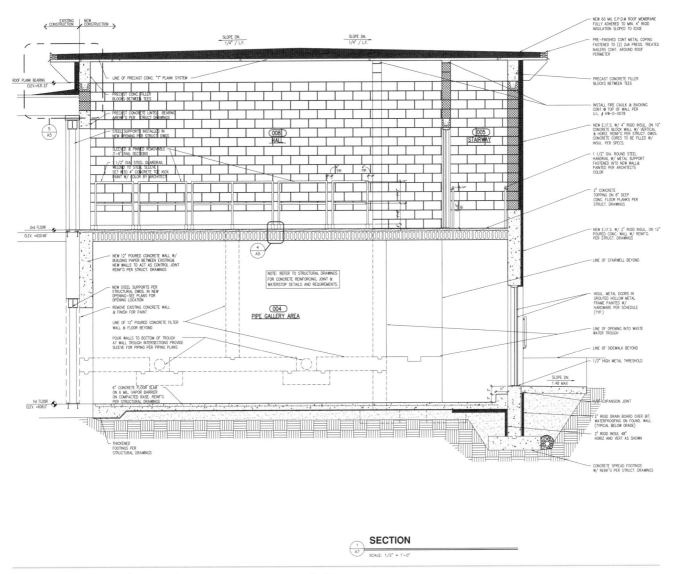

FIGURE 18.39. General section for Baraga water treatment facility.

Figure 18.39 shows a general section for the Baraga water treatment facility upgrade. This section shows the general building layout, clearly indicating where the pipe gallery is in relation to the hall above it. Notice that not much detail and very few dimensions are provided in this section; however, the drawing is helpful in understanding the overall design of the facility.

Detail sections provide a great deal of information. They show how the different components in a building system fit together, and they provide information that cannot be shown in large-scale drawings, such as floor plans or elevation views. **Wall sections** are among the most prevalent type of detail sectional drawing in a set of construction plans, although roof framing and foundation sections are also common. Refer to the foundation plan shown for the Baraga project in Figure 18.35. On the wall of the foundation plan toward the top of the drawing, a cutting plane line is shown with an arrow pointing toward the right side of the page. The label for this section line is given as 2/S2. This means that the cross section indicated by the cutting plane line is drawing number 2 found on section sheet 2. Figure 18.40 shows the wall section that corresponds to that cutting plane line. You should note that unlike manufacturing section views, this section did not project orthographically (it was even on another sheet); further, the section view is not

FIGURE 18.40. Detailed wall section for Baraga water treatment facility.

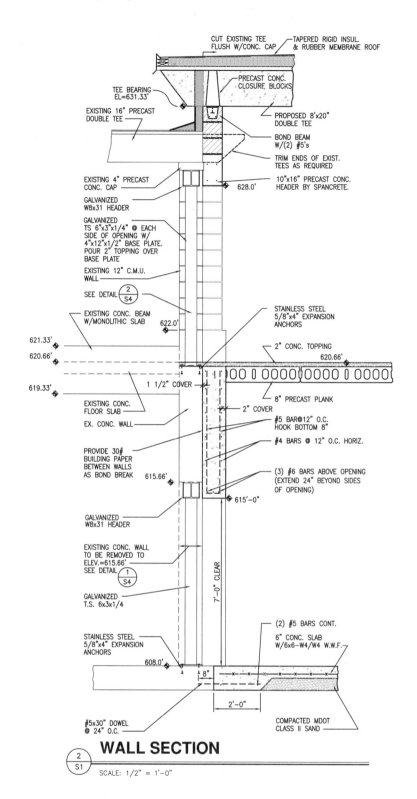

CUT EXISTING TEE FLUSH W/CONC. CAP
TAPERED RIGID INSUL. & RUBBER MEMBRANE ROOF

PRECAST CONC. CLOSURE BLOCKS

TEE BEARING EL=631.33'

EXISTING 16" PRECAST DOUBLE TEE

PROPOSED 8'x20' DOUBLE TEE

BOND BEAM W/(2) #5's

TRIM ENDS OF EXIST. TEES AS REQUIRED

EXISTING 4" PRECAST CONC. CAP

10"x16" PRECAST CONC. HEADER BY SPANCRETE.

GALVANIZED W8x31 HEADER

628.0'

GALVANIZED TS 6"x3"x1/4" @ EACH SIDE OF OPENING W/ 4"x12"x1/2" BASE PLATE. POUR 2" TOPPING OVER BASE PLATE

EXISTING 12" C.M.U. WALL

SEE DETAIL 2/S4

EXISTING CONC. BEAM W/MONOLITHIC SLAB

622.0'

STAINLESS STEEL 5/8"x4" EXPANSION ANCHORS

621.33'
620.66'

2" CONC. TOPPING

620.66'

619.33'

1 1/2" COVER

8" PRECAST PLANK

EXISTING CONC. FLOOR SLAB

2" COVER

EX. CONC. WALL

#5 BAR@12" O.C. HOOK BOTTOM 8"

#4 BARS @ 12" O.C. HORIZ.

PROVIDE 30# BUILDING PAPER BETWEEN WALLS AS BOND BREAK

615.66'

(3) #6 BARS ABOVE OPENING (EXTEND 24" BEYOND SIDES OF OPENING)

615'-0"

GALVANIZED W8x31 HEADER

EXISTING CONC. WALL TO BE REMOVED TO ELEV.=615.66' SEE DETAIL 1/S4

7'-0" CLEAR

GALVANIZED T.S. 6x3x1/4

STAINLESS STEEL 5/8"x4" EXPANSION ANCHORS

(2) #5 BARS CONT.

6" CONC. SLAB W/6x6-W4/W4 W.W.F.

608.0'

8"

2'-0"

#5x30" DOWEL @ 24" O.C.

COMPACTED MDOT CLASS II SAND

WALL SECTION

2/S1

SCALE: 1/2" = 1'-0"

drawn to the same scale as the top view from which it is projecting. The plan view is drawn at a scale of ¼"=1'-0"; the wall section is drawn at a scale of ½"=1'-0".

The wall section shown in Figure 18.40 includes details about the reinforcing (welded wire fabric, dowels, stainless steel expansion anchors, and #6 bars); it includes information about elevations of various portions of the wall (the top of the foundation slab is at 608.0', the top of the slab for the first floor is at 620.66', and the bottom of the

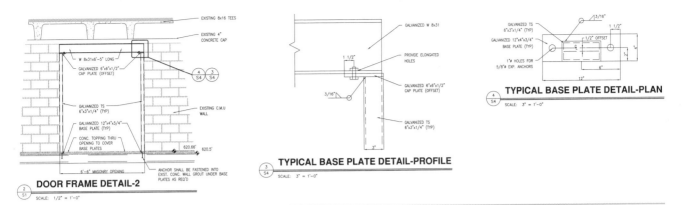

FIGURE 18.41. Detail drawings showing how a door will be installed in the Baraga water treatment facility.

existing precast concrete cap is at 628.0′); it also shows the various components that extend out from the walls (the slabs, the double tee, the existing structure, and the roof).

18.08.06 Detail Construction Drawings

Detail drawings are made to show one or two particular features on the constructed facility so that it can be built. Because constructed facilities are typically large, some of the finer details of the construction cannot be shown adequately on other types of drawings. Thus, detail views show one specific area on a drawing that has been enlarged. Detail views are referenced from existing drawings, and all detail drawings may be shown on one sheet. Figure 18.41 shows the door frame detail for the Baraga project. In the upper-right corner of the detail drawing for the door frame, two new details are referenced—3/S4 and 4/S4, which are also shown in the figure. Detail 3/S4 shows how the cap plate will be bolted to the crossbeam from a profile viewpoint, and Detail 4/S4 shows the connection from a plan viewpoint. You should note that the plan and profile views of the detail do not project orthographically on the sheet. You must mentally line these drawings up in order to understand how the door frame is to be constructed.

18.08.07 Plan and Profile Drawings

Another common type of construction drawing is a **plan and profile drawing**. Recall that plan views show a structure from above and that profile views show the structure from the side or front. In other words, plan views show changes in bearings of lines and profile views show changes in elevations of features. Figure 18.42 shows a plan and profile drawing for a street and a corresponding sewage pipe for a wastewater system in Baraga. Note that in this drawing, things do project orthographically between the plan and the profile views; however, the drawing scales are different between views. For the plan view, the entire view is drawn at a scale of 1″=30′. For the profile view, the scale is 1″=30′ on the horizontal dimension and 1″=10′ on the vertical dimension. The reason for this change in scale is to show the changes in elevation in greater detail.

FIGURE 18.42. Plan and profile drawing showing the street and corresponding sewage pipe for wastewater system in Baraga.

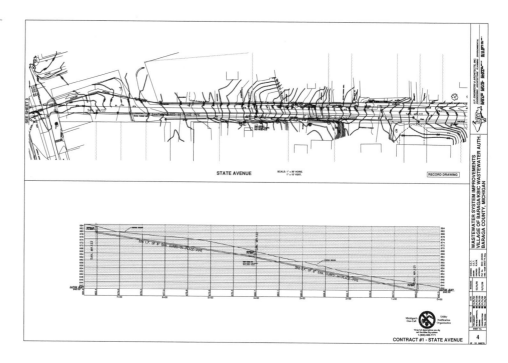

18.09 Engineering Scales

As you learned previously, virtually all engineering drawings are made to scale. This is especially true with construction drawings that represent large projects that do not fit on a single sheet of paper. In this age of CAD, engineering designs can be printed to any scale desired. Further, if you decide that you need the drawing at a scale that differs from the one you first chose, you merely adjust the font sizes and reprint the drawing at the new scale. Previously, if you needed the drawing at a new scale, you were required to re-create the entire drawing from the beginning—a tedious task.

It is important to understand that when an object is drawn to scale, its actual size does not change—just its appearance on the paper. Figure 18.43 illustrates the concept of drawing something to scale. Here the objects are the same size; the one on the right just appears to be twice as large as the one on the left. The notation of a 2:1 scale means

FIGURE 18.43. Scaled drawing of object.

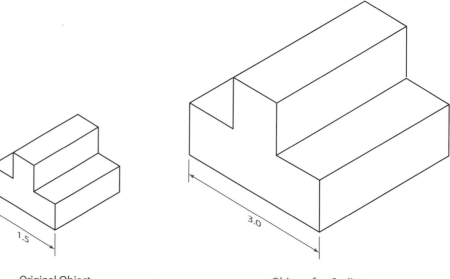

Original Object

Object after Scaling

that 2 inches on paper equals 1 inch on the object. Therefore, the drawing looks larger than the actual object. Conversely, a 1:2 scale would mean that 1 inch on paper represents 2 inches on the physical object; hence, the drawing would look smaller than the actual object.

Another way to think of drawing objects to scale is that the scale indicates how close you are to the object. If you are a substantial distance from the object, it appears very small; whereas if you are very close to the object, it appears large. However, the true object size does not change. Similarly, from an airplane, a house on the ground looks tiny; but if you are standing a few inches from the same house, it appears enormous. It is your perception of the house that changes, not the size of the house.

Scales for drawings are usually reported as ratios. In denoting scales, the first number in the ratio corresponds to the drawing and the second number corresponds to the physical object. However, sometimes drawing scales are denoted with an equal sign rather than a ratio. This is particularly true when scales are given in the English system of units. Thus, a scale may be reported as 1″=50′ or ¼″=1′-0″. The first scale (1″=50′) means that 1 inch on the drawing corresponds to 50 feet on the actual object. These drawing scales can also relate back to their ratio equivalents, i.e., 1″=50′ corresponds to a scale of 1:600 (there are 12 inches in a foot, so 50 feet = 600 inches, resulting in a 1:600 ratio), and a scale of ¼″=1′-0″ corresponds to 1:48.

A scale is a device that was developed over the years to aid in making a drawing to scale; it is usually a triangular prism with six to twelve different drawing scales depicted on one piece of equipment. Figure 18.44 shows three common scales used by engineers—an Engineer's scale, an Architect's scale, and a Metric scale. With modern-day mechanical CAD systems, you typically create a 3-D object in true size and print it out to the scale you need. In civil engineering applications, you create your drawings full-size and print them out to scale. In either case, you must ensure that the text on the drawings is legible when printed to the desired scale.

Due to advances in computer software, physical scales such as those shown in Figure 18.44 are, for the most part, a relic of the past. However, in a few instances, knowledge of scales is helpful—and possibly necessary. Because construction projects

FIGURE 18.44. Three common scales used in creating or measuring dimension on engineering drawings.

are built as one-of-a-kind structures, there may be times when dimensions are inadvertently left off drawings; and despite the diligence of the engineers who check the designs, the lack of a dimension is not known until the project is under construction. In this case, scales can be used in the field to quickly determine the dimension and construction can continue. Since tolerances in civil engineering projects are typically large (or nonexistent), reading a dimension using a scale is often "close enough." Further, in civil engineering projects, scales can be used in the field to measure a dimension on a given sheet rather than looking through a large set of drawings to find the specific sheet where the dimension is "officially" located. In manufacturing applications, scales can be used to quickly estimate dimensions as needed.

In determining a dimension from a drawing that has been drawn to scale, many novices use a calculator. For example, if a drawing has been made at a scale of 1"=40' and you measured a line that is ⅝" long, you could calculate that the line represents 25' on the actual object (⅝ of 40 is 25). Using a calculator to figure out dimension is extremely tedious and would likely result in error. Fortunately, this tedium can be avoided with the use of an appropriate scale. In the following sections, you will learn about the three primary types of scales used in engineering.

18.09.01 Engineer's Scale

An **Engineer's scale** (sometimes called a Civil Engineer's scale) usually consists of 10, 20, 30, 40, 50, and 60 scales. These scales are based on the English system of units, with the inch as the basis for measurement. The divisions on the scales are in increments of tenths of an inch, not eighths of an inch as on ordinary rulers. Engineer's scales can be used to measure a line in any multiple of ten of the basic unit. For example, the 30 scale can be used for reading the following scales from drawings: 1"=3', 1"=300', or 1"=30 mi. Similarly, the 50 scale can be used for drawings with scales of 1"=50', 1"=5 yds, or 1"= 500 mi.

Figure 18.45 shows a line being measured with a 20 scale. The actual length of the line on paper is 3.5"; but since it is drawn at a scale of 1"=200', this line represents a length of 700' on the actual object. By reading the scale in this figure, what is the length of the actual line to point A? (The actual line to point A is 580' long.)

Figure 18.46 shows lines drawn at a scale of 1"=40' and a corresponding 40 Engineer's scale. What is the length of each line segment (OA, OB, OC)? These values can be read directly from the scale, making proper adjustments for decimal places. The line is drawn at a scale of 1"=40'; therefore, the first 2 on the scale represents 20', the 4 represents 40', the 6 represents 60', etc. The unlabeled long tic marks represent 10', 30', 50', etc. The intermediate-length tic marks occur at 5' intervals, and the smaller tic marks represent 1' intervals. Therefore, the length of line OA on this scale can be read as 67'. The line OB is read as 103'. Many times novice scale readers will incorrectly interpret the length of OB as 130'. When the scale is read, care should be taken to put the

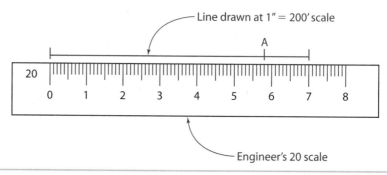

FIGURE 18.45. Line to be measured at a scale of 1"=200' and a 20 Engineer's scale.

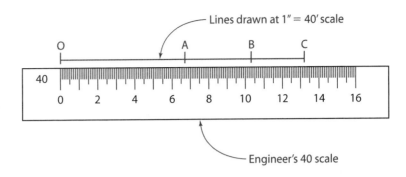

FIGURE 18.46. Lines drawn at a scale of 1"=40' and a 40 Engineer's scale.

decimal in the correct place. The distance OB is read directly as 10.3; but since the scale is 1"=40', the decimal is moved to the right one unit and the correct scale reading becomes 103'. The length of the line OC can be read from the scale as 132'.

In Figure 18.46, what are the lengths of the lines if they are drawn at a scale of 1"=4000'? Note that you still use the same Engineer's scale (the 40 scale) to make this reading but you add more zeros to the number that you read on the scale. Thus, the line OA has a length of 6700', OB has a length of 10,300', and OC has a length of 13,400' at a scale of 1"=4000'. What if the lines are drawn at a scale of 1"=4 yds? At that scale, the line OA has a length of 6.7 yds, OB has a length of 10.3 yds, and OC has a length of 13.4 yds.

18.09.02 Metric Scale

Metric scales are similar to Engineer's scales except that they are based on the metric system of units. Because metric units are based on decimals, unlike the English system of units (12" per foot, 3' per yard, 1,760 yds per mile, etc.), Metric scales are reported as ratios. Thus, typical Metric scales are reported as 1:1, 1:2, 1:5, and 1:10, for example. The same principal used to measure distances with an Engineer's scale is used for Metric scales. Like an Engineer's scale, the Metric scales can be used for multiples of ten of the basic unit. Thus, a 1:5 scale can also be used to measure 1:50, 1:500, and 1:5000 scales. Figure 18.47 shows a line drawn at a 1:2000 scale and a 1:20 Metric scale. On a Metric scale, the numbers (0.5, 1.0, 1.5, etc.) generally represent meters; and you adjust the decimal according to the specific scale at which you are measuring. If you read the scale directly, the length of the line is 1.84 m. But since the scale depicts a drawing scale of 1:20 and the line was drawn at a scale of 1:2000, you must move the decimal two units to the right to account for the difference. Thus, the length of the line is equal to 184 m. Similarly, if the line was drawn at a 1:200 scale, the length of the line would be 18.4 m.

Figure 18.48 shows a Metric scale of 1:100 and a set of lines drawn at a 1:1 scale. What are the lengths of each line? If you read the length of OA directly from the scale, you see that it is 7.7 m. Since the scale is 1:100 and the line is drawn at 1:1, you move the decimal place two units to the left; therefore, the length of the line is 0.077 m. Alternatively, you could report the length of the line as 7.7 cm or 77 mm. What is the length of OB? The value read from the scale is 10.7 m. If you move the decimal place two units to the left, the length is determined as 0.107 m (or 10.7 cm or 107 mm). Similarly, the length of line OC is 0.124 m (12.4 cm).

FIGURE 18.47. Line drawn at a scale of 1:2000 and a 1:20 Metric scale.

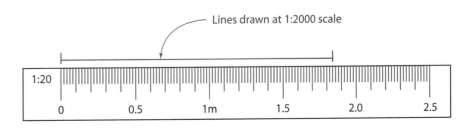

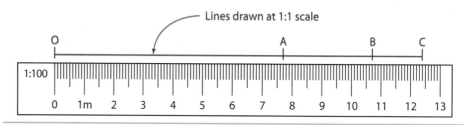

FIGURE 18.48. Lines drawn at 1:1 scale and a 1:100 Metric scale.

18.09.03 Architect's Scale

An **Architect's scale** is similar to an Engineer's scale in that it is based on the English system of units. One of the differences between the two scales is that the Architect's scale is based on fractions of an inch. (Recall that the Engineer's scale is based on tenths.) Another significant difference is that with an Architect's scale, drawing scales are always reported as something=1'-0". Thus, a scale might be reported as ¼"=1'-0" or as ⅜"=1'-0". Some of the more common scales depicted on an Architect's scale are as follows:

12"=1'0" (full size)	6"=1'-0" (half size)	3"=1'-0" (quarter size)
1½"=1'-0" (⅛ size)	1"=1'-0" (1/12 size)	¾"=1'-0" (1/16 size)
½"=1'-0" (1/24 size)	⅜"=1'-0" (1/32 size)	¼"=1'-0" (1/48 size)
3/16"=1'-0" (1/64 size)	⅛"=1'-0" (1/96 size)	3/32"=1'-0" (1/128 size)

Architect's scales usually look significantly different than Engineer's or Metric scales. The biggest difference is that each edge of the Architect's scale typically depicts two scales—one reading from left to right and the other reading from right to left. Thus, twice as many scales (twelve versus six) are depicted on an Architect's scale when compared to an Engineer's or Metric scale. The other difference is that fractional gradations are shown only at the ends of the scale. Thus, when you are measuring a distance with an Architect's scale, you must place one end of the line at the nearest whole number foot on the scale and read the fractional foot at the end with the gradation. Figure 18.49 shows an Architect's ¼ scale (this means the ¼"=1'-0") and line to be measured with this scale. In this figure, the ¼ scale is read from right to left on the scale and the ⅛ scale is read from left to right. To read the length of this line, you place one end of the line on the nearest even foot mark of the scale. In this case, it is 11'. (Remember that you are reading from right to left for the ¼ scale.) Notice that the closest foot mark is not labeled for you. For the ¼ scale, the even foot markers are labeled but the odd ones are not. The smaller tic marks for this scale represent one-half foot divisions. Be careful not to line up the end of the line with the half-foot marks instead of the foot markers. The fractional feet are shown in the last foot of the scale (past the 0). This last foot is divided into twelve gradations, so each tic mark on the scale represents 1" because there are 12 inches in a foot. Thus, the length of this line is 11'-7".

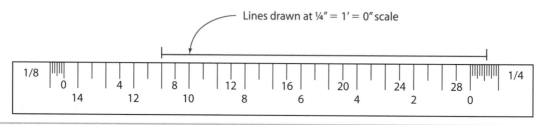

FIGURE 18.49. Line drawn at a scale of ¼"=1'-0" and a ¼" Architect's scale.

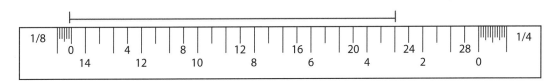

FIGURE 18.50. Line drawn at a scale of ⅛"=1'-0" and a ⅛" Architect's scale.

What happens if you read the length of this line using the ⅛ scale? Figure 18.50 shows the same line being measured with the ⅛ scale. The same procedure is followed to read the length of the line at this scale. In this case, the nearest even foot mark is 23'. Notice that on this scale, only every fourth (4, 8, 12, etc.) foot marker is labeled and that the long tic marks from left to right represent the odd foot marks. The short tic marks from left to right represent the intermediate even foot markers. The final foot of this scale is divided into six increments compared to twelve for the ¼ scale. Thus, each division in the final foot represents 2". As shown in this figure, the length of the line at a ⅛ scale is 23'-2". (Note that this makes sense because 2 × 11'-7" = 22'-14", or 23'-2"). The Architect's scale usually requires a great deal of practice on your part to be able to read it with confidence.

As you may have realized from the previous discussion of drawing scales (Engineer's, Architect's, and Metric), these devices are time-saving and relatively easy to use. Unfortunately, many students have a tendency to use calculators when working with scaled drawings for the first time. It is important that you learn to use a scale for working with engineering drawings.

CAUTION

The guidelines for creating working drawings are structured to minimize the number of errors and amount of missing information. New engineers who are not familiar with these guidelines (or choose to ignore them) sometimes create errors. Errors in working drawings are likely to cause mild embarrassment for the originator at best. When errors are more serious, they can slow the process of the drawing being interpreted or cause confusion in the cataloging or organizing of the part. The following sections are a compilation of the most common beginner errors and ways to avoid them.

No Drawing Border

The absence of a border on a formal drawing is usually the result of an inexperienced attempt to create a custom drawing header. A well-defined border defines the limits of a drawing. Without a border, as shown in Figure 18.51, it is sometime unclear, especially when copying the drawing and especially when the drawing's full size is unknown, to know what should be included. When additional views, details, comments, or corrections are added, this information may become lost. Including a border clearly shows what is part of the drawing and what is not.

No Title Block or Poor Title Block

A poor or missing title block, as shown in Figure 18.52, is also a sign of an inexperienced attempt to create a formal drawing header. Although drawing headers vary between organizations, title blocks are always expected along with a minimum amount of information. When creating a custom title block, a good place to start is with the ANSI blocks shown in Figure 18.14. Spaces can then be added for the information required for the specific needs of your company. For example, products that carry high financial or safety risks may consistently require additional levels of engineering or management approval for the release of a drawing to fabricators. Some companies require that their material specialists approve all drawings to ensure that hazardous materials are not used and that all parts are recyclable at their end of life.

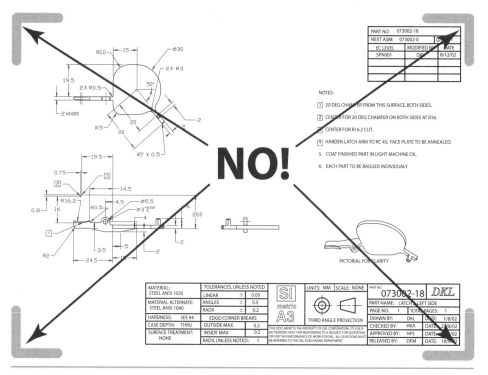

FIGURE 18.51. A common error. Without a border, the size and limits of a drawing are uncertain.

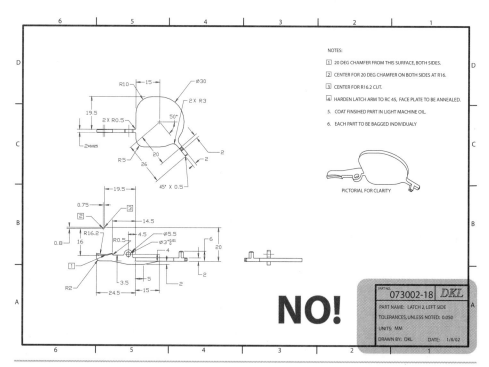

FIGURE 18.52. A common error. A poor header makes it too easy to omit important information.

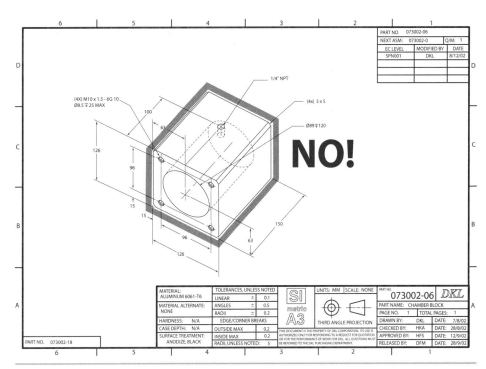

FIGURE 18.53. A common error. Applying dimensions to a pictorial is considered incorrect practice for formal working drawings.

No Multiview Presentation

The use of multiple orthogonal views to present an object, showing as many of its edges in true length or true shapes as possible, is considered the standard for manufacturing drawings; however, recall that doing so usually is not standard practice in the construction industry. The use of pictorials for manufacturing drawings is to provide additional clarity only; pictorial drawings are rarely included with construction plans due to the complexity of the designed systems. Showing dimensions on a pictorial, as in Figure 18.53, may seem reasonable but is generally not accepted as being correct because true shapes on the object are distorted and some features may be partially or completely hidden.

Poor Multiview Presentation

When a multiview presentation is used for manufacturing drawings, the object should be oriented to show as many of its edges as visible, rather than hidden, edges for defining dimensions. In the example shown in Figure 18.54, the object is oriented such that its edges can be seen in their true shape in at least one view. However, hidden lines define the edges of the bore and groove. It would be much better to turn the object so that the opening of the bore faces the right side; that view would show the edges as visible. An alternative solution would be to add a left side view to the object and show the dimension of the bore in that view.

FIGURE 18.54. A common error. Poor orientation of the object in a multiview presentation produces hidden lines instead of solid edges on the face containing the bore opening and four tapped holes. The opening of the bore should have been placed facing the reader in the front view.

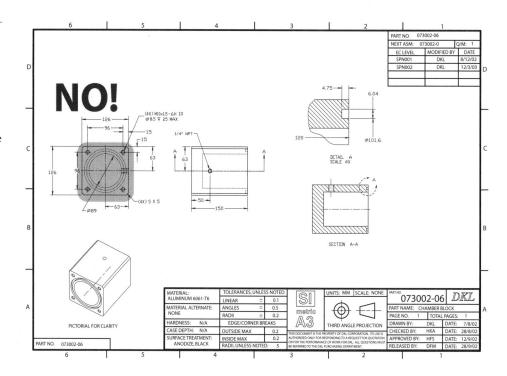

Crowding or Poor Dimension Placement

The dimensions on a drawing should be placed so that they are easy to see and interpret. When the dimensions are crowded, placed inside the object, or placed such that many dimension lines and extension lines cross, as in Figure 18.55, the presentation appears unorganized and is confusing.

FIGURE 18.55. A common error. Poorly placed and/or crowded dimensions make the drawing difficult and time-consuming to read.

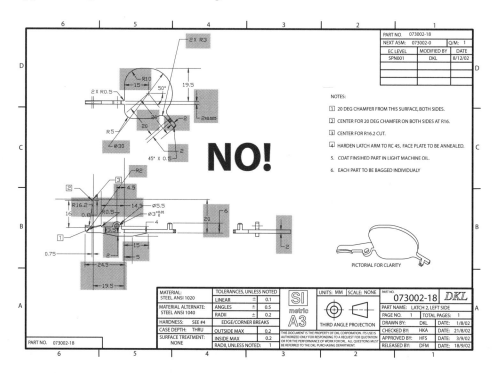

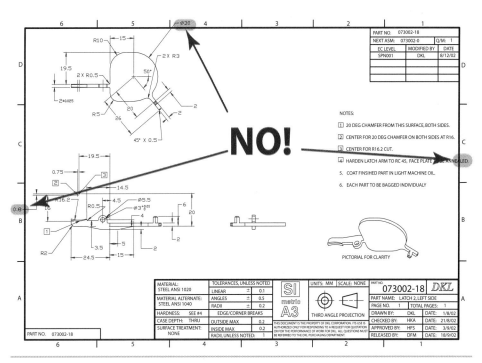

FIGURE 18.56. A common error. Information that overspills the border must be contained within the border to be a part of the drawing.

Content That Is Outside the Border

Everything that is of importance to a drawing must be contained entirely within its border. In Figure 18.56, some dimension text and notes overspill the border. This is considered sloppy work and should be avoided. When there is not enough room on the sheet to contain all of the information within the border, a larger sheet must be used.

Bad Choice for Sheet Size

Objects that are of a simple geometry, with few features that need to be defined and dimensioned, can be drawn on smaller sheets. Objects with more complicated geometries that have many features must be drawn on larger sheets. The choice of a proper sheet size is subjective, but the cases in Figure 18.57 show sheet size that is either too small or too large. Too small a sheet results in crowding of information on the drawing. Too large a sheet is a waste of paper and results in a drawing that is more difficult to handle than is necessary.

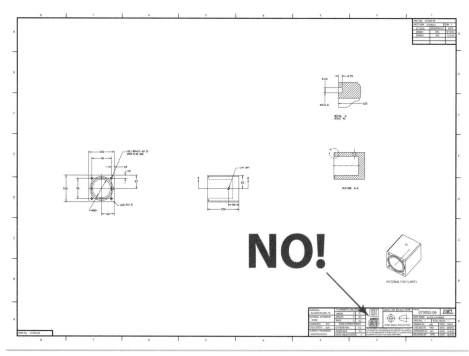

FIGURE 18.57. A common error. Poor choice of sheet size: too small (above) and too large (below).

Bad Choice for Drawing Scale

Objects that are of a simple geometry, with few large features that need to be defined and dimensioned, can be drawn to a smaller scale. Objects with more complicated geometries that have many features must be drawn to a larger scale so that the geometries can be seen and defined. As with the selection of sheet size, the choice of a proper drawing scale is subjective; but the cases in Figure 18.58 provide examples of drawing scales that are too small and too big. Too small a scale results in crowding of information and indiscernible object features on the drawing. Too large a scale results in an unnecessarily large sheet size and text that is unnecessarily small when the entire object is presented.

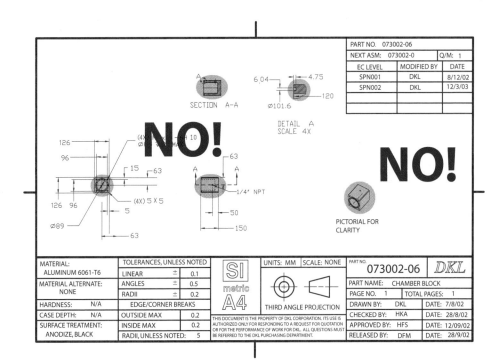

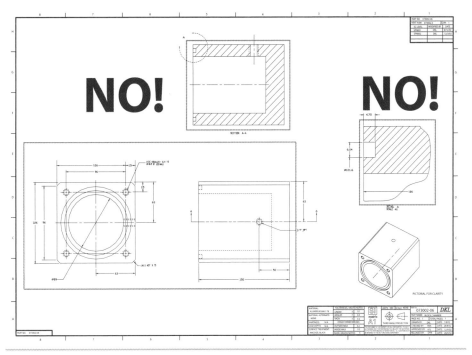

FIGURE 18.58. A common error. Poor choice of drawing scale: too small (above) and too large (below).

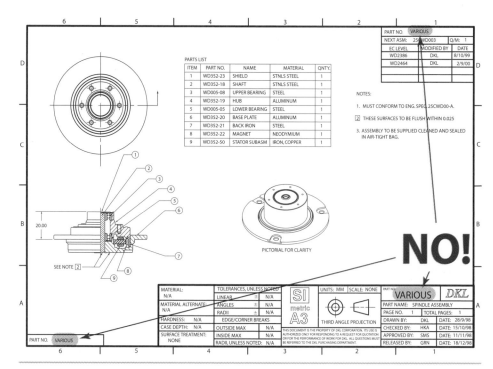

FIGURE 18.59. A common error. Omitted part numbers. As with individual parts, a unique part number is required for each subassembly and assembly.

No Part Number

Every piece in a device or manufactured system must have its own unique part number within the company that designed it. Part numbers are often neglected for assemblies and subassemblies, as shown in Figure 18.59. One reason for this common error is the misconception that part numbers are for parts only. Part numbers are required to identify assemblies and subassemblies as well.

Same Part Number for Different Parts

Occasionally, due to carelessness or poor record keeping, different parts within the same company or organization end up having the same part number, as shown in Figure 18.60. This error will undoubtedly cause much confusion when the time comes to fabricate the correct part.

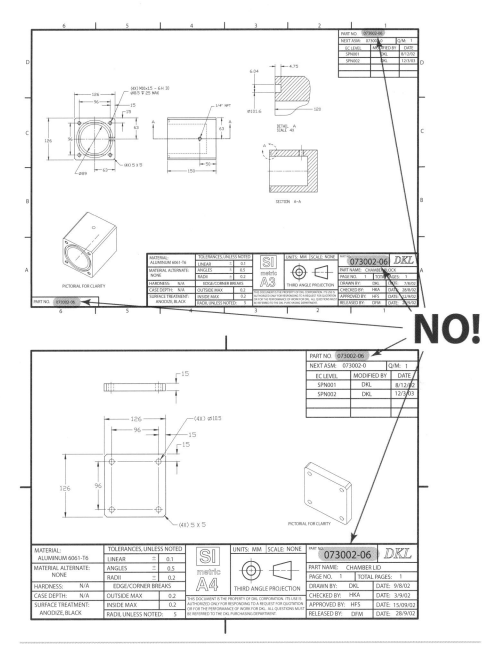

FIGURE 18.60. A common error. These two drawings claim to have the same part number.

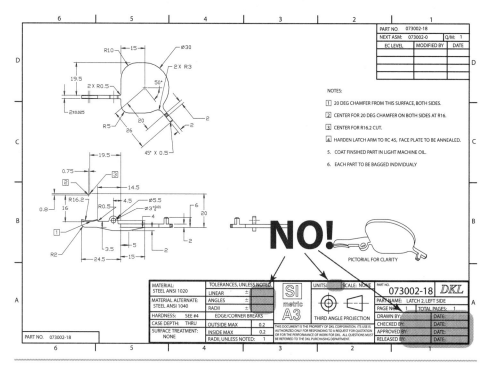

FIGURE 18.61. A common error. Important information is missing from the header.

Missing Information in the Title Block

One purpose of using a drawing header with a comprehensive title block is to prompt the creator of the drawing to include information that may otherwise be neglected. If such information is not included, as shown in Figure 18.61, there is little point in using the drawing header. All of the information requested in the title block should be supplied. If the information has no relevance for a particular drawing (for example, the default tolerances on an assembly drawing with no assembly dimensions), that space should be marked with N/A or a similar notation.

Portrait Instead of Landscape Orientation

Although portrait orientation, shown in Figure 18.62, is permitted in formal engineering drawings, landscape orientation is preferred. New engineers unfamiliar with formal drawing sometimes use portrait orientation (especially for size A or A4 drawings) because it is the same orientation used to create text documents, with which they are familiar from school. Although some companies use portrait orientation for drawings, the majority of drawings are done in landscape orientation.

Nonstandard Sheet Size

In the strictest sense, it is not incorrect to create a drawing in portrait orientation, where the height of the sheet is larger than the width (shown in Figure 18.63). However, engineering drawings are almost exclusively created using landscape orientation, where the width is larger than the height. To maintain a more professional appearance, landscape orientation should be used for drawings.

FIGURE 18.62. A common error. A portrait sheet orientation is not preferred in engineering drawings; landscape orientation is.

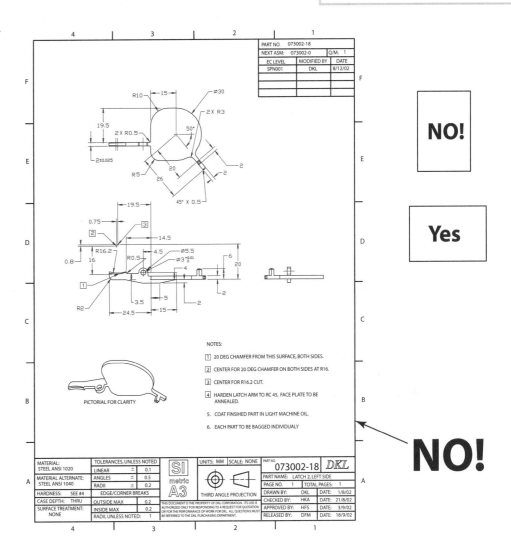

FIGURE 18.63. A common error. Nonstandard sheet sizes. Landscape orientation is used almost exclusively for drawings.

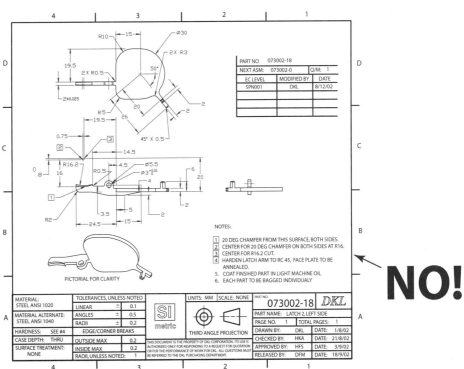

FIGURE 18.64. A common error. Lettering that is too large, too small, or inconsistent in size. Font sizes should be appropriate and used consistently on a drawing.

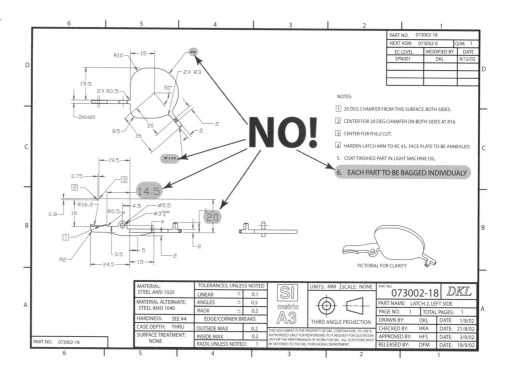

Poor or Inconsistent Fonts

The lettering size for the text and numbers on a drawing should be in the range of 3–6 mm in height when the drawing is printed to its specified sheet size. Of course, when the drawing is reduced in size (for example, for the convenience of printing on a letter-sized sheet from a desktop printer), the fonts will appear smaller. Lettering that is too large, too small, or inconsistent in size on a drawing implies that not enough thought was given to a professional appearance. Incorrect font sizes are shown in Figure 18.64.

FIGURE 18.65. A common error. Detail drawings showing multiple parts. Each drawing should contain only one part.

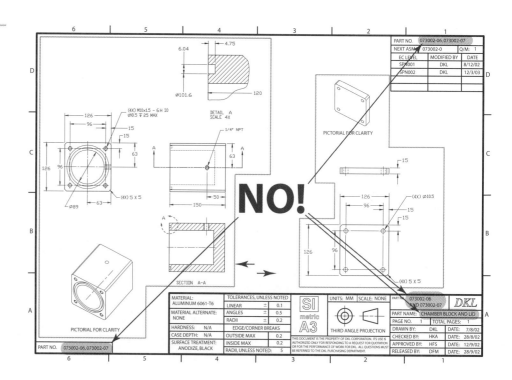

Multiple Parts on a Single Detail Drawing

It is sometimes tempting to save time, effort, and paper by putting more than one part on a single detail drawing, as shown in Figure 18.65. Each part must have its own detail drawing. The practice of putting multiple parts on a single drawing is considered incorrect for manufacturing drawings; however, construction drawings often show several details or sections on a single sheet, as shown in Figure 18.66. In the case of construction drawings, one drawing per sheet is considered poor practice. The reason for this difference between manufacturing and construction drawings is that in

FIGURE 18.66. Drawing showing multiple details from a set of construction plans.

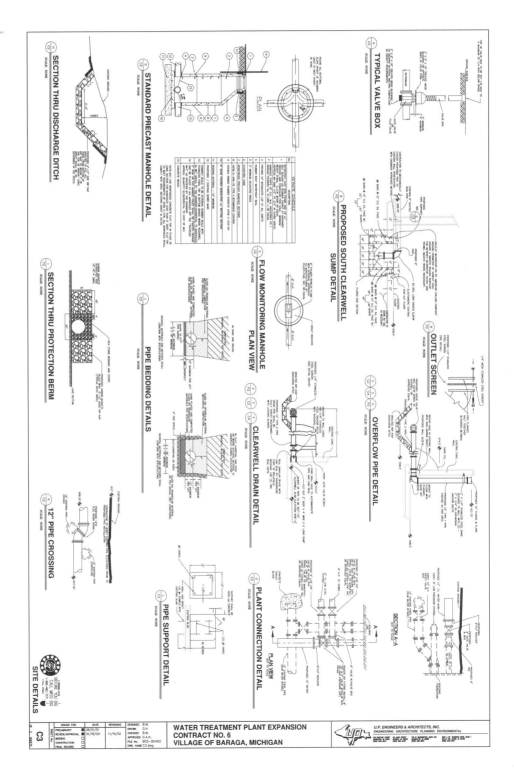

manufacturing, it is common to have different parts made by different fabricators. For construction projects, the same contractor is working on the entire project and needs to be able to see all of the details and the way they fit in the overall project. Further, the set of construction drawings is typically so large—as is the sheet size (size E)—that having one detail per sheet would make a thick set of plans even thicker. Having multiple manufactured parts on the same sheet creates confusion about which part is to be made and which drawing details belong to which part. The exception in manufacturing drawings is in the case of a family of parts with the same general appearance and function that differ in a few dimensions only. Such parts are generally intended to be made at the same fabricator.

Detail Dimensions on an Assembly Drawing

Putting part dimensions on an assembly drawing for a manufactured system, as shown in Figure 18.67, is incorrect. Part dimensions belong on the detail drawing for that part. It is quite common for dimensions and tolerances to be modified on a part. If these dimensions or tolerances change, it is easier and less confusing when the changes are made to the detail drawing only. Adding part dimensions to assembly drawings is redundant information, which should be unnecessary for assembly drawings.

Handwritten Notes on an Electronic Drawing

When an electronic (CAD) drawing is modified, its data file must be changed. Although it seems easy to modify the drawing by hand, as shown in Figure 18.68, hand-written notes are not reflected in the drawing's electronic file. When a manufacturing drawing is submitted for approval or is provided to a fabricator, it should contain no handwriting. If errors or corrections are noted on a submitted drawing, these errors must be corrected in the original electronic file and a new drawing issued. The exception to this general rule is in construction projects where a contractor applies hand-written notes to a drawing in the creation of the as-built drawings. These notes should be transferred to the electronic files at a later date.

FIGURE 18.67. A common error. Dimensions for individual parts shown on assembly drawings. The dimensions belong on the detail drawings.

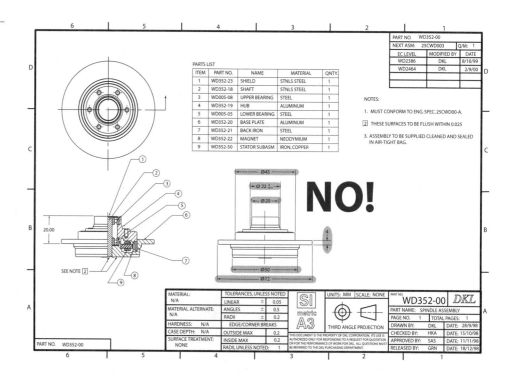

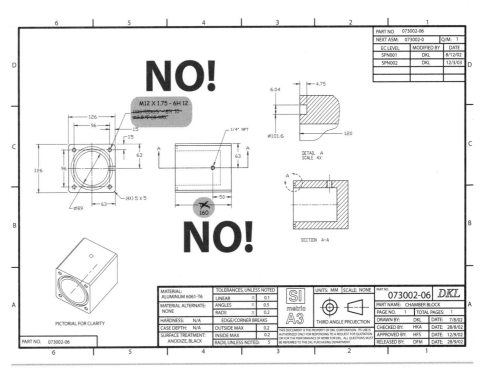

FIGURE 18.68. A common error. Amending or editing by hand an electronically generated drawing. Doing so does not alter the original data file; it needs to be updated.

18.10 Considerations for 3-D Modeling

The development of 3-D computer modeling has greatly reduced the time and effort required to produce a manufacturing drawing; however, as stated previously, 3-D modeling is not predominant in the construction industry and is not likely to be so for several years. In the following paragraphs, the considerations for 3-D modeling are given for projects in the realm of manufacturing.

There are provisions on most 3-D modeling software to easily generate different views of an object or assembly, including multiviews, section and detail views, auxiliary views, and pictorials. Dimensions can also be made to appear on any of the views. Because of the ease with which these graphics are generated, there is no excuse not to include as many different views as needed to communicate the geometry of the part or device. Formal drawing headers also are easily created, usually recalled from a library of premade headers with different complexities as demanded by the application of the device to be made.

Three-dimensional modeling software, however, cannot fully interpret the functional requirements of the device that is to be built. That knowledge resides with the designer or engineer. For example, depending on the functional requirements of a part, only the engineer or designer can know what dimension tolerances are acceptable for the part to work properly. Since most numerically controlled machine tools (described in the chapter on fabrication processes) can easily hold tolerances to within 25 microns for most small parts, it is sometimes tempting to use this number as a default tolerance for every dimension. However, if tighter tolerances are required by the engineer, special manufacturing processes may be required. An example is in the computer disk drive spindle detailed in Figure 18.27; it shows that tolerances in the range of 5 microns are required for some dimensions. Only the engineer or designer can know those requirements. The software can present only what the engineer or designer wants.

18.11 Chapter Summary

With any type of engineering drawing, the key word is *communication*. The drawing must be able to communicate to the reader the desires of the engineer or designer for a part or assembly. When working drawings are created, this communication must occur even in the absence of the drawing's originator. Use of the formal drawing format—with proper views, sheet sizes, headers, and drawing organization—serves to maximize the probability that the device will be built correctly. Almost as important is the fact that the quality of a working drawing is a reflection of the person, company, or organization that produced it. A high-quality and professional presentation must be maintained.

A formal working drawing succeeds not because it looks good, but because it clearly and unambiguously tells a fabricator or contractor how to produce a desired product. What you have designed may well be beautiful once it is produced, but that is irrelevant initially. The only goal at the start is to produce a working drawing that allows your conception to be made into reality.

18.12 glossary of key terms

approval signatures: The dated signatures or initials of the people responsible for certain aspects of a formal drawing, such as the people who did the drafting or the engineer responsible for the function of the part.

Architect's scale: A device used to measure or draw lines in the English system of units with a base unit of inches and fractions of an inch.

as-built plans: Drawings that show exactly how buildings were constructed, especially when variations exist between the final building and the plans created during the design phase.

assembly: A collection of parts and/or subassemblies that have been put together to make a device or structure that performs a specific function.

assembly dimensions: Dimensions that show where parts must be placed relative to other parts when the device is being put together.

balloons: Closed geometric shapes, usually circles, containing identification numbers and placed beside parts on a layout or assembly drawing to help identify those parts.

bearing: The angle that a line makes with a North-South line as seen in a plan view.

benchmarks: Points established by the U.S. Geological Survey that can be used to accurately locate control points on a construction site.

bill of materials (BOM): A drawing or table in a drawing that lists all of the parts needed to build a device by (at least) the part number, part name, type of material used, and number of times the part is used in the device.

blueprints: The name sometimes given to construction drawings based on historical blue-on-white drawings that were produced from ink drawings.

border: A thick line that defines the perimeter of a drawing.

construction drawings: Working drawings, often created by civil engineers, that are used to build large-scale, one-of-a-kind structures.

continuation blocks: Header blocks used on the second and subsequent pages of multipage drawings.

control points: Points at a construction site that are referenced to an origin by north, south, east, or west coordinates.

cover sheet: The first page in a set of construction drawings showing a map of the location of the project and possibly an index.

default tolerances: Usually appearing in the drawing header, the tolerances to be assumed for any dimension show on a part when that dimension does not specify any tolerances.

detail drawing: A formal drawing that shows the geometry, dimensions, tolerances, materials, and any processes needed to fabricate a part.

detail sections: Drawings included in a set of construction plans that show how the various components are assembled.

EC Level: A number included in the title block of a drawing indicating that the part has undergone a revision.

electrical plan: A plan view showing the layout of electrical devices on a floor in a building.

18.12 glossary of key terms (continued)

elevation views: Views of a structure that show changes in elevation (side or front views).

Engineer's scale: A device used to measure or draw lines in the English system of units with a base unit of inches and tenths of an inch.

engineering change (EC) number: A dated number that defines the degree to which the specifications of a part have been updated.

exploded assembly drawing: A formal drawing, usually in pictorial form, that shows the orientation and sequence in which parts are put together to make a device.

floor plan: A plan view of a single floor in a building that shows the layout of the rooms.

foundation plan: A plan view of the foundation of a building showing footings and other support structures.

general sections: Sections through entire structures that show the layout of rooms but provide little detail.

header: A premade outline on which working drawings are created to ensure that all information required for fabrication and record keeping is entered.

heating and ventilation plan: A plan view of the ventilation systems on a specific floor of a building, including ductwork and devices such as air conditioning units.

index: A list of all sheets of drawings contained in a set of construction plans.

item number: A number used to identify a part on a layout or assembly drawing.

international sheet sizes: The internationally accepted paper dimensions used when drawings are created or printed to their full intended size.

landscape: The drawing orientation in which the horizontal size is larger than the vertical size.

layout drawing: A formal drawing that shows a device in its assembled state with all of its parts identified.

location grid: An imaginary alphanumeric grid, similar to that of a street map, on a drawing that is used to specify area locations on the drawing.

main assembly: A completed device usually composed of multiple smaller parts and/or subassemblies.

main title block: A bordered area of a drawing (and part of the drawing header) that contains important information about the identification, fabrication, history, and ownership of the item shown on the drawing.

manufacturing drawings: Working drawings, often created by mechanical engineers, that are used to mass-produce products for consumers.

Metric scale: A device used to measure or draw lines in the metric system of units with drawings scales reported as ratios.

notes: Additional information or instructions placed on a drawing that are not contained on the dimensions, tolerances, or header.

one-off: A one-of-a-kind engineering project for which no physical prototypes are created.

outline assembly drawing: *See* layout drawing.

part: An object expected to be delivered from a fabricator as a single unit with only its external dimensions and functional requirements specified.

part name: A very short descriptive title given to a part, subassembly, or device.

part number: Within a company, a string of alphanumeric characters used to identify a part, a subassembly, an assembly, or a device.

parts list: *See* bill of materials.

plan and profile drawings: Construction drawings typically used for roads or other linear entities that show the road from above as well as from the side, with the profile view usually drawn with an exaggerated vertical scale.

plan views: Drawings created from a viewpoint above the structure (top view).

portrait: The drawing orientation in which the vertical size is larger than the horizontal size.

professional engineer (PE): An individual who has received an engineering degree, who has worked under the supervision of a PE for a number of years, and who has passed two examinations certifying knowledge of engineering practice.

profile views: Views of a structure that show horizontal surfaces in edge view (side or front views).

quantity per machine (Q/M): The number of times a part is required to build its next highest assembly.

rebars: Steel bars added to concrete for reinforcement or for temperature control.

reference dimensions: Unneeded dimensions shown for the convenience of the reader used to show overall dimensions that could be extracted from other dimensions on the part or from other drawings.

schedule of materials: A list of the materials, such as doors and windows, necessary for a construction project.

secondary title block: An additional bordered area of a drawing (and part of the drawing header) that contains important information about the identification, fabrication, and history of the item shown on the drawing.

sectioned assembly drawing: A formal drawing, usually in pictorial form, that shows the device in its assembled form but with sections removed from obscuring parts to reveal formerly hidden parts.

18.12 glossary of key terms (continued)

set of construction plans: A collection of drawings, not necessarily all of them plan views, needed to construct a building or infrastructure project.

site plan: A plan view showing the construction site for an infrastructure project.

site survey: Data regarding the existing topography and structures gathered during the preliminary design stages by trained surveying crews.

specifications (specs): The written instructions that accompany a set of construction plans used to build an infrastructure project.

subassemblies: Collections of parts that have been put together for the purpose of installing the collections as single units into larger assemblies.

title block: Usually the main title block, which is a bordered area of the drawing (and part of the drawing header) that contains important information about the identification, fabrication, history, and ownership of the item shown on the drawing.

trail: Dashed lines on an assembly drawing that show how various parts or subassemblies are inserted to create a larger assembly.

US sheet sizes: The accepted paper dimensions used in the United States when drawings are created or printed to their intended size.

wall sections: Sectional views of walls from foundation to roof for a construction project.

working drawings: A collection of all drawings needed to fabricate and put together a device or structure.

18.13 questions for review

1. What is the purpose of a header on a formal engineering drawing?

2. What type of information is typically included on a drawing header?

3. What signatures (or initials) typically appear in a drawing header?

4. Why is it important that dates be included on a drawing?

5. Why is it important that part numbers be unique to each part?

6. When should the part number for a particular part be changed?

7. What considerations need to be made in the selection of a sheet size for a drawing?

8. What considerations need to be made in the selection of a scale for a drawing?

9. What are the three different types of assembly drawings? How do they differ?

10. What is a revision (or engineering change) to a drawing?

11. How is a subassembly different from a main assembly?

12. What sort of information is typically included in a bill of materials?

13. What types of dimensions are permitted on an assembly drawing?

14. List three ways that manufacturing drawings differ from construction drawings.

15. Construction projects are site-specific. What does that mean?

16. What is the bearing of a line? In which view is it seen?

17. What does the term *professional engineer* mean?

18. What are plan, profile, and elevation views?

19. What is meant by the term *one-off*?

20. For construction drawings, what is a general section?

21. What are the three types of scales used in engineering?

22. Which scales are based on the English system of units?

18.14 problems

1. The parts shown in Figure P18.1 are to be assembled into a screw clamp. Create a complete set of working drawings for the device, including an outline assembly drawing, an exploded assembly drawing, a bill of materials, and all detailed part drawings. Specify appropriate tolerances for all dimensions. All parts are made of steel. You may use metric dimensions or convert the metric dimensions to their nearest inch equivalents.

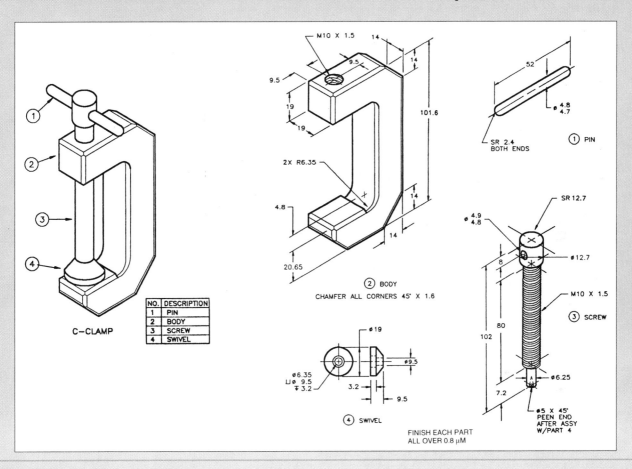

FIGURE P18.1.

18.14 problems (continued)

2. The parts shown in Figure P18.2 are to be assembled into a tool holder. Create a complete set of working drawings for the device, including an outline assembly drawing, an exploded assembly drawing, a sectioned assembly drawing, a bill of materials, and all detailed part drawings. Specify appropriate tolerances for all dimensions. All parts are made of steel. You may use metric dimensions or convert the metric dimensions to their nearest inch equivalents.

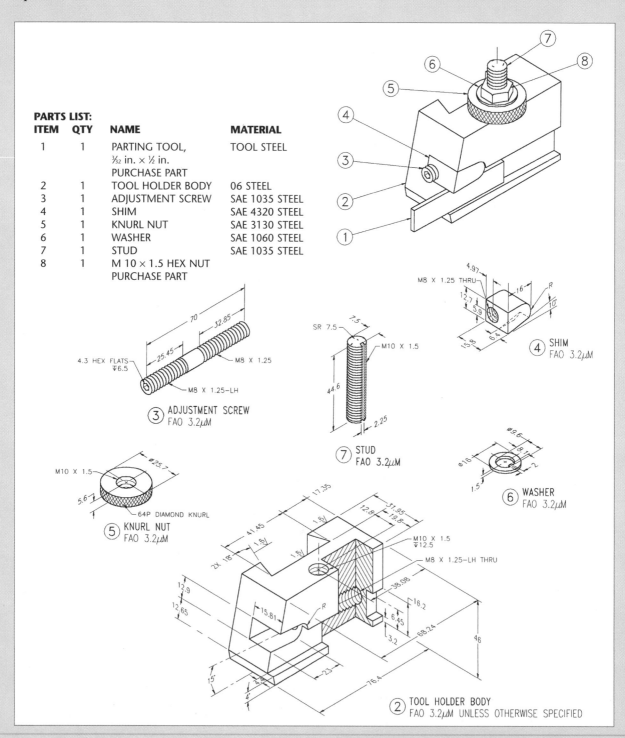

PARTS LIST:

ITEM	QTY	NAME	MATERIAL
1	1	PARTING TOOL, ³⁄₃₂ in. × ½ in. PURCHASE PART	TOOL STEEL
2	1	TOOL HOLDER BODY	06 STEEL
3	1	ADJUSTMENT SCREW	SAE 1035 STEEL
4	1	SHIM	SAE 4320 STEEL
5	1	KNURL NUT	SAE 3130 STEEL
6	1	WASHER	SAE 1060 STEEL
7	1	STUD	SAE 1035 STEEL
8	1	M 10 × 1.5 HEX NUT PURCHASE PART	

FIGURE P18.2.

18.14 problems (continued)

3. A conceptual layout of a wood clamp is shown in Figure P18.3. Detail the design by specifying appropriate dimensions and tolerances for each part. Create a complete set of working drawings for the device, including an outline assembly drawing, an exploded assembly drawing, a bill of materials, and all detailed part drawings. All parts are made of steel. You may use the given inch dimensions or their nearest metric equivalents.

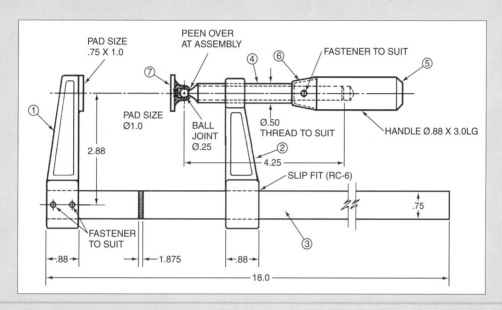

FIGURE P18.3.

4. A conceptual layout of an adjustable drawing compass is shown in Figure P18.4. Detail the design by specifying appropriate dimensions and tolerances for each part. Create a complete set of working drawings for the device, including an outline assembly drawing, an exploded assembly drawing, a bill of materials, and all detailed part drawings. All parts are made of steel. It is not necessary to create a drawing of the LEAD. You may use the given inch dimensions or their nearest metric equivalents.

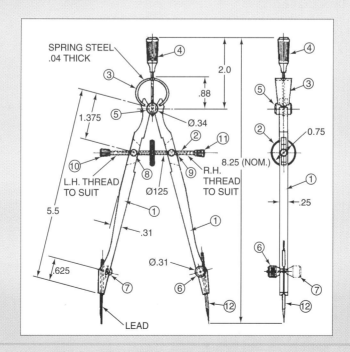

FIGURE P18.4.

18.14 problems (continued)

5. A conceptual sketch of a general duty clamp is shown in Figure P18.5. Detail the design by specifying appropriate dimensions and tolerances for each part. Create a complete set of working drawings for the device, including an outline assembly drawing, an exploded assembly drawing, a bill of materials, and all detailed part drawings. All parts are made of steel. You may use metric dimensions or convert the metric dimensions to their nearest inch equivalents.

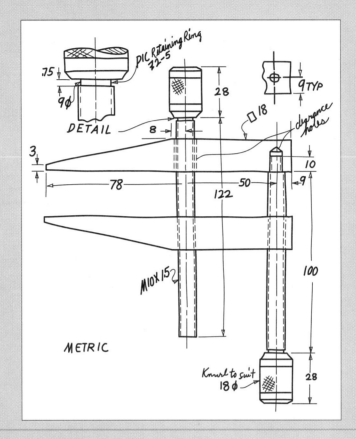

FIGURE P18.5.

18.14 problems (continued)

6. A conceptual sketch of a toggle clamp is shown in Figure P18.6. Detail the design by specifying appropriate dimensions and tolerances for each part. Create a complete set of working drawings for the device, including an outline assembly drawing, an exploded assembly drawing, a bill of materials, and all detailed part drawings. All parts are made of steel. You may use the given inch dimensions or their nearest metric equivalents.

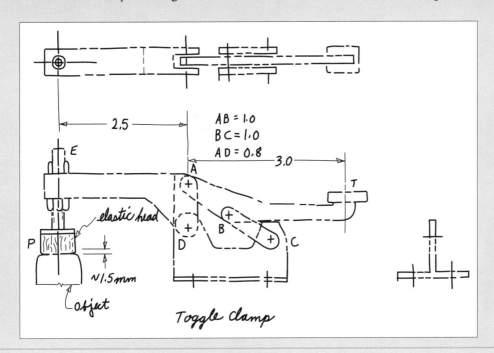

FIGURE P18.6.

18.14 problems (continued)

7. A conceptual layout of an adjustable lifting clamp is shown in Figure P18.7. Detail the design by specifying appropriate dimensions and tolerances for each part. Create a complete set of working drawings for the device, including an outline assembly drawing, an exploded assembly drawing, a bill of materials, and all detailed part drawings. All parts are made of steel. You may use the given inch dimensions or their nearest metric equivalents.

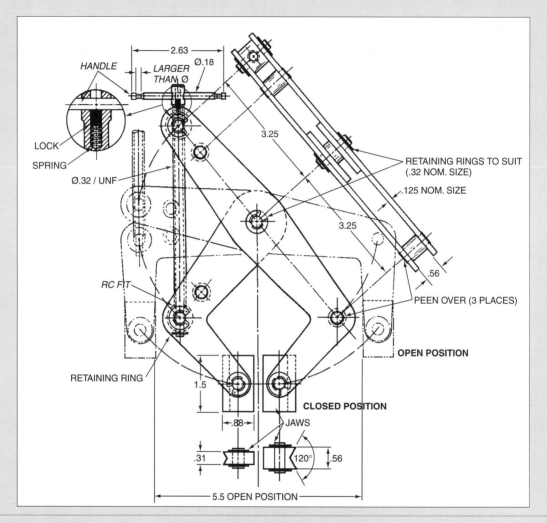

FIGURE P18.7.

18.14 problems (continued)

8. A conceptual model for a pen-type eraser is shown in whole and in cutaway view in Figure P18.8. Using reasonable materials and dimensions of your choice, expand the concept to create a complete set of working drawings for the device, including an outline assembly drawing, an exploded assembly drawing, a sectioned assembly drawing, a bill of materials, and all detailed part drawings. Specify appropriate tolerances for all dimensions.

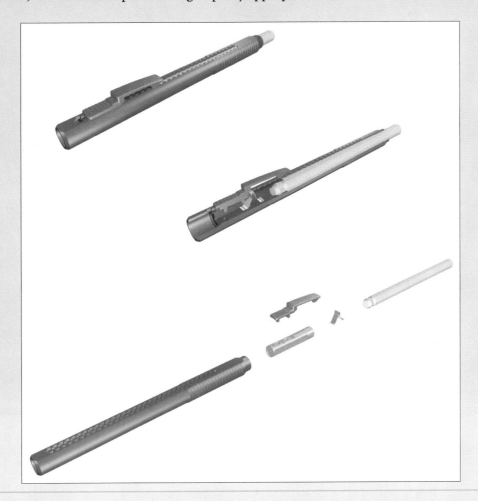

FIGURE P18.8.

18.14 problems (continued)

9. A conceptual model for a garden hose nozzle is shown in whole, cutaway, and exploded views in Figure P18.9. Using reasonable materials and dimensions of your choice, expand the concept to create a complete set of working drawings for the device, including an outline assembly drawing, an exploded assembly drawing, a sectioned assembly drawing, a bill of materials, and all detailed part drawings. Specify appropriate tolerances for all dimensions.

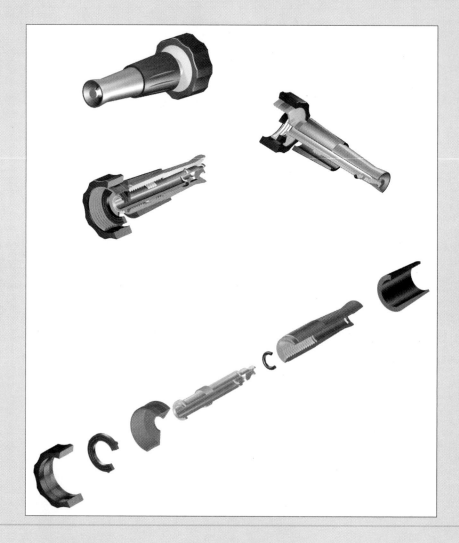

FIGURE P18.9.

18.14 problems (continued)

10. Conceptual sketches for a wheelbarrow are shown in Figure P18.10. Using reasonable materials and dimensions of your choice, expand the concept to create a complete set of working drawings for the device, including an outline assembly drawing, an exploded assembly drawing, a sectioned assembly drawing, a bill of materials, and all detailed part drawings. You may use either inch or metric dimensions. Specify appropriate tolerances for all dimensions.

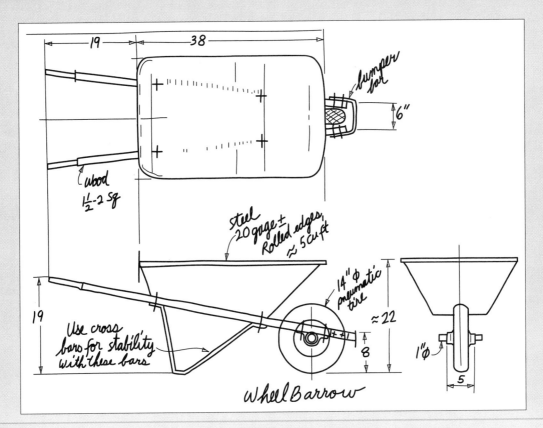

FIGURE P18.10.

18.14 problems (continued)

11. Conceptual sketches for a caster are shown in Figure P18.11. Using reasonable materials and dimensions of your choice, expand the concept to create a complete set of working drawings for the device, including an outline assembly drawing, an exploded assembly drawing, a sectioned assembly drawing, a bill of materials, and all detailed part drawings. You may use either inch or metric dimensions. Specify appropriate tolerances for all dimensions.

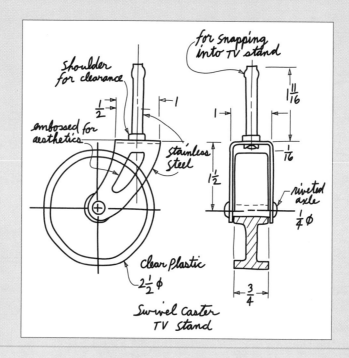

FIGURE P18.11.

18.14 problems (continued)

12. Find the errors and poor practices in these drawings.

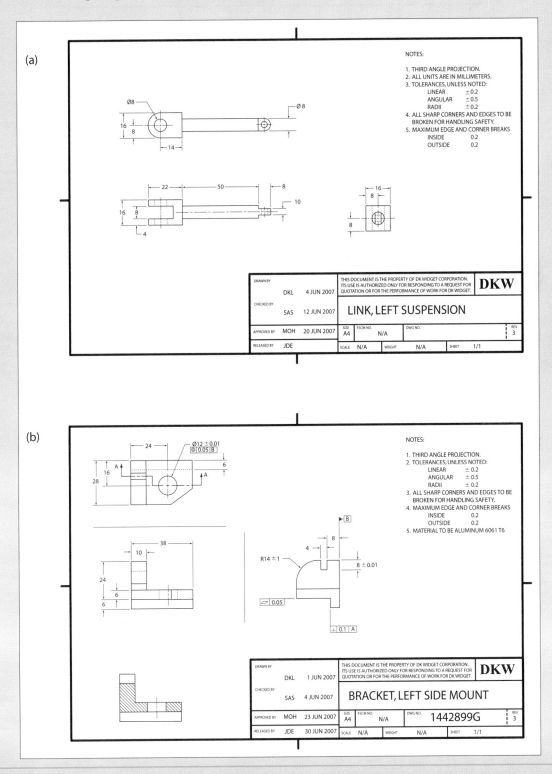

FIGURES P18.12.

18.14 problems (continued)

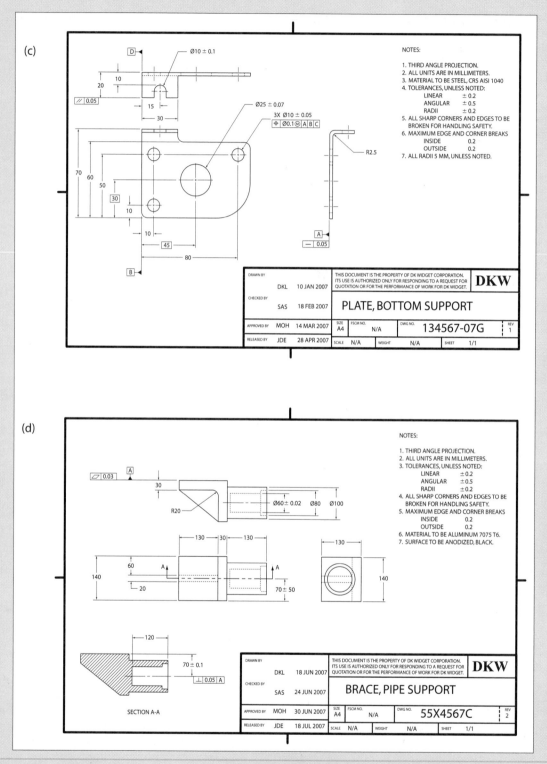

FIGURES P18.12. (CONTINUED)

18.14 problems (continued)

13. Answer the following questions regarding the site plan for the water main extension project in the village of Baraga shown here.

  a. What are the names of the four streets bordering the area under consideration?

  b. How many existing fire hydrants are shown on the plan?

  c. How many proposed fire hydrants are shown on the plan?

  d. Counting all houses and separate garages, how many buildings are in the area?

  e. What is the diameter of the supply main to be abandoned?

  f. What is the diameter of the new water main? How many total linear feet of it is required?

  g. For the houses and garages shown on the plan, how many have gravel driveways and how many have bituminous driveways?

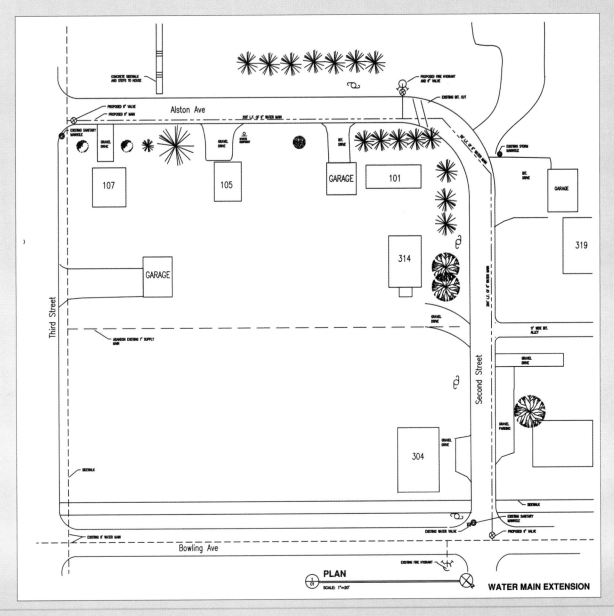

FIGURE P18.13.

18.14 problems (continued)

14. Answer the following questions regarding the trench detail for the water main extension project in the village of Baraga shown here.

a. What is the trench width for an 8" pipe? for a 12" pipe?

b. What is the minimum depth from the ground to the top of the pipe? Who can approve a smaller minimum depth?

c. What is the slope of the sides of the trench?

d. Where will the contractor find the specifications for the bedding requirements?

e. What is the minimum distance between the bottom of the pipe and the bottom of the trench?

f. What type of compacted material surrounds the pipe?

g. This drawing is made N.T.S. (meaning "not to scale"). Why do you suppose this is an acceptable practice?

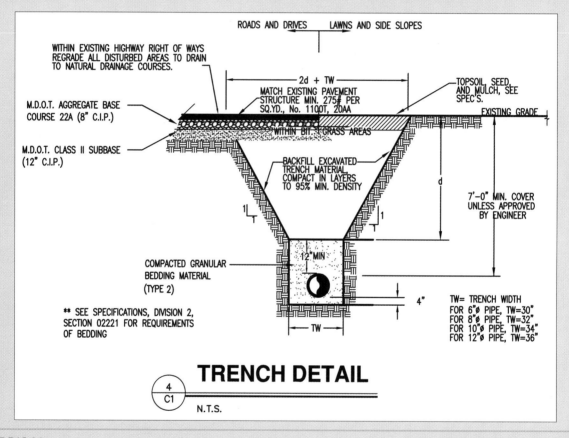

FIGURE P18.14.

18.14 problems (continued)

15. Answer the following questions regarding the wall section for the water treatment plant expansion project in the village of Baraga shown here.

  a. What is the elevation of the top of the footing?

  b. What is the elevation of the top of the concrete slab?

  c. What is the elevation of the top of the concrete sidewalk?

  d. What is the elevation of the bottom of the proposed double tee?

  e. What is the depth of the concrete topping that covers the 8" precast plank?

  f. What is the size and type of insulation for the upper portion of the wall?

  g. What is the minimum concrete cover for the steel rebars in the wall?

  h. How many rebars are required at the top of the door opening? What is the size of the bars there?

  i. What is the width of the footing?

  j. #4 and #5 rebars are used as reinforcement throughout the wall and footing. What size is used in the footing? What size is used for horizontal reinforcement? What size is used for vertical reinforcement?

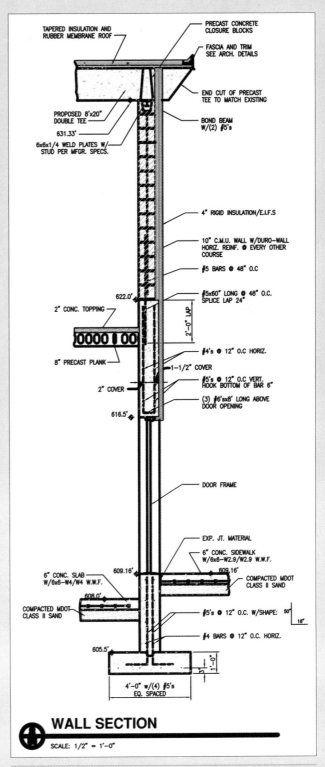

FIGURE P18.15.

18.14 problems (continued)

16. For the figure shown here, measure the lengths of the lines at the indicated scales. (Do not use a calculator for this exercise.) What are the lengths of lines A through F if they are drawn at the indicated scales?

  a. 1"=4000'

  b. 1"=5 yds

  c. 1"=60'

  d. 1"=2'

  e. ¼"=1'-0"

  f. ⅜"=1'-0"

  g. ¾"=1'-0"

  h. ½"=1'-0"

  i. 1:2 (use Metric scale)

  j. 1:500 (use Metric scale)

  k. 1:75 (use Metric scale)

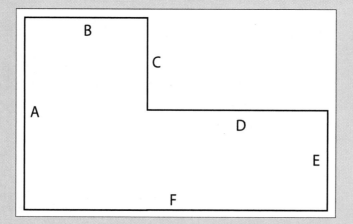

FIGURE P18.16.

Appendix

casestudy
TiLite Wheelchairs—"The Ultimate Ride"

The freedom to get around is important to everyone, but especially to people with disabilities. Users of manual wheelchairs must be independently mobile to enjoy work, travel, sports, and other social activities. They require comfortable, lightweight wheelchairs with features to suit their active lifestyle. A properly designed and fitted wheelchair not only is comfortable but also minimizes energy expenditure and reduces stresses on the user's body. Today people with disabilities can benefit from breakthroughs in design, materials, and manufacturing methods to obtain a unique, customized wheelchair that fits their personal abilities and active lifestyle.

Founded in 1998, TiLite's goal is to provide a twenty-first-century solution to the age-old problem of mobility. TiLite has successfully combined the unique material properties of titanium; traditional fabrication methods; and modern design tools such as parametric modeling, finite element analysis, and rapid prototyping to provide a unique line of affordable, lightweight, and custom-fit manual wheelchairs. TiLite wheelchairs are fabricated from a titanium alloy that is lightweight and has superior strength. Unlike steel, titanium does not corrode and is very durable. The unique combination of these properties is ideal for wheelchair design.

TiLite designs wheelchairs for a variety of users. Ultralightweight chairs are ideal for sports enthusiasts such as wheelchair basketball players and marathon racers. A TiLite chair has even carried the Olympic Torch. Children require chairs that are lightweight and that adapt to children's growth. Elderly users also benefit from lightweight chairs that are easy to propel. Lightweight folding models are easy to transport. TiLite wheelchairs are designed not only to be functional but also to be stylish, displaying the beautiful patina of polished titanium metal. The ability to custom-design and fabricate a unique chair to fit each individual means that there is a TiLite chair for every user. Modern CAD tools enable designers to modify their designs for custom fabrication.

VARIATIONAL DESIGN OF THE TILITE WHEELCHAIR

Over half of all manual wheelchair users suffer from repetitive motion injuries such as carpal tunnel syndrome, chronic shoulder injury, pressure sores, back pain, postural deformities, and reduced heart and lung function.

Proper fit and low weight are critical to wheelchair design to reduce these injuries. Studies have shown that wheelchair users suffer fewer long-term health problems with a properly fitted wheelchair. The rear axle of the wheelchair should be positioned forward of the user's shoulder, and the center of gravity of the user and chair should be just forward of the rear axle. The seat should be as narrow as possible to keep the rear wheels close to the frame and the arms close to the body during propulsion. The wheelchair frame must be sized to fit the user's body measurements. These requirements translate into specific dimensions on the wheelchair frame.

The TiLite XC Ultralightweight wheelchair.

For the TiLite TX model, the user must specify twelve measurements or parameters, such as seat width, back angle, footrest width, and wheel camber; there is a choice of between three and twenty-five possible values for each measurement. With all of these geometric variables and constraints, the designers of TiLite chairs must utilize parametric models to create solid models and drawings of the custom-fit wheelchair design. Based on the user's desired dimensions, the Design Table function in the solid modeling software allows the designer to create all of the necessary configurations of basic wheelchair frame members. When the user's desired dimensions are inserted into the design tables, all of the remaining dimensions of the parts are automatically adjusted to ensure that the parts fit together and fit the user. From these solid models, all of the necessary drawings for a custom wheelchair can be created in only a few minutes. This saves time for the designer and speeds up delivery of the wheelchair to the user.

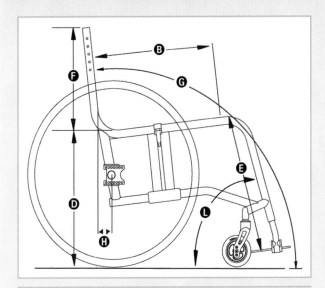

Measurements for ordering a custom wheelchair design.

ASSEMBLY MODELING OF THE TILITE WHEELCHAIR

For a custom-fit wheelchair design, a vast number of different configurations are available depending on the user's body dimensions and seating preferences. Therefore, it is impossible and impractical to build a physical prototype of each wheelchair frame configuration. Nonetheless, the wheelchair must function properly regardless of the size of the frame members. Solid modeling can be used to create virtual prototypes instead of physical models of any wheelchair design.

A folding wheelchair based on a familiar x-frame design is composed of two cross tubes (shown in gray), seat tubes (blue), and hinge members (pink). When designing a folding wheelchair, the designer must check for interference between parts in the open and folded configurations as well as all positions in between. When the sizes of the parts vary for different users, the model must be carefully checked for each configuration. This can be done most efficiently using a solid model. Stick figure models are created to represent the centerlines of each moving part, measured from their attachment points at the pin joints. These skeleton models are manipulated to make sure that the mechanism does not lock up, invert, or toggle. A trial-and-error method is

used to move the locations of the hinge pins until an acceptable design is found that works for all possible sizes of the design.

Although a range of sizes is available for seat tubes and cross tubes, the goal is to have a single design for the hinge members, which may be manufactured by an outside vendor. After the positions of the hinge pins are established with the stick figure models, the hinge members are fleshed out and given a shape that will avoid interference with the cross tubes and seat tubes. A variational solid model allows the designer to check multiple configurations quickly and to ensure that all sizes of the wheelchair frame will function as desired.

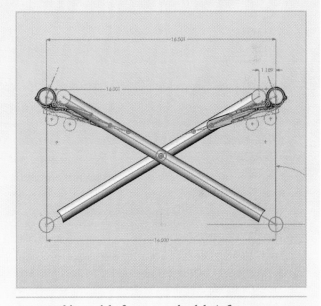

An assembly model of an open wheelchair frame.

Another important design consideration is that the wheelchair can be folded compactly. Solid models can be used to ensure that none of the parts interfere during folding. Changes in the design are easily checked for multiple sizes and configurations of the wheelchair. With the use of solid models, the designer can be assured that the wheelchair will fold to the most compact form possible and function smoothly in the folding operation.

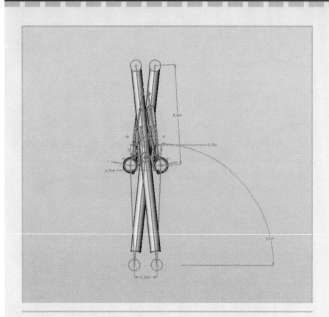

An assembly model of a folded wheelchair frame.

FABRICATION OF THE TILITE WHEELCHAIR

Each custom-fitted wheelchair frame is unique and must be manufactured individually. To begin the fabrication process, TiLite designer Lindy Anderlini uses the parametric models of the wheelchair frame to generate its full-scale layout. The frame drawing is then laid on the surface of a modular fixture, and the stop blocks on the fixture are bolted down in the proper positions to hold each piece of the tubing. Setting up the modular fixture takes only about ten minutes.

Each tube member is carefully bent to the proper angle using a special bending machine. The tubing is then measured and cut to the correct length based on the scale drawing, and the ends are shaped to fit snugly to the mating parts. Proper sizing and positioning of the frame members is critical to obtain sturdy weld joints. By using the full-scale drawing as a template, the manufacturer can ensure a perfect fit for every customer. After each piece of tubing has been formed and cut, they are laid in the fixture and clamped in the proper position. The parts are tack-welded together, then removed from the fixture and finish-welded. In completion of the fabrication process, the frame is drilled in the necessary locations for assembly of other parts and bead-blasted, hand-buffed, or painted according to the user's preference for surface finish.

TiLite designer Lindy Anderlini creates full-scale drawings of wheelchair frames.

DISCUSSION QUESTIONS/ACTIVITIES

1. Explain how a parametric solid modeler can be used to customize the design of wheelchairs to fit individual users. How is the model used in the design process? the manufacturing process?

2. Compare a custom design to a standard wheelchair with adjustable components. What are the advantages and disadvantages of each design?

3. Make a list of the important design and performance specifications for a lightweight wheelchair. How can a solid model be used to check wheelchair design to ensure that the design meets the desired specifications?

Modular.

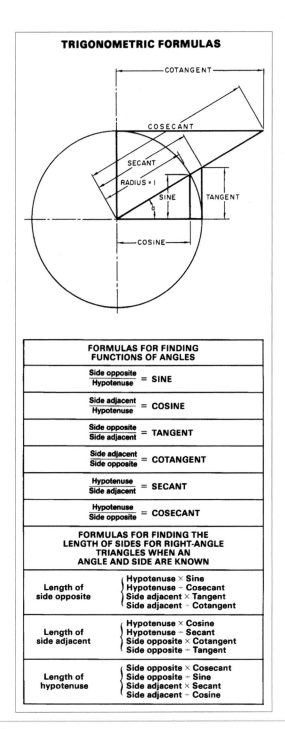

Trigonometric Formulas for Triangles.

RIGHT-TRIANGLE FORMULAS

TO FIND SIDES	FORMULAS		TO FIND ANGLES	FORMULAS	
a	$\sqrt{b^2 + c^2}$		C	$\frac{c}{a} = $ Sine C	90°−B
a	$c \times$ Csc C	$\frac{c}{\text{sine } C}$	C	$\frac{b}{a} = $ Cosine C	90°−B
	$c \times$ Secant B	$\frac{c}{\text{Cosine } B}$	C	$\frac{c}{b} = $ Tan C	90°−B
	$b \times$ Csc B	$\frac{b}{\text{Sine } B}$	C	$\frac{b}{c} = $ Cot C	90°−B
	$\times$ Secant C	$\frac{b}{\text{Cosine } C}$	C	$\frac{a}{b} = $ Secant C	90°−B
	$= c^2$		C	$\frac{a}{c} = $ Csc C	90°−B
?		$\frac{a}{\text{Cosecant } B}$	B	$\frac{b}{a} = $ Sine B	90°−C
		$\frac{a}{\text{Secant } C}$	B	$\frac{c}{a} = $ Cosine B	90°−C
	$\frac{c}{\text{Cotangent } B}$		B	$\frac{b}{c} = $ Tan B	90°−C
	$\frac{c}{\text{ent } C}$		B	$\frac{c}{b} = $ Cot B	90°−C
	B	$\frac{a}{c} = $ Secant B	90°−C		
	B	$\frac{a}{b} = $ Csc B	90°−C		
			c	$a \times$ Cos B	$\frac{a}{\text{Secant } B}$
			c	$a \times$ Sine C	$\frac{a}{\text{Cosecant } C}$
			c	$b \times$ Cot B	$\frac{b}{\text{Tangent } B}$
			c	$b \times$ Tan C	$\frac{b}{\text{Cotangent } C}$

Trigonometric Formulas for Triangles. (CONTINUED)

OBLIQUE-ANGLED TRIANGLE FORMULAS

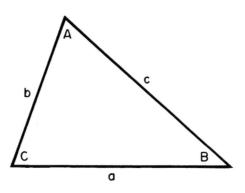

TO FIND	KNOWN	SOLUTION
C	A-B	$180° - (A + B)$
b	a-B-A	$\dfrac{a \times Sin\ B}{Sin\ A}$
c	a-A-C	$\dfrac{a \times Sin\ C}{Sin\ A}$
Tan A	a-C-b	$\dfrac{a \times Sin\ C}{b - (a \times Cos\ C)}$
B	A-C	$180° - (A + C)$
Sin B	b-A-a	$\dfrac{b \times Sin\ A}{a}$
A	B-C	$180° - (B + C)$
Cos A	a-b-c	$\dfrac{b^2 + c^2 - a^2}{2bc}$
Sin C	c-A-a	$\dfrac{c \times Sin\ A}{a}$
Cot B	a-C-b	$\dfrac{a \times Csc\ C}{b} - Cot\ C$
c	b-C-B	$b \times Sin\ C \times Csc\ B$

Trigonometric Formulas for Triangles. (CONTINUED)

RULES RELATIVE TO THE CIRCLE

To Find Circumference—
Multiply diameter by 3.1416 .... Or divide diameter by 0.3183

To Find Diameter—
Multiply circumference by 0.3183 .... Or divide circumference by 3.1416

To Find Radius—
Multiply circumference by 0.15915 .... Or divide circumference by 6.28318

To Find Side of an Inscribed Square—
Multiply diameter by 0.7071
Or multiply circumference by 0.2251 .... Or divide circumference by 4.4428

To Find Side of an Equal Square—
Multiply diameter by 0.8862 .... Or divide diameter by 1.1284
Or multiply circumference by 0.2821 .... Or divide circumference by 3.545

Square—
A side multiplied by 1.4142   equals diameter of its circumscribing circle.
A side multiplied by 4.443   equals circumference of its circumscribing circle.
A side multiplied by 1.128   equals diameter of an equal circle.
A side multiplied by 3.547   equals circumference of an equal circle.

To Find the Area of a Circle—
Multiply circumference by one-quarter of the diameter.
Or multiply the square of diameter by 0.7854
Or multiply the square of circumference by .07958
Or multiply the square of 1/2 diameter by 3.1416

To Find the Surface of a Sphere or Globe—
Multiply the diameter by the circumference.
Or multiply the square of diameter by 3.1416
Or multiply four times the square of radius by 3.1416

Trigonometric Formulas for Circles.

STANDARD LINE TYPES

VISIBLE OBJECT LINES	THICK	THICK LINE APPROXIMATE WIDTH: 0.6 mm
HIDDEN LINE	THIN	THIN LINE APPROXIMATE WIDTH: 0.3 mm
SECTION LINE	THIN	
CENTERLINE	THIN	THICK
SYMMETRY LINE	THIN	
DIMENSION LINE EXTENSION LINE AND LEADER LINE	LEADER EXTENSION LINE DIMENSION LINE THIN 76	
CUTTING-PLANE LINE OR VIEWING-PLANE LINE	THICK THICK THICK	
BREAK LINE	THICK THIN	SHORT BREAKS LONG BREAKS
PHANTOM LINE	THIN	
STITCH LINE	THIN DOTS	
CHAIN LINE	THICK	

Standard Line Types for Drafting.

Inches to Millimeters Conversion.

INCHES TO MILLIMETERS

in.	mm	in.	mm	in.	mm	in.	mm
1	25.4	26	660.4	51	1295.4	76	1930.4
2	50.8	27	685.8	52	1320.8	77	1955.8
3	76.2	28	711.2	53	1346.2	78	1981.2
4	101.6	29	736.6	54	1371.6	79	2006.6
5	127.0	30	762.0	55	1397.0	80	2032.0
6	152.4	31	787.4	56	1422.4	81	2057.4
7	177.8	32	812.8	57	1447.8	82	2082.8
8	203.2	33	838.2	58	1473.2	83	2108.2
9	228.6	34	863.6	59	1498.6	84	2133.6
10	254.0	35	889.0	60	1524.0	85	2159.0
11	279.4	36	914.4	61	1549.4	86	2184.4
12	304.8	37	939.8	62	1574.8	87	2209.8
13	330.2	38	965.2	63	1600.2	88	2235.2
14	355.6	39	990.6	64	1625.6	89	2260.6
15	381.0	40	1016.0	65	1651.0	90	2286.0
16	406.4	41	1041.4	66	1676.4	91	2311.4
17	431.8	42	1066.8	67	1701.8	92	2336.8
18	457.2	43	1092.2	68	1727.2	93	2362.2
19	482.6	44	1117.6	69	1752.6	94	2387.6
20	508.0	45	1143.0	70	1778.0	95	2413.0
21	533.4	46	1168.4	71	1803.4	96	2438.4
22	558.8	47	1193.8	72	1828.8	97	2463.8
23	584.2	48	1219.2	73	1854.2	98	2489.2
24	609.6	49	1244.6	74	1879.6	99	2514.6
25	635.0	50	1270.0	75	1905.0	100	2540.0

The above table is exact on the basis: 1 in. = 25.4 mm

Millimeters to Inches Conversion.

MILLIMETERS TO INCHES

in.	mm	in.	mm	in.	mm	in.	mm
1	0.039370	26	1.023622	51	2.007874	76	2.992126
2	0.078740	27	1.062992	52	2.047244	77	3.031496
3	0.118110	28	1.102362	53	2.086614	78	3.070866
4	0.157480	29	1.141732	54	2.125984	79	3.110236
5	0.196850	30	1.181102	55	2.165354	80	3.149606
6	0.236220	31	1.220472	56	2.204724	81	3.188976
7	0.275591	32	1.259843	57	2.244094	82	3.228346
8	0.314961	33	1.299213	58	2.283465	83	3.267717
9	0.354331	34	1.338583	59	2.322835	84	3.307087
10	0.393701	35	1.377953	60	2.362205	85	3.346457
11	0.433071	36	1.417323	61	2.401575	86	3.385827
12	0.472441	37	1.456693	62	2.440945	87	3.425197
13	0.511811	38	1.496063	63	2.480315	88	3.464567
14	0.551181	39	1.535433	64	2.519685	89	3.503937
15	0.590551	40	1.574803	65	2.559055	90	3.543307
16	0.629921	41	1.614173	66	2.598425	91	3.582677
17	0.669291	42	1.653543	67	2.637795	92	3.622047
18	0.708661	43	1.692913	68	2.677165	93	3.661417
19	0.748031	44	1.732283	69	2.716535	94	3.700787
20	0.787402	45	1.771654	70	2.755906	95	3.740157
21	0.826772	46	1.811024	71	2.795276	96	3.779528
22	0.866142	47	1.850394	72	2.834646	97	3.818898
23	0.905512	48	1.889764	73	2.874016	98	3.858268
24	0.944882	49	1.929134	74	2.913386	99	3.897638
25	0.984252	50	1.968504	75	2.952756	100	3.937008

The above table is approximate on the basis: 1 in. = 25.4 mm, 1/25.4 = 0.039370078740+

INCH/METRIC EQUIVALENTS

Fraction	Decimal Equivalent Customary (in.)	Metric (mm)	Fraction	Decimal Equivalent Customary (in.)	Metric (mm)
1/64	.015625	0.3969	33/64	.515625	13.0969
1/32	.03125	0.7938	17/32	.53125	13.4938
3/64	.046875	1.1906	35/64	.546875	13.8906
1/16	.0625	1.5875	9/16	.5625	14.2875
5/64	.078125	1.9844	37/64	.578125	14.6844
3/32	.09375	2.3813	19/32	.59375	15.0813
7/64	.109375	2.7781	39/64	.609375	15.4781
1/8	.1250	3.1750	5/8	.6250	15.8750
9/64	.140625	3.5719	41/64	.640625	16.2719
5/32	.15625	3.9688	21/32	.65625	16.6688
11/64	.171875	4.3656	43/64	.671875	17.0656
3/16	.1875	4.7625	11/16	.6875	17.4625
13/64	.203125	5.1594	45/64	.703125	17.8594
7/32	.21875	5.5563	23/32	.71875	18.2563
15/64	.234375	5.9531	47/64	.734375	18.6531
1/4	.250	6.3500	3/4	.750	19.0500
17/64	.265625	6.7469	49/64	.765625	19.4469
9/32	.28125	7.1438	25/32	.78125	19.8438
19/64	.296875	7.5406	51/64	.796875	20.2406
5/16	.3125	7.9375	13/16	.8125	20.6375
21/64	.328125	8.3384	53/64	.828125	21.0344
11/32	.34375	8.7313	27/32	.84375	21.4313
23/64	.359375	9.1281	55/64	.859375	21.8281
3/8	.3750	9.5250	7/8	.8750	22.2250
25/64	.390625	9.9219	57/64	.890625	22.6219
13/32	.40625	10.3188	29/32	.90625	23.0188
27/64	.421875	10.7156	59/64	.921875	23.4156
7/16	.4375	11.1125	15/16	.9375	23.8125
29/64	.453125	11.5094	61/64	.953125	24.2094
15/32	.46875	11.9063	31/32	.96875	24.6063
31/64	.484375	12.3031	63/64	.984375	25.0031
1/2	.500	12.7000	1	1.000	25.4000

Inch/Metric Equivalents.

Measures of Length
1 millimeter (mm) = 0.03937 inch
1 centimeter (cm) = 0.39370 inch
1 meter (m) = 39.37008 inches
= 3.2808 feet
= 1.0936 yards
1 kilometer (km) = 0.6214 mile
1 inch = 25.4 millimeters (mm)
= 2.54 centimeters (cm)
1 foot = 304.8 millimeters (mm)
= 0.3048 meter (m)
1 yard = 0.9144 meter (m)
1 mile = 1.609 kilometers (km)

Measures of Area
1 square millimeter = 0.00155 square inch
1 square centimeter = 0.155 square inch
1 square meter = 10.764 square feet
= 1.196 square yards
1 square kilometer = 0.3861 square mile
1 square inch = 645.2 square millimeters
= 6.452 square centimeters
1 square foot = 929 square centimeters
= 0.0929 square meter
1 square yard = 0.836 square meter
1 square mile = 2.5899 square kilometers

Measures of Capacity (Dry)
1 cubic centimeter (cm^3) = 0.061 cubic inch
1 liter = 0.0353 cubic foot
= 61.023 cubic inches
1 cubic meter (m^3) = 35.315 cubic feet
= 1.308 cubic yards
1 cubic inch = 16.38706 cubic centimeters (cm^3)
1 cubic foot = 0.02832 cubic meter (m^3)
= 28.317 liters
1 cubic yard = 0.7646 cubic meter (m^3)

Measures of Capacity (Liquid)
1 liter = 1.0567 U.S. quarts
= 0.2642 U.S. gallon
= 0.2200 Imperial gallon
1 cubic meter (m^3) = 264.2 U.S. gallons
= 219.969 Imperial gallons
1 U.S. quart = 0.946 liter
1 Imperial quart = 1.136 liters
1 U.S. gallon = 3.785 liters
1 Imperial gallon = 4.546 liters

Measures of Weight
1 gram (g) = 15.432 grains
= 0.03215 ounce troy
= 0.03527 ounce avoirdupois
1 kilogram (kg) = 35.274 ounces avoirdupois
= 2.2046 pounds
1000 kilograms (kg) = 1 metric ton (t)
= 1.1023 tons of 2000 pounds
= 0.9842 ton of 2240 pounds
1 ounce avoirdupois = 28.35 grams (g)
1 ounce troy = 31.103 grams (g)
1 pound = 453.6 grams
= 0.4536 kilogram (kg)
1 ton of 2240 pounds = 1016 kilograms (kg)
= 1.016 metric tons
1 grain = 0.0648 gram (g)
1 metric ton = 0.9842 ton of 2240 pounds
= 2204.6 pounds

Inch/Metric Conversion.

Grade Marking	Specification	Material
NO MARK	SAE—Grade 1	Low or Medium Carbon Steel
	ASTM—A307	Low Carbon Steel
	SAE—Grade 2	Low or Medium Carbon Steel
	SAE—Grade 5	Medium Carbon Steel, Quenched and Tempered
	ASTM—A 449	
	SAE—Grade 5.2	Low Carbon Martensite Steel, Quenched and Tempered
A 325	ASTM—A 325 Type 1	Medium Carbon Steel, Quenched and Tempered Radial dashes optional
A 325	ASTM—A 325 Type 2	Low Carbon Martensite Steel, Quenched and Tempered
A 325	ASTM—A 325 Type 3	Atmospheric Corrosion (Weathering) Steel, Quenched and Tempered
BC	ASTM—A 354 Grade BC	Alloy Steel, Quenched and Tempered
	SAE—Grade 7	Medium Carbon Alloy Steel, Quenched and Tempered, Roll Threaded After Heat Treatment
	SAE—Grade 8	Medium Carbon Alloy Steel, Quenched and Tempered
	ASTM—A 354 Grade BD	Alloy Steel, Quenched and Tempered
	SAE—Grade 8.2	Low Carbon Martensite Steel, Quenched and Tempered
A 490	ASTM—A 490 Type 1	Alloy Steel, Quenched and Tempered
A 490	ASTM—A 490 Type 3	Atmospheric Corrosion (Weathering) Steel, Quenched and Tempered

Reprinted from ASME B18.2.1-1981 (R1992), B18.2.2-1987 (R1993), B18.3-1986 (R1993), B18.6.2-1972 (R1993), B18.6.3-1972 (R1991), B18.21.1-1994, B18.22.1-1965 (R1990), B17.1-1967 (R1998), B17.2-1967 (R1990) and B4.2-1978 (R1994), by permission of The American Society of Mechanical Engineers. All rights reserved.

ASTM and SAE Grade Markings for Steel Bolts and Screws.

Sizes Primary	Sizes Secondary	Basic Major Diameter	Coarse UNC	Fine UNF	Extra fine UNEF	4UN	6UN	8UN	12UN	16UN	20UN	28UN	32UN	Sizes
0		0.0600	—	80	—	—	—	—	—	—	—	—	—	0
	1	0.0730	64	72	—	—	—	—	—	—	—	—	—	1
2		0.0860	56	64	—	—	—	—	—	—	—	—	—	2
	3	0.0990	48	56	—	—	—	—	—	—	—	—	—	3
4		0.1120	40	48	—	—	—	—	—	—	—	—	—	4
5		0.1250	40	44	—	—	—	—	—	—	—	—	—	5
6		0.1380	32	40	—	—	—	—	—	—	—	—	UNC	6
8		0.1640	32	36	—	—	—	—	—	—	—	—	UNC	8
10		0.1900	24	32	—	—	—	—	—	—	—	UNF	UNEF	10
	12	0.2160	24	28	32	—	—	—	—	—	—	UNF	UNEF	12
1/4		0.2500	20	28	32	—	—	—	—	—	UNC	UNF	UNEF	1/4
5/16		0.3125	18	24	32	—	—	—	—	—	20	28	UNEF	5/16
3/8		0.3750	16	24	32	—	—	—	—	UNC	20	28	UNEF	3/8
7/16		0.4375	14	20	28	—	—	—	—	16	UNF	UNEF	32	7/16
1/2		0.5000	13	20	28	—	—	—	—	16	UNF	UNEF	32	1/2
9/16		0.5625	12	18	24	—	—	—	UNC	16	20	28	32	9/16
5/8		0.6250	11	18	24	—	—	—	12	16	20	28	32	5/8
	11/16	0.6875	—	—	24	—	—	—	12	16	20	28	32	11/16
3/4		0.7500	10	16	20	—	—	—	12	UNF	UNEF	28	32	3/4
	13/16	0.8125	—	—	20	—	—	—	12	16	UNEF	28	32	13/16
7/8		0.8750	9	14	20	—	—	—	12	16	UNEF	28	32	7/8
	15/16	0.9375	—	—	20	—	—	—	12	16	UNEF	28	32	15/16
1		1.0000	8	12	20	—	—	UNC	UNF	16	UNEF	28	32	1
	1 1/16	1.0625	—	—	18	—	—	8	12	16	20	28	—	1 1/16
1 1/8		1.1250	7	12	18	—	—	8	UNF	16	20	28	—	1 1/8
	1 3/16	1.1875	—	—	18	—	—	8	12	16	20	28	—	1 3/16
1 1/4		1.2500	7	12	18	—	—	8	UNF	16	20	28	—	1 1/4
	1 5/16	1.3125	—	—	18	—	—	8	12	16	20	28	—	1 5/16
1 3/8		1.3750	6	12	18	—	UNC	8	UNF	16	20	28	—	1 3/8
	1 7/16	1.4375	—	—	18	—	6	8	12	16	20	28	—	1 7/16
1 1/2		1.5000	6	12	18	—	UNC	8	UNF	16	20	28	—	1 1/2
	1 9/16	1.5625	—	—	18	—	6	8	12	16	20	—	—	1 9/16
1 5/8		1.6250	—	—	18	—	6	8	12	16	20	—	—	1 5/8
	1 11/16	1.6875	—	—	18	—	6	8	12	16	20	—	—	1 11/16
1 3/4		1.7500	5	—	—	—	6	8	12	16	20	—	—	1 3/4
	1 13/16	1.8125	—	—	—	—	6	8	12	16	20	—	—	1 13/16
1 7/8		1.8750	—	—	—	—	6	8	12	16	20	—	—	1 7/8
	1 15/16	1.9375	—	—	—	—	6	8	12	16	20	—	—	1 15/16
2		2.0000	4 1/2	—	—	—	6	8	12	16	20	—	—	2
	2 1/8	2.1250	—	—	—	—	6	8	12	16	20	—	—	2 1/8
2 1/4		2.2500	4 1/2	—	—	—	6	8	12	16	20	—	—	2 1/4
	2 3/8	2.3750	—	—	—	—	6	8	12	16	20	—	—	2 3/8
2 1/2		2.5000	4	—	—	UNC	6	8	12	16	20	—	—	2 1/2
	2 5/8	2.6250	—	—	—	4	6	8	12	16	20	—	—	2 5/8
2 3/4		2.7500	4	—	—	UNC	6	8	12	16	20	—	—	2 3/4
	2 7/8	2.8750	—	—	—	4	6	8	12	16	20	—	—	2 7/8
3		3.0000	4	—	—	UNC	6	8	12	16	20	—	—	3
	3 1/8	3.1250	—	—	—	4	6	8	12	16	—	—	—	3 1/8
3 1/4		3.2500	4	—	—	UNC	6	8	12	16	—	—	—	3 1/4
	3 3/8	3.3750	—	—	—	4	6	8	12	16	—	—	—	3 3/8
3 1/2		3.5000	4	—	—	UNC	6	8	12	16	—	—	—	3 1/2
	3 5/8	3.6250	—	—	—	4	6	8	12	16	—	—	—	3 5/8
3 3/4		3.7500	4	—	—	UNC	6	8	12	16	—	—	—	3 3/4
	3 7/8	3.8750	—	—	—	4	6	8	12	16	—	—	—	3 7/8
4		4.0000	4	—	—	UNC	6	8	12	16	—	—	—	4
	4 1/8	4.1250	—	—	—	4	6	8	12	16	—	—	—	4 1/8
4 1/4		4.2500	—	—	—	4	6	8	12	16	—	—	—	4 1/4
	4 3/8	4.3750	—	—	—	4	6	8	12	16	—	—	—	4 3/8
4 1/2		4.5000	—	—	—	4	6	8	12	16	—	—	—	4 1/2
	4 5/8	4.6250	—	—	—	4	6	8	12	16	—	—	—	4 5/8
4 3/4		4.7500	—	—	—	4	6	8	12	16	—	—	—	4 3/4
	4 7/8	4.8750	—	—	—	4	6	8	12	16	—	—	—	4 7/8
5		5.0000	—	—	—	4	6	8	12	16	—	—	—	5
	5 1/8	5.1250	—	—	—	4	6	8	12	16	—	—	—	5 1/8
5 1/4		5.2500	—	—	—	4	6	8	12	16	—	—	—	5 1/4
	5 3/8	5.3750	—	—	—	4	6	8	12	16	—	—	—	5 3/8
5 1/2		5.5000	—	—	—	4	6	8	12	16	—	—	—	5 1/2
	5 5/8	5.6250	—	—	—	4	6	8	12	16	—	—	—	5 5/8
5 3/4		5.7500	—	—	—	4	6	8	12	16	—	—	—	5 3/4
	5 7/8	5.8750	—	—	—	4	6	8	12	16	—	—	—	5 7/8
6		6.0000	—	—	—	4	6	8	12	16	—	—	—	6

Unified Standard Screw Thread Series.

ISO BASIC METRIC THREAD INFORMATION

Basic Major DIA & Pitch	Tap Drill DIA	INTERNAL THREADS		EXTERNAL THREADS		Clearance Hole
		Minor DIA MAX	Minor DIA MIN	Major DIA MAX	Major DIA MIN	
M1.6 × 0.35	1.25	1.321	1.221	1.576	1.491	1.9
M2 × 0.4	1.60	1.679	1.567	1.976	1.881	2.4
M2.5 × 0.45	2.05	2.138	2.013	2.476	2.013	2.9
M3 × 0.5	2.50	2.599	2.459	2.976	2.870	3.4
M3.5 × 0.6	2.90	3.010	2.850	3.476	3.351	4.0
M4 × 0.7	3.30	3.422	3.242	3.976	3.836	4.5
M5 × 0.8	4.20	4.334	4.134	4.976	4.826	5.5
M6 × 1	5.00	5.153	4.917	5.974	5.794	6.6
M8 × 1.25	6.80	6.912	6.647	7.972	7.760	9.0
M10 × 1.5	8.50	8.676	8.376	9.968	9.732	11.0
M12 × 1.75	10.20	10.441	10.106	11.966	11.701	13.5
M14 × 2	12.00	12.210	11.835	13.962	13.682	15.5
M16 × 2	14.00	14.210	13.835	15.962	15.682	17.5
M20 × 2.5	17.50	17.744	17.294	19.958	19.623	22.0
M24 × 3	21.00	21.252	20.752	23.952	23.577	26.0
M30 × 3.5	26.50	26.771	26.211	29.947	29.522	33.0
M36 × 4	32.00	32.270	31.670	35.940	35.465	39.0
M42 × 4.5	37.50	37.799	37.129	41.937	41.437	45.0
M48 × 5	43.00	43.297	42.587	47.929	47.399	52.0
M56 × 5.5	50.50	50.796	50.046	55.925	55.365	62.0
M64 × 6	58.00	58.305	57.505	63.920	63.320	70.0
M72 × 6	66.00	66.305	65.505	71.920	71.320	78.0
M80 × 6	74.00	74.305	73.505	79.920	79.320	86.0
M90 × 6	84.00	84.305	83.505	89.920	89.320	96.0
M100 × 6	94.00	94.305	93.505	99.920	99.320	107.0

ISO Metric Thread Information.

INCH—METRIC THREAD COMPARISON

INCH SERIES				METRIC		
Size	Dia.(In.)	TPI	Size	Dia. (In.)	Pitch (mm)	TPI (Approx)
			M1.4	.055	.3 .2	85 127
#0	.060	80				
			M1.6	.063	.35 .2	74 127
#1	.073	64 72				
			M2	.079	.4 .25	64 101
#2	.086	56 64				
			M2.5	.098	.45 .35	56 74
#3	.099	48 56				
#4	.112	40 48				
			M3	.118	.5 .35	51 74
#5	.125	40 44				
#6	.138	32 40				
			M4	.157	.7 .5	36 51
#8	.164	32 36				
#10	.190	24 32				
			M5	.196	.8 .5	32 51
			M6	.236	1.0 .75	25 34
¼	.250	20 28				
5/16	.312	18 24				
			M8	.315	1.25 1.0	20 25
3/8	.375	16 24				
			M10	.393	1.5 1.25	17 20
7/16	.437	14 20				
			M12	.472	1.75 1.25	14.5 20
½	.500	13 20				
			M14	.551	2 1.5	12.5 17
5/8	.625	11 18				
			M16	.630	2 1.5	12.5 17
			M18	.709	2.5 1.5	10 17
¾	.750	10 16				
			M20	.787	2.5 1.5	10 17
			M22	.866	2.5 1.5	10 17
7/8	.875	9 14				
			M24	.945	3 2	8.5 12.5
1"	1.000	8 12				
			M27	1.063	3 2	8.5 12.5

Inch-Metric Thread Comparison.

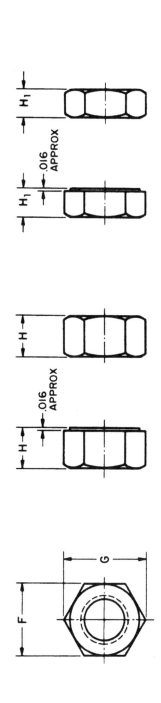

Nominal Size or Basic Major Dia. of Thread		F Width Across Flats			G Width Across Corners		H Thickness Hex Nuts			H₁ Thickness Hex Jam Nuts			Hex Nuts Specified Proof Load — Runout of Bearing Face, FIR Max		Jam Nuts All Strength Levels
		Basic	Max	Min	Max	Min	Basic	Max	Min	Basic	Max	Min	Up to 150,000 psi	150,000 psi and Greater	
1/4	0.2500	7/16	0.438	0.428	0.505	0.488	7/32	0.226	0.212	5/32	0.163	0.150	0.015	0.010	0.015
5/16	0.3125	1/2	0.500	0.489	0.577	0.557	17/64	0.273	0.258	3/16	0.195	0.180	0.016	0.011	0.016
3/8	0.3750	9/16	0.562	0.551	0.650	0.628	21/64	0.337	0.320	7/32	0.227	0.210	0.017	0.012	0.017
7/16	0.4375	11/16	0.688	0.675	0.794	0.768	3/8	0.385	0.365	1/4	0.260	0.240	0.018	0.013	0.018
1/2	0.5000	3/4	0.750	0.736	0.866	0.840	7/16	0.448	0.427	5/16	0.323	0.302	0.019	0.014	0.019
9/16	0.5625	7/8	0.875	0.861	1.010	0.982	31/64	0.496	0.473	5/16	0.324	0.301	0.020	0.015	0.020
5/8	0.6250	15/16	0.938	0.922	1.083	1.051	35/64	0.559	0.535	3/8	0.387	0.363	0.021	0.016	0.021
3/4	0.7500	1 1/8	1.125	1.088	1.299	1.240	41/64	0.665	0.617	27/64	0.446	0.398	0.023	0.018	0.023
7/8	0.8750	1 5/16	1.312	1.269	1.516	1.447	3/4	0.776	0.724	31/64	0.510	0.458	0.025	0.020	0.025
1	1.0000	1 1/2	1.500	1.450	1.732	1.653	55/64	0.887	0.831	35/64	0.575	0.519	0.027	0.022	0.027
1 1/8	1.1250	1 11/16	1.688	1.631	1.949	1.859	31/32	0.999	0.939	39/64	0.639	0.579	0.030	0.025	0.030
1 1/4	1.2500	1 7/8	1.875	1.812	2.165	2.066	1 1/16	1.094	1.030	23/32	0.751	0.687	0.033	0.028	0.033
1 3/8	1.3750	2 1/16	2.062	1.994	2.382	2.273	1 11/64	1.206	1.138	25/32	0.815	0.747	0.036	0.031	0.036
1 1/2	1.5000	2 1/4	2.250	2.175	2.598	2.480	1 9/32	1.317	1.245	27/32	0.880	0.808	0.039	0.034	0.039
See Notes	9		3		4									2	2

Inch-Metric Thread Comparison. (**continued**)

Reprinted from ASME B18.2.1-1981 (R1992), B18.2.2-1987 (R1993), B18.3-1986 (R1993), B18.6.2-1972 (R1993), B18.6.3-1972 (R1991), B18.21.1-1994, B18.22.1-1965 (R1990), B17.1-1967 (R1998), B17.2-1967 (R1990) and B4.2-1978 (R1994), by permission of The American Society of Mechanical Engineers. All rights reserved.

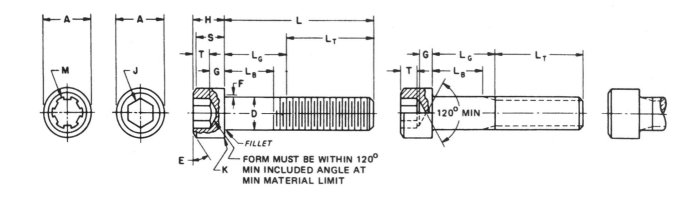

Nominal Size or Basic Screw Diameter		D Body Diameter		A Head Diameter		H Head Height		S Head Side Height	M Spline Socket Size	J Hexagon Socket Size		T Key Engagement	G Wall Thickness	K Chamfer or Radius
		Max	Min	Max	Min	Max	Min	Min	Nom	Nom		Min	Min	Max
0	0.0600	0.0600	0.0568	0.096	0.091	0.060	0.057	0.054	0.060		0.050	0.025	0.020	0.003
1	0.0730	0.0730	0.0695	0.118	0.112	0.073	0.070	0.066	0.072	1/16	0.062	0.031	0.025	0.003
2	0.0860	0.0860	0.0822	0.140	0.134	0.086	0.083	0.077	0.096	5/64	0.078	0.038	0.029	0.003
3	0.0990	0.0990	0.0949	0.161	0.154	0.099	0.095	0.089	0.096	5/64	0.078	0.044	0.034	0.003
4	0.1120	0.1120	0.1075	0.183	0.176	0.112	0.108	0.101	0.111	3/32	0.094	0.051	0.038	0.005
5	0.1250	0.1250	0.1202	0.205	0.198	0.125	0.121	0.112	0.111	3/32	0.094	0.057	0.043	0.005
6	0.1380	0.1380	0.1329	0.226	0.218	0.138	0.134	0.124	0.133	7/64	0.109	0.064	0.047	0.005
8	0.1640	0.1640	0.1585	0.270	0.262	0.164	0.159	0.148	0.168	9/64	0.141	0.077	0.056	0.005
10	0.1900	0.1900	0.1840	0.312	0.303	0.190	0.185	0.171	0.183	5/52	0.156	0.090	0.065	0.005
1/4	0.2500	0.2500	0.2435	0.375	0.365	0.250	0.244	0.225	0.216	3/16	0.188	0.120	0.095	0.008
5/16	0.3125	0.3125	0.3053	0.469	0.457	0.312	0.306	0.281	0.291	1/4	0.250	0.151	0.119	0.008
3/8	0.3750	0.3750	0.3678	0.562	0.550	0.375	0.368	0.337	0.372	5/16	0.312	0.182	0.143	0.008
7/16	0.4375	0.4375	0.4294	0.656	0.642	0.438	0.430	0.394	0.454	3/8	0.375	0.213	0.166	0.010
1/2	0.5000	0.5000	0.4919	0.750	0.735	0.500	0.492	0.450	0.454	3/8	0.375	0.245	0.190	0.010
5/8	0.6250	0.6250	0.6163	0.938	0.921	0.625	0.616	0.562	0.595	1/2	0.500	0.307	0.238	0.010
3/4	0.7500	0.7500	0.7406	1.125	1.107	0.750	0.740	0.675	0.620	5/8	0.625	0.370	0.285	0.010
7/8	0.8750	0.8750	0.8647	1.312	1.293	0.875	0.864	0.787	0.698	3/4	0.750	0.432	0.333	0.015
1	1.0000	1.0000	0.9886	1.500	1.479	1.000	0.988	0.900	0.790	3/4	0.750	0.495	0.380	0.015
1 1/8	1.1250	1.1250	1.1086	1.688	1.665	1.125	1.111	1.012	....	7/8	0.875	0.557	0.428	0.015
1 1/4	1.2500	1.2500	1.2336	1.875	1.852	1.250	1.236	1.125	....	7/8	0.875	0.620	0.475	0.015
1 3/8	1.3750	1.3750	1.3568	2.062	2.038	1.375	1.360	1.237	....	1	1.000	0.682	0.523	0.015
1 1/2	1.5000	1.5000	1.4818	2.250	2.224	1.500	1.485	1.350	....	1	1.000	0.745	0.570	0.015
1 3/4	1.7500	1.7500	1.7295	2.625	2.597	1.750	1.734	1.575	....	1 1/4	1.250	0.870	0.665	0.015
2	2.0000	2.0000	1.9780	3.000	2.970	2.000	1.983	1.800	....	1 1/2	1.500	0.995	0.760	0.015
2 1/4	2.2500	2.2500	2.2280	3.375	3.344	2.250	2.232	2.025	....	1 3/4	1.750	1.120	0.855	0.031
2 1/2	2.5000	2.5000	2.4762	3.750	3.717	2.500	2.481	2.250	....	1 3/4	1.750	1.245	0.950	0.031
2 3/4	2.7500	2.7500	2.7262	4.125	4.090	2.750	2.730	2.475	....	2	2.000	1.370	1.045	0.031
3	3.0000	3.0000	2.9762	4.500	4.464	3.000	2.979	2.700	....	2 1/4	2.250	1.495	1.140	0.031
3 1/4	3.2500	3.2500	3.2262	4.875	4.837	3.250	3.228	2.925	....	2 1/4	2.250	1.620	1.235	0.031
3 1/2	3.5000	3.5000	3.4762	5.250	5.211	3.500	3.478	3.150	....	2 3/4	2.750	1.745	1.330	0.031
3 3/4	3.7500	3.7500	3.7262	5.625	5.584	3.750	3.727	3.375	....	2 3/4	2.750	1.870	1.425	0.031
4	4.0000	4.0000	3.9762	6.000	5.958	4.000	3.976	3.600	....	3	3.000	1.995	1.520	0.031

Reprinted from ASME B18.2.1-1981 (R1992), B18.2.2-1987 (R1993), B18.3-1986 (R1993), B18.6.2-1972 (R1993), B18.6.3-1972 (R1991), B18.21.1-1994, B18.22.1-1965 (R1990), B17.1-1967 (R1998), B17.2-1967 (R1990) and B4.2-1978 (R1994), by permission of The American Society of Mechanical Engineers. All rights reserved.

Cap Screw Specifications.

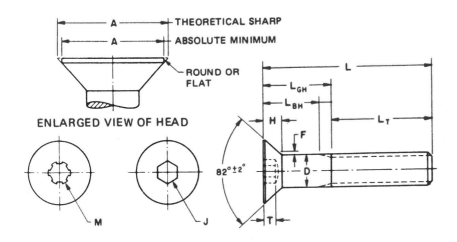

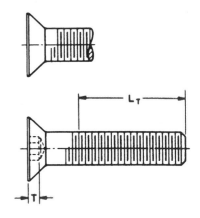

Nominal Size or Basic Screw Diameter		D Body Diameter		A Head Diameter		H Heat Height		M Spline Socket Size	J Hexagon Socket Size		T Key Engagement	F Fillet Extension Above D Max
		Max	Min	Theoretical Sharp Max	Abs. Min	Reference	Flushness Tolerance		Nom		Min	Max
0	0.0600	0.0600	0.0568	0.138	0.117	0.044	0.006	0.048		0.035	0.025	0.006
1	0.0730	0.0730	0.0695	0.168	0.143	0.054	0.007	0.060		0.050	0.031	0.008
2	0.0860	0.0860	0.0822	0.197	0.168	0.064	0.008	0.060		0.050	0.038	0.010
3	0.0990	0.0990	0.0949	0.226	0.193	0.073	0.010	0.072	1/16	0.062	0.044	0.010
4	0.1120	0.1120	0.1075	0.255	0.218	0.083	0.011	0.072	1/16	0.062	0.055	0.012
5	0.1250	0.1250	0.1202	0.281	0.240	0.090	0.012	0.096	5/64	0.078	0.061	0.014
6	0.1380	0.1380	0.1329	0.307	0.263	0.097	0.013	0.096	5/64	0.078	0.066	0.015
8	0.1640	0.1640	0.1585	0.359	0.311	0.112	0.014	0.111	3/32	0.094	0.076	0.015
10	0.1900	0.1900	0.1840	0.411	0.359	0.127	0.015	0.145	1/8	0.125	0.087	0.015
1/4	0.2500	0.2500	0.2435	0.531	0.480	0.161	0.016	0.183	5/32	0.156	0.111	0.015
5/16	0.3125	0.3125	0.3053	0.656	0.600	0.198	0.017	0.216	3/16	0.188	0.135	0.015
3/8	0.3750	0.3750	0.3678	0.781	0.720	0.234	0.018	0.251	7/32	0.219	0.159	0.015
7/16	0.4375	0.4375	0.4294	0.844	0.781	0.234	0.018	0.291	1/4	0.250	0.159	0.015
1/2	0.5000	0.5000	0.4919	0.938	0.872	0.251	0.018	0.372	5/16	0.312	0.172	0.015
5/8	0.6250	0.6250	0.6163	1.188	1.112	0.324	0.022	0.454	3/8	0.375	0.220	0.015
3/4	0.7500	0.7500	0.7406	1.438	1.355	0.396	0.024	0.454	1/2	0.500	0.220	0.015
7/8	0.8750	0.8750	0.8647	1.688	1.604	0.468	0.025	. . .	9/16	0.562	0.248	0.015
1	1.0000	1.0000	0.9886	1.938	1.841	0.540	0.028	. . .	5/8	0.625	0.297	0.015
1 1/8	1.1250	1.1250	1.1086	2.188	2.079	0.611	0.031	. . .	3/4	0.750	0.325	0.031
1 1/4	1.2500	1.2500	1.2336	2.438	2.316	0.683	0.035	. . .	7/8	0.875	0.358	0.031
1 3/8	1.3750	1.3750	1.3568	2.688	2.553	0.755	0.038	. . .	7/8	0.875	0.402	0.031
1 1/2	1.5000	1.5000	1.4818	2.938	2.791	0.827	0.042	. . .	1	1.000	0.435	0.031

Reprinted from ASME B18.2.1-1981 (R1992), B18.2.2-1987 (R1993), B18.3-1986 (R1993), B18.6.2-1972 (R1993), B18.6.3-1972 (R1991), B18.21.1-1994, B18.22.1-1965 (R1990), B17.1-1967 (R1998), B17.2-1967 (R1990) and B4.2-1978 (R1994), by permission of The American Society of Mechanical Engineers. All rights reserved.

Cap Screw Specifications. (CONTINUED)

CAP SCREWS

FLAT

Type of Head

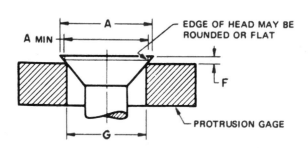

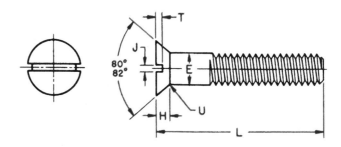

Nominal Size[1] or Basic Screw Diameter		E Body Diameter		A Head Diameter		H[2] Head Height	J Slot Width		T Slot Depth		U Fillet Radius	F[3] Protrusion Above Gaging Diameter		G[3] Gaging Diameter
		Max	Min	Max, Edge Sharp	Min, Edge Rounded or Flat	Ref	Max	Min	Max	Min	Max	Max	Min	
1/4	0.2500	0.2500	0.2450	0.500	0.452	0.140	0.075	0.064	0.068	0.045	0.100	0.046	0.030	0.424
5/16	0.3125	0.3125	0.3070	0.625	0.567	0.177	0.084	0.072	0.086	0.057	0.125	0.053	0.035	0.538
3/8	0.3750	0.3750	0.3690	0.750	0.682	0.210	0.094	0.081	0.103	0.068	0.150	0.060	0.040	0.651
7/16	0.4375	0.4375	0.4310	0.812	0.736	0.210	0.094	0.081	0.103	0.068	0.175	0.065	0.044	0.703
1/2	0.5000	0.5000	0.4930	0.875	0.791	0.210	0.106	0.091	0.103	0.068	0.200	0.071	0.049	0.756
9/16	0.5625	0.5625	0.5550	1.000	0.906	0.244	0.118	0.102	0.120	0.080	0.225	0.078	0.054	0.869
5/8	0.6250	0.6250	0.6170	1.125	1.020	0.281	0.133	0.116	0.137	0.091	0.250	0.085	0.058	0.982
3/4	0.7500	0.7500	0.7420	1.375	1.251	0.352	0.149	0.131	0.171	0.115	0.300	0.099	0.068	1.208
7/8	0.8750	0.8750	0.8660	1.625	1.480	0.423	0.167	0.147	0.206	0.138	0.350	0.113	0.077	1.435
1	1.0000	1.0000	0.9900	1.875	1.711	0.494	0.188	0.166	0.240	0.162	0.400	0.127	0.087	1.661
1 1/8	1.1250	1.1250	1.1140	2.062	1.880	0.529	0.196	0.178	0.257	0.173	0.450	0.141	0.096	1.826
1 1/4	1.2500	1.2500	1.2390	2.312	2.110	0.600	0.211	0.193	0.291	0.197	0.500	0.155	0.105	2.052
1 3/8	1.3750	1.3750	1.3630	2.562	2.340	0.665	0.226	0.208	0.326	0.220	0.550	0.169	0.115	2.279
1 1/2	1.5000	1.5000	1.4880	2.812	2.570	0.742	0.258	0.240	0.360	0.244	0.600	0.183	0.124	2.505

[1] Where specifying nominal size in decimals, zeros preceding decimal and in the fourth decimal place shall be omitted.
[2] Tabulated values determined from formula for maximum H, Appendix III.
[3] No tolerance for gaging diameter is given. If the gaging diameter of the gage used differs from tabulated value, the protrusion will be affected accordingly and the proper protrusion values must be recalculated using the formulas shown in Appendix II.
FOOTNOTES REFER TO ANSI B18.6.2–1972 (R1993).

Reprinted from ASME B18.2.1-1981 (R1992), B18.2.2-1987 (R1993), B18.3-1986 (R1993), B18.6.2-1972 (R1993), B18.6.3-1972 (R1991), B18.21.1-1994, B18.22.1-1965 (R1990), B17.1-1967 (R1998), B17.2-1967 (R1990) and B4.2-1978 (R1994), by permission of The American Society of Mechanical Engineers. All rights reserved.

Cap Screw Specifications. (CONTINUED)

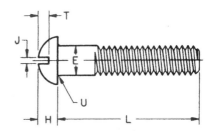

CAP SCREWS
ROUND

Type of Head

Nominal Size[1] or Basic Screw Diameter		E Body Diameter		A Head Diameter		H Head Height		J Slot Width		T Slot Depth		U Fillet Radius	
		Max	Min	Max	Min	Max	Min	Max	Min	Max	Min	Max	Min
1/4	0.2500	0.2500	0.2450	0.437	0.418	0.191	0.175	0.075	0.064	0.117	0.097	0.031	0.016
5/16	0.3125	0.3125	0.3070	0.562	0.540	0.245	0.226	0.084	0.072	0.151	0.126	0.031	0.016
3/8	0.3750	0.3750	0.3690	0.625	0.603	0.273	0.252	0.094	0.081	0.168	0.138	0.031	0.016
7/16	0.4375	0.4375	0.4310	0.750	0.725	0.328	0.302	0.094	0.081	0.202	0.167	0.047	0.016
1/2	0.5000	0.5000	0.4930	0.812	0.786	0.354	0.327	0.106	0.091	0.218	0.178	0.047	0.016
9/16	0.5625	0.5625	0.5550	0.937	0.909	0.409	0.378	0.118	0.102	0.252	0.207	0.047	0.016
5/8	0.6250	0.6250	0.6170	1.000	0.970	0.437	0.405	0.133	0.116	0.270	0.220	0.062	0.031
3/4	0.7500	0.7500	0.7420	1.250	1.215	0.546	0.507	0.149	0.131	0.338	0.278	0.062	0.031

[1] Where specifying nominal size in decimals, zeros preceding decimal and in the fourth decimal place shall be omitted.

Reprinted from ASME B18.2.1-1981 (R1992), B18.2.2-1987 (R1993), B18.3-1986 (R1993), B18.6.2-1972 (R1993), B18.6.3-1972 (R1991), B18.21.1-1994, B18.22.1-1965 (R1990), B17.1-1967 (R1998), B17.2-1967 (R1990) and B4.2-1978 (R1994), by permission of The American Society of Mechanical Engineers. All rights reserved.

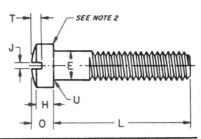

CAP SCREWS
FILLISTER

Type of Head

Nominal Size[1] or Basic Screw Diameter		E Body Diameter		A Head Diameter		H Head Side Height		O Total Head Height		J Slot Width		T Slot Depth		U Fillet Radius	
		Max	Min	Max	Min	Max	Min	Max	Min	Max	Min	Max	Min	Max	Min
1/4	0.2500	0.2500	0.2450	0.375	0.363	0.172	0.157	0.216	0.194	0.075	0.064	0.097	0.077	0.031	0.016
5/16	0.3125	0.3125	0.3070	0.437	0.424	0.203	0.186	0.253	0.230	0.084	0.072	0.115	0.090	0.031	0.016
3/8	0.3750	0.3750	0.3690	0.562	0.547	0.250	0.229	0.314	0.284	0.094	0.081	0.142	0.112	0.031	0.016
7/16	0.4375	0.4375	0.4310	0.625	0.608	0.297	0.274	0.368	0.336	0.094	0.081	0.168	0.133	0.047	0.016
1/2	0.5000	0.5000	0.4930	0.750	0.731	0.328	0.301	0.413	0.376	0.106	0.091	0.193	0.153	0.047	0.016
9/16	0.5625	0.5625	0.5550	0.812	0.792	0.375	0.346	0.467	0.427	0.118	0.102	0.213	0.168	0.047	0.016
5/8	0.6250	0.6250	0.6170	0.875	0.853	0.422	0.391	0.521	0.478	0.133	0.116	0.239	0.189	0.062	0.031
3/4	0.7500	0.7500	0.7420	1.000	0.976	0.500	0.466	0.612	0.566	0.149	0.131	0.283	0.223	0.062	0.031
7/8	0.8750	0.8750	0.8660	1.125	1.098	0.594	0.556	0.720	0.668	0.167	0.147	0.334	0.264	0.062	0.031
1	1.0000	1.0000	0.9900	1.312	1.282	0.656	0.612	0.803	0.743	0.188	0.166	0.371	0.291	0.062	0.031

[1] Where specifying nominal size in decimals, zeros preceding decimal and in the fourth decimal place shall be omitted.
[2] A slight rounding of the edges at periphery of head shall be permissible provided the diameter of the bearing circle is equal to no less than 90 percent of the specified minimum head diameter.

Reprinted from ASME B18.2.1-1981 (R1992), B18.2.2-1987 (R1993), B18.3-1986 (R1993), B18.6.2-1972 (R1993), B18.6.3-1972 (R1991), B18.21.1-1994, B18.22.1-1965 (R1990), B17.1-1967 (R1998), B17.2-1967 (R1990) and B4.2-1978 (R1994), by permission of The American Society of Mechanical Engineers. All rights reserved.

Cap Screw Specifications. (CONTINUED)

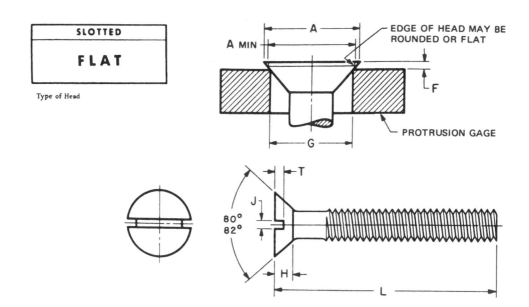

SLOTTED

FLAT

Type of Head

Nominal Size[1] or Basic Screw Diameter		L[2] These Lengths or Shorter are Undercut	A Head Diameter		H[3] Head Height	J Slot Width		T Slot Depth		F[4] Protrusion Above Gaging Diameter		G[4] Gaging Diameter
			Max. Edge Sharp	Min, Edge Rounded or Flat	Ref	Max	Min	Max	Min	Max	Min	
0000	0.0210	—	0.043	0.037	0.011	0.008	0.004	0.007	0.003	*	*	*
000	0.0340	—	0.064	0.058	0.016	0.011	0.007	0.009	0.005	*	*	*
00	0.0470	—	0.093	0.085	0.028	0.017	0.010	0.014	0.009	*	*	*
0	0.0600	1/8	0.119	0.099	0.035	0.023	0.016	0.015	0.010	0.026	0.016	0.078
1	0.0730	1/8	0.146	0.123	0.043	0.026	0.019	0.019	0.012	0.028	0.016	0.101
2	0.0860	1/8	0.172	0.147	0.051	0.031	0.023	0.023	0.015	0.029	0.017	0.124
3	0.0990	1/8	0.199	0.171	0.059	0.035	0.027	0.027	0.017	0.031	0.018	0.148
4	0.1120	3/16	0.225	0.195	0.067	0.039	0.031	0.030	0.020	0.032	0.019	0.172
5	0.1250	3/16	0.252	0.220	0.075	0.043	0.035	0.034	0.022	0.034	0.020	0.196
6	0.1380	3/16	0.279	0.244	0.083	0.048	0.039	0.038	0.024	0.036	0.021	0.220
8	0.1640	1/4	0.332	0.292	0.100	0.054	0.045	0.045	0.029	0.039	0.023	0.267
10	0.1900	5/16	0.385	0.340	0.116	0.060	0.050	0.053	0.034	0.042	0.025	0.313
12	0.2160	3/8	0.438	0.389	0.132	0.067	0.056	0.060	0.039	0.045	0.027	0.362
1/4	0.2500	7/16	0.507	0.452	0.153	0.075	0.064	0.070	0.046	0.050	0.029	0.424
5/16	0.3125	1/2	0.635	0.568	0.191	0.084	0.072	0.088	0.058	0.057	0.034	0.539
3/8	0.3750	9/16	0.762	0.685	0.230	0.094	0.081	0.106	0.070	0.065	0.039	0.653
7/16	0.4375	5/8	0.812	0.723	0.223	0.094	0.081	0.103	0.066	0.073	0.044	0.690
1/2	0.5000	3/4	0.875	0.775	0.223	0.106	0.091	0.103	0.065	0.081	0.049	0.739
9/16	0.5625	—	1.000	0.889	0.260	0.118	0.102	0.120	0.077	0.089	0.053	0.851
5/8	0.6250	—	1.125	1.002	0.298	0.133	0.116	0.137	0.088	0.097	0.058	0.962
3/4	0.7500	—	1.375	1.230	0.372	0.149	0.131	0.171	0.111	0.112	0.067	1.186

[1] Where specifying nominal size in decimals, zeros preceding decimal and in the fourth decimal place shall be omitted.
[2] Screws of these lengths and shorter shall have undercut heads as shown in Table 5.
[3] Tabulated values determined from formula for maximum H, Appendix V.
[4] No tolerance for gaging diameter is given. If the gaging diameter of the gage used differs from tabulated value, the protrusion will be affected accordingly and the proper protrusion values must be recalculated using the formulas shown in Appendix I.
* Not practical to gage.
For additional requirements refer to General Data on Pages 3, 4 and 5.
FOOTNOTES REFER TO ANSI B18.6.3-1972 (R1991).

Reprinted from ASME B18.2.1-1981 (R1992), B18.2.2-1987 (R1993), B18.3-1986 (R1993), B18.6.2-1972 (R1993), B18.6.3-1972 (R1991), B18.21.1-1994, B18.22.1-1965 (R1990), B17.1-1967 (R1998), B17.2-1967 (R1990) and B4.2-1978 (R1994), by permission of The American Society of Mechanical Engineers. All rights reserved.

Machine Screw Specifications.

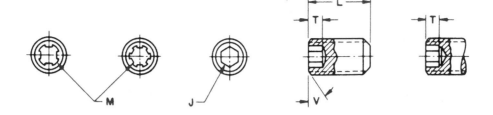

Nominal Size or Basic Screw Diameter		P		Q		B Shortest Optimum Nominal Length To Which Column T_H Applies			B_1 Shortest Optimum Nominal Length To Which Column T_S Applies		
		Half Dog Point									
		Diameter		Length		Cup and Flat Points	90° Cone and Oval Points	Half Dog Points	Cup and Flat Points	90° Cone and Oval Points	Half Dog Point
		Max	Min	Max	Min						
0	0.0600	0.040	0.037	0.017	0.013	7/64	1/8	7/64	1/16	1/8	7/64
1	0.0730	0.049	0.045	0.021	0.017	1/8	9/64	1/8	3/32	9/64	1/8
2	0.0860	0.057	0.053	0.024	0.020	1/8	9/64	9/64	3/32	9/64	9/64
3	0.0990	0.066	0.062	0.027	0.023	9/64	5/32	5/32	3/32	5/32	5/32
4	0.1120	0.075	0.070	0.030	0.026	9/64	11/64	5/32	3/32	11/64	5/32
5	0.1250	0.083	0.078	0.033	0.027	3/16	3/16	11/64	1/8	3/16	11/64
6	0.1380	0.092	0.087	0.038	0.032	11/64	13/64	3/16	1/8	13/64	3/16
8	0.1640	0.109	0.103	0.043	0.037	3/16	7/32	13/64	3/16	7/32	13/64
10	0.1900	0.127	0.120	0.049	0.041	3/16	1/4	15/64	3/16	1/4	15/64
1/4	0.2500	0.156	0.149	0.067	0.059	1/4	5/16	19/64	1/4	5/16	19/64
5/16	0.3125	0.203	0.195	0.082	0.074	5/16	25/64	23/64	5/16	25/64	23/64
3/8	0.3750	0.250	0.241	0.099	0.089	3/8	7/16	7/16	3/8	7/16	7/16
7/16	0.4375	0.297	0.287	0.114	0.104	7/16	35/64	31/64	7/16	35/64	31/64
1/2	0.5000	0.344	0.334	0.130	0.120	1/2	39/64	35/64	1/2	39/64	35/64
5/8	0.6250	0.469	0.456	0.164	0.148	5/8	49/64	43/64	5/8	49/64	43/64
3/4	0.7500	0.562	0.549	0.196	0.180	3/4	29/32	51/64	3/4	29/32	51/64
7/8	0.8750	0.656	0.642	0.227	0.211	7/8	1 1/8	63/64	7/8	1 1/8	63/64
1	1.0000	0.750	0.734	0.260	0.240	1	1 17/64	1 1/8	. . .	. . .	. . .
1 1/8	1.1250	0.844	0.826	0.291	0.271	1 1/8	1 25/64	1 3/16	. . .	. . .	. . .
1 1/4	1.2500	0.938	0.920	0.323	0.303	1 1/4	1 1/2	1 5/16	. . .	. . .	. . .
1 3/8	1.3750	1.031	1.011	0.354	0.334	1 3/8	1 21/64	1 7/16	. . .	. . .	. . .
1 1/2	1.5000	1.125	1.105	0.385	0.365	1 1/2	1 51/64	1 9/16	. . .	. . .	. . .
1 3/4	1.7500	1.312	1.289	0.448	0.428	1 3/4	2 7/32	1 61/64	. . .	. . .	. . .
2	2.0000	1.500	1.474	0.510	0.490	2	2 25/64	2 5/64	. . .	. . .	. . .

Reprinted from ASME B18.2.1-1981 (R1992), B18.2.2-1987 (R1993), B18.3-1986 (R1993), B18.6.2-1972 (R1993), B18.6.3-1972 (R1991), B18.21.1-1994, B18.22.1-1965 (R1990), B17.1-1967 (R1998), B17.2-1967 (R1990) and B4.2-1978 (R1994), by permission of The American Society of Mechanical Engineers. All rights reserved.

Set Screw Specifications.

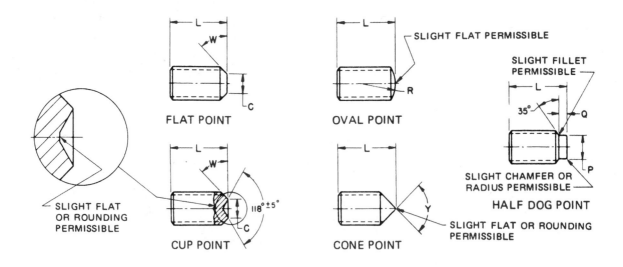

FLAT POINT

OVAL POINT

CUP POINT

CONE POINT

HALF DOG POINT

SLIGHT FLAT OR ROUNDING PERMISSIBLE

Nominal Size or Basic Screw Diameter		P		Q		B			B₁		
		Half Dog Point				Shortest Optimum Nominal Length To Which Column T_H Applies			Shortest Optimum Nominal Length To Which Column T_S Applies		
		Diameter		Length		Cup and Flat Points	90° Cone and Oval Points	Half Dog Points	Cup and Flat Points	90° Cone and Oval Points	Half Dog Point
		Max	Min	Max	Min						
0	0.0600	0.040	0.037	0.017	0.013	7/64	1/8	7/64	1/16	1/8	7/64
1	0.0730	0.049	0.045	0.021	0.017	1/8	9/64	1/8	3/32	9/64	1/8
2	0.0860	0.057	0.053	0.024	0.020	1/8	9/64	9/64	3/32	9/64	9/64
3	0.0990	0.066	0.062	0.027	0.023	9/64	5/32	5/32	3/32	5/32	5/32
4	0.1120	0.075	0.070	0.030	0.026	9/64	11/64	5/32	3/32	11/64	5/32
5	0.1250	0.083	0.078	0.033	0.027	3/16	3/16	11/64	1/8	3/16	11/64
6	0.1380	0.092	0.087	0.038	0.032	11/64	13/64	3/16	1/8	13/64	3/16
8	0.1640	0.109	0.103	0.043	0.037	3/16	7/32	13/64	3/16	7/32	13/64
10	0.1900	0.127	0.120	0.049	0.041	3/16	1/4	15/64	3/16	1/4	15/64
1/4	0.2500	0.156	0.149	0.067	0.059	1/4	5/16	19/64	1/4	5/16	19/64
5/16	0.3125	0.203	0.195	0.082	0.074	5/16	25/64	23/64	5/16	25/64	23/64
3/8	0.3750	0.250	0.241	0.099	0.089	3/8	7/16	7/16	3/8	7/16	7/16
7/16	0.4375	0.297	0.287	0.114	0.104	7/16	35/64	31/64	7/16	35/64	31/64
1/2	0.5000	0.344	0.334	0.130	0.120	1/2	39/64	35/64	1/2	39/64	35/64
5/8	0.6250	0.469	0.456	0.164	0.148	5/8	49/64	43/64	5/8	49/64	43/64
3/4	0.7500	0.562	0.549	0.196	0.180	3/4	29/32	51/64	3/4	29/32	51/64
7/8	0.8750	0.656	0.642	0.227	0.211	7/8	1 1/8	63/64	7/8	1 1/8	63/64
1	1.0000	0.750	0.734	0.260	0.240	1	1 17/64	1 1/8	. . .	. . .	. . .
1 1/8	1.1250	0.844	0.826	0.291	0.271	1 1/8	1 25/64	1 3/16	. . .	. . .	. . .
1 1/4	1.2500	0.938	0.920	0.323	0.303	1 1/4	1 1/2	1 5/16	. . .	. . .	. . .
1 3/8	1.3750	1.031	1.011	0.354	0.334	1 3/8	1 21/32	1 7/16	. . .	. . .	. . .
1 1/2	1.5000	1.125	1.105	0.385	0.365	1 1/2	1 51/64	1 9/16	. . .	. . .	. . .
1 3/4	1.7500	1.312	1.289	0.448	0.428	1 3/4	2 7/32	1 61/64	. . .	. . .	. . .
2	2.0000	1.500	1.474	0.510	0.490	2	2 25/64	2 5/64	. . .	. . .	. . .

Reprinted from ASME B18.2.1-1981 (R1992), B18.2.2-1987 (R1993), B18.3-1986 (R1993), B18.6.2-1972 (R1993), B18.6.3-1972 (R1991), B18.21.1-1994, B18.22.1-1965 (R1990), B17.1-1967 (R1998), B17.2-1967 (R1990) and B4.2-1978 (R1994), by permission of The American Society of Mechanical Engineers. All rights reserved.

Set Screw Specifications. (CONTINUED)

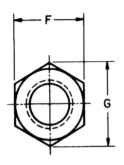

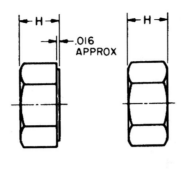

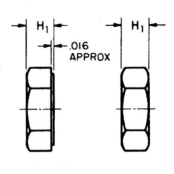

Nominal Size or Basic Major Dia of Thread		F Width Across Flats			G Width Across Corners		H Thickness Hex Nuts			H₁ Thickness Hex Jam Nuts			Hex Nuts Specified Proof Load		Jam Nuts All Strength Levels
		Basic	Max	Min	Max	Min	Basic	Max	Min	Basic	Max	Min	Up to 150,000 psi	150,000 psi and Greater	
													Runout of Bearing Face, FIR Max		
1/4	0.2500	7/16	0.438	0.428	0.505	0.488	7/32	0.226	0.212	5/32	0.163	0.150	0.015	0.010	0.015
5/16	0.3125	1/2	0.500	0.489	0.577	0.557	17/64	0.273	0.258	3/16	0.195	0.180	0.016	0.011	0.016
3/8	0.3750	9/16	0.562	0.551	0.650	0.628	21/64	0.337	0.320	7/32	0.227	0.210	0.017	0.012	0.017
7/16	0.4375	11/16	0.688	0.675	0.794	0.768	3/8	0.385	0.365	1/4	0.260	0.240	0.018	0.013	0.018
1/2	0.5000	3/4	0.750	0.736	0.866	0.840	7/16	0.448	0.427	5/16	0.323	0.302	0.019	0.014	0.019
9/16	0.5625	7/8	0.875	0.861	1.010	0.982	31/64	0.496	0.473	5/16	0.324	0.301	0.020	0.015	0.020
5/8	0.6250	15/16	0.938	0.922	1.083	1.051	35/64	0.559	0.535	3/8	0.387	0.363	0.021	0.016	0.021
3/4	0.7500	1 1/8	1.125	1.088	1.299	1.240	41/64	0.665	0.617	27/64	0.446	0.398	0.023	0.018	0.023
7/8	0.8750	1 5/16	1.312	1.269	1.516	1.447	3/4	0.776	0.724	31/64	0.510	0.458	0.025	0.020	0.025
1	1.0000	1 1/2	1.500	1.450	1.732	1.653	55/64	0.887	0.831	35/64	0.575	0.519	0.027	0.022	0.027
1 1/8	1.1250	1 11/16	1.688	1.631	1.949	1.859	31/32	0.999	0.939	39/64	0.639	0.579	0.030	0.025	0.030
1 1/4	1.2500	1 7/8	1.875	1.812	2.165	2.066	1 1/16	1.094	1.030	23/32	0.751	0.687	0.033	0.028	0.033
1 3/8	1.3750	2 1/16	2.062	1.994	2.382	2.273	1 11/64	1.206	1.138	25/32	0.815	0.747	0.036	0.031	0.036
1 1/2	1.5000	2 1/4	2.250	2.175	2.598	2.480	1 9/32	1.317	1.245	27/32	0.880	0.808	0.039	0.034	0.039

Reprinted from ASME B18.2.1-1981 (R1992), B18.2.2-1987 (R1993), B18.3-1986
(R1993), B18.6.2-1972 (R1993), B18.6.3-1972 (R1991), B18.21.1-1994, B18.22.1-1965
(R1990), B17.1-1967 (R1998), B17.2-1967 (R1990) and B4.2-1978 (R1994), by
permission of The American Society of Mechanical Engineers. All rights reserved.

Hex Nut Specifications.

AMERICAN STANDARD

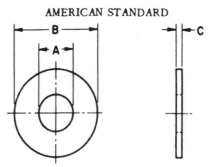

DIMENSIONS OF PREFERRED SIZES OF TYPE A PLAIN WASHERS **

Nominal Washer Size***			Inside Diameter A			Outside Diameter B			Thickness C		
			Basic	Tolerance Plus	Tolerance Minus	Basic	Tolerance Plus	Tolerance Minus	Basic	Max	Min
—	—		0.078	0.000	0.005	0.188	0.000	0.005	0.020	0.025	0.016
—	—		0.094	0.000	0.005	0.250	0.000	0.005	0.020	0.025	0.016
—	—		0.125	0.008	0.005	0.312	0.008	0.005	0.032	0.040	0.025
No. 6	0.138		0.156	0.008	0.005	0.375	0.015	0.005	0.049	0.065	0.036
No. 8	0.164		0.188	0.008	0.005	0.438	0.015	0.005	0.049	0.065	0.036
No. 10	0.190		0.219	0.008	0.005	0.500	0.015	0.005	0.049	0.065	0.036
3/16	0.188		0.250	0.015	0.005	0.562	0.015	0.005	0.049	0.065	0.036
No. 12	0.216		0.250	0.015	0.005	0.562	0.015	0.005	0.065	0.080	0.051
1/4	0.250	N	0.281	0.015	0.005	0.625	0.015	0.005	0.065	0.080	0.051
1/4	0.250	W	0.312	0.015	0.005	0.734*	0.015	0.007	0.065	0.080	0.051
5/16	0.312	N	0.344	0.015	0.005	0.688	0.015	0.007	0.065	0.080	0.051
5/16	0.312	W	0.375	0.015	0.005	0.875	0.030	0.007	0.083	0.104	0.064
3/8	0.375	N	0.406	0.015	0.005	0.812	0.015	0.007	0.065	0.080	0.051
3/8	0.375	W	0.438	0.015	0.005	1.000	0.030	0.007	0.083	0.104	0.064
7/16	0.438	N	0.469	0.015	0.005	0.922	0.015	0.007	0.065	0.080	0.051
7/16	0.438	W	0.500	0.015	0.005	1.250	0.030	0.007	0.083	0.104	0.064
1/2	0.500	N	0.531	0.015	0.005	1.062	0.030	0.007	0.095	0.121	0.074
1/2	0.500	W	0.562	0.015	0.005	1.375	0.030	0.007	0.109	0.132	0.086
9/16	0.562	N	0.594	0.015	0.005	1.156*	0.030	0.007	0.095	0.121	0.074
9/16	0.562	W	0.625	0.015	0.005	1.469*	0.030	0.007	0.109	0.132	0.086
5/8	0.625	N	0.656	0.030	0.007	1.312	0.030	0.007	0.095	0.121	0.074
5/8	0.625	W	0.688	0.030	0.007	1.750	0.030	0.007	0.134	0.160	0.108
3/4	0.750	N	0.812	0.030	0.007	1.469	0.030	0.007	0.134	0.160	0.108
3/4	0.750	W	0.812	0.030	0.007	2.000	0.030	0.007	0.148	0.177	0.122
7/8	0.875	N	0.938	0.030	0.007	1.750	0.030	0.007	0.134	0.160	0.108
7/8	0.875	W	0.938	0.030	0.007	2.250	0.030	0.007	0.165	0.192	0.136
1	1.000	N	1.062	0.030	0.007	2.000	0.030	0.007	0.134	0.160	0.108
1	1.000	W	1.062	0.030	0.007	2.500	0.030	0.007	0.165	0.192	0.136
1 1/8	1.125	N	1.250	0.030	0.007	2.250	0.030	0.007	0.134	0.160	0.108
1 1/8	1.125	W	1.250	0.030	0.007	2.750	0.030	0.007	0.165	0.192	0.136
1 1/4	1.250	N	1.375	0.030	0.007	2.500	0.030	0.007	0.165	0.192	0.136
1 1/4	1.250	W	1.375	0.030	0.007	3.000	0.030	0.007	0.165	0.192	0.136
1 3/8	1.375	N	1.500	0.030	0.007	2.750	0.030	0.007	0.165	0.192	0.136
1 3/8	1.375	W	1.500	0.045	0.010	3.250	0.045	0.010	0.180	0.213	0.153
1 1/2	1.500	N	1.625	0.030	0.007	3.000	0.030	0.007	0.165	0.192	0.136
1 1/2	1.500	W	1.625	0.045	0.010	3.500	0.045	0.010	0.180	0.213	0.153
1 5/8	1.625		1.750	0.045	0.010	3.750	0.045	0.010	0.180	0.213	0.153
1 3/4	1.750		1.875	0.045	0.010	4.000	0.045	0.010	0.180	0.213	0.153
1 7/8	1.875		2.000	0.045	0.010	4.250	0.045	0.010	0.180	0.213	0.153
2	2.000		2.125	0.045	0.010	4.500	0.045	0.010	0.180	0.213	0.153
2 1/4	2.250		2.375	0.045	0.010	4.750	0.045	0.010	0.220	0.248	0.193
2 1/2	2.500		2.625	0.045	0.010	5.000	0.045	0.010	0.238	0.280	0.210
2 3/4	2.750		2.875	0.065	0.010	5.250	0.065	0.010	0.259	0.310	0.228
3	3.000		3.125	0.065	0.010	5.500	0.065	0.010	0.284	0.327	0.249

*The 0.734 in., 1.156 in., and 1.469 in. outside diameters avoid washers which could be used in coin operated devices.
**Preferred sizes are for the most part from series previously designated "Standard Plate" and "SAE." Where common sizes existed in the two series, the SAE size is designated "N" (narrow) and the Standard Plate "W" (wide). These sizes as well as all other sizes of Type A Plain Washers are to be ordered by ID, OD, and thickness dimensions.
***Nominal washer sizes are intended for use with comparable nominal screw or bolt sizes.

Reprinted from ASME B18.2.1-1981 (R1992), B18.2.2-1987 (R1993), B18.3-1986 (R1993), B18.6.2-1972 (R1993), B18.6.3-1972 (R1991), B18.21.1-1994, B18.22.1-1965 (R1990), B17.1-1967 (R1998), B17.2-1967 (R1990) and B4.2-1978 (R1994), by permission of The American Society of Mechanical Engineers. All rights reserved.

Dimensions of Preferred Sizes of Type A Plain Washers.

AMERICAN NATIONAL STANDARD
LOCK WASHERS

ANSI B18.21.1-1990

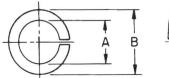

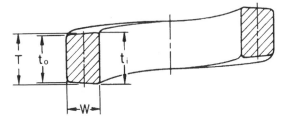

ENLARGED SECTION

DIMENSIONS OF REGULAR HELICAL SPRING LOCK WASHERS[1]

Nominal Washer Size		A Inside Diameter		B Outside Diameter	T Mean Section Thickness $\left(\dfrac{t_i + t_o}{2}\right)$	W Section Width
		Max	Min	Max[2]	Min	Min
No. 4	0.112	0.120	0.114	0.173	0.022	0.022
No. 5	0.125	0.133	0.127	0.202	0.030	0.030
No. 6	0.138	0.148	0.141	0.216	0.030	0.030
No. 8	0.164	0.174	0.167	0.267	0.047	0.042
No. 10	0.190	0.200	0.193	0.294	0.047	0.042
1/4	0.250	0.262	0.254	0.365	0.078	0.047
5/16	0.312	0.326	0.317	0.460	0.093	0.062
3/8	0.375	0.390	0.380	0.553	0.125	0.076
7/16	0.438	0.455	0.443	0.647	0.140	0.090
1/2	0.500	0.518	0.506	0.737	0.172	0.103
5/8	0.625	0.650	0.635	0.923	0.203	0.125
3/4	0.750	0.775	0.760	1.111	0.218	0.154
7/8	0.875	0.905	0.887	1.296	0.234	0.182
1	1.000	1.042	1.017	1.483	0.250	0.208
1 1/8	1.125	1.172	1.144	1.669	0.313	0.236
1 1/4	1.250	1.302	1.271	1.799	0.313	0.236
1 3/8	1.375	1.432	1.398	2.041	0.375	0.292
1 1/2	1.500	1.561	1.525	2.170	0.375	0.292
1 3/4	1.750	1.811	1.775	2.602	0.469	0.383
2	2.000	2.061	2.025	2.852	0.469	0.383
2 1/4	2.250	2.311	2.275	3.352	0.508	0.508
2 1/2	2.500	2.561	2.525	3.602	0.508	0.508
2 3/4	2.750	2.811	2.775	4.102	0.633	0.633
3	3.000	3.061	3.025	4.352	0.633	0.633

[1]For use with 1960 Series Socket Head Cap Screws specified in American National Standard, ANSI B18.3.
[2]The maximum outside diameters specified allow for the commercial tolerances on cold-drawn wire.

Reprinted from ASME B18.2.1-1981 (R1992), B18.2.2-1987 (R1993), B18.3-1986 (R1993), B18.6.2-1972 (R1993), B18.6.3-1972 (R1991), B18.21.1-1994, B18.22.1-1965 (R1990), B17.1-1967 (R1998), B17.2-1967 (R1990) and B4.2-1978 (R1994), by permission of The American Society of Mechanical Engineers. All rights reserved.

Dimensions of Spring Lock Washers.

AMERICAN NATIONAL STANDARD
LOCK WASHERS

ASME/ANSI B18.21.1-1994

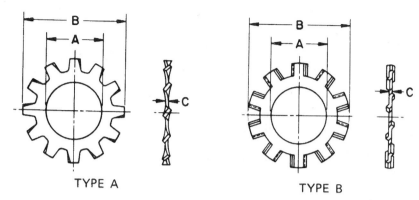

TYPE A   TYPE B

DIMENSIONS OF EXTERNAL TOOTH LOCK WASHERS

Nominal Washer Size		A Inside Diameter		B Outside Diameter		C Thickness	
		Max	Min	Max	Min	Max	Min
No. 3	0.099	0.109	0.102	0.235	0.220	0.015	0.012
No. 4	0.112	0.123	0.115	0.260	0.245	0.019	0.015
No. 5	0.125	0.136	0.129	0.285	0.270	0.019	0.014
No. 6	0.138	0.150	0.141	0.320	0.305	0.022	0.016
No. 8	0.164	0.176	0.168	0.381	0.365	0.023	0.018
No. 10	0.190	0.204	0.195	0.410	0.395	0.025	0.020
No. 12	0.216	0.231	0.221	0.475	0.460	0.028	0.023
1/4	0.250	0.267	0.256	0.510	0.494	0.028	0.023
5/16	0.312	0.332	0.320	0.610	0.588	0.034	0.028
3/8	0.375	0.398	0.384	0.694	0.670	0.040	0.032
7/16	0.438	0.464	0.448	0.760	0.740	0.040	0.032
1/2	0.500	0.530	0.513	0.900	0.880	0.045	0.037
9/16	0.562	0.596	0.576	0.985	0.960	0.045	0.037
5/8	0.625	0.663	0.641	1.070	1.045	0.050	0.042
11/16	0.688	0.728	0.704	1.155	1.130	0.050	0.042
3/4	0.750	0.795	0.768	1.260	1.220	0.055	0.047
13/16	0.812	0.861	0.833	1.315	1.290	0.055	0.047
7/8	0.875	0.927	0.897	1.410	1.380	0.060	0.052
1	1.000	1.060	1.025	1.620	1.590	0.067	0.059

Reprinted from ASME B18.2.1-1981 (R1992), B18.2.2-1987 (R1993), B18.3-1986 (R1993), B18.6.2-1972 (R1993), B18.6.3-1972 (R1991), B18.21.1-1994, B18.22.1-1965 (R1990), B17.1-1967 (R1998), B17.2-1967 (R1990) and B4.2-1978 (R1994), by permission of The American Society of Mechanical Engineers. All rights reserved.

Dimensions of Internal and External Tooth Lock Washers.

AMERICAN NATIONAL STANDARD
LOCK WASHERS

ASME/ANSI B18.21.1-1994

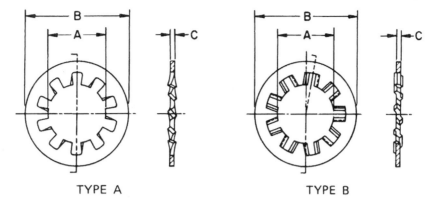

TYPE A   TYPE B

DIMENSIONS OF INTERNAL TOOTH LOCK WASHERS

Nominal Washer Size		A Inside Diameter		B Outside Diameter		C Thickness	
		Max	Min	Max	Min	Max	Min
No. 2	0.086	0.095	0.089	0.200	0.175	0.015	0.010
No. 3	0.099	0.109	0.102	0.232	0.215	0.019	0.012
No. 4	0.112	0.123	0.115	0.270	0.255	0.019	0.015
No. 5	0.125	0.136	0.129	0.280	0.245	0.021	0.017
No. 6	0.138	0.150	0.141	0.295	0.275	0.021	0.017
No. 8	0.164	0.176	0.168	0.340	0.325	0.023	0.018
No. 10	0.190	0.204	0.195	0.381	0.365	0.025	0.020
No. 12	0.216	0.231	0.221	0.410	0.394	0.025	0.020
1/4	0.250	0.267	0.256	0.478	0.460	0.028	0.023
5/16	0.312	0.332	0.320	0.610	0.594	0.034	0.028
3/8	0.375	0.398	0.384	0.692	0.670	0.040	0.032
7/16	0.438	0.464	0.448	0.789	0.740	0.040	0.032
1/2	0.500	0.530	0.512	0.900	0.867	0.045	0.037
9/16	0.562	0.596	0.576	0.985	0.957	0.045	0.037
5/8	0.625	0.663	0.640	1.071	1.045	0.050	0.042
11/16	0.688	0.728	0.704	1.166	1.130	0.050	0.042
1/4	0.750	0.795	0.769	1.245	1.220	0.055	0.047
13/16	0.812	0.861	0.832	1.315	1.290	0.055	0.047
7/8	0.875	0.927	0.894	1.410	1.364	0.060	0.052
1	1.000	1.060	1.019	1.637	1.590	0.067	0.059
1 1/8	1.125	1.192	1.144	1.830	1.799	0.067	0.059
1 1/4	1.250	1.325	1.275	1.975	1.921	0.067	0.059

Reprinted from ASME B18.2.1-1981 (R1992), B18.2.2-1987 (R1993), B18.3-1986
(R1993), B18.6.2-1972 (R1993), B18.6.3-1972 (R1991), B18.21.1-1994, B18.22.1-1965
(R1990), B17.1-1967 (R1998), B17.2-1967 (R1990) and B4.2-1978 (R1994), by
permission of The American Society of Mechanical Engineers. All rights reserved.

Dimensions of Internal and External Tooth Lock Washers. (CONTINUED)

Tap Drill Sizes.

Fraction or Drill Size	Decimal Equivalent	Tap Size
80 (Number Size Drills)	.0135	
79	.0145	
1/64	.0156	
78	.0160	
77	.0180	
76	.0200	
75	.0210	
74	.0225	
73	.0240	
72	.0250	
71	.0260	
70	.0280	
69	.0292	
68	.0310	
1/32	.0312	
67	.0320	
66	.0330	
65	.0350	
64	.0360	
63	.0370	
62	.0380	
61	.0390	
60	.0400	
59	.0410	
58	.0420	
57	.0430	
56	.0465	
3/64	.0469	0-80
55	.0520	
54	.0550	1-56
53	.0595	1-64, 72
1/16	.0625	
52	.0635	
51	.0670	
50	.0700	2-56, 64
49	.0730	
48	.0760	
5/64	.0781	3-48
47	.0785	
46	.0810	
45	.0820	3-56, 4-32
44	.0860	4-36
43	.0890	4-40
42	.0935	4-48
3/32	.0938	
41	.0960	
40	.0980	

Fraction or Drill Size	Decimal Equivalent	Tap Size
39	.0995	
38	.1015	
37	.1040	5-40
36	.1065	5-44
7/64	.1094	6-32
35	.1100	
34	.1110	
33	.1130	6-36
32	.1160	6-40
31	.1200	
1/8	.1250	
30	.1285	
29	.1360	8-32,36
28	.1405	8-40
9/64	.1406	
27	.1440	
26	.1470	
25	.1495	10-24
24	.1520	
23	.1540	
5/32	.1562	
22	.1570	
21	.1590	10-30
20	.1610	10-32
19	.1660	
18	.1695	
11/64	.1719	
17	.1730	
16	.1770	12-24
15	.1800	
14	.1820	12-28
13	.1850	12-32
3/16	.1875	
12	.1890	
11	.1910	
10	.1935	
9	.1960	
8	.1990	
7	.2010	1/4-20
13/64	.2031	
6	.2040	
5	.2055	
4	.2090	
3	.2130	1/4-28
7/32	.2188	
2	.2210	
1	.2280	
A (Letter Size Drills)	.2340	

Fraction or Drill Size	Decimal Equivalent	Tap Size
15/64	.2344	
B	.2380	
C	.2420	
D	.2460	
1/4 / E	.2500	5/16-18
F	.2570	
G	.2610	
17/64	.2656	
H	.2660	
I	.2720	
J	.2770	5/16-24
K	.2810	
9/32	.2812	
L	.2900	
M	.2950	
19/64	.2969	
N	.3020	
5/16	.3125	
O	.3160	3/8-16
P	.3230	
21/64	.3281	
Q	.3320	3/8-24
R	.3390	
11/32	.3438	
S	.3480	
T	.3580	
23/64	.3594	7/16-14
U	.3680	
3/8	.3750	
V	.3770	
W	.3860	7/16-20
25/64	.3906	
X	.3970	
Y	.4040	
13/32	.4062	1/2-13
Z	.4130	
27/64	.4219	1/2-20
7/16	.4375	
29/64	.4531	9/16-12
15/32	.4688	
1/2	.5000	9/16-18, 5/8-11
33/64	.5156	
17/32	.5312	
35/64	.5469	
9/16	.5625	5/8-18
37/64	.5781	

Fraction or Drill Size	Decimal Equivalent	Tap Size
19/32	.5938	11/16-11
39/64	.6094	11/16-16
5/8	.6250	
41/64	.6406	3/4-10
21/32	.6562	
43/64	.6719	
11/16	.6875	3/4-16
45/64	.7031	
23/32	.7188	
47/64	.7344	
3/4	.7500	
49/64	.7656	7/8-9
25/32	.7812	
51/64	.7969	
13/16	.8125	7/8-14
53/64	.8281	
27/32	.8438	
55/64	.8594	
7/8	.8750	
57/64	.8906	1-8
29/32	.9062	
59/64	.9219	
15/16	.9375	1-12, 14
61/64	.9531	
31/32	.9688	
63/64	.9844	
1	1.0000	1 1/8-7
1 3/64	1.0469	1 1/8-12
1 7/64	1.0938	1 1/4-7
1 1/8	1.1250	
1 11/64	1.1719	1 1/4-12
1 7/32	1.2188	1 3/8-6
1 1/4	1.2500	
1 19/64	1.2969	1 3/8-12
1 11/32	1.3438	1 1/2-6
1 3/8	1.3750	
1 27/64	1.4219	1 1/2-12
1 1/2	1.5000	

Pipe Thread Sizes

Thread	Drill	Thread	Drill
1/8-27	R	1 1/2-11 1/2	1 47/64
1/4-18	7/16	2-11 1/2	2 7/32
3/8-18	37/64	2 1/2-8	2 5/8
1/2-14	23/32	3-8	3 1/4
3/4-14	59/64	3 1/2-8	3 3/4
1-11 1/2	1 5/32	4-8	4 1/4
1 1/4-11 1/2	1 1/2		

KEY & KEYWAY SIZES

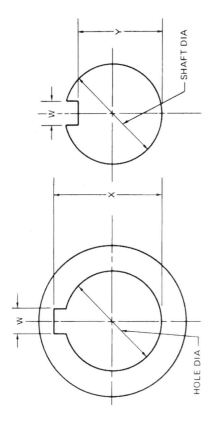

Nom. Size (Inch)	DIA. – (Shaft) Inch	mm	'X' (Collar) Inch	mm	'Y' (Shaft) Inch	mm
1/2	.500	12.700	.560	14.224	.430	10.922
9/16	.562	14.290	.623	15.824	.493	12.522
5/8	.625	15.875	.709	18.008	.517	13.132
11/16	.688	17.470	.773	18.618	.581	14.757
3/4	.750	19.050	.837	21.259	.644	16.357
13/16	.812	20.640	.900	22.860	.708	17.983
7/8	.875	22.225	.964	24.485	.771	19.583
15/16	.938	23.820	1.051	26.695	.791	20.091
1	1.000	25.400	1.114	28.295	.859	21.818
1 1/16	1.062	26.985	1.178	29.921	.923	23.444
1 1/8	1.125	28.575	1.241	31.521	.986	25.044
1 3/16	1.188	30.165	1.304	33.121	1.049	26.644
1 1/4	1.250	31.750	1.367	34.722	1.112	28.244
1 5/16	1.312	33.340	1.455	36.957	1.137	28.879
1 3/8	1.375	34.923	1.518	38.557	1.201	30.505

From DRAFTING FOR TRADES AND INDUSTRY, Mechanical and Electronic (Drafting for Trades & Industry Series) 1st edition by NELSON.1979. Reprinted with permission of Delmar Learning, a division of Thomson Learning: www.thomsonrights.com. Fax 800 730-2215.

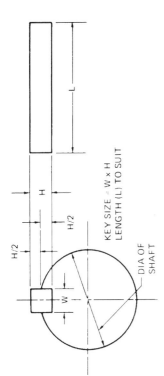

KEY SIZE = W x H
LENGTH (L) TO SUIT

Shaft Nom. Size – DIA. – From	To & Incl.	Square (W = H)	Type	Square Key From	To & Incl.	Tolerance
5/16 (8)	7/16 (11)	3/32 (2.38)	Bar Stock	—	3/4 (19.05)	+.000 –.002 (+.0000 –.0254)
7/16 (11)	9/16 (14)	1/8 (3.175)	Bar Stock	—		
9/16 (14)	7/8 (22)	3/16 (4.76)	Bar Stock	3/4 (19.05)	1 1/2 (38.1)	+.000 –.003 (+.0000 –.0762)
7/8 (22)	1 1/4 (32)	1/4 (6.35)	Bar Stock	1 1/2 (38.1)	2 1/2 (63.5)	+.000 –.004 (+.0000 –.1016)
1 1/4 (32)	1 3/8 (35)	5/16 (7.94)	Bar Stock	2 1/2 (63.5)	3 1/2 (88.9)	+.000 –.006 (+.0000 –.1524)
1 3/8 (35)	1 3/4 (44)	3/8 (9.53)	Keystock	—	1 1/4 (31.75)	+.001 –.000 (+.0254 –.0000)
1 3/4 (44)	2 1/4 (57)	1/2 (12.7)	Keystock	1 1/4 (31.75)	3 (76.2)	+.002 –.000 (+.0508 –.0000)
2 1/4 (57)	2 3/4 (70)	5/8 (15.88)	Keystock	3 (76.2)	3 1/2 (88.9)	+.003 –.000 (+.0762 –.0000)
2 3/4 (70)	3 1/4 (82)	3/4 (19.05)				
3 1/4 (82)	3 3/4 (95)	7/8 (22.23)				

(Figures in parenthesis = mm)

Dimensions of Keys and Slots.

USA STANDARD

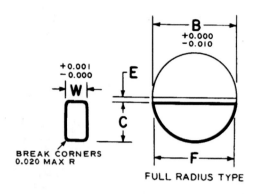

FULL RADIUS TYPE

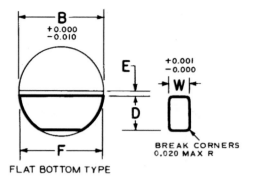

FLAT BOTTOM TYPE

WOODRUFF KEYS

Key No.	Nominal Key Size W × B	Actual Length F +0.000-0.010	Height of Key				Distance Below Center E
			C		D		
			Max	Min	Max	Min	
202	1/16 × 1/4	0.248	0.109	0.104	0.109	0.104	1/64
202.5	1/16 × 5/16	0.311	0.140	0.135	0.140	0.135	1/64
302.5	3/32 × 5/16	0.311	0.140	0.135	0.140	0.135	1/64
203	1/16 × 3/8	0.374	0.172	0.167	0.172	0.167	1/64
303	3/32 × 3/8	0.374	0.172	0.167	0.172	0.167	1/64
403	1/8 × 3/8	0.374	0.172	0.167	0.172	0.167	1/64
204	1/16 × 1/2	0.491	0.203	0.198	0.194	0.188	3/64
304	3/32 × 1/2	0.491	0.203	0.198	0.194	0.188	3/64
404	1/8 × 1/2	0.491	0.203	0.198	0.194	0.188	3/64
305	3/32 × 5/8	0.612	0.250	0.245	0.240	0.234	1/16
405	1/8 × 5/8	0.612	0.250	0.245	0.240	0.234	1/16
505	5/32 × 5/8	0.612	0.250	0.245	0.240	0.234	1/16
605	3/16 × 5/8	0.612	0.250	0.245	0.240	0.234	1/16
406	1/8 × 3/4	0.740	0.313	0.308	0.303	0.297	1/16
506	5/32 × 3/4	0.740	0.313	0.308	0.303	0.297	1/16
606	3/16 × 3/4	0.740	0.313	0.308	0.303	0.297	1/16
806	1/4 × 3/4	0.740	0.313	0.308	0.303	0.297	1/16
507	5/32 × 7/8	0.866	0.375	0.370	0.365	0.359	1/16
607	3/16 × 7/8	0.866	0.375	0.370	0.365	0.359	1/16
707	7/32 × 7/8	0.866	0.375	0.370	0.365	0.359	1/16
807	1/4 × 7/8	0.866	0.375	0.370	0.365	0.359	1/16
608	3/16 × 1	0.992	0.438	0.433	0.428	0.422	1/16
708	7/32 × 1	0.992	0.438	0.433	0.428	0.422	1/16
808	1/4 × 1	0.992	0.438	0.433	0.428	0.422	1/16
1008	5/16 × 1	0.992	0.438	0.433	0.428	0.422	1/16
1208	3/8 × 1	0.992	0.438	0.433	0.428	0.422	1/16
609	3/16 × 1 1/8	1.114	0.484	0.479	0.475	0.469	5/64
709	7/32 × 1 1/8	1.114	0.484	0.479	0.475	0.469	5/64
809	1/4 × 1 1/8	1.114	0.484	0.479	0.475	0.469	5/64
1009	5/16 × 1 1/8	1.114	0.484	0.479	0.475	0.469	5/64

Dimensions of Keys and Slots. (CONTINUED)

WOODRUFF KEYS (CONCLUDED)

Key No.	Nominal Key Size W × B	Actual Length F +0.000-0.010	Height of Key				Distance Below Center E
			C		D		
			Max	Min	Max	Min	
610	$\frac{3}{16} \times 1\frac{1}{4}$	1.240	0.547	0.542	0.537	0.531	$\frac{5}{64}$
710	$\frac{7}{32} \times 1\frac{1}{4}$	1.240	0.547	0.542	0.537	0.531	$\frac{5}{64}$
810	$\frac{1}{4} \times 1\frac{1}{4}$	1.240	0.547	0.542	0.537	0.531	$\frac{5}{64}$
1010	$\frac{5}{16} \times 1\frac{1}{4}$	1.240	0.547	0.542	0.537	0.531	$\frac{5}{64}$
1210	$\frac{3}{8} \times 1\frac{1}{4}$	1.240	0.547	0.542	0.537	0.531	$\frac{5}{64}$
811	$\frac{1}{4} \times 1\frac{3}{8}$	1.362	0.594	0.589	0.584	0.578	$\frac{3}{32}$
1011	$\frac{5}{16} \times 1\frac{3}{8}$	1.362	0.594	0.589	0.584	0.578	$\frac{3}{32}$
1211	$\frac{3}{8} \times 1\frac{3}{8}$	1.362	0.594	0.589	0.584	0.578	$\frac{3}{32}$
812	$\frac{1}{4} \times 1\frac{1}{2}$	1.484	0.641	0.636	0.631	0.625	$\frac{7}{64}$
1012	$\frac{5}{16} \times 1\frac{1}{2}$	1.484	0.641	0.636	0.631	0.625	$\frac{7}{64}$
1212	$\frac{3}{8} \times 1\frac{1}{2}$	1.484	0.641	0.636	0.631	0.625	$\frac{7}{64}$

All dimensions given are in inches.

The key numbers indicate nominal key dimensions. The last two digits give the nominal diameter B in eighths of an inch and the digits preceding the last two give the nominal width W in thirty-seconds of an inch.

Example:
　　No. 204 indicates a key $\frac{2}{32} \times \frac{4}{8}$ or $\frac{1}{16} \times \frac{1}{2}$.
　　No. 808 indicates a key $\frac{8}{32} \times \frac{8}{8}$ or $\frac{1}{4} \times 1$.
　　No. 1212 indicates a key $\frac{12}{32} \times \frac{12}{8}$ or $\frac{3}{8} \times 1\frac{1}{2}$.

Reprinted from ASME B18.2.1-1981 (R1992), B18.2.2-1987 (R1993), B18.3-1986 (R1993), B18.6.2-1972 (R1993), B18.6.3-1972 (R1991), B18.21.1-1994, B18.22.1-1965 (R1990), B17.1-1967 (R1998), B17.2-1967 (R1990) and B4.2-1978 (R1994), by permission of The American Society of Mechanical Engineers. All rights reserved.

Dimensions of Keys and Slots. (CONTINUED)

WOODRUFF KEYS AND KEYSEATS

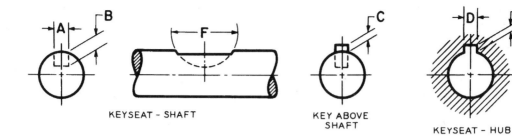

KEYSEAT – SHAFT   KEY ABOVE SHAFT   KEYSEAT – HUB

| Key Number | Nominal Size Key | Keyseat – Shaft | | | | | Key Above Shaft | Keyseat – Hub | |
| | | Width A* | | Depth B | Diameter F | | Height C | Width D | Depth E |
		Min	Max	+0.005 -0.000	Min	Max	+0.005 -0.005	+0.002 -0.000	+0.005 -0.000
202	1/16 × 1/4	0.0615	0.0630	0.0728	0.250	0.268	0.0312	0.0635	0.0372
202.5	1/16 × 5/16	0.0615	0.0630	0.1038	0.312	0.330	0.0312	0.0635	0.0372
302.5	3/32 × 5/16	0.0928	0.0943	0.0882	0.312	0.330	0.0469	0.0948	0.0529
203	1/16 × 3/8	0.0615	0.0630	0.1358	0.375	0.393	0.0312	0.0635	0.0372
303	3/32 × 3/8	0.0928	0.0943	0.1202	0.375	0.393	0.0469	0.0948	0.0529
403	1/8 × 3/8	0.1240	0.1255	0.1045	0.375	0.393	0.0625	0.1260	0.0685
204	1/16 × 1/2	0.0615	0.0630	0.1668	0.500	0.518	0.0312	0.0635	0.0372
304	3/32 × 1/2	0.0928	0.0943	0.1511	0.500	0.518	0.0469	0.0948	0.0529
404	1/8 × 1/2	0.1240	0.1255	0.1355	0.500	0.518	0.0625	0.1260	0.0685
305	3/32 × 5/8	0.0928	0.0943	0.1981	0.625	0.643	0.0469	0.0948	0.0529
405	1/8 × 5/8	0.1240	0.1255	0.1825	0.625	0.643	0.0625	0.1260	0.0685
505	5/32 × 5/8	0.1553	0.1568	0.1669	0.625	0.643	0.0781	0.1573	0.0841
605	3/16 × 5/8	0.1863	0.1880	0.1513	0.625	0.643	0.0937	0.1885	0.0997
406	1/8 × 3/4	0.1240	0.1255	0.2455	0.750	0.768	0.0625	0.1260	0.0685
506	5/32 × 3/4	0.1553	0.1568	0.2299	0.750	0.768	0.0781	0.1573	0.0841
606	3/16 × 3/4	0.1863	0.1880	0.2143	0.750	0.768	0.0937	0.1885	0.0997
806	1/4 × 3/4	0.2487	0.2505	0.1830	0.750	0.768	0.1250	0.2510	0.1310
507	5/32 × 7/8	0.1553	0.1568	0.2919	0.875	0.895	0.0781	0.1573	0.0841
607	3/16 × 7/8	0.1863	0.1880	0.2763	0.875	0.895	0.0937	0.1885	0.0997
707	7/32 × 7/8	0.2175	0.2193	0.2607	0.875	0.895	0.1093	0.2198	0.1153
807	1/4 × 7/8	0.2487	0.2505	0.2450	0.875	0.895	0.1250	0.2510	0.1310
608	3/16 × 1	0.1863	0.1880	0.3393	1.000	1.020	0.0937	0.1885	0.0997
708	7/32 × 1	0.2175	0.2193	0.3237	1.000	1.020	0.1093	0.2198	0.1153
808	1/4 × 1	0.2487	0.2505	0.3080	1.000	1.020	0.1250	0.2510	0.1310
1008	5/16 × 1	0.3111	0.3130	0.2768	1.000	1.020	0.1562	0.3135	0.1622
1208	3/8 × 1	0.3735	0.3755	0.2455	1.000	1.020	0.1875	0.3760	0.1935
609	3/16 × 1 1/8	0.1863	0.1880	0.3853	1.125	1.145	0.0937	0.1885	0.0997
709	7/32 × 1 1/8	0.2175	0.2193	0.3697	1.125	1.145	0.1093	0.2198	0.1153
809	1/4 × 1 1/8	0.2487	0.2505	0.3540	1.125	1.145	0.1250	0.2510	0.1310
1009	5/16 × 1 1/8	0.3111	0.3130	0.3228	1.125	1.145	0.1562	0.3135	0.1622

From The American Society of Mechanical Engineers—ANSI B17.2—1967—R1990

Dimensions of Keys and Slots. (CONTINUED)

KEYS AND KEYSEATS

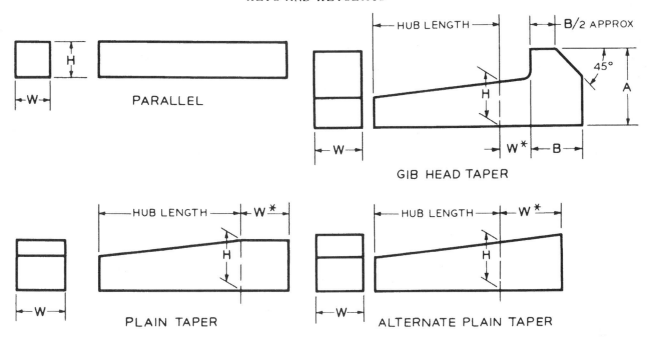

PARALLEL

GIB HEAD TAPER

PLAIN TAPER

ALTERNATE PLAIN TAPER

Plain and Gib Head Taper Keys Have a 1/8″ Taper in 12″

KEY DIMENSIONS AND TOLERANCES

KEY			NOMINAL KEY SIZE		TOLERANCE	
			Width, W		Width, W	Height, H
			Over	To (Incl)		
Parallel	Square	Bar Stock	— 3/4 1-1/2 2-1/2	3/4 1-1/2 2-1/2 3-1/2	+0.000 −0.002 +0.000 −0.003 +0.000 −0.004 +0.000 −0.006	+0.000 −0.002 +0.000 −0.003 +0.000 −0.004 +0.000 −0.006
		Keystock	— 1-1/4 3	1-1/4 3 3-1/2	+0.001 −0.000 +0.002 −0.000 +0.003 −0.000	+0.001 −0.000 +0.002 −0.000 +0.003 −0.000
	Rectangular	Bar Stock	— 3/4 1-1/2 3 4 6	3/4 1-1/2 3 4 6 7	+0.000 −0.003 +0.000 −0.004 +0.000 −0.005 +0.000 −0.006 +0.000 −0.008 +0.000 −0.013	+0.000 −0.003 +0.000 −0.004 +0.000 −0.005 +0.000 −0.006 +0.000 −0.008 +0.000 −0.013
		Keystock	— 1-1/4 3	1-1/4 3 7	+0.001 −0.000 +0.002 −0.000 +0.003 −0.000	+0.005 −0.005 +0.005 −0.005 +0.005 −0.005
Taper	Plain or Gib Head Square or Rectangular		— 1-1/4 3	1-1/4 3 7	+0.001 −0.000 +0.002 −0.000 +0.003 −0.000	+0.005 −0.000 +0.005 −0.000 +0.005 −0.000

*For locating position of dimension H. Tolerance does not apply.
See Table 41 for dimensions on gib heads.
All dimensions given in inches.

Reprinted from ASME B18.2.1-1981 (R1992), B18.2.2-1987 (R1993), B18.3-1986
(R1993), B18.6.2-1972 (R1993), B18.6.3-1972 (R1991), B18.21.1-1994, B18.22.1-1965
(R1990), B17.1-1967 (R1998), B17.2-1967 (R1990) and B4.2-1978 (R1994), by
permission of The American Society of Mechanical Engineers. All rights reserved.

Dimensions of Keys and Slots. **(CONTINUED)**

WOODRUFF KEY SIZES FOR DIFFERENT SHAFT DIAMETERS

Shaft Diameter	5/16 to 3/8	7/16 to 1/2	9/16 to 3/4	13/16 to 15/16	1 to 1 3/16	1 1/4 to 1 7/16	1 1/2 to 1 3/4	1 13/16 to 2 1/8	2 3/16 to 2 1/2
Key Numbers	204	304 305	404 405 406	505 506 507	606 607 608 609	807 808 809	810 811 812	1011 1012	1211 1212

Dimensions of Keys and Slots. **(CONTINUED)**

USA STANDARD

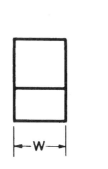
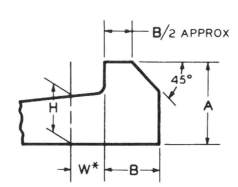

GIB HEAD NOMINAL DIMENSIONS

Nominal Key Size Width, W	SQUARE			RECTANGULAR		
	H	A	B	H	A	B
1/8	1/8	1/4	1/4	3/32	3/16	1/8
3/16	3/16	5/16	5/16	1/8	1/4	1/4
1/4	1/4	7/16	3/8	3/16	5/16	5/16
5/16	5/16	1/2	7/16	1/4	7/16	3/8
3/8	3/8	5/8	1/2	1/4	7/16	3/8
1/2	1/2	7/8	5/8	3/8	5/8	1/2
5/8	5/8	1	3/4	7/16	3/4	9/16
3/4	3/4	1-1/4	7/8	1/2	7/8	5/8
7/8	7/8	1-3/8	1	5/8	1	3/4
1	1	1-5/8	1-1/8	3/4	1-1/4	7/8
1-1/4	1-1/4	2	1-7/16	7/8	1-3/8	1
1-1/2	1-1/2	2-3/8	1-3/4	1	1-5/8	1-1/8
1-3/4	1-3/4	2-3/4	2	1-1/2	2-3/8	1-3/4
2	2	3-1/2	2-1/4	1-1/2	2-3/8	1-3/4
2-1/2	2-1/2	4	3	1-3/4	2-3/4	2
3	3	5	3-1/2	2	3-1/2	2-1/4
3-1/2	3-1/2	6	4	2-1/2	4	3

*For locating position of dimension H.

For larger sizes the following relationships are suggested as guides for establishing A and B.

$$A = 1.8 H \qquad B = 1.2 H$$

All dimensions given in inches.

Reprinted from ASME B18.2.1-1981 (R1992), B18.2.2-1987 (R1993), B18.3-1986 (R1993), B18.6.2-1972 (R1993), B18.6.3-1972 (R1991), B18.21.1-1994, B18.22.1-1965 (R1990), B17.1-1967 (R1998), B17.2-1967 (R1990) and B4.2-1978 (R1994), by permission of The American Society of Mechanical Engineers. All rights reserved.

Dimensions of Keys and Slots. **(CONTINUED)**

Application	SAE No.	Application	SAE No.
Adapters	1145	Chain pins, transmission	4320
Agricultural steel	1070	" " "	4815
" "	1080	" " "	4820
Aircraft forgings	4140	Chains, transmission	3135
Axles, front or rear	1040	" "	3140
" " "	4140	Clutch disks	1060
Axle shafts	1045	" "	1070
" "	2340	" "	1085
" "	2345	Clutch springs	1060
" "	3135	Coil springs	4063
" "	3140	Cold-headed bolts	4042
" "	3141	Cold-heading steel	30905
" "	4063	Cold-heading wire or rod	rimmed*
" "	4340	" " " "	1035
Ball-bearing races	52100	Cold-rolled steel	1070
Balls for ball bearings	52100	Connecting-rods	1040
Body stock for cars	rimmed*	" "	3141
Bolts, anchor	1040	Connecting-rod bolts	3130
Bolts and screws	1035	Corrosion resisting	51710
Bolts, cold-headed	4042	" "	30805
Bolts, connecting-rod	3130	Covers, transmission	rimmed*
Bolts, heat-treated	2330	Crankshafts	1045
Bolts, heavy-duty	4815	"	1145
" " "	4820	"	3135
Bolts, steering-arm	3130	"	3140
Brake levers	1030	"	3141
" "	1040	Crankshafts, Diesel engine	4340
Bumper bars	1085	Cushion, springs	1060
Cams, free-wheeling	4615	Cutlery, stainless	51335
" " "	4620	Cylinder studs	3130
Camshafts	1020	Deep-drawing steel	rimmed*
"	1040	" " "	30905
Carburized parts	1020	Differential gears	4023
" "	1022	Disks, clutch	1070
" "	1024	" "	1060
" "	1320	Ductile steel	30905
" "	2317	Fan blades	1020
" "	2515	Fatigue resisting	4340
" "	3310	" "	4640
" "	3115	Fender stock for cars	rimmed*
" "	3120	Forgings, aircraft	4140
" "	4023	Forgings, carbon steel	1040
" "	4032	" " "	1045
" "	1117	Forgings, heat-treated	3240
" "	1118	" " "	5140

General Applications of SAE Steels.

Application	SAE No.	Application	SAE No.
Forgings, heat-treated	6150	Key stock	1030
Forgings, high-duty	6150	" "	2330
Forgings, small or medium .	1035	" "	3130
Forgings, large .	1036	Leaf springs	1085
Free-cutting carbon steel.....	1111	" "	9260
" " " "	1113	Levers, brake	1030
Free-cutting chro.-ni.steel	30615	" "	1040
Free-cutting mang. steel......	1132	Levers, gear shift	1030
" " " "	1137	Levers, heat-treated	2330
Gears, carburized.............	1320	Lock-washers	1060
" "	2317	Mower knives	1085
" "	3115	Mower sections	1070
" "	3120	Music wire........................	1085
" "	3310	Nuts	3130
" "	4119	Nuts, heat-treated	2330
" "	4125	Oil-pans, automobile	rimmed*
" "	4320	Pinions, carburized.............	3115
" "	4615	" "	3120
" "	4620	" "	4320
" "	4815	Piston-pins	3115
" "	4820	" "	3120
Gears, heat-treated............	2345	Plow beams	1070
Gears, car and truck	4027	Plow disks	1080
" " " "	4032	Plow shares	1080
Gears, cyanide-hardening..	5140	Propeller shafts....................	2340
Gears, differential	4023	" "	2345
Gears, high duty...............	4640	" "	4140
" " "	6150	Races, ball-bearing.............	52100
Gears, oil-hardening.........	3145	Ring gears	3115
" " "	3150	" "	3120
" " "	4340	" "	4119
" " "	5150	Rings, snap......................	1060
Gears, ring......................	1045	Rivets	rimmed*
" "	3115	Rod and wire....................	killed*
" "	3120	Rod, cold-heading	1035
" "	4119	Roller bearings....................	4815
Gears, transmission	3115	Rollers for bearings..............	52100
" "	3120	Screws and bolts.................	1035
" "	4119	Screw stock, Bessemer	1111
Gears, truck and bus	3310	" " "	1112
" " " "	4320	" " "	1113
Gear shift levers...............	1030	Screw stock, open hearth	1115
Harrow disks	1080	Screws, heat-treated............	2330
" "	1095	Seat springs......................	1095
Hay-rake teeth	1095	Shafts, axle......................	1045

General Applications of SAE Steels. (CONTINUED)

Application	SAE No.	Application	SAE No.
Shafts, cyanide-hardening ..	5140	Steel, cold-heading	30905
Shafts, heavy-duty	4340	Steel, free-cutting carbon	11111
" " "	6150	" " " "	1113
" " "	4615	Steel, free-cutting chro.-ni.	30615
" " "	4620	Steel, free-cutting mang.	1132
Shafts, oil-hardening	5150	" " " "	0000
Shafts, propeller	2340	Steel, minimum distortion	4615
" "	2345	" " " "	4620
" "	4140	" " " "	4640
Shafts, transmission	4140	Steel, soft ductile	30905
Sheets and strips	rimmed*	Steering arms	4042
Snap rings	1060	Steering-arm bolts	3130
Spline shafts	1045	Steering knuckles	3141
" "	1320	Steering-knuckle pins	4815
" "	2340	" " "	4820
" "	2345	Studs	1040
" "	3115	" "	1111
" "	3120	Studs, cold-headed	4042
" "	3135	Studs, cylinder	3130
" "	3140	Studs, heat-treated	2330
" "	4023	Studs, heavy-duty	4815
Spring clips	1060	" " "	4820
Springs, coil	1095	Tacks	rimmed*
" "	4063	Thrust washers	1060
" "	6150	Thrust washers, oil-harden	5150
Springs, clutch	1060	Transmission shafts	4140
Springs, cushion	1060	Tubing	1040
Springs, leaf	1085	Tubing, front axle	4140
" "	1095	Tubing, seamless	1030
" "	4063	Tubing, welded	1020
" "	4068	Universal joints	1145
" "	9260	Valve springs	1060
" "	6150	Washers, lock	1060
Springs, hard-drawn coiled	1066	Welded structures	30705
Springs, oil-hardening	5150	Wire and rod	killed*
Springs, oil-tempered wire ..	1066	Wire, cold-heading	rimmed*
Springs, seat	1095	" " "	1035
Springs, valve	1060	Wire, hard-drawn spring	1045
Spring wire	1045	" " "	1055
Spring wire, hard-drawn	1055	Wire, music	1085
Spring wire, oil-tempered ...	1055	Wire, oil-tempered spring	1055
Stainless irons	51210	Wrist-pins, automobile	1020
" "	51710	Yokes	1145
Steel, cold-rolled	1070		

General Applications of SAE Steels. **(CONTINUED)**

Element	Sym-bol	Melting point, °F	Boiling point, °F	Specific heat,[a] cal/g/°C	Thermal conductivity,[a] Btu/hr/sq ft/°F/ft	Density,[a] g/cm³	Modulus of elasticity in tension, million psi	Coefficient of linear thermal expansion,[a] μ in./in./°F	Electrical resistivity, microhm-cm	Crystal structure
Aluminum	Al	1220	4442	0.215	128.	2.70	9	13.1	2.65	f.c.c
Antimony	Sb	1167	2516	0.049	10.8	6.62	11.3	4.7	39	Rhomb.
Arsenic	As	1503 (28 atm)	1135[b]	0.082	.....	5.72	.....	2.6	33.3	Rhomb.
Barium	Ba	1317	2980	0.068		3.5	.....	....	....	b.c.c.
Beryllium	Be	2332	5020	0.45	84.4	1.85	42	6.4	4	h.c.p.
Bismuth	Bi	520	2840	0.029	4.8	9.80	4.6	7.4	107	Rhomb.
Boron	B	3690	.....	0.309	.....	2.34	.....	4.6	10	Orthorhomb
Cadmium	Cd	610	1409	0.055	53.	8.65	8	16.55	6.83	h.c.p.
Calcium	Ca	1540	2625	0.149	72.3	1.55	3.5	12.4	3.91	f.c.c.
Carbon (graphite)	C	6740[b]	8730	0.165	13.8	2.25	0.7	0.3 to 2.4	1375	Hexag.
Cerium	Ce	1479	6280	0.045	6.6	6.77	6	4.4	75	f.c.c.
Cesium	Cs	84	1273	0.048	.....	1.90	.....	54	20	b.c.c.
Chromium	Cr	3407	4829	0.11	40.3	7.19	36	3.4	12.9	b.c.c.
Cobalt	Co	2723	5250	0.099	41.5	8.85	30	7.66	6.24	h.c.p.
Columbium	Cb	4474	8901	0.065	31.5	8.57	.....	4.06	12.5	b.c.c.
Copper	Cu	1981	4703	0.092	226.	8.96	16	9.2	1.67	f.c.c.
Gallium	Ga	86	4059	0.079	19.4	5.91	.....	10	17.4	Orthorhomb.
Germanium[c]	Ge	1719	5125	0.073	33.7	5.32	.....	3.19	46×10^5	Diam. cubic
Gold	Au	1954	5380	0.031	171.	19.32	11.6	7.9	2.35	f.c.c.
Indium	In	313	3632	0.057	13.8	7.31	1.57	18	8.37	f.c.tetr.
Iridium	Ir	4449	9570	0.031	33.7	22.50	76	3.8	5.3	f.c.c.
Iron	Fe	2798	5430	0.11	43.3	7.87	28.5	6.53	9.71	b.c.c.
Lanthanum	La	1688	6280	0.048	8.	6.19	10.5	2.77	57	Hexag.
Lead	Pb	621	3137	0.031	20.	11.36	2	16.3	20.6	f.c.c.
Lithium	Li	357	2426	0.79	41.	0.534	.....	31	8.55	b.c.c.
Magnesium	Mg	1202	2025	0.245	88.5	1.74	6.35	15.05	4.45	h.c.p.
Manganese	Mn	2273	3900	0.115	.....	7.73	23	12.22	185	Complex cubic
Mercury	Hg	−37	675	0.033	4.7	13.55	.....	....	98.4	Rhomb.
Molybdenum	Mo	4730	10040	0.000	82.	10.22	47	2.7	5.2	b.c.c.
Nickel	Ni	2647	4950	0.105	53.	8.90	30	7.39	6.84	f.c.c.
Osmium	Os	4900	9950	0.031	.....	22.57	81	2.6	9.5	h.c.p.
Palladium	Pd	2826	7200	0.058	40.5	12.02	16.3	6.53	10.8	f.c.c.
Phosphorus (white)	P	112	536	0.177	.....	1.83	.....	70	10	Cubic
Platinum	Pt	3217	8185	0.0314	39.8	21.45	21.3	4.9	10.6	f.c.c.
Plutonium	Pu	1184	6000	0.033	4.8	19.00	14	30.55	141.4	Monoclinic
Potassium	K	147	1400	0.177	58.	0.86	.....	46	6.15	b.c.c.
Rhenium	Re	5755	10650	0.033	41.	21.04	66.7	3.7	19.3	h.c.p.
Rhodium	Rh	3571	8130	0.059	50.6	12.44	42.5	4.6	4.51	f.c.c.
Rubidium	Rb	102	1270	0.080	.....	1.53	.....	50	12.5	b.c.c.
Ruthenium	Ru	4530	8850	0.057	.....	12.20	60	5.1	7.6	h.c.p.
Selenium	Se	423	1265	0.084	.....	4.70	8.4	21	12	Hexag.
Silicon[c]	Si	2570	48660	0.162	48.2	2.33	16.35	1.6 to 1.4	10	Diam. cubic
Silver	Ag	1761	4010	0.056	242.	10.49	11	10.9	1.59	f.c.c.
Sodium	Na	208	1638	0.295	77.2	0.971	.....	39	4.2	b.c.c.
Strontium	Sr	1414	2520	0.176	.....	2.60	.....	.....	23	f.c.c.
Tantalum	Ta	5425	9800	0.034	31.3	16.60	27	3.6	12.45	b.c.c.
Tellurium	Te	841	1814	0.047	3.3	6.24	6	9.3	46×10^5	Hexag.
Thallium	Tl	577	2655	0.031	22.5	11.85	.....	16	18	h.c.p.
Thorium	Th	3182	7000	0.034	21.7	11.66	.....	6.9	13	f.c.c.
Tin	Sn	449	4120	0.054	36.2	7.30	6.3	13	11	Tetrag.
Titanium	Ti	3035	5900	0.124	9.8	4.51	16.8	4.67	42	h.c.p.
Tungsten	W	6170	10706	0.033	96.	19.30	50	2.55	5.65	b.c.c.
Uranium	U	2070	6904	0.028	17.1	19.07	24	3.8 to 7.8	30	Orthorhomb.
Vanadium	V	3450	6150	0.119	16.9	6.1	19	4.6	26	h.c.c.
Yttrium	Y	2748	5490	0.071	8.5	4.47	17	....	57	h.c.p.
Zinc	Zn	787	1663	0.092	65.	7.13	.....	22	5.92	h.c.p.
Zirconium	Zr	3366	6470	0.067	9.6	6.49	13.7	3.2	40	h.c.p.

[a] Near 68°F (20°C)

[b] Sublimes—triple point at 2028 atm.

[c] Semiconductor.

Courtesy of "Metals Handbook," vol. 1, 8th ed., American Society for Metals, Cleveland, 1961.

Properties of Common Metals (density, Young's modules, coefficient of thermal expansion).

Metal	Modulus of elasticity E, million psi	Ultimate tensile strength σ_u, thousand psi	Yield strength σ_y, thousand psi	Endurance limit σ_{end}, thousand psi	Hardness Brinell
Gray cast iron, ASTM 20, med. sec.	12	22	....	10	180
Gray cast iron, ASTM 50, med. sec.	19	53	....	25	240
Nodular ductile cast iron:					
Type 60-45-10....................	22–25	60–80	45–60	35	140–190
Type 120-90-02....................	22–25	120–150	90–125	52	240–325
Austenitic	18.5	58–68	32–38	32	140–200
Malleable cast iron, ferritic 32510..	25	50	33.5	28	110–156
Malleable cast iron, pearlitic 60003	28	80–100	60–80	39–40	197–269
Ingot iron, hot rolled.....................	29.8	44	23	28	83
Ingot iron, cold drawn	29.8	73	69	33	142
Wrought iron, hot rolled longit........	29.5	48	27	23	97–105
Cast carbon steel, normalized 70000	30	70	38	31	140
Cast steel, low alloy, 100,000 norm.					
and temp	29–30	100	68	45	209
Cast steel, low alloy, 200,000					
quench. and temp	29–30	200	170	85	400
Wrought plain C steel:					
C1020 hot rolled..................	29–30	66	44	32	143
C1045 hard. and temp. 100°F	29–30	118	88	....	277
C1095 hard. and temp. 700°F	29–30	180	118	....	375
Low-alloy steels:					
Wrought 1330, HT and temp					
1000°F..............................	29–30	122	100	....	248
Wrought 2317, HT and temp					
1000°F..............................	29–30	107	72	....	222
Wrought 4340, HT and temp					
800°F...............................	29–30	220	200	....	445
Wrought 6150, HT and temp					
1000°F..............................	29–30	187	179	....	444
Wrought 2317, HT and temp					
800°F...............................	29–30	214	194	....	423
Ultra high strength steel H11, HT	30	295–311	241–247	132	
300M HT and temp. 500°F......	....	289	242	116	
4340 HT and temp. 400°F.......	30	287	270	107	
25 Ni Maraging	24	319	284		
Austenitic Stainless Steel 302, cold					
worked	28	110	75	34	240
Ferritic Stainless Steel 302, cold					
worked	29	75–90	45–80		
Martensitic Stainless Steel 410, HT	29	90–190	60–145	40	180–390
Martensitic Stainless Steel 440A,					
HT..	29	260	240	....	510
Nitriding Steels, 135 Mod, hard					
and temp. (core properties)	29–30	145–159	125–141	45–90	285–320
Nitiding Steels 5Ni-2A, hard. and					
temp..	29–30	206	202	90	
Structural Steel.............................	30	50–65	30–40	....	120
Aluminum Alloys, cast:					
195 SHT and aged	10.1	36	24	8	75
220 SHT................................	9.5	48	26	8	75
142 SHT and aged	10.3	28–47	25–42	9.5	75–110
355 SHT and aged	10.2	35–42	25–27	9–10	80–90
A13 as cast............................	10.3	39	27	19	

ANSI Grades for Steel and Aluminum Alloys (yield strength and ultimate strength for alloys for various conditions including Cold Rolled and Hot Rolled).

Metal	Modulus of elasticity E, million psi	Ultimate tensile strength σ_u, thousand psi	Yield strength σ_y, thousand psi	Endurance limit σ_{end}, thousand psi	Hardness Brinell
Aluminum Alloys, wrought:					
EC ann	10	12	4		
EC H 19, hard	10	27	24	7	
3003 H 18 hard	10	29	27	10	55
2024 H T (T3)	10.6	70	50	20	120
5052 H 38, hard	10.2	42	37	20	77
7075 HT (T6)	10.4	83	73	23	150
7079 HT (T6)	10.3	78	68	23	145
Copper alloys, cast:					
Leaded red brass BB11-4A	9–14.8	33–46	17–24	....	55
Leaded tin bronze BB11-2A	12–16	36–48	16–21	....	60–72
Yellow brass BB11-7A	12–14	60–78	25–40	....	80–95
Aluminum bronze BB11-9BHT	15	90	40	....	180
Copper alloys, wrought:					
Oxygen-free 102 ann	17	32–35	10	11	
Hard	....	50–55	45	13	
Beryllium copper, 172 HT	19	165–183	150–170	35–40	
Cartridge Brass, 260 hard	16	76	63	21	
Muntz metal, 280 ann	15	54	21		
Admiralty, 442 ann	16	53	22		
Manganese bronze, 675 hard	15	84	60		
Phosphor bronze, 521 spring	16	112	70		
Silicon bronze, 647 HT	18	100	88		
Cupro-Nickel, 715 hard	22	80	73		
Magnesium alloys, cast:					
AZ63A, aged	6.5	30–40	14-19	11–15	55–73
AZ92A, aged	6.5	36–40	16-21	11–15	80–84
HK31A, T6	6.5	31	16	9–11	55
Magnesium Alloys, wrought:					
AZ61AF, forged	6.5	43	26	17–22	55
ZE-10A-H24	6.5	34-38	19-28	20–24	
HM31A-T5	6.5	42	33	12–14	
Nickel-alloy castings 210	21.5	45–60	20–30	....	80–125
Monel 411 cast	19	65–90	32–45	....	125–150
Inconel 610 cast	23	70–95	30–45	....	190
Nickel alloys, wrought:					
200 Spring	30	90–130	70–115		
Duranickel, 301 Spring	30	155–190			
K Monel, K500 Spring	26	145–165	130–180		
Titanium alloys, wrought, unalloyed	15–16	60–110	40–95	60–70	
5A1-2.5 Sn	16–17	115–140	110–135	95	
13V-11 Cr3A1 HT	14.5–16	190–240	170–220	50–55	
Zinc, wrought, comm. rolled	....	25–31	....	4.1	
Zirconium, wrought:	14	64	53		
Reactor grade	14	49	29		
Zircaloy 2	13.8	68	61		
Pure metals, wrought:					
Beryllium, ann	44	60–90	45–55		
Hafnium, ann	20	77	32		
Thorium, ann	10	34	26		
Vanadium, ann	20	72	64		
Uranium, ann	30	90	25		

ANSI Grades for Steel and Aluminum Alloys (yield strength and ultimate strength for alloys for various conditions including Cold Rolled and Hot Rolled). **(CONTINUED)**

Metal	Modulus of elasticity E, million psi	Ultimate tensile strength σ_u, thousand psi	Yield strength σ_y, thousand psi	Endurance limit σ_{end}, thousand psi	Hardness Brinell
Precious metals:	12	19		46	25
Gold, ann......................	11	22	8		25–35
Silver, ann	21	17–26	2–5.5		38–52
Platinum, ann	17	30	5		46
Rhodium, ann..................	42	73			55–156
Osmium, cast	80	......			350
Iridium, ann	74	......			170

Babbitt has a compressive elastic limit of 1.3 to 2.5 ksi and a Brinell hardness of 20.
Compressive yield strength of all metals, except those cold-worked = tensile yield strength.
Poisson's ratio is in the range 0.25 to 0.35 for metals.
Yield strength is determined at 0.2 per cent permanent deformation.
Modulus of elasticity in shear for metals is approximately 0.4 of modulus of elasticity in tension E.
Compressive yield strength of cast iron 80,000 to 150,000 ksi.
From Materials in Design Engineering, Materials Selector Issue, vol. 56, No. 5, 1962.
Courtesy of McGraw-Hill Companies.

ANSI Grades for Steel and Aluminum Alloys (yield strength and ultimate strength for alloys for various conditions including Cold Rolled and Hot Rolled). (CONTINUED)

Type	Specific gravity	Coefficient of thermal expansion, 10^{-6} °F	Thermal conductivity, Btu/hr/ sq ft/ °F/ft	Volume resistivity, ohm-cm	Dialectric strength [a], volts/mil	Modulus of elasticity in tension 10^6 psi	Tensile strength, 10^3 psi
Acrylic, general purpose, type I.............................	1.17–1.19	4.5	0.12	$>10^{15}$	450–530	3.5–4.5	6–9
Cellulose acetnte, type I (med.)	1.24–1.34	4.4–9.0	0.1–0.19	10^{12}	250–600	......	2.7–6.5
Epoxy, general purpose	1.12–2.4	1.7–5.0	0.1–0.8	10^{13}	350–550	......	2–12
Nylon 6..........................	1.13–1.14	4.6–5.4	0.1–0.14	10^{14}	420–485	2.5–3.4	10.2–12
Phenolic, type I (mech.)..........	1.31	3.3–4.4	......	1.7×10^{12}	350–400	4–5	6–9
Polyester, Allyl type	1.30–1.45	2.8–5.6	0.12	$>10^{13}$	330–500	2–3	4.5–7
Silicone, general (mineral)......	1.80–2.0	2.8–3.2	0.09	$>10^{13}$	350–400	......	4.2
Polystyrene, general purpose	1.04–1.07	3.3–4.8	0.00–0.09	10^{18}	>500	4–5	5–8
Polyethylene, low density	0.92	8.9–11	0.19	10^{18}	480	0.22	1.4–2
Polyethylene, medium density.............................	0.93	8.3–16.7	0.19	$>10^{15}$	480	......	2
Polyethylene, high density	0.96	8.3–16.7	0.19	$>10^{15}$	480	......	4.4
Polypropylene......................	0.89–0.91	6.2	0.08	10^{16}	769–820	1.4–1.7	5

[a] Short time.

Harold A. Rothbart, Mechanical Design and Systems Handbook, © 1985, McGraw-Hill.
Reprinted with permission of The McGraw-Hill Companies

Properties of Common Plastics (density, Young's Modulus, coefficient of thermal expansion, strength).

SHEET METAL AND WIRE GAGE DESIGNATION

GAGE NO.	AMERICAN OR BROWN & SHARPE'S A.W.G. OR B. & S.	UNITED STATES STANDARD	MANU- FACTURERS' STANDARD FOR SHEET STEEL	GAGE NO.
0000000	. . . .	.500	. . . .	0000000
000000	.5800	.469	. . . .	000000
00000	.5165	.438	. . . .	00000
0000	.4600	.406	. . . .	0000
000	.4096	.375	. . . .	000
00	.3648	.344	. . . .	00
0	.3249	.312	. . . .	0
1	.2893	.281	. . . .	1
2	.2576	.266	. . . .	2
3	.2294	.250	.2391	3
4	.2043	.234	.2242	4
5	.1819	.219	.2092	5
6	.1620	.203	.1943	6
7	.1443	.188	.1793	7
8	.1285	.172	.1644	8
9	.1144	.156	.1495	9
10	.1019	.141	.1345	10
11	.0907	.125	.1196	11
12	.0808	.109	.1046	12
13	.0720	.0938	.0897	13
14	.0642	.0781	.0747	14
15	.0571	.0703	.0673	15
16	.0508	.0625	.0598	16
17	.0453	.0562	.0538	17
18	.0403	.0500	.0478	18
19	.0359	.0438	.0418	19
20	.0320	.0375	.0359	20
21	.0285	.0344	.0329	21
22	.0253	.0312	.0299	22
23	.0226	.0281	.0269	23
24	.0201	.0250	.0239	24
25	.0179	.0219	.0209	25
26	.0159	.0188	.0179	26
27	.0142	.0172	.0164	27
28	.0126	.0156	.0149	28
29	.0113	.0141	.0135	29
30	.0100	.0125	.0120	30
31	.0089	.0109	.0105	31
32	.0080	.0102	.0097	32
33	.0071	.00938	.0090	33
34	.0063	.00859	.0082	34
35	.0056	.00781	.0075	35
36	.0050	.00703	.0067	36

Sheet Metal and Wire Gage Designation.

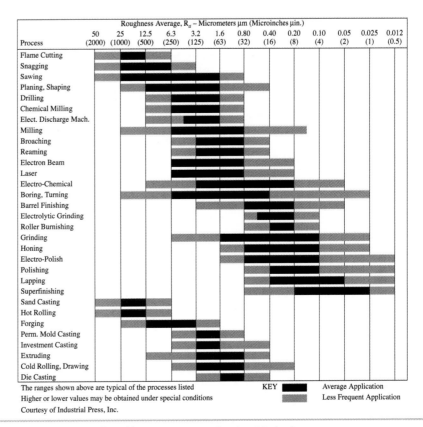

Surface Roughness Produced by Common Production Methods.

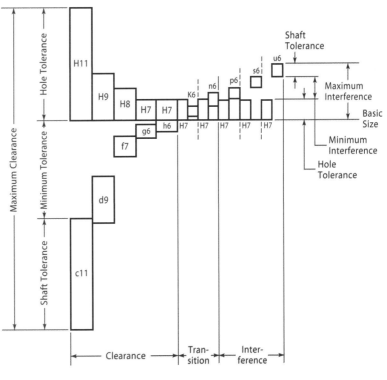

Courtesy of Industrial Press, Inc.

Standard Allowances, Tolerances, and Fits.

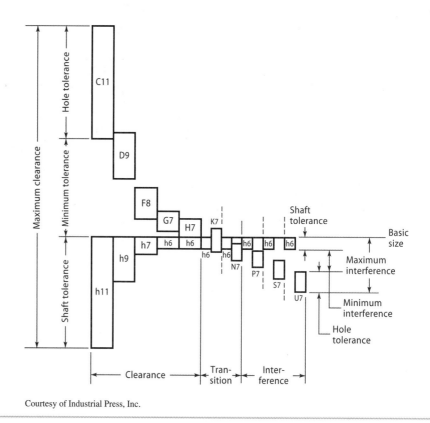

Courtesy of Industrial Press, Inc.

Standard Allowances, Tolerances, and Fits. **(CONTINUED)**

ISO SYMBOL		DESCRIPTION	
Hole Basis	**Shaft Basis**		
H11/c11	C11/h11	*Loose running* fit for wide commercial tolerances or allowances on external members.	
H9/d9	D9/h9	*Free running* fit not for use where accuracy is essential, but good for large temperature variations, high running speeds, or heavy journal pressures.	
H8/f7	F8/h7	*Close Running* fit for running on accurate machines and for accurate moderate speeds and journal pressures.	More Clearance ↑
H7/g6	G7/h6	*Sliding fit* not intended to run freely, but to move and turn freely and locate accurately.	
H7/h6	H7/h6	*Locational clearance* fit provides snug fit for locating stationary parts; but can be freely assembled and disassembled.	
H7/k6	K7/h6	*Locational transition* fit for accurate location, a compromise between clearance and interference.	
H7/n6	N7/h6	*Locational transition* fit for more accurate location where greater interference is permissible.	
H7/p6[a]	P7/h6	*Locational interference* fit for parts requiring rigidity and alignment with prime accuracy of location but without special bore pressure requirements.	More Interferance ↓
H7/s6	S7/h6	*Medium drive* fit for ordinary steel parts or shrink fits on light sections, the tightest fit usable with cast iron.	
H7/u6	U7/h6	*Force* fit suitable for parts which can be highly stressed or for shrink fits where the heavy pressing forces required are impractical.	

Clearance Fits: H11/c11–H7/h6
Transition Fits: H7/k6, H7/n6
Interference Fits: H7/p6[a], H7/s6, H7/u6

[a] Transition fit for basic sizes in range from 0 through 3 mm.

Courtesy of Industrial Press, Inc.

Standard Allowances, Tolerances, and Fits. **(CONTINUED)**

**AMERICAN NATIONAL STANDARD
PREFERRED METRIC LIMITS AND FITS**

ANSI B4.2–1978

Dimensions in mm.

PREFERRED HOLE BASIS CLEARANCE FITS

BASIC SIZE		LOOSE RUNNING Hole H11	Shaft c11	Fit	FREE RUNNING Hole H9	Shaft d9	Fit	CLOSE RUNNING Hole H8	Shaft f7	Fit	SLIDING Hole H7	Shaft g6	Fit	LOCATIONAL CLEARANCE Hole H7	Shaft h6	Fit
1	MAX	1.060	0.940	0.180	1.025	0.980	0.070	1.014	0.994	0.030	1.010	0.998	0.018	1.010	1.000	0.016
	MIN	1.000	0.880	0.060	1.000	0.955	0.020	1.000	0.984	0.006	1.000	0.992	0.002	1.000	0.994	0.000
1.2	MAX	1.260	1.140	0.180	1.225	1.180	0.070	1.214	1.194	0.030	1.210	1.198	0.018	1.210	1.200	0.016
	MIN	1.200	1.080	0.060	1.200	1.155	0.020	1.200	1.184	0.006	1.200	1.192	0.002	1.200	1.194	0.000
1.6	MAX	1.660	1.540	0.180	1.625	1.580	0.070	1.614	1.594	0.030	1.610	1.598	0.018	1.610	1.600	0.016
	MIN	1.600	1.480	0.060	1.600	1.555	0.020	1.600	1.584	0.006	1.600	1.592	0.002	1.600	1.594	0.000
2	MAX	2.060	1.940	0.180	2.025	1.980	0.070	2.014	1.994	0.030	2.010	1.998	0.018	2.010	2.000	0.016
	MIN	2.000	1.880	0.060	2.000	1.955	0.020	2.000	1.984	0.006	2.000	1.992	0.002	2.000	1.994	0.000
2.5	MAX	2.560	2.440	0.180	2.525	2.480	0.070	2.514	2.494	0.030	2.510	2.498	0.018	2.510	2.500	0.016
	MIN	2.500	2.380	0.060	2.500	2.455	0.020	2.500	2.484	0.006	2.500	2.492	0.002	2.500	2.494	0.000
3	MAX	3.060	2.940	0.180	3.025	2.980	0.070	3.014	2.994	0.030	3.010	2.998	0.018	3.010	3.000	0.016
	MIN	3.000	2.880	0.060	3.000	2.955	0.020	3.000	2.984	0.006	3.000	2.992	0.002	3.000	2.994	0.000
4	MAX	4.075	3.930	0.220	4.030	3.970	0.090	4.018	3.990	0.040	4.012	3.996	0.024	4.012	4.000	0.020
	MIN	4.000	3.855	0.070	4.000	3.940	0.030	4.000	3.978	0.010	4.000	3.988	0.004	4.000	3.992	0.000
5	MAX	5.075	4.930	0.220	5.030	4.970	0.090	5.018	4.990	0.040	5.012	4.996	0.024	5.012	5.000	0.020
	MIN	5.000	4.855	0.070	5.000	4.940	0.030	5.000	4.978	0.010	5.000	4.988	0.004	5.000	4.992	0.000
6	MAX	6.075	5.930	0.220	6.030	5.970	0.090	6.018	5.990	0.040	6.012	5.996	0.024	6.012	6.000	0.020
	MIN	6.000	5.855	0.070	6.000	5.940	0.030	6.000	5.978	0.010	6.000	5.988	0.004	6.000	5.992	0.000
8	MAX	8.090	7.920	0.260	8.036	7.960	0.112	8.022	7.987	0.050	8.015	7.995	0.029	8.015	8.000	0.024
	MIN	8.000	7.830	0.080	8.000	7.924	0.040	8.000	7.972	0.013	8.000	7.986	0.005	8.000	7.991	0.000
10	MAX	10.090	9.920	0.260	10.036	9.960	0.112	10.022	9.987	0.050	10.015	9.995	0.029	10.015	10.000	0.024
	MIN	10.000	9.830	0.080	10.000	9.924	0.040	10.000	9.972	0.013	10.000	9.986	0.005	10.000	9.991	0.000
12	MAX	12.110	11.905	0.315	12.043	11.950	0.136	12.027	11.984	0.061	12.018	11.994	0.035	12.018	12.000	0.029
	MIN	12.000	11.795	0.095	12.000	11.907	0.050	12.000	11.966	0.016	12.000	11.983	0.006	12.000	11.989	0.000
16	MAX	16.110	15.905	0.315	16.043	15.950	0.136	16.027	15.984	0.061	16.018	15.994	0.035	16.018	16.000	0.029
	MIN	16.000	15.795	0.095	16.000	15.907	0.050	16.000	15.966	0.016	16.000	15.983	0.006	16.000	15.989	0.000
20	MAX	20.130	19.890	0.370	20.052	19.935	0.169	20.033	19.980	0.074	20.021	19.993	0.041	20.021	20.000	0.034
	MIN	20.000	19.760	0.110	20.000	19.883	0.065	20.000	19.959	0.020	20.000	19.980	0.007	20.000	19.987	0.000
25	MAX	25.130	24.890	0.370	25.052	24.935	0.169	25.033	24.980	0.074	25.021	24.993	0.041	25.021	25.000	0.034
	MIN	25.000	24.760	0.110	25.000	24.883	0.065	25.000	24.959	0.020	25.000	24.980	0.007	25.000	24.987	0.000
30	MAX	30.130	29.890	0.370	30.052	29.935	0.169	30.033	29.980	0.074	30.021	29.993	0.041	30.021	30.000	0.034
	MIN	30.000	29.760	0.110	30.000	29.883	0.065	30.000	29.959	0.020	30.000	29.980	0.007	30.000	29.987	0.000

Reprinted from ASME B18.2.1-1981 (R1992), B18.2.2-1987 (R1993), B18.3-1986 (R1993), B18.6.2-1972 (R1993), B18.6.3-1972 (R1991), B18.21.1-1994, B18.22.1-1965 (R1990), B17.1-1967 (R1998), B17.2-1967 (R1990) and B4.2-1978 (R1994), by permission of The American Society of Mechanical Engineers. All rights reserved. ANSI B4.2-1978

Metric Limits and Fits.

RUNNING AND SLIDING FITS

VALUES IN THOUSANDTHS OF AN INCH

Nominal Size Range Inches		Class RC1 Precision Sliding			Class RC2 Sliding Fit			Class RC3 Precision Running			Class RC4 Close Running			Class RC5 Medium Running		
		Hole Tol. GR5	Minimum Clearance	Shaft Tol. GR4	Hole Tol. GR6	Minimum Clearance	Shaft Tol. GR5	Hole Tol. GR7	Minimum Clearance	Shaft Tol. GR6	Hole Tol. GR8	Minimum Clearance	Shaft Tol. GR7	Hole Tol. GR8	Minimum Clearance	Shaft Tol. GR7
Over	To	-0		+0	-0		+0	-0		+0	-0		+0	-0		+0
0	.12	+0.15	0.10	-0.12	+0.25	0.10	-0.15	+0.40	0.30	-0.25	+0.60	0.30	-0.40	+0.60	0.60	-0.40
.12	.24	+0.20	0.15	-0.15	+0.30	0.15	-0.20	+0.50	0.40	-0.30	+0.70	0.40	-0.50	+0.70	0.80	-0.50
.24	.40	+0.25	0.20	-0.15	+0.40	0.20	-0.25	+0.60	0.50	-0.40	+0.90	0.50	-0.60	+0.90	1.00	-0.60
.40	.71	+0.30	0.25	-0.20	+0.40	0.25	-0.30	+0.70	0.60	-0.40	+1.00	0.60	-0.70	+1.00	1.20	-0.70
.71	1.19	+0.40	0.30	-0.25	+0.50	0.30	-0.40	+0.80	0.80	-0.50	+1.20	0.80	-0.80	+1.20	1.60	-0.80
1.19	1.97	+0.40	0.40	-0.30	+0.60	0.40	-0.40	+1.00	1.00	-0.60	+1.60	1.00	-1.00	+1.60	2.00	-1.00
1.97	3.15	+0.50	0.40	-0.30	+0.70	0.40	-0.50	+1.20	1.20	-0.70	+1.80	1.20	-1.20	+1.80	2.50	-1.20
3.15	4.73	+0.60	0.50	-0.40	+0.90	0.50	-0.60	+1.40	1.40	-0.90	+2.20	1.40	-1.40	+2.20	3.00	-1.40
4.73	7.09	+0.70	0.60	-0.50	+1.00	0.60	-0.70	+1.60	1.60	-1.00	+2.50	1.60	-1.60	+2.50	3.50	-1.60
7.09	9.85	+0.80	0.60	-0.60	+1.20	0.60	-0.80	+1.80	2.00	-1.20	+2.80	2.00	-1.80	+2.80	4.50	-1.80
9.85	12.41	+0.90	0.80	-0.60	+1.20	0.80	-0.90	+2.00	2.50	-1.20	+3.00	2.50	-2.00	+3.00	5.00	-2.00
12.41	15.75	+1.00	1.00	-0.70	+1.40	1.00	-1.00	+2.20	3.00	-1.40	+3.50	3.00	-2.20	+3.50	6.00	-2.20

Nominal Size Range Inches		Class RC6 Medium Running			Class RC7 Free Running			Class RC8 Loose Running			Class RC9 Loose Running		
		Hole Tol. GR9	Minimum Clearance	Shaft Tol. GR8	Hole Tol. GR9	Minimum Clearance	Shaft Tol. GR8	Hole Tol. GR10	Minimum Clearance	Shaft Tol. GR9	Hole Tol. GR11	Minimum Clearance	Shaft Tol. GR10
Over	To	-0		+0	-0		+0	-0		+0	-0		+0
0	.12	+1.00	0.60	-0.60	+1.00	1.00	-0.60	+1.60	2.50	-1.00	+2.50	4.00	-1.60
.12	.24	+1.20	0.80	-0.70	+1.20	1.20	-0.70	+1.80	2.80	-1.20	+3.00	4.50	-1.80
.24	.40	+1.40	1.00	-0.90	+1.40	1.60	-0.90	+2.20	3.00	-1.40	+3.50	6.00	-2.20
.40	.71	+1.60	1.20	-1.00	+1.60	2.00	-1.00	+2.80	3.50	-1.60	+4.00	6.00	-2.80
.71	1.19	+2.00	1.60	-1.20	+2.00	2.50	-1.20	+3.50	4.50	-2.00	+5.00	7.00	-3.50
1.19	1.97	+2.50	2.00	-1.60	+2.50	3.00	-1.60	+4.00	5.00	-2.50	+6.00	8.00	-4.00
1.97	3.15	+3.00	2.50	-1.80	+3.00	4.00	-1.80	+4.50	6.00	-3.00	+7.00	9.00	-4.50
3.15	4.73	+3.50	3.00	-2.20	+3.50	5.00	-2.20	+5.00	7.00	-3.50	+9.00	10.00	-5.00
4.73	7.09	+4.00	3.50	-2.50	+4.00	6.00	-2.50	+6.00	8.00	-4.00	+10.00	12.00	-6.00
7.09	9.85	+4.50	4.00	-2.80	+4.50	7.00	-2.80	+7.00	10.00	-4.50	+12.00	15.00	-7.00
9.85	12.41	+5.00	5.00	-3.00	+5.00	8.00	-3.00	+8.00	12.00	-5.00	+12.00	18.00	-8.00
12.41	15.75	+6.00	6.00	-3.50	+6.00	10.00	-3.50	+9.00	14.00	-6.00	+14.00	22.00	-9.00

VALUES IN MILLIMETERS

Nominal Size Range Millimeters		Class RC1 Precision Sliding			Class RC2 Sliding Fit			Class RC3 Precision Running			Class RC4 Close Running			Class RC5 Medium Running		
		Hole Tol. H5	Minimum Clearance	Shaft Tol. g4	Hole Tol. H6	Minimum Clearance	Shaft Tol. g5	Hole Tol. H7	Minimum Clearance	Shaft Tol. f6	Hole Tol. H8	Minimum Clearance	Shaft Tol. f7	Hole Tol. H8	Minimum Clearance	Shaft Tol. e7
Over	To	-0		+0	-0		+0	-0		+0	-0		+0	-0		+0
0	3	+0.004	0.003	-0.003	+0.006	0.003	-0.004	+0.010	0.008	-0.006	+0.015	0.008	-0.010	+0.015	0.015	-0.010
3	6	+0.005	0.004	-0.004	+0.008	0.004	-0.005	+0.013	0.010	-0.008	+0.018	0.010	-0.013	+0.018	0.020	-0.013
6	10	+0.006	0.005	-0.004	+0.010	0.005	-0.006	+0.015	0.013	-0.010	+0.023	0.013	-0.015	+0.023	0.025	-0.015
10	18	+0.008	0.006	-0.005	+0.010	0.006	-0.008	+0.018	0.015	-0.010	+0.025	0.015	-0.018	+0.025	0.030	-0.018
18	30	+0.010	0.008	-0.006	+0.013	0.008	-0.010	+0.020	0.020	-0.013	+0.030	0.020	-0.020	+0.030	0.040	-0.020
30	50	+0.010	0.010	-0.008	+0.015	0.010	-0.010	+0.030	0.030	-0.015	+0.040	0.030	-0.030	+0.040	0.050	-0.030
50	80	+0.013	0.010	-0.008	+0.018	0.010	-0.013	+0.030	0.030	-0.020	+0.050	0.030	-0.030	+0.050	0.060	-0.030
80	120	+0.015	0.013	-0.010	+0.023	0.013	-0.015	+0.040	0.040	-0.020	+0.060	0.040	-0.040	+0.060	0.080	-0.040
120	180	+0.018	0.015	-0.013	+0.025	0.015	-0.018	+0.040	0.040	-0.030	+0.060	0.040	-0.040	+0.060	0.090	-0.040
180	250	+0.020	0.015	-0.015	+0.030	0.015	-0.020	+0.050	0.050	-0.030	+0.070	0.050	-0.050	+0.070	0.110	-0.050
250	315	+0.023	0.020	-0.015	+0.030	0.020	-0.023	+0.050	0.060	-0.030	+0.080	0.060	-0.050	+0.080	0.130	-0.050
315	400	+0.025	0.025	-0.018	+0.036	0.025	-0.025	+0.060	0.080	-0.040	+0.090	0.080	-0.060	+0.090	0.150	-0.060

Nominal Size Range Millimeters		Class RC6 Medium Running			Class RC7 Free Running			Class RC8 Loose Running			Class RC9 Loose Running		
		Hole Tol. H9	Minimum Clearance	Shaft Tol. e8	Hole Tol. H9	Minimum Clearance	Shaft Tol. d8	Hole Tol. H10	Minimum Clearance	Shaft Tol. e9	Hole Tol. GR11	Minimum Clearance	Shaft Tol. gr10
Over	To	-0		+0	-0		+0	-0		+0	-0		+0
0	3	+0.025	0.015	-0.015	+0.025	0.025	-0.015	+0.041	0.064	-0.025	+0.060	0.100	-0.040
3	6	+0.030	0.015	-0.018	+0.030	0.030	-0.018	+0.046	0.071	-0.030	+0.080	0.110	-0.050
6	10	+0.036	0.025	-0.023	+0.036	0.040	-0.023	+0.056	0.076	-0.036	+0.070	0.130	-0.060
10	18	+0.040	0.030	-0.025	+0.040	0.050	-0.025	+0.070	0.090	-0.040	+0.100	0.150	-0.070
18	30	+0.050	0.040	-0.030	+0.050	0.060	-0.030	+0.090	0.110	-0.050	+0.130	0.180	-0.090
30	50	+0.060	0.050	-0.040	+0.060	0.080	-0.040	+0.100	0.130	-0.060	+0.150	0.200	-0.100
50	80	+0.080	0.060	-0.050	+0.080	0.100	-0.050	+0.110	0.150	-0.080	+0.180	0.230	-0.120
80	120	+0.090	0.080	-0.060	+0.090	0.130	-0.060	+0.130	0.180	-0.090	+0.230	0.250	-0.130
120	180	+0.100	0.090	-0.060	+0.100	0.150	-0.060	+0.150	0.200	-0.100	+0.250	0.300	-0.150
180	250	+0.110	0.100	-0.070	+0.110	0.180	-0.070	+0.180	0.250	-0.110	+0.300	0.380	-0.180
250	315	+0.130	0.130	-0.080	+0.130	0.200	-0.080	+0.200	0.300	-0.130	+0.300	0.460	-0.200
315	400	+0.150	0.150	-0.090	+0.150	0.250	-0.090	+0.230	0.360	-0.150	+0.360	0.560	-0.230

Running and Sliding Fits.

LOCATIONAL CLEARANCE FITS

VALUES IN THOUSANDTHS OF AN INCH

Nominal Size Range Inches		Class LC1			Class LC2			Class LC3			Class LC4			Class LC5			Class LC6		
		Hole Tol. GR6	Minimum Clearance	Shaft Tol. GR5	Hole Tol. GR8	Minimum Clearance	Shaft Tol. GR7	Hole Tol. GR10	Minimum Clearance	Shaft Tol. GR9	Hole Tol. GR7	Minimum Clearance	Shaft Tol. GR6	Hole Tol. GR9	Minimum Clearance	Shaft Tol. GR8	Hole Tol. GR9	Minimum Clearance	Shaft Tol. GR8
Over	To	-0		+0	-0		+0	-0		+0	-0		+0	-0		+0	-0		+0
0	.12	+0.25	0	-0.15	+0.4	0	-0.25	+0.6	0	-0.4	+1.6	0	-1.0	+0.4	0.10	-0.25	+1.0	0.3	-0.6
.12	.24	+0.30	0	-0.20	+0.5	0	-0.30	+0.7	0	-0.5	+1.8	0	-1.2	+0.5	0.15	-0.30	+1.2	0.4	-0.7
.24	.40	+0.40	0	-0.25	+0.6	0	-0.40	+0.9	0	-0.6	+2.2	0	-1.4	+0.6	0.20	-0.40	+1.4	0.5	-0.9
.40	.71	+0.40	0	-0.30	+0.7	0	-0.40	+1.0	0	-0.7	+2.8	0	-1.6	+0.7	0.25	-0.40	+1.6	0.6	-1.0
.71	1.19	+0.50	0	-0.40	+0.8	0	-0.50	+1.2	0	-0.8	+3.5	0	-2.0	+0.8	0.30	-0.50	+2.0	0.8	-1.2
1.19	1.97	+0.60	0	-0.40	+1.0	0	-0.60	+1.6	0	-1.0	+4.0	0	-2.5	+1.0	0.40	-0.60	+2.5	1.0	-1.6
1.97	3.15	+0.70	0	-0.50	+1.2	0	-0.70	+1.8	0	-1.2	+4.5	0	-3.0	+1.2	0.40	-0.70	+3.0	1.2	-1.8
3.15	4.73	+0.90	0	-0.60	+1.4	0	-0.90	+2.2	0	-1.4	+5.0	0	-3.5	+1.4	0.50	-0.90	+3.5	1.6	-2.2
4.73	7.09	+1.00	0	-0.70	+1.6	0	-1.00	+2.5	0	-1.6	+6.0	0	-4.0	+1.6	0.60	-1.00	+4.0	1.6	-2.5
7.09	9.85	+1.20	0	-0.80	+1.8	0	-1.20	+2.8	0	-1.8	+7.0	0	-4.5	+1.8	0.60	-1.20	+4.5	2.0	-2.8
9.85	12.41	+1.20	0	-0.90	+2.0	0	-1.20	+3.0	0	-2.0	+8.0	0	-5.0	+2.0	0.70	-1.20	+5.0	2.2	-3.0
12.41	15.75	+1.40	0	-1.00	+2.2	0	-1.40	+3.5	0	-2.2	+9.0	0	-6.0	+2.2	0.70	-1.40	+6.0	2.5	-3.5

Nominal Size Range Inches		Class LC7			Class LC8			Class LC9			Class LC10			Class LC11		
		Hole Tol. GR10	Minimum Clearance	Shaft Tol. GR9	Hole Tol. GR10	Minimum Clearance	Shaft Tol. GR9	Hole Tol. GR11	Minimum Clearance	Shaft Tol. GR10	Hole Tol. GR12	Minimum Clearance	Shaft Tol. GR11	Hole Tol. GR13	Minimum Clearance	Shaft Tol. GR12
Over	To	-0		+0	-0		+0	-0		+0	-0		+0	-0		+0
0	.12	+1.6	0.6	-1.0	+1.6	1.0	-1.0	+2.5	2.5	-1.6	+4.0	4.0	-2.5	+6.0	5.0	-4.0
.12	.24	+1.8	0.8	-1.2	+1.8	1.2	-1.2	+3.0	2.8	-1.8	+5.0	4.5	-3.0	+7.0	6.0	-5.0
.24	.40	+2.2	1.0	-1.4	+2.2	1.6	-1.4	+3.5	3.0	-2.2	+6.0	5.0	-3.5	+9.0	7.0	-6.0
.40	.71	+2.8	1.2	-1.6	+2.8	2.0	-1.6	+4.0	3.5	-2.8	+7.0	6.0	-4.0	+10.0	8.0	-7.0
.71	1.19	+3.5	1.6	-2.0	+3.5	2.5	-2.0	+5.0	4.5	-3.5	+8.0	7.0	-5.0	+12.0	10.0	-8.0
1.19	1.97	+4.0	2.0	-2.5	+4.0	3.6	-2.5	+6.0	5.0	-4.0	+10.0	8.0	-6.0	+16.0	12.0	-10.0
1.97	3.15	+4.5	2.5	-3.0	+4.5	4.0	-3.0	+7.0	6.0	-4.5	+12.0	10.0	-7.0	+18.0	14.0	-12.0
3.15	4.73	+5.0	3.0	-3.5	+5.0	5.0	-3.5	+9.0	7.0	-5.0	+14.0	11.0	-9.0	+22.0	16.0	-14.0
4.73	7.09	+6.0	3.5	-4.0	+6.0	6.0	-4.0	+10.0	8.0	-6.0	+16.0	12.0	-10.0	+25.0	18.0	-16.0
7.09	9.85	+7.0	4.0	-4.5	+7.0	7.0	-4.5	+12.0	10.0	-7.0	+18.0	16.0	-12.0	+28.0	22.0	-18.0
9.85	12.41	+8.0	4.5	-5.0	+8.0	7.0	-5.0	+12.0	12.0	-8.0	+20.0	20.0	-12.0	+30.0	28.0	-20.0
12.41	15.75	+9.0	5.0	-6.0	+9.0	8.0	-6.0	+14.0	14.0	-9.0	+22.0	22.0	-14.0	+35.0	30.0	-22.0

VALUES IN MILLIMETERS

Nominal Size Range Millimeters		Class LC1			Class LC2			Class LC3			Class LC4			Class LC5			Class LC6		
		Hole Tol. H6	Minimum Clearance	Shaft Tol. h5	Hole Tol. H7	Minimum Clearance	Shaft Tol. h6	Hole Tol. H8	Minimum Clearance	Shaft Tol. h7	Hole Tol. H10	Minimum Clearance	Shaft Tol. h9	Hole Tol. H7	Minimum Clearance	Shaft Tol. g6	Hole Tol. H9	Minimum Clearance	Shaft Tol. f8
Over	To	-0		+0	-0		+0	-0		+0	-0		+0	-0		+0	-0		+0
0	3	+0.006	0	-0.004	+0.010	0	-0.006	+0.015	0	-0.010	+0.041	0	-0.025	+0.010	0.002	-0.006	+0.025	0.008	-0.015
3	6	+0.008	0	-0.005	+0.013	0	-0.008	+0.018	0	-0.013	+0.046	0	-0.030	+0.013	0.004	-0.008	+0.030	0.010	-0.018
6	10	+0.010	0	-0.006	+0.015	0	-0.010	+0.023	0	-0.015	+0.056	0	-0.036	+0.015	0.005	-0.010	+0.036	0.013	-0.023
10	18	+0.010	0	-0.008	+0.018	0	-0.010	+0.025	0	-0.018	+0.070	0	-0.040	+0.018	0.006	-0.010	+0.041	0.015	-0.025
18	30	+0.013	0	-0.010	+0.020	0	-0.013	+0.030	0	-0.020	+0.090	0	-0.050	+0.020	0.008	-0.013	+0.050	0.020	-0.030
30	50	+0.015	0	-0.010	+0.025	0	-0.015	+0.041	0	-0.025	+0.100	0	-0.060	+0.025	0.010	-0.015	+0.060	0.030	-0.040
50	80	+0.018	0	-0.013	+0.030	0	-0.018	+0.046	0	-0.030	+0.110	0	-0.080	+0.030	0.010	-0.018	+0.080	0.030	-0.050
80	120	+0.023	0	-0.015	+0.036	0	-0.023	+0.056	0	-0.036	+0.130	0	-0.080	+0.036	0.013	-0.023	+0.090	0.040	-0.060
120	180	+0.025	0	-0.018	+0.041	0	-0.025	+0.064	0	-0.041	+0.150	0	-0.100	+0.041	0.015	-0.025	+0.100	0.040	-0.060
180	250	+0.030	0	-0.020	+0.046	0	-0.030	+0.071	0	-0.046	+0.180	0	-0.110	+0.046	0.015	-0.030	+0.110	0.050	-0.070
250	315	+0.020	0	-0.023	+0.051	0	-0.030	+0.076	0	-0.051	+0.200	0	-0.130	+0.051	0.018	-0.030	+0.130	0.060	-0.080
315	400	+0.036	0	-0.025	+0.056	0	-0.036	+0.089	0	-0.056	+0.230	0	-0.150	+0.056	0.018	-0.036	+0.150	0.060	-0.090

Nominal Size Range Millimeters		Class LC7			Class LC8			Class LC9			Class LC10			Class LC11		
		Hole Tol. H10	Minimum Clearance	Shaft Tol. e9	Hole Tol. H10	Minimum Clearance	Shaft Tol. d9	Hole Tol. H11	Minimum Clearance	Shaft Tol. c10	Hole Tol. GR12	Minimum Clearance	Shaft Tol. gr11	Hole Tol. GR13	Minimum Clearance	Shaft Tol. gr12
Over	To	-0		+0	-0		+0	-0		+0	-0		+0	-0		+0
0	3	+0.041	0.015	-0.025	+0.041	0.025	-0.025	+0.064	0.06	-0.041	+0.10	0.10	-0.06	+0.15	0.13	-0.10
3	6	+0.046	0.020	-0.030	+0.046	0.030	-0.030	+0.076	0.07	-0.46	+0.13	0.11	-0.08	+0.18	0.15	-0.13
6	10	+0.056	0.025	-0.036	+0.056	0.041	-0.036	+0.089	0.08	-0.56	+0.15	0.13	-0.09	+0.23	0.18	-0.15
10	18	+0.070	0.030	-0.040	+0.070	0.050	-0.040	+0.100	0.09	-0.70	+0.18	0.15	-0.10	+0.25	0.20	-0.18
18	30	+0.090	0.040	-0.050	+0.090	0.060	-0.050	+0.130	0.11	-0.90	+0.20	0.18	-0.13	+0.31	0.25	-0.20
30	50	+0.100	0.050	-0.060	+0.100	0.090	-0.060	+0.150	0.13	-0.100	+0.25	0.20	-0.15	+0.41	0.31	-0.25
50	80	+0.110	0.060	-0.080	+0.110	0.100	-0.080	+0.180	0.15	-0.110	+0.31	0.25	-0.18	+0.46	0.36	-0.31
80	120	+0.130	0.080	-0.090	+0.130	0.130	-0.090	+0.230	0.18	-0.130	+0.36	0.28	-0.23	+0.56	0.41	-0.36
120	180	+0.150	0.090	-0.100	+0.150	0.150	-0.100	+0.250	0.20	-0.150	+0.41	0.31	-0.25	+0.64	0.46	-0.41
180	250	+0.180	0.100	-0.110	+0.180	0.180	-0.110	+0.310	0.25	-0.180	+0.46	0.41	-0.31	+0.71	0.56	-0.46
250	315	+0.200	0.110	-0.130	+0.200	0.180	-0.130	+0.310	0.31	-0.200	+0.51	0.51	-0.31	+0.76	0.71	-0.51
315	400	+0.230	0.130	-0.150	+0.230	0.200	-0.150	+0.360	0.36	-0.230	+0.56	0.56	-0.36	+0.89	0.76	-0.56

Running and Sliding Fits. (CONTINUED)

LOCATIONAL TRANSITION FITS

VALUES IN THOUSANDTHS OF AN INCH

Nominal Size Range Inches		Class LT1			Class LT2			Class LT3			Class LT4			Class LT5			Class LT6		
		Hole Tol. GR7	Maximum Interference	Shaft Tol. GR6	Hole Tol. GR8	Maximum Interference	Shaft Tol. GR7	Hole Tol. GR7	Maximum Interference	Shaft Tol. GR6	Hole Tol. GR8	Maximum Interference	Shaft Tol. GR7	Hole Tol. GR7	Maximum Interference	Shaft Tol. GR6	Hole Tol. GR8	Maximum Interference	Shaft Tol. GR7
Over	To	-0		+0	-0		+0	-0		+0	-0		+0	-0		+0	-0		+0
0	.12	+0.4	0.10	-0.25	+0.6	0.20	-0.4	+0.4	0.25	-0.25	+0.6	0.4	-0.4	+0.4	0.5	-0.25	+0.6	0.65	-0.4
.12	.24	+0.5	0.15	-0.30	+0.7	0.25	-0.5	+0.5	0.40	-0.30	+0.7	0.6	-0.5	+0.5	0.6	-0.30	+0.7	0.80	-0.5
.24	.40	+0.6	0.20	-0.40	+0.9	0.30	-0.6	+0.6	0.50	-0.40	+0.9	0.7	-0.6	+0.6	0.8	-0.40	+0.9	1.00	-0.6
.40	.71	+0.7	0.20	-0.40	+1.0	0.30	-0.7	+0.7	0.50	-0.40	+1.0	0.8	-0.7	+0.7	0.9	-0.40	+1.0	1.20	-0.7
.71	1.19	+0.8	0.25	-0.50	+1.2	0.40	-0.8	+0.8	0.60	-0.50	+1.2	0.9	-0.8	+0.8	1.1	-0.50	+1.2	1.40	-0.8
1.19	1.97	+1.0	0.30	-0.60	+1.6	0.50	-1.0	+1.0	0.70	-0.60	+1.6	1.1	-1.0	+1.0	1.3	-0.60	+1.6	1.70	-1.0
1.97	3.15	+1.2	0.30	-0.70	+1.8	0.60	-1.2	+1.2	0.80	-0.70	+1.8	1.3	-1.2	+1.2	1.5	-0.70	+1.8	2.00	-1.2
3.15	4.73	+1.4	0.40	-0.90	+2.2	0.70	-1.4	+1.4	1.00	-0.90	+2.2	1.5	-1.4	+1.4	1.9	-0.90	+2.2	2.40	-1.4
4.73	7.09	+1.6	0.50	-1.00	+2.5	0.80	-1.6	+1.6	1.10	-1.00	+2.5	1.7	-1.6	+1.6	2.2	-1.00	+2.5	2.80	-1.6
7.09	9.85	+1.8	0.60	-1.20	+2.8	0.90	-1.8	+1.8	1.40	-1.20	+2.8	2.0	-1.8	+1.8	2.6	-1.20	+2.8	3.20	-1.8
9.85	12.41	+2.0	0.60	-1.20	+3.0	1.00	-2.0	+2.0	1.40	-1.20	+3.0	2.2	-2.0	+2.0	2.6	-1.20	+3.0	3.40	-2.0
12.41	15.75	+2.2	0.70	-1.40	+3.5	1.00	-2.2	+2.2	1.60	-1.40	+3.5	2.4	-2.2	+2.2	3.0	-1.40	+3.5	3.80	-2.2

VALUES IN MILLIMETERS

Nominal Size Range Millimeters		Class LT1			Class LT2			Class LT3			Class LT4			Class LT5			Class LT6		
		Hole Tol. H7	Maximum Clearance	Shaft Tol. js6	Hole Tol. H8	Maximum Clearance	Shaft Tol. js7	Hole Tol. H7	Maximum Clearance	Shaft Tol. k6	Hole Tol. H8	Maximum Clearance	Shaft Tol. k7	Hole Tol. H7	Maximum Clearance	Shaft Tol. n6	Hole Tol. H8	Maximum Clearance	Shaft Tol. n7
Over	To	-0		+0	-0		+0	-0		+0	-0		+0	-0		+0	-0		+0
0	3	+0.010	0.002	-0.006	+0.015	0.005	-0.010	+0.010	0.006	-0.006	+0.015	0.010	-0.010	+0.010	0.013	-0.006	+0.015	0.016	-0.010
3	6	+0.013	0.004	-0.008	+0.018	0.006	-0.013	+0.013	0.010	-0.008	+0.018	0.015	-0.013	+0.013	0.015	-0.008	+0.018	0.020	-0.013
6	10	+0.015	0.005	-0.010	+0.023	0.008	-0.015	+0.015	0.013	-0.010	+0.023	0.018	-0.015	+0.015	0.020	-0.010	+0.023	0.025	-0.015
10	18	+0.018	0.005	-0.010	+0.025	0.008	-0.018	+0.018	0.013	-0.010	+0.025	0.020	-0.018	+0.018	0.023	-0.010	+0.025	0.030	-0.018
18	30	+0.020	0.006	-0.013	+0.030	0.010	-0.020	+0.020	0.015	-0.013	+0.030	0.023	-0.020	+0.020	0.028	-0.013	+0.030	0.036	-0.020
30	50	+0.025	0.008	-0.015	+0.041	0.013	-0.025	+0.025	0.018	-0.015	+0.041	0.028	-0.025	+0.025	0.033	-0.015	+0.041	0.044	-0.025
50	80	+0.030	0.008	-0.018	+0.046	0.015	-0.030	+0.030	0.020	-0.018	+0.046	0.033	-0.030	+0.030	0.038	-0.018	+0.046	0.051	-0.030
80	120	+0.036	0.010	-0.023	+0.056	0.018	-0.036	+0.036	0.025	-0.023	+0.056	0.038	-0.036	+0.036	0.048	-0.023	+0.056	0.062	-0.036
120	180	+0.041	0.013	-0.025	+0.064	0.020	-0.041	+0.041	0.028	-0.025	+0.064	0.044	-0.041	+0.041	0.056	-0.025	+0.064	0.071	-0.041
180	250	+0.046	0.015	-0.030	+0.071	0.023	-0.046	+0.046	0.036	-0.030	+0.071	0.051	-0.046	+0.046	0.066	-0.030	+0.071	0.081	-0.046
250	315	+0.051	0.015	-0.030	+0.076	0.025	-0.051	+0.051	0.036	-0.030	+0.076	0.056	-0.051	+0.051	0.066	-0.030	+0.076	0.086	-0.051
315	400	+0.056	0.018	-0.036	+0.089	0.025	-0.056	+0.056	0.041	-0.036	+0.089	0.062	-0.056	+0.056	0.076	-0.036	+0.089	0.096	-0.056

Running and Sliding Fits. (CONTINUED)

LOCATIONAL INTERFERENCE FITS

VALUES IN THOUSANDTHS OF AN INCH

Nominal Size Range Inches		Class LN1 Light Press Fit			Class LN2 Medium Press Fit			Class LN3 Heavy Press Fit			Class LN4			Class LN5			Class LN6		
		Hole Tol. GR6	Maximum Interference	Shaft Tol. GR5	Hole Tol. GR7	Maximum Interference	Shaft Tol. GR6	Hole Tol. GR7	Maximum Interference	Shaft Tol. GR6	Hole Tol. GR8	Maximum Interference	Shaft Tol. GR7	Hole Tol. GR9	Maximum Interference	Shaft Tol. GR8	Hole Tol. GR10	Maximum Interference	Shaft Tol. GR9
Over	To	-0		+0	-0		+0	-0		+0	-0		+0	-0		+0	-0		+0
0	.12	+0.25	0.40	-0.15	+0.4	0.65	-0.25	+0.4	0.75	-0.25	+0.6	1.2	-0.4	+1.0	1.8	-0.6	+1.6	3.0	-1.0
.12	.24	+0.30	0.50	-0.20	+0.5	0.80	-0.30	+0.5	0.90	-0.30	+0.7	1.5	-0.5	+1.2	2.3	-0.7	+1.8	3.6	-1.2
.24	.40	+0.40	0.65	-0.25	+0.6	1.00	-0.40	+0.6	1.20	-0.40	+0.9	1.8	-0.6	+1.4	2.8	-0.9	+2.2	4.4	-1.4
.40	.71	+0.40	0.70	-0.30	+0.7	1.10	-0.40	+0.7	1.40	-0.40	+1.0	2.2	-0.7	+1.6	3.4	-1.0	+2.8	5.6	-1.6
.71	1.19	+0.50	0.90	-0.40	+0.8	1.30	-0.50	+0.8	1.70	-0.50	+1.2	2.6	-0.8	+2.0	4.2	-1.2	+3.5	7.0	-2.0
1.19	1.97	+0.60	1.00	-0.40	+1.0	1.60	-0.60	+1.0	2.00	-0.60	+1.6	3.4	-1.0	+2.5	5.3	-1.6	+4.0	8.5	-2.5
1.97	3.15	+0.70	1.30	-0.50	+1.2	2.10	-0.70	+1.2	2.30	-0.70	+1.8	4.0	-1.2	+3.0	6.3	-1.8	+4.5	10.0	-3.0
3.15	4.73	+0.90	1.60	-0.60	+1.4	2.50	-0.90	+1.4	2.90	-0.90	+2.2	4.8	-1.4	+4.0	7.7	-2.2	+5.0	11.5	-3.5
4.73	7.09	+1.00	1.90	-0.70	+1.6	2.80	-1.00	+1.6	3.50	-1.00	+2.5	5.6	-1.6	+4.5	8.7	-2.5	+6.0	13.5	-4.0
7.09	9.85	+1.20	2.20	-0.80	+1.8	3.20	-1.20	+1.8	4.20	-1.20	+2.8	6.6	-1.8	+5.0	10.3	-2.8	+7.0	16.5	-4.5
9.85	12.41	+1.20	2.30	-0.90	+2.0	3.40	-1.20	+2.0	4.70	-1.20	+3.0	7.5	-2.0	+6.0	12.0	-3.0	+8.0	19.0	-5.0
12.41	15.75	+1.40	2.60	-1.00	+2.2	3.90	-1.40	+2.2	5.90	-1.40	+3.5	8.7	-2.2	+6.0	14.5	-3.5	+9.0	23.0	-6.0

VALUES IN MILLIMETERS

Nominal Size Range Millimeters		Class LN1 Light Press Fit			Class LN2 Medium Press Fit			Class LN3 Heavy Press Fit			Class LN4			Class LN5			Class LN6		
		Hole Tol. GR6	Maximum Interference	Shaft Tol. gr5	Hole Tol. H7	Maximum Interference	Shaft Tol. p6	Hole Tol. H7	Maximum Interference	Shaft Tol. t6	Hole Tol. GR8	Maximum Interference	Shaft Tol. gr7	Hole Tol. GR9	Maximum Interference	Shaft Tol. gr8	Hole Tol. GR10	Maximum Interference	Shaft Tol. gr9
Over	To	-0		+0	-0		+0	-0		+0	-0		+0	-0		+0	-0		+0
0	3	+0.006		-0.004	+0.010	0.016	-0.006	+0.010	0.019	-0.006	+0.015	0.030	-0.010	+0.025	0.046	-0.015	+0.041	0.076	-0.025
3	6	+0.008		-0.005	+0.013	0.020	-0.008	+0.013	0.023	-0.008	+0.018	0.038	-0.013	+0.030	0.059	-0.018	+0.046	0.091	-0.030
6	10	+0.010		-0.006	+0.015	0.025	-0.010	+0.015	0.030	-0.010	+0.023	0.046	-0.015	+0.036	0.071	-0.023	+0.056	0.112	-0.036
10	18	+0.010		-0.008	+0.018	0.028	-0.010	+0.018	0.036	-0.010	+0.025	0.056	-0.018	+0.041	0.086	-0.025	+0.071	0.142	-0.041
18	30	+0.013		-0.010	+0.020	0.033	-0.013	+0.020	0.044	-0.013	+0.030	0.066	-0.020	+0.051	0.107	-0.030	+0.089	0.178	-0.051
30	50	+0.015		-0.010	+0.025	0.041	-0.015	+0.025	0.051	-0.015	+0.041	0.086	-0.025	+0.064	0.135	-0.041	+0.102	0.216	-0.064
50	80	+0.018		-0.013	+0.030	0.054	-0.018	+0.030	0.059	-0.018	+0.046	0.102	-0.030	+0.076	0.160	-0.046	+0.114	0.254	-0.076
80	120	+0.023		-0.015	+0.036	0.064	-0.023	+0.036	0.074	-0.023	+0.056	0.122	-0.036	+0.102	0.196	-0.056	+0.127	0.292	-0.102
120	180	+0.025		-0.018	+0.041	0.071	-0.025	+0.041	0.089	-0.025	+0.064	0.142	-0.041	+0.114	0.221	-0.064	+0.152	0.343	-0.114
180	250	+0.030		-0.020	+0.046	0.081	-0.030	+0.046	0.107	-0.030	+0.071	0.168	-0.046	+0.127	0.262	-0.071	+0.178	0.419	-0.127
250	315	+0.030		-0.023	+0.051	0.086	-0.030	+0.051	0.119	-0.030	+0.076	0.191	-0.051	+0.152	0.305	-0.076	+0.203	0.483	-0.152
315	400	+0.036		-0.025	+0.056	0.099	-0.036	+0.056	0.150	-0.036	+0.089	0.221	-0.056	+0.152	0.368	-0.089	+0.229	0.584	-0.152

Running and Sliding Fits. (CONTINUED)

FORCE AND SHRINK FITS

VALUES IN THOUSANDTHS OF AN INCH

Nominal Size Range Inches		Class FN1 Light Drive Fit			Class FN2 Medium Drive Fit			Class FN3 Heavy Drive Fit			Class FN4 Shrink Fit			Class FN5 Heavy Shrink Fit		
Over	To	Hole Tol. GR6 -0	Maximum Interference	Shaft Tol. GR5 +0	Hole Tol. GR7 -0	Maximum Interference	Shaft Tol. GR6 +0	Hole Tol. GR7 -0	Maximum Interference	Shaft Tol. GR6 +0	Hole Tol. GR7 -0	Maximum Interference	Shaft Tol. GR6 +0	Hole Tol. GR8 -0	Maximum Interference	Shaft Tol. GR7 +0
0	.12	+0.25	0.50	-0.15	+0.40	0.85	-0.25				+0.40	0.95	-0.25	+0.60	1.30	-0.40
.12	.24	+0.30	0.60	-0.20	+0.50	1.00	-0.30				+0.50	1.20	-0.30	+0.70	1.70	-0.50
.24	.40	+0.40	0.75	-0.25	+0.60	1.40	-0.40				+0.60	1.60	-0.40	+0.90	2.00	-0.60
.40	.56	+0.40	0.80	-0.30	+0.70	1.60	-0.40				+0.70	1.80	-0.40	+1.00	2.30	-0.70
.56	.71	+0.40	0.90	-0.30	+0.70	1.60	-0.40				+0.70	1.80	-0.40	+1.00	2.50	-0.70
.71	.95	+0.50	1.10	-0.40	+0.80	1.90	-0.50				+0.80	2.10	-0.50	+1.20	3.00	-0.80
.95	1.19	+0.50	1.20	-0.40	+0.80	1.90	-0.50	+0.80	2.10	-0.50	+0.80	2.30	-0.50	+1.20	3.30	-0.80
1.19	1.58	+0.60	1.30	-0.40	+1.00	2.40	-0.60	+1.00	2.60	-0.60	+1.00	3.10	-0.60	+1.60	4.00	-1.00
1.58	1.97	+0.60	1.40	-0.40	+1.00	2.40	-0.60	+1.00	2.80	-0.60	+1.00	3.40	-0.60	+1.60	5.00	-1.00
1.97	2.56	+0.70	1.80	-0.50	+1.20	2.70	-0.70	+1.20	3.20	-0.70	+1.20	4.20	-0.70	+1.80	6.20	-1.20
2.56	3.15	+0.70	1.90	-0.50	+1.20	2.90	-0.70	+1.20	3.70	-0.70	+1.20	4.70	-0.70	+1.80	7.20	-1.20
3.15	3.94	+0.90	2.40	-0.60	+1.40	3.70	-0.90	+1.40	4.40	-0.70	+1.40	5.90	-0.90	+2.20	8.40	-1.40

VALUES IN MILLIMETERS

Nominal Size Range Millimeters		Class FN1 Light Drive Fit			Class FN2 Medium Drive Fit			Class FN3 Heavy Drive Fit			Class FN4 Shrink Fit			Class FN5 Heavy Shrink Fit		
Over	To	Hole Tol. GR6 -0	Maximum Interference	Shaft Tol. gr5 +0	Hole Tol. H7 -0	Maximum Interference	Shaft Tol. s6 +0	Hole Tol. H7 -0	Maximum Interference	Shaft Tol. t6 +0	Hole Tol. GR8 -0	Maximum Interference	Shaft Tol. gr7 +0	Hole Tol. H8 -0	Maximum Interference	Shaft Tol. t7 +0
0	3	+0.006	0.013	-0.004	+0.010	0.216	-0.006				+0.010	0.024	-0.006	+0.015	0.033	-0.010
3	6	+0.007	0.015	-0.005	+0.013	0.025	-0.007				+0.013	0.030	-0.007	+0.018	0.043	-0.013
6	10	+0.010	0.019	-0.006	+0.015	0.036	-0.010				+0.015	0.041	-0.010	+0.023	0.051	-0.015
10	14	+0.010	0.020	-0.008	+0.018	0.041	-0.010				+0.018	0.046	-0.010	+0.025	0.058	-0.018
14	18	+0.010	0.023	-0.008	+0.018	0.041	-0.010				+0.018	0.046	-0.010	+0.025	0.064	-0.018
18	24	+0.013	0.028	-0.010	+0.020	0.048	-0.013				+0.020	0.053	-0.013	+0.030	0.076	-0.020
24	30	+0.013	0.030	-0.010	+0.020	0.048	-0.013	+0.020	0.053	-0.013	+0.020	0.058	-0.013	+0.030	0.084	-0.020
30	40	+0.015	0.033	-0.010	+0.025	0.061	-0.015	+0.025	0.066	-0.015	+0.025	0.079	-0.015	+0.041	0.102	-0.025
40	50	+0.015	0.036	-0.010	+0.025	0.061	-0.015	+0.025	0.071	-0.015	+0.025	0.086	-0.015	+0.041	0.127	-0.025
50	65	+0.018	0.046	-0.013	+0.030	0.069	-0.018	+0.030	0.082	-0.018	+0.030	0.107	-0.018	+0.046	0.157	-0.030
65	80	+0.018	0.048	-0.013	+0.030	0.074	-0.018	+0.030	0.094	-0.018	+0.030	0.119	-0.018	+0.046	0.183	-0.030
80	100	+0.023	0.061	-0.015	+0.035	0.094	-0.023	+0.035	0.112	-0.023	+0.036	0.150	-0.023	+0.056	0.213	-0.036

Running and Sliding Fits. (CONTINUED)

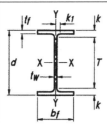

Table 1–1
W Shapes
Dimensions

Shape	Area, A	Depth, d		Web Thickness, t_w		$\frac{t_w}{2}$	Flange Width, b_f		Flange Thickness, t_f		Distance k k_{des}	k k_{det}	k_1	T	Workable Gage
	in.²	in.		in.		in.	in.		in.		in.	in.	in.	in.	in.
W36×800[h]	236	42.6	42½	2.38	2⅜	1³/₁₆	18.0	18	4.29	4⁵/₁₆	5.24	5⁹/₁₆	2³/₈	31³/₈	7½
×652[h]	192	41.1	41	1.97	2	1	17.6	17⅝	3.54	3⁹/₁₆	4.49	4¹³/₁₆	2³/₁₆		
×529[h]	156	39.8	39¾	1.61	1⅝	¹³/₁₆	17.2	17¼	2.91	2¹⁵/₁₆	3.86	4³/₁₆	2		
×487[h]	143	39.3	39⅜	1.50	1½	¾	17.1	17⅛	2.68	2¹¹/₁₆	3.63	4	1¹⁵/₁₆		
×441[h]	130	38.9	38⅞	1.36	1⅜	¹¹/₁₆	17.0	17	2.44	2⁷/₁₆	3.39	3¾	1⅞		
×395[h]	116	38.4	38⅜	1.22	1¼	⅝	16.8	16⅞	2.20	2³/₁₆	3.15	3⁷/₁₆	1¹³/₁₆		
×361[h]	106	38.0	38	1.12	1⅛	⁹/₁₆	16.7	16¾	2.01	2	2.96	3⁵/₁₆	1¾		
×330	97.0	37.7	37⅝	1.02	1	½	16.6	16⅝	1.85	1⅞	2.80	3⅛	1¾		
×302	88.8	37.3	37⅜	0.945	¹⁵/₁₆	½	16.7	16⅝	1.68	1¹¹/₁₆	2.63	3	1¹¹/₁₆		
×282[c]	82.9	37.1	37⅛	0.885	⅞	⁷/₁₆	16.6	16⅝	1.57	1⁹/₁₆	2.52	2⅞	1⅝		
×262[c]	77.0	36.9	36⅞	0.840	¹³/₁₆	⁷/₁₆	16.6	16½	1.44	1⁷/₁₆	2.39	2¾	1⅝		
×247[c]	72.5	36.7	36⅝	0.800	¹³/₁₆	⁷/₁₆	16.5	16½	1.35	1⅜	2.30	2⅝	1⅝		
×231[c]	68.1	36.5	36½	0.760	¾	⅜	16.5	16½	1.26	1¼	2.21	2⁹/₁₆	1⁹/₁₆		
W36×256	75.4	37.4	37⅜	0.960	¹⁵/₁₆	½	12.2	12¼	1.73	1¾	2.48	2⅝	1⁵/₁₆	32⅛	5½
×232[c]	68.1	37.1	37⅛	0.870	⅞	⁷/₁₆	12.1	12⅛	1.57	1⁹/₁₆	2.32	2⁷/₁₆	1¼		
×210[c]	61.8	36.7	36¾	0.830	¹³/₁₆	⁷/₁₆	12.2	12⅛	1.36	1⅜	2.11	2⁵/₁₆	1¼		
×194[c]	57.0	36.5	36½	0.765	¾	⅜	12.1	12⅛	1.26	1¼	2.01	2³/₁₆	1³/₁₆		
×182[c]	53.6	36.3	36⅜	0.725	¾	⅜	12.1	12⅛	1.18	1³/₁₆	1.93	2⅛	1³/₁₆		
×170[c]	50.1	36.2	36⅛	0.680	¹¹/₁₆	⅜	12.0	12	1.10	1⅛	1.85	2	1³/₁₆		
×160[c]	47.0	36.0	36	0.650	⅝	⁵/₁₆	12.0	12	1.02	1	1.77	1¹⁵/₁₆	1⅛		
×150[c]	44.2	35.9	35⅞	0.625	⅝	⁵/₁₆	12.0	12	0.940	¹⁵/₁₆	1.69	1⅞	1⅛		
×135[c,v]	39.7	35.6	35½	0.600	⅝	⁵/₁₆	12.0	12	0.790	¹³/₁₆	1.54	1¹¹/₁₆	1⅛		
W33×387[h]	114	36.0	36	1.26	1¼	⅝	16.2	16¼	2.28	2¼	3.07	3³/₁₆	1⁷/₁₆	29⅝	5½
×354[h]	104	35.6	35½	1.16	1³/₁₆	⅝	16.1	16⅛	2.09	2¹/₁₆	2.88	2¹⁵/₁₆	1⅜		
×318	93.6	35.2	35⅛	1.04	1¹/₁₆	⁹/₁₆	16.0	16	1.89	1⅞	2.68	2¾	1⁵/₁₆		
×291	85.7	34.8	34⅞	0.960	¹⁵/₁₆	½	15.9	15⅞	1.73	1¾	2.52	2⅝	1⁵/₁₆		
×263	77.5	34.5	34½	0.870	⅞	⁷/₁₆	15.8	15¾	1.57	1⁹/₁₆	2.36	2⁷/₁₆	1¼		
×241[c]	71.0	34.2	34⅛	0.830	¹³/₁₆	⁷/₁₆	15.9	15⅞	1.40	1⅜	2.19	2¼	1¼		
×221[c]	65.2	33.9	33⅞	0.775	¾	⅜	15.8	15¾	1.28	1¼	2.06	2⅛	1³/₁₆		
×201[c]	59.2	33.7	33⅝	0.715	¹¹/₁₆	⅜	15.7	15¾	1.15	1⅛	1.94	2	1³/₁₆		
W33×169[c]	49.5	33.8	33⅞	0.670	¹¹/₁₆	⅜	11.5	11½	1.22	1¼	1.92	2⅛	1³/₁₆	29⅝	5½
×152[c]	44.8	33.5	33½	0.635	⅝	⁵/₁₆	11.6	11⅝	1.06	1¹/₁₆	1.76	1¹⁵/₁₆	1⅛		
×141[c]	41.6	33.3	33¼	0.605	⅝	⁵/₁₆	11.5	11½	0.960	¹⁵/₁₆	1.66	1¹³/₁₆	1⅛		
×130[c]	38.3	33.1	33⅛	0.580	⁹/₁₆	⁵/₁₆	11.5	11½	0.855	⅞	1.56	1¾	1⅛		
×118[c,v]	34.7	32.9	32⅞	0.550	⁹/₁₆	⁵/₁₆	11.5	11½	0.740	¾	1.44	1⅝	1⅛		

[c] Shape is slender for compression with F_y = 50 ksi.
[h] Flange thickness greater than 2 in. Special requirements may apply per AISC Specification Section A3.1c.
[v] Shape does not meet the h/t_w limit for shear in Specification Section G2.1a with F_y = 50 ksi.

Copyright © American Institute of Steel Construction, Inc. Reprinted with permission.
All rights reserved.

Structural Metal Shape Designations.

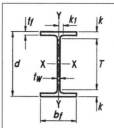

Table 1–1 (continued)
W Shapes
Dimensions

Shape	Area, A	Depth, d		Web Thickness, t_w		$\frac{t_w}{2}$	Flange Width, b_f		Flange Thickness, t_f		k_{des}	k_{det}	k_1	T	Workable Gage
	in.²	in.		in.		in.	in.		in.		in.	in.	in.	in.	in.
W30×391[h]	115	33.2	33¼	1.36	1⅜	11/16	15.6	15⅝	2.44	2 7/16	3.23	3⅜	1½	26½	5½
×357[h]	105	32.8	32¾	1.24	1¼	⅝	15.5	15½	2.24	2¼	3.03	3⅛	1 7/16		
×326[h]	95.8	32.4	32⅜	1.14	1⅛	9/16	15.4	15⅜	2.05	2 1/16	2.84	2 15/16	1⅜		
×292	85.9	32.0	32	1.02	1	½	15.3	15¼	1.85	1⅞	2.64	2¾	1 5/16		
×261	76.9	31.6	31⅝	0.930	15/16	½	15.2	15⅛	1.65	1⅝	2.44	2 9/16	1 5/16		
×235	69.2	31.3	31¼	0.830	13/16	7/16	15.1	15	1.50	1½	2.29	2⅜	1¼		
×211	62.2	30.9	31	0.775	¾	⅜	15.1	15⅛	1.32	1 5/16	2.10	2¼	1 3/16		
×191[c]	56.3	30.7	30⅝	0.710	11/16	⅜	15.0	15	1.19	1 3/16	1.97	2 1/16	1 3/16	↓	↓
×173[c]	51.0	30.4	30½	0.655	⅝	5/16	15.0	15	1.07	1 1/16	1.85	2	1⅛		
W30×148[c]	43.5	30.7	30⅝	0.650	⅝	5/16	10.5	10½	1.18	1 3/16	1.83	2 1/16	1⅛	26½	5½
×132[c]	38.9	30.3	30¼	0.615	⅝	5/16	10.5	10½	1.00	1	1.65	1⅞	1⅛		
×124[c]	36.5	30.2	30⅛	0.585	9/16	5/16	10.5	10½	0.930	15/16	1.58	1 13/16	1⅛		
×116[c]	34.2	30.0	30	0.565	9/16	5/16	10.5	10½	0.850	⅞	1.50	1¾	1⅛		
×108[c]	31.7	29.8	29⅞	0.545	9/16	5/16	10.5	10½	0.760	¾	1.41	1 11/16	1⅛		
×99[c]	29.1	29.7	29⅝	0.520	½	¼	10.5	10½	0.670	11/16	1.32	1 9/16	1 1/16	↓	↓
×90[c,v]	26.4	29.5	29½	0.470	½	¼	10.4	10⅜	0.610	⅝	1.26	1½	1 1/16		
W27×539[h]	159	32.5	32½	1.97	2	1	15.3	15¼	3.54	3 9/16	4.33	4 7/16	1 13/16	23⅝	5½[g]
×368[h]	108	30.4	30⅜	1.38	1⅜	11/16	14.7	14⅝	2.48	2½	3.27	3⅜	1½		5½
×336[h]	98.9	30.0	30	1.26	1¼	⅝	14.6	14½	2.28	2¼	3.07	3 3/16	1 7/16		
×307[h]	90.4	29.6	29⅝	1.16	1 3/16	⅝	14.4	14½	2.09	2 1/16	2.88	3	1 7/16		
×281	82.9	29.3	29¼	1.06	1 1/16	9/16	14.4	14⅜	1.93	1 15/16	2.72	2 13/16	1⅜		
×258	76.0	29.0	29	0.980	1	½	14.3	14¼	1.77	1¾	2.56	2 11/16	1 5/16		
×235	69.4	28.7	28⅝	0.910	15/16	½	14.2	14¼	1.61	1⅝	2.40	2½	1 5/16		
×217	64.0	28.4	28⅜	0.830	13/16	7/16	14.1	14⅛	1.50	1½	2.29	2⅜	1¼		
×194	57.2	28.1	28⅛	0.750	¾	⅜	14.0	14	1.34	1 5/16	2.13	2¼	1 3/16		
×178	52.5	27.8	27¾	0.725	¾	⅜	14.1	14⅛	1.19	1 3/16	1.98	2 1/16	1 3/16		
×161[c]	47.6	27.6	27⅝	0.660	11/16	⅜	14.0	14	1.08	1 1/16	1.87	2	1 3/16	↓	↓
×146[c]	43.1	27.4	27⅜	0.605	⅝	5/16	14.0	14	0.975	1	1.76	1⅞	1⅛		
W27×129[c]	37.8	27.6	27⅝	0.610	⅝	5/16	10.0	10	1.10	1⅛	1.70	2	1⅛	23⅝	5½
×114[c]	33.5	27.3	27¼	0.570	9/16	5/16	10.1	10⅛	0.930	15/16	1.53	1 13/16	1⅛		
×102[c]	30.0	27.1	27⅛	0.515	½	¼	10.0	10	0.830	13/16	1.43	1¾	1 1/16		
×94[c]	27.7	26.9	26⅞	0.490	½	¼	10.0	10	0.745	¾	1.34	1⅝	1 1/16	↓	↓
×84[c]	24.8	26.7	26¾	0.460	7/16	¼	10.0	10	0.640	⅝	1.24	1 9/16	1 1/16		

[c] Shape is slender for compression with F_y = 50 ksi.
[g] The actual size, combination, and orientation of fastener components should be compared with the geometry of the cross-section to ensure compatibility.
[h] Flange thickness greater than 2 in. Special requirements may apply per AISC Specification Section A3.1c.
[v] Shape does not meet the h/t_w limit for shear in Specification Section G2.1a with F_y = 50 ksi.

Copyright © American Institute of Steel Construction, Inc. Reprinted with permission. All rights reserved.

Structural Metal Shape Designations. (CONTINUED)

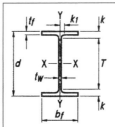

Table 1–1 (continued)
W Shapes
Dimensions

Shape	Area, A	Depth, d		Web Thickness, t_w		$\frac{t_w}{2}$	Flange Width, b_f		Thickness, t_f		k k_{des}	k_{det}	k_1	T	Workable Gage
	in.²	in.		in.		in.	in.		in.		in.	in.	in.	in.	in.
W24×370[h]	109	28.0	28	1.52	$1\frac{1}{2}$	$\frac{3}{4}$	13.7	$13\frac{5}{8}$	2.72	$2\frac{3}{4}$	3.22	$3\frac{5}{8}$	$1\frac{9}{16}$	$20\frac{3}{4}$	$5\frac{1}{2}$
×335[h]	98.4	27.5	$27\frac{1}{2}$	1.38	$1\frac{3}{8}$	$\frac{11}{16}$	13.5	$13\frac{1}{2}$	2.48	$2\frac{1}{2}$	2.98	$3\frac{3}{8}$	$1\frac{1}{2}$		
×306[h]	89.8	27.1	$27\frac{1}{8}$	1.26	$1\frac{1}{4}$	$\frac{5}{8}$	13.4	$13\frac{3}{8}$	2.28	$2\frac{1}{4}$	2.78	$3\frac{3}{16}$	$1\frac{7}{16}$		
x279[h]	82.0	26.7	$26\frac{3}{4}$	1.16	$1\frac{3}{16}$	$\frac{5}{8}$	13.3	$13\frac{1}{4}$	2.09	$2\frac{1}{16}$	2.59	3	$1\frac{7}{16}$		
×250	73.5	26.3	$26\frac{3}{8}$	1.04	$1\frac{1}{16}$	$\frac{9}{16}$	13.2	$13\frac{1}{8}$	1.89	$1\frac{7}{8}$	2.39	$2\frac{13}{16}$	$1\frac{3}{8}$		
×229	67.2	26.0	26	0.960	$\frac{15}{16}$	$\frac{1}{2}$	13.1	$13\frac{1}{8}$	1.73	$1\frac{3}{4}$	2.23	$2\frac{5}{8}$	$1\frac{5}{16}$		
×207	60.7	25.7	$25\frac{3}{4}$	0.870	$\frac{7}{8}$	$\frac{7}{16}$	13.0	13	1.57	$1\frac{9}{16}$	2.07	$2\frac{1}{2}$	$1\frac{1}{4}$		
×192	56.3	25.5	$25\frac{1}{2}$	0.810	$\frac{13}{16}$	$\frac{7}{16}$	13.0	13	1.46	$1\frac{7}{16}$	1.96	$2\frac{3}{8}$	$1\frac{1}{4}$		
×176	51.7	25.2	$25\frac{1}{4}$	0.750	$\frac{3}{4}$	$\frac{3}{8}$	12.9	$12\frac{7}{8}$	1.34	$1\frac{5}{16}$	1.84	$2\frac{1}{4}$	$1\frac{3}{16}$		
×162	47.7	25.0	25	0.705	$\frac{11}{16}$	$\frac{3}{8}$	13.0	13	1.22	$1\frac{1}{4}$	1.72	$2\frac{1}{8}$	$1\frac{3}{16}$		
×146	43.0	24.7	$24\frac{3}{4}$	0.650	$\frac{5}{8}$	$\frac{5}{16}$	12.9	$12\frac{7}{8}$	1.09	$1\frac{1}{16}$	1.59	2	$1\frac{1}{8}$		
×131	38.5	24.5	$24\frac{1}{2}$	0.605	$\frac{5}{8}$	$\frac{5}{16}$	12.9	$12\frac{7}{8}$	0.960	$\frac{15}{16}$	1.46	$1\frac{7}{8}$	$1\frac{1}{8}$		
×117[c]	34.4	24.3	$24\frac{1}{4}$	0.550	$\frac{9}{16}$	$\frac{5}{16}$	12.8	$12\frac{3}{4}$	0.850	$\frac{7}{8}$	1.35	$1\frac{3}{4}$	$1\frac{1}{8}$		
×104[c]	30.6	24.1	24	0.500	$\frac{1}{2}$	$\frac{1}{4}$	12.8	$12\frac{3}{4}$	0.750	$\frac{3}{4}$	1.25	$1\frac{5}{8}$	$1\frac{1}{16}$	↓	↓
W24×103[c]	30.3	24.5	$24\frac{1}{2}$	0.550	$\frac{9}{16}$	$\frac{5}{16}$	9.00	9	0.980	1	1.48	$1\frac{7}{8}$	$1\frac{1}{8}$	$20\frac{3}{4}$	$5\frac{1}{2}$
×94[c]	27.7	24.3	$24\frac{1}{4}$	0.515	$\frac{1}{2}$	$\frac{1}{4}$	9.07	$9\frac{1}{8}$	0.875	$\frac{7}{8}$	1.38	$1\frac{3}{4}$	$1\frac{1}{16}$		
×84[c]	24.7	24.1	$24\frac{1}{8}$	0.470	$\frac{1}{2}$	$\frac{1}{4}$	9.02	9	0.770	$\frac{3}{4}$	1.27	$1\frac{11}{16}$	$1\frac{1}{16}$		
×76[c]	22.4	23.9	$23\frac{7}{8}$	0.440	$\frac{7}{16}$	$\frac{1}{4}$	8.99	9	0.680	$\frac{11}{16}$	1.18	$1\frac{9}{16}$	$1\frac{1}{16}$		
×68[c]	20.1	23.7	$23\frac{3}{4}$	0.415	$\frac{7}{16}$	$\frac{1}{4}$	8.97	9	0.585	$\frac{9}{16}$	1.09	$1\frac{1}{2}$	$1\frac{1}{16}$	↓	↓
W24×62[c]	18.2	23.7	$23\frac{3}{4}$	0.430	$\frac{7}{16}$	$\frac{1}{4}$	7.04	7	0.590	$\frac{9}{16}$	1.09	$1\frac{1}{2}$	$1\frac{1}{16}$	$20\frac{3}{4}$	$3\frac{1}{2}$[g]
×55[c,v]	16.2	23.6	$23\frac{5}{8}$	0.395	$\frac{3}{8}$	$\frac{3}{16}$	7.01	7	0.505	$\frac{1}{2}$	1.01	$1\frac{7}{16}$	1	$20\frac{3}{4}$	$3\frac{1}{2}$[g]
W21×201	59.2	23.0	23	0.910	$\frac{15}{16}$	$\frac{1}{2}$	12.6	$12\frac{5}{8}$	1.63	$1\frac{5}{8}$	2.13	$2\frac{1}{2}$	$1\frac{5}{16}$	18	$5\frac{1}{2}$
×182	53.6	22.7	$22\frac{3}{4}$	0.830	$\frac{13}{16}$	$\frac{7}{16}$	12.5	$12\frac{1}{2}$	1.48	$1\frac{1}{2}$	1.98	$2\frac{3}{8}$	$1\frac{1}{4}$		
×166	48.8	22.5	$22\frac{1}{2}$	0.750	$\frac{3}{4}$	$\frac{3}{8}$	12.4	$12\frac{3}{8}$	1.36	$1\frac{3}{8}$	1.86	$2\frac{1}{4}$	$1\frac{3}{16}$		
×147	43.2	22.1	22	0.720	$\frac{3}{4}$	$\frac{3}{8}$	12.5	$12\frac{1}{2}$	1.15	$1\frac{1}{8}$	1.65	2	$1\frac{3}{16}$		
×132	38.8	21.8	$21\frac{7}{8}$	0.650	$\frac{5}{8}$	$\frac{5}{16}$	12.4	$12\frac{1}{2}$	1.04	$1\frac{1}{16}$	1.54	$1\frac{15}{16}$	$1\frac{1}{8}$		
×122	35.9	21.7	$21\frac{5}{8}$	0.600	$\frac{5}{8}$	$\frac{5}{16}$	12.4	$12\frac{3}{8}$	0.960	$\frac{15}{16}$	1.46	$1\frac{13}{16}$	$1\frac{1}{8}$		
×111	32.7	21.5	$21\frac{1}{2}$	0.550	$\frac{9}{16}$	$\frac{5}{16}$	12.3	$12\frac{3}{8}$	0.875	$\frac{7}{8}$	1.38	$1\frac{3}{4}$	$1\frac{1}{8}$		
×101[c]	29.8	21.4	$21\frac{3}{8}$	0.500	$\frac{1}{2}$	$\frac{1}{4}$	12.3	$12\frac{1}{4}$	0.800	$\frac{13}{16}$	1.30	$1\frac{11}{16}$	$1\frac{1}{16}$	↓	↓

[c] Shape is slender for compression with F_y = 50 ksi.
[g] The actual size, combination, and orientation of fastener components should be compared with the geometry of the cross-section to ensure compatibility.
[h] Flange thickness greater than 2 in. Special requirements may apply per AISC Specification Section A3.1c.
[v] Shape does not meet the h/t_w limit for shear in Specification Section G2.1a with F_y = 50 ksi.

Copyright © American Institute of Steel Construction, Inc. Reprinted with permission.
All rights reserved.

Structural Metal Shape Designations. (CONTINUED)

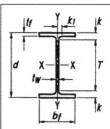

Table 1–1 (continued)
W Shapes
Dimensions

Shape	Area, A	Depth, d		Web Thickness, t_w		$\frac{t_w}{2}$	Flange Width, b_f		Flange Thickness, t_f		k k_{des}	k k_{det}	k_1	T	Workable Gage
	in.²	in.		in.		in.	in.		in.		in.	in.	in.	in.	in.
W21×93	27.3	21.6	21⁵⁄₈	0.580	⁹⁄₁₆	⁵⁄₁₆	8.42	8³⁄₈	0.930	¹⁵⁄₁₆	1.43	1⁵⁄₈	¹⁵⁄₁₆	18³⁄₈	5¹⁄₂
×83ᶜ	24.3	21.4	21³⁄₈	0.515	¹⁄₂	¹⁄₄	8.36	8³⁄₈	0.835	¹³⁄₁₆	1.34	1¹⁄₂	⁷⁄₈		
×73ᶜ	21.5	21.2	21¹⁄₄	0.455	⁷⁄₁₆	¹⁄₄	8.30	8¹⁄₄	0.740	³⁄₄	1.24	1⁷⁄₁₆	⁷⁄₈		
×68ᶜ	20.0	21.1	21¹⁄₈	0.430	⁷⁄₁₆	¹⁄₄	8.27	8¹⁄₄	0.685	¹¹⁄₁₆	1.19	1³⁄₈	⁷⁄₈		
×62ᶜ	18.3	21.0	21	0.400	³⁄₈	³⁄₁₆	8.24	8¹⁄₄	0.615	⁵⁄₈	1.12	1⁵⁄₁₆	¹³⁄₁₆		
×55ᶜ	16.2	20.8	20³⁄₄	0.375	³⁄₈	³⁄₁₆	8.22	8¹⁄₄	0.522	¹⁄₂	1.02	1³⁄₁₆	¹³⁄₁₆		
×48ᶜ,ᶠ	14.1	20.6	20⁵⁄₈	0.350	³⁄₈	³⁄₁₆	8.14	8¹⁄₈	0.430	⁷⁄₁₆	0.930	1¹⁄₈	¹³⁄₁₆	▼	▼
W21×57ᶜ	16.7	21.1	21	0.405	³⁄₈	³⁄₁₆	6.56	6¹⁄₂	0.650	⁵⁄₈	1.15	1⁵⁄₁₆	¹³⁄₁₆	18³⁄₈	3¹⁄₂
×50ᶜ	14.7	20.8	20⁷⁄₈	0.380	³⁄₈	³⁄₁₆	6.53	6¹⁄₂	0.535	⁹⁄₁₆	1.04	1¹⁄₄	¹³⁄₁₆		
×44ᶜ	13.0	20.7	20⁵⁄₈	0.350	³⁄₈	³⁄₁₆	6.50	6¹⁄₂	0.450	⁷⁄₁₆	0.950	1¹⁄₈	¹³⁄₁₆	▼	▼
W18×311ʰ	91.6	22.3	22³⁄₈	1.52	1¹⁄₂	³⁄₄	12.0	12	2.74	2³⁄₄	3.24	3⁷⁄₁₆	1³⁄₈	15¹⁄₂	5¹⁄₂
×283ʰ	83.3	21.9	21⁷⁄₈	1.40	1³⁄₈	¹¹⁄₁₆	11.9	11⁷⁄₈	2.50	2¹⁄₂	3.00	3³⁄₁₆	1⁵⁄₁₆		
×258ʰ	75.9	21.5	21¹⁄₂	1.28	1¹⁄₄	⁵⁄₈	11.8	11³⁄₄	2.30	2⁵⁄₁₆	2.70	3	1¹⁄₄		
×234ʰ	68.8	21.1	21	1.16	1³⁄₁₆	⁵⁄₈	11.7	11⁵⁄₈	2.11	2¹⁄₈	2.51	2³⁄₄	1³⁄₁₆		
×211	62.1	20.7	20⁵⁄₈	1.06	1¹⁄₁₆	⁹⁄₁₆	11.6	11¹⁄₂	1.91	1¹⁵⁄₁₆	2.31	2⁹⁄₁₆	1³⁄₁₆		
×192	56.4	20.4	20³⁄₈	0.960	¹⁵⁄₁₆	¹⁄₂	11.5	11¹⁄₂	1.75	1³⁄₄	2.15	2⁷⁄₁₆	1¹⁄₈	▼	
×175	51.3	20.0	20	0.890	⁷⁄₈	⁷⁄₁₆	11.4	11³⁄₈	1.59	1⁹⁄₁₆	1.99	2⁷⁄₁₆	1¹⁄₄	15¹⁄₈	
×158	46.3	19.7	19³⁄₄	0.810	¹³⁄₁₆	⁷⁄₁₆	11.3	11¹⁄₄	1.44	1⁷⁄₁₆	1.84	2³⁄₈	1¹⁄₄		
×143	42.1	19.5	19¹⁄₂	0.730	³⁄₄	³⁄₈	11.2	11¹⁄₄	1.32	1⁵⁄₁₆	1.72	2³⁄₁₆	1³⁄₁₆		
×130	38.2	19.3	19¹⁄₄	0.670	¹¹⁄₁₆	³⁄₈	11.2	11¹⁄₈	1.20	1³⁄₁₆	1.60	2¹⁄₁₆	1³⁄₁₆		
×119	35.1	19.0	19	0.655	⁵⁄₈	⁵⁄₁₆	11.3	11¹⁄₄	1.06	1¹⁄₁₆	1.46	1¹⁵⁄₁₆	1³⁄₁₆		
×106	31.1	18.7	18³⁄₄	0.590	⁹⁄₁₆	⁵⁄₁₆	11.2	11¹⁄₄	0.940	¹⁵⁄₁₆	1.34	1¹³⁄₁₆	1¹⁄₈		
×97	28.5	18.6	18⁵⁄₈	0.535	⁹⁄₁₆	⁵⁄₁₆	11.1	11¹⁄₈	0.870	⁷⁄₈	1.27	1³⁄₄	1¹⁄₈		
×86	25.3	18.4	18³⁄₈	0.480	¹⁄₂	¹⁄₄	11.1	11¹⁄₈	0.770	³⁄₄	1.17	1⁵⁄₈	1¹⁄₁₆		
×76ᶜ	22.3	18.2	18¹⁄₄	0.425	⁷⁄₁₆	¹⁄₄	11.0	11	0.680	¹¹⁄₁₆	1.08	1⁹⁄₁₆	1¹⁄₁₆	▼	▼
W18×71	20.8	18.5	18¹⁄₂	0.495	¹⁄₂	¹⁄₄	7.64	7⁵⁄₈	0.810	¹³⁄₁₆	1.21	1¹⁄₂	⁷⁄₈	15¹⁄₂	3¹⁄₂ᵍ
×65	19.1	18.4	18³⁄₈	0.450	⁷⁄₁₆	¹⁄₄	7.59	7⁵⁄₈	0.750	³⁄₄	1.15	1⁷⁄₁₆	⁷⁄₈		
×60ᶜ	17.6	18.2	18¹⁄₄	0.415	⁷⁄₁₆	¹⁄₄	7.56	7¹⁄₂	0.695	¹¹⁄₁₆	1.10	1³⁄₈	¹³⁄₁₆		
×55ᶜ	16.2	18.1	18¹⁄₈	0.390	³⁄₈	³⁄₁₆	7.53	7¹⁄₂	0.630	⁵⁄₈	1.03	1⁵⁄₁₆	¹³⁄₁₆		
×50ᶜ	14.7	18.0	18	0.355	³⁄₈	³⁄₁₆	7.50	7¹⁄₂	0.570	⁹⁄₁₆	0.972	1¹⁄₄	¹³⁄₁₆	▼	▼
W18×46ᶜ	13.5	18.1	18	0.360	³⁄₈	³⁄₁₆	6.06	6	0.605	⁵⁄₈	1.01	1¹⁄₄	¹³⁄₁₆	15¹⁄₂	3¹⁄₂ᵍ
×40ᶜ	11.8	17.9	17⁷⁄₈	0.315	⁵⁄₁₆	³⁄₁₆	6.02	6	0.525	¹⁄₂	0.927	1³⁄₁₆	¹³⁄₁₆		
×35ᶜ	10.3	17.7	17³⁄₄	0.300	⁵⁄₁₆	³⁄₁₆	6.00	6	0.425	⁷⁄₁₆	0.827	1¹⁄₈	³⁄₄	▼	▼

ᶜ Shape is slender for compression with F_y = 50 ksi.
ᶠ Shape exceeds compact limit for flexure with F_y = 50 ksi.
ᵍ The actual size, combination, and orientation of fastener components should be compared with the geometry of the cross-section to ensure compatibility.
ʰ Flange thickness greater than 2 in. Special requirements may apply per AISC Specification Section A3.1c.

Copyright © American Institute of Steel Construction, Inc. Reprinted with permission. All rights reserved.

Structural Metal Shape Designations. (CONTINUED)

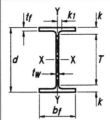

Table 1–1 (continued)
W Shapes
Dimensions

Shape	Area, A	Depth, d	Web Thickness, t_w	$\dfrac{t_w}{2}$	Flange Width, b_f	Flange Thickness, t_f	k k_{des}	k k_{det}	k_1	T	Workable Gage
	in.²	in.	in.	in.	in.	in.	in.	in.	in.	in.	in.
W16×100	29.5	17.0 17	0.585 9/16	5/16	10.4 10 3/8	0.985 1	1.39	1 7/8	1 1/8	13 1/4	5 1/2
×89	26.2	16.8 16 3/4	0.525 1/2	1/4	10.4 10 3/8	0.875 7/8	1.28	1 3/4	1 1/16	↓	↓
×77	22.6	16.5 16 1/2	0.455 7/16	1/4	10.3 10 1/4	0.760 3/4	1.16	1 5/8	1 1/16		
×67ᶜ	19.7	16.3 16 3/8	0.395 3/8	3/16	10.2 10 1/4	0.665 11/16	1.07	1 9/16	1		
W16×57	16.8	16.4 16 3/8	0.430 7/16	1/4	7.12 7 1/8	0.715 11/16	1.12	1 3/8	7/8	13 5/8	3 1/2ᵍ
×50ᶜ	14.7	16.3 16 1/4	0.380 3/8	3/16	7.07 7 1/8	0.630 5/8	1.03	1 5/16	13/16		
×45ᶜ	13.3	16.1 16 1/8	0.345 3/8	3/16	7.04 7	0.565 9/16	0.967	1 1/4	13/16		
×40ᶜ	11.8	16.0 16	0.305 5/16	3/16	7.00 7	0.505 1/2	0.907	1 3/16	13/16		
×36ᶜ	10.6	15.9 15 7/8	0.295 5/16	3/16	6.99 7	0.430 7/16	0.832	1 1/8	3/4	↓	↓
W16×31ᶜ	9.13	15.9 15 7/8	0.275 1/4	1/8	5.53 5 1/2	0.440 7/16	0.842	1 1/8	3/4	13 5/8	3 1/2
×26ᶜ·ᵛ	7.68	15.7 15 3/4	0.250 1/4	1/8	5.50 5 1/2	0.345 3/8	0.747	1 1/16	3/4	13 5/8	3 1/2
W14×730ʰ	215	22.4 22 3/8	3.07 3 1/16	1 9/16	17.9 17 7/8	4.91 4 15/16	5.51	6 3/16	2 3/4	10	3-7 1/2-3ᵍ
×665ʰ	196	21.6 21 5/8	2.83 2 13/16	1 7/16	17.7 17 5/8	4.52 4 1/2	5.12	5 13/16	2 5/8		3-7 1/2-3ᵍ
×605ʰ	178	20.9 20 7/8	2.60 2 5/8	1 5/16	17.4 17 3/8	4.16 4 3/16	4.76	5 7/16	2 1/2		3-7 1/2-3
×550ʰ	162	20.2 20 1/4	2.38 2 3/8	1 3/16	17.2 17 1/4	3.82 3 13/16	4.42	5 1/8	2 3/8		
×500ʰ	147	19.6 19 5/8	2.19 2 3/16	1 1/8	17.0 17	3.50 3 1/2	4.10	4 13/16	2 5/16		
×455ʰ	134	19.0 19	2.02 2	1	16.8 16 7/8	3.21 3 3/16	3.81	4 1/2	2 1/4		
×426ʰ	125	18.7 18 5/8	1.88 1 7/8	15/16	16.7 16 3/4	3.04 3 1/16	3.63	4 5/16	2 1/8		
×398ʰ	117	18.3 18 1/4	1.77 1 3/4	7/8	16.6 16 5/8	2.85 2 7/8	3.44	4 1/8	2 1/8		
×370ʰ	109	17.9 17 7/8	1.66 1 5/8	13/16	16.5 16 1/2	2.66 2 11/16	3.26	3 15/16	2 1/16		
×342ʰ	101	17.5 17 1/2	1.54 1 9/16	13/16	16.4 16 3/8	2.47 2 1/2	3.07	3 3/4	2		
×311ʰ	91.4	17.1 17 1/8	1.41 1 7/16	3/4	16.2 16 1/4	2.26 2 1/4	2.86	3 9/16	1 15/16		
×283ʰ	83.3	16.7 16 3/4	1.29 1 5/16	11/16	16.1 16 1/8	2.07 2 1/16	2.67	3 3/8	1 7/8		
×257	75.6	16.4 16 3/8	1.18 1 3/16	5/8	16.0 16	1.89 1 7/8	2.49	3 3/16	1 13/16		
×233	68.5	16.0 16	1.07 1 1/16	9/16	15.9 15 7/8	1.72 1 3/4	2.32	3	1 3/4		
×211	62.0	15.7 15 3/4	0.980 1	1/2	15.8 15 3/4	1.56 1 9/16	2.16	2 7/8	1 11/16		
×193	56.8	15.5 15 1/2	0.890 7/8	7/16	15.7 15 3/4	1.44 1 7/16	2.04	2 3/4	1 11/16		
×176	51.8	15.2 15 1/4	0.830 13/16	7/16	15.7 15 5/8	1.31 1 5/16	1.91	2 5/8	1 5/8		
×159	46.7	15.0 15	0.745 3/4	3/8	15.6 15 5/8	1.19 1 3/16	1.79	2 1/2	1 9/16	↓	↓
×145	42.7	14.8 14 3/4	0.680 11/16	3/8	15.5 15 1/2	1.09 1 1/16	1.69	2 3/8	1 9/16		

ᶜ Shape is slender for compression with F_y = 50 ksi.
ᵍ The actual size, combination, and orientation of fastener components should be compared with the geometry of the cross-section to ensure compatibility.
ʰ Flange thickness greater than 2 in. Special requirements may apply per AISC Specification Section A3.1c.
ᵛ Shape does not meet the h/t_w limit for shear in Specification Section G2.1a with F_y = 50 ksi.

Copyright © American Institute of Steel Construction, Inc. Reprinted with permission.
All rights reserved.

Structural Metal Shape Designations. (CONTINUED)

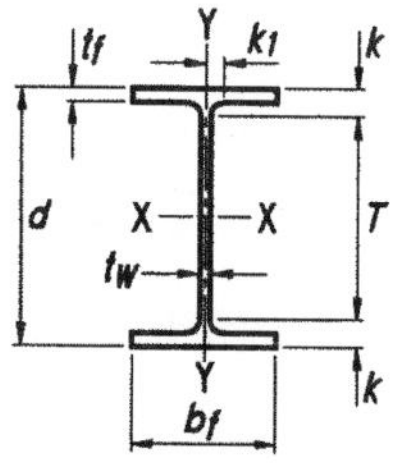

Table 1–1 (continued)
W Shapes
Dimensions

Shape	Area, A	Depth, d		Web Thickness, t_w		Web $\frac{t_w}{2}$	Flange Width, b_f		Flange Thickness, t_f		Distance k k_{des}	Distance k k_{det}	Distance k_1	Distance T	Workable Gage
	in.²	in.		in.		in.	in.		in.		in.	in.	in.	in.	in.
W14×132	38.8	14.7	14 5/8	0.645	5/8	5/16	14.7	14 3/4	1.03	1	1.63	2 5/16	1 9/16	10	5 1/2
×120	35.3	14.5	14 1/2	0.590	9/16	5/16	14.7	14 5/8	0.940	15/16	1.54	2 1/4	1 1/2		
×109	32.0	14.3	14 3/8	0.525	1/2	1/4	14.6	14 5/8	0.860	7/8	1.46	2 3/16	1 1/2		
×99[f]	29.1	14.2	14 1/8	0.485	1/2	1/4	14.6	14 5/8	0.780	3/4	1.38	2 1/16	1 7/16		
×90[f]	26.5	14.0	14	0.440	7/16	1/4	14.5	14 1/2	0.710	11/16	1.31	2	1 7/16	↓	↓
W14×82	24.0	14.3	14 1/4	0.510	1/2	1/4	10.1	10 1/8	0.855	7/8	1.45	1 11/16	1 1/16	10 7/8	5 1/2
×74	21.8	14.2	14 1/8	0.450	7/16	1/4	10.1	10 1/8	0.785	13/16	1.38	1 5/8	1 1/16		
×68	20.0	14.0	14	0.415	7/16	1/4	10.0	10	0.720	3/4	1.31	1 9/16	1 1/16		
×61	17.9	13.9	13 7/8	0.375	3/8	3/16	10.0	10	0.645	5/8	1.24	1 1/2	1	↓	↓
W14×53	15.6	13.9	13 7/8	0.370	3/8	3/16	8.06	8	0.660	11/16	1.25	1 1/2	1	10 7/8	5 1/2
×48	14.1	13.8	13 3/4	0.340	5/16	3/16	8.03	8	0.595	5/8	1.19	1 7/16	1		
×43[c]	12.6	13.7	13 5/8	0.305	5/16	3/16	8.00	8	0.530	1/2	1.12	1 3/8	1	↓	↓
W14×38[c]	11.2	14.1	14 1/8	0.310	5/16	3/16	6.77	6 3/4	0.515	1/2	0.915	1 1/4	13/16	11 5/8	3 1/2[g]
×34[c]	10.0	14.0	14	0.285	5/16	3/16	6.75	6 3/4	0.455	7/16	0.855	1 3/16	3/4		3 1/2
×30[c]	8.85	13.8	13 7/8	0.270	1/4	1/8	6.73	6 3/4	0.385	3/8	0.785	1 1/8	3/4	↓	3 1/2
W14×26[c]	7.69	13.9	13 7/8	0.255	1/4	1/8	5.03	5	0.420	7/16	0.820	1 1/8	3/4	11 5/8	2 3/4[g]
×22[c]	6.49	13.7	13 3/4	0.230	1/4	1/8	5.00	5	0.335	5/16	0.735	1 1/16	3/4	11 5/8	2 3/4[g]
W12×336[h]	98.8	16.8	16 7/8	1.78	1 3/4	7/8	13.4	13 3/8	2.96	2 15/16	3.55	3 7/8	1 11/16	9 1/8	5 1/2
×305[h]	89.6	16.3	16 3/8	1.63	1 5/8	13/16	13.2	13 1/4	2.71	2 11/16	3.30	3 5/8	1 5/8		
×279[h]	81.9	15.9	15 7/8	1.53	1 1/2	3/4	13.1	13 1/8	2.47	2 1/2	3.07	3 3/8	1 5/8		
×252[h]	74.0	15.4	15 3/8	1.40	1 3/8	11/16	13.0	13	2.25	2 1/4	2.85	3 1/8	1 1/2		
×230[h]	67.7	15.1	15	1.29	1 5/16	11/16	12.9	12 7/8	2.07	2 1/16	2.67	2 15/16	1 1/2		
×210	61.8	14.7	14 3/4	1.18	1 3/16	5/8	12.8	12 3/4	1.90	1 7/8	2.50	2 13/16	1 7/16		
×190	55.8	14.4	14 3/8	1.06	1 1/16	9/16	12.7	12 5/8	1.74	1 3/4	2.33	2 5/8	1 3/8		
×170	50.0	14.0	14	0.960	15/16	1/2	12.6	12 5/8	1.56	1 9/16	2.16	2 7/16	1 5/16		
×152	44.7	13.7	13 3/4	0.870	7/8	7/16	12.5	12 1/2	1.40	1 3/8	2.00	2 5/16	1 1/4		
×136	39.9	13.4	13 3/8	0.790	13/16	7/16	12.4	12 3/8	1.25	1 1/4	1.85	2 1/8	1 1/4		
×120	35.3	13.1	13 1/8	0.710	11/16	3/8	12.3	12 3/8	1.11	1 1/8	1.70	2	1 3/16		
×106	31.2	12.9	12 7/8	0.610	5/8	5/16	12.2	12 1/4	0.990	1	1.59	1 7/8	1 1/8		
×96	28.2	12.7	12 3/4	0.550	9/16	5/16	12.2	12 1/8	0.900	7/8	1.50	1 13/16	1 1/8		
×87	25.6	12.5	12 1/2	0.515	1/2	1/4	12.1	12 1/8	0.810	13/16	1.41	1 11/16	1 1/16		
×79	23.2	12.4	12 3/8	0.470	1/2	1/4	12.1	12 1/8	0.735	3/4	1.33	1 5/8	1 1/16		
×72	21.1	12.3	12 1/4	0.430	7/16	1/4	12.0	12	0.670	11/16	1.27	1 9/16	1 1/16		
×65[f]	19.1	12.1	12 1/8	0.390	3/8	3/16	12.0	12	0.605	5/8	1.20	1 1/2	1	↓	↓

[c] Shape is slender for compression with $F_y = 50$ ksi.
[f] Shape exceeds compact limit for flexure with $F_y = 50$ ksi.
[g] The actual size, combination, and orientation of fastener components should be compared with the geometry of the cross-section to ensure compatibility.
[h] Flange thickness greater than 2 in. Special requirements may apply per AISC Specification Section A3.1c.

Copyright © American Institute of Steel Construction, Inc. Reprinted with permission.
All rights reserved.

Structural Metal Shape Designations. **(CONTINUED)**

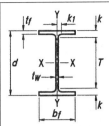

Table 1–1 (continued)
W Shapes
Dimensions

Shape	Area, A	Depth, d		Web Thickness, t_w		$\frac{t_w}{2}$	Flange Width, b_f		Thickness, t_f		Distance k k_{des}	k_{det}	k_1	T	Work-able Gage
	in.²	in.		in.		in.	in.		in.		in.	in.	in.	in.	in.
W12×58	17.0	12.2	12¼	0.360	³/₈	³/₁₆	10.0	10	0.640	⁵/₈	1.24	1½	¹⁵/₁₆	9¼	5½
×53	15.6	12.1	12	0.345	³/₈	³/₁₆	10.0	10	0.575	⁹/₁₆	1.18	1³/₈	¹⁵/₁₆	9¼	5½
W12×50	14.6	12.2	12¼	0.370	³/₈	³/₁₆	8.08	8¹/₈	0.640	⁵/₈	1.14	1½	¹⁵/₁₆	9¼	5½
×45	13.1	12.1	12	0.335	⁵/₁₆	³/₁₆	8.05	8	0.575	⁹/₁₆	1.08	1³/₈	¹⁵/₁₆	↓	↓
×40	11.7	11.9	12	0.295	⁵/₁₆	³/₁₆	8.01	8	0.515	½	1.02	1³/₈	⁷/₈	↓	↓
W12×35ᶜ	10.3	12.5	12½	0.300	⁵/₁₆	³/₁₆	6.56	6½	0.520	½	0.820	1³/₁₆	¾	10¹/₈	3½
×30ᶜ	8.79	12.3	12³/₈	0.260	¼	¹/₈	6.52	6½	0.440	⁷/₁₆	0.740	1¹/₈	¾	↓	↓
×26ᶜ	7.65	12.2	12¼	0.230	¼	¹/₈	6.49	6½	0.380	³/₈	0.680	1¹/₁₆	¾	↓	↓
W12×22ᶜ	6.48	12.3	12¼	0.260	¼	¹/₈	4.03	4	0.425	⁷/₁₆	0.725	¹⁵/₁₆	⁵/₈	10³/₈	2¼ᵍ
×19ᶜ	5.57	12.2	12¹/₈	0.235	¼	¹/₈	4.01	4	0.350	³/₈	0.650	⁷/₈	⁹/₁₆	↓	↓
×16ᶜ	4.71	12.0	12	0.220	¼	¹/₈	3.99	4	0.265	¼	0.565	¹³/₁₆	⁹/₁₆	↓	↓
×14ᶜ·ᵛ	4.16	11.9	11⁷/₈	0.200	³/₁₆	¹/₈	3.97	4	0.225	¼	0.525	¾	⁹/₁₆	↓	↓
W10×112	32.9	11.4	11³/₈	0.755	¾	³/₈	10.4	10³/₈	1.25	1¼	1.75	1¹⁵/₁₆	1	7½	5½
×100	29.4	11.1	11¹/₈	0.680	¹¹/₁₆	³/₈	10.3	10³/₈	1.12	1¹/₈	1.62	1¹³/₁₆	1		
×88	25.9	10.8	10⁷/₈	0.605	⁵/₈	⁵/₁₆	10.3	10¼	0.990	1	1.49	1¹¹/₁₆	¹⁵/₁₆		
×77	22.6	10.6	10⁵/₈	0.530	½	¼	10.2	10¼	0.870	⁷/₈	1.37	1⁹/₁₆	⁷/₈		
×68	20.0	10.4	10³/₈	0.470	½	¼	10.1	10¹/₈	0.770	¾	1.27	1⁷/₁₆	⁷/₈		
×60	17.6	10.2	10¼	0.420	⁷/₁₆	¼	10.1	10¹/₈	0.680	¹¹/₁₆	1.18	1³/₈	¹³/₁₆		
×54	15.8	10.1	10¹/₈	0.370	³/₈	³/₁₆	10.0	10	0.615	⁵/₈	1.12	1⁵/₁₆	¹³/₁₆	↓	↓
×49	14.4	10.0	10	0.340	⁵/₁₆	³/₁₆	10.0	10	0.560	⁹/₁₆	1.06	1¼	¹³/₁₆		
W10×45	13.3	10.1	10¹/₈	0.350	³/₈	³/₁₆	8.02	8	0.620	⁵/₈	1.12	1⁵/₁₆	¹³/₁₆	7½	5½
×39	11.5	9.92	9⁷/₈	0.315	⁵/₁₆	³/₁₆	7.99	8	0.530	½	1.03	1³/₁₆	¹³/₁₆	↓	↓
×33	9.71	9.73	9¾	0.290	⁵/₁₆	³/₁₆	7.96	8	0.435	⁷/₁₆	0.935	1¹/₈	¾		
W10×30	8.84	10.5	10½	0.300	⁵/₁₆	³/₁₆	5.81	5¾	0.510	½	0.810	1¹/₈	¹¹/₁₆	8¼	2¾ᵍ
×26	7.61	10.3	10³/₈	0.260	¼	¹/₈	5.77	5¾	0.440	⁷/₁₆	0.740	1¹/₁₆	¹¹/₁₆	↓	↓
×22ᶜ	6.49	10.2	10¹/₈	0.240	¼	¹/₈	5.75	5¾	0.360	³/₈	0.660	¹⁵/₁₆	⁵/₈		
W10×19	5.62	10.2	10¼	0.250	¼	¹/₈	4.02	4	0.395	³/₈	0.695	¹⁵/₁₆	⁵/₈	8³/₈	2¼ᵍ
×17ᶜ	4.99	10.1	10¹/₈	0.240	¼	¹/₈	4.01	4	0.330	⁵/₁₆	0.630	⁷/₈	⁹/₁₆	↓	↓
×15ᶜ	4.41	10.0	10	0.230	¼	¹/₈	4.00	4	0.270	¼	0.570	¹³/₁₆	⁹/₁₆		
×12ᶜ·ᶠ	3.54	9.87	9⁷/₈	0.190	³/₁₆	¹/₈	3.96	4	0.210	³/₁₆	0.510	¾	⁹/₁₆		

ᶜ Shape is slender for compression with F_y = 50 ksi.
ᶠ Shape exceeds compact limit for flexure with F_y = 50 ksi.
ᵍ The actual size, combination, and orientation of fastener components should be compared with the geometry of the cross-section to ensure compatibility.
ᵛ Shape does not meet the h/t_w limit for shear in Specification Section G2.1a with F_y = 50 ksi.

Copyright © American Institute of Steel Construction, Inc. Reprinted with permission.
All rights reserved.

Structural Metal Shape Designations. (CONTINUED)

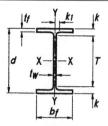

Table 1–1 (continued)
W Shapes
Dimensions

Shape	Area, A	Depth, d		Web Thickness, t_w		$\frac{t_w}{2}$	Flange Width, b_f		Flange Thickness, t_f		Distance k k_{des}	k_{det}	k_1	T	Workable Gage
	in.²	in.		in.		in.	in.		in.		in.	in.	in.	in.	in.
W8×67	19.7	9.00	9	0.570	9/16	5/16	8.28	8¼	0.935	15/16	1.33	1⅝	15/16	5¾	5½
×58	17.1	8.75	8¾	0.510	½	¼	8.22	8¼	0.810	13/16	1.20	1½	⅞		
×48	14.1	8.50	8½	0.400	⅜	3/16	8.11	8⅛	0.685	11/16	1.08	1⅜	13/16		
×40	11.7	8.25	8¼	0.360	⅜	3/16	8.07	8⅛	0.560	9/16	0.954	1¼	13/16		
×35	10.3	8.12	8⅛	0.310	5/16	3/16	8.02	8	0.495	½	0.889	1 3/16	13/16	↓	↓
×31ᶠ	9.12	8.00	8	0.285	5/16	3/16	8.00	8	0.435	7/16	0.829	1⅛	¾		
W8×28	8.24	8.06	8	0.285	5/16	3/16	6.54	6½	0.465	7/16	0.859	15/16	⅝	6⅛	4
×24	7.08	7.93	7⅞	0.245	¼	⅛	6.50	6½	0.400	⅜	0.794	⅞	9/16	6⅛	4
W8×21	6.16	8.28	8¼	0.250	¼	⅛	5.27	5¼	0.400	⅜	0.700	⅞	9/16	6½	2¾ᵍ
×18	5.26	8.14	8⅛	0.230	¼	⅛	5.25	5¼	0.330	5/16	0.630	13/16	9/16	6½	2¾ᵍ
W8×15	4.44	8.11	8⅛	0.245	¼	⅛	4.02	4	0.315	5/16	0.615	13/16	9/16	6½	2¼ᵍ
×13	3.84	7.99	8	0.230	¼	⅛	4.00	4	0.255	¼	0.555	¾	9/16	↓	↓
×10ᶜ,ᶠ	2.96	7.89	7⅞	0.170	3/16	⅛	3.94	4	0.205	3/16	0.505	11/16	½		
W6×25	7.34	6.38	6⅜	0.320	5/16	3/16	6.08	6⅛	0.455	7/16	0.705	15/16	9/16	4½	3½
×20	5.87	6.20	6¼	0.260	¼	⅛	6.02	6	0.365	⅜	0.615	⅞	9/16	↓	↓
×15ᶠ	4.43	5.99	6	0.230	¼	⅛	5.99	6	0.260	¼	0.510	¾	9/16		
W6×16	4.74	6.28	6¼	0.260	¼	⅛	4.03	4	0.405	⅜	0.655	⅞	9/16	4½	2¼ᵍ
×12	3.55	6.03	6	0.230	¼	⅛	4.00	4	0.280	¼	0.530	¾	9/16		
×9ᶠ	2.68	5.90	5⅞	0.170	3/16	⅛	3.94	4	0.215	3/16	0.465	11/16	½	↓	↓
×8.5ᶠ	2.52	5.83	5⅞	0.170	3/16	⅛	3.94	4	0.195	3/16	0.445	11/16	½		
W5×19	5.56	5.15	5⅛	0.270	¼	⅛	5.03	5	0.430	7/16	0.730	13/16	7/16	3½	2¾ᵍ
×16	4.71	5.01	5	0.240	¼	⅛	5.00	5	0.360	⅜	0.660	¾	7/16	3½	2¾ᵍ
W4×13	3.83	4.16	4⅛	0.280	¼	⅛	4.06	4	0.345	⅜	0.595	¾	½	2⅝	2¼ᵍ

ᶜ Shape is slender for compression with F_y = 50 ksi.
ᶠ Shape exceeds compact limit for flexure with F_y = 50 ksi.
ᵍ The actual size, combination, and orientation of fastener components should be compared with the geometry of the cross-section to ensure compatibility.

Copyright © American Institute of Steel Construction, Inc. Reprinted with permission.
All rights reserved.

Structural Metal Shape Designations. (CONTINUED)

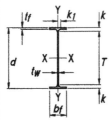

Table 1–2
M Shapes
Dimensions

Shape	Area, A	Depth, d		Web			Flange				Distance			Workable Gage
				Thickness, t_w		$\frac{t_w}{2}$	Width, b_f		Thickness, t_f		k	k_1	T	
	in.²	in.		in.		in.	in.		in.		in.	in.	in.	in.
M12.5×12.4[c,v]	3.63	12.5	12½	0.155	⅛	1/16	3.75	3¾	0.228	¼	9/16	⅜	11⅜	—
×11.6[c,v]	3.40	12.5	12½	0.155	⅛	1/16	3.50	3½	0.211	3/16	9/16	⅜	11⅜	—
M12×11.8[c]	3.47	12.0	12	0.177	3/16	⅛	3.07	3⅛	0.225	¼	9/16	⅜	10⅞	—
×10.8[c]	3.18	12.0	12	0.160	3/16	⅛	3.07	3⅛	0.210	3/16	9/16	⅜	10⅞	—
M12×10[c,v]	2.95	12.0	12	0.149	⅛	1/16	3.25	3¼	0.180	3/16	½	⅜	11	—
M10×9[c]	2.65	10.0	10	0.157	3/16	⅛	2.69	2¾	0.206	3/16	9/16	⅜	8⅞	—
×8[c]	2.37	9.95	10	0.141	⅛	1/16	2.69	2¾	0.182	3/16	9/16	⅜	8⅞	—
M10×7.5[c,v]	2.22	9.99	10	0.130	⅛	1/16	2.69	2¾	0.173	3/16	7/16	5/16	9⅛	—
M8×6.5[c]	1.92	8.00	8	0.135	⅛	1/16	2.28	2¼	0.189	3/16	9/16	⅜	6⅞	—
×6.2[c]	1.82	8.00	8	0.129	⅛	1/16	2.28	2¼	0.177	3/16	7/16	¼	7⅛	—
M6×4.4[c]	1.29	6.00	6	0.114	⅛	1/16	1.84	1⅞	0.171	3/16	⅜	¼	5¼	—
×3.7[c]	1.09	5.92	5⅞	0.0980	⅛	1/16	2.00	2	0.129	⅛	5/16	¼	5¼	—
M5×18.9[t]	5.56	5.00	5	0.316	5/16	3/16	5.00	5	0.416	7/16	13/16	½	3⅜	2¾[g]
M4×6[f]	1.75	3.80	3¾	0.130	⅛	1/16	3.80	3¾	0.160	3/16	½	⅜	2¾	—
×4.08	1.27	4.00	4	0.115	⅛	1/16	2.25	2¼	0.170	3/16	9/16	⅜	2⅞	—
×3.45	1.01	4.00	4	0.0920	1/16	1/16	2.25	2¼	0.130	⅛	½	⅜	3	—
×3.2	1.01	4.00	4	0.0920	1/16	1/16	2.25	2¼	0.130	⅛	½	⅜	3	—
M3×2.9	0.914	3.00	3	0.0900	1/16	1/16	2.25	2¼	0.130	⅛	½	⅜	2	—

[c] Shape is slender for compression with F_y = 36 ksi.
[f] Shape exceeds compact limit for flexure with F_y = 36 ksi.
[g] The actual size, combination, and orientation of fastener components should be compared with the geometry of the cross-section to ensure compatibility.
[t] Shape has tapered flanges while other M-shapes have parallel flange surfaces.
[v] Shape does not meet the h/t_w limit for shear in Specification Section G2.1b(i) with F_y = 36 ksi.
— Flange is too narrow to establish a workable gage.

Copyright © American Institute of Steel Construction, Inc. Reprinted with permission.
All rights reserved.

Structural Metal Shape Designations. (CONTINUED)

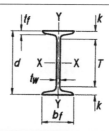

Table 1–3
S Shapes
Dimensions

Shape	Area, A	Depth, d		Web Thickness, t_w		$\frac{t_w}{2}$	Flange Width, b_f		Thickness, t_f		k	T	Workable Gage
	in.²	in.		in.		in.	in.		in.		in.	in.	in.
S24×121	35.5	24.5	24½	0.800	13/16	7/16	8.05	8	1.09	1 1/16	2	20½	4
×106	31.1	24.5	24½	0.620	5/8	5/16	7.87	7⅞	1.09	1 1/16	2	20½	4
S24×100	29.3	24.0	24	0.745	3/4	3/8	7.25	7¼	0.870	7/8	1¾	20½	4
×90	26.5	24.0	24	0.625	5/8	5/16	7.13	7⅛	0.870	7/8	1¾	20½	4
×80	23.5	24.0	24	0.500	1/2	1/4	7.00	7	0.870	7/8	1¾	20½	4
S20×96	28.2	20.3	20¼	0.800	13/16	7/16	7.20	7¼	0.920	15/16	1¾	16¾	4
×86	25.3	20.3	20¼	0.660	11/16	3/8	7.06	7	0.920	15/16	1¾	16¾	4
S20×75	22.0	20.0	20	0.635	5/8	5/16	6.39	6⅜	0.795	13/16	1⅝	16¾	3½⁹
×66	19.4	20.0	20	0.505	1/2	1/4	6.26	6¼	0.795	13/16	1⅝	16¾	3½⁹
S18×70	20.5	18.0	18	0.711	11/16	3/8	6.25	6¼	0.691	11/16	1½	15	3½⁹
×54.7	16.0	18.0	18	0.461	7/16	1/4	6.00	6	0.691	11/16	1½	15	3½⁹
S15×50	14.7	15.0	15	0.550	9/16	5/16	5.64	5⅝	0.622	5/8	1⅜	12¼	3½⁹
×42.9	12.6	15.0	15	0.411	7/16	1/4	5.50	5½	0.622	5/8	1⅜	12¼	3½⁹
S12×50	14.6	12.0	12	0.687	11/16	3/8	5.48	5½	0.659	11/16	1 7/16	9⅛	3⁹
×40.8	11.9	12.0	12	0.462	7/16	1/4	5.25	5¼	0.659	11/16	1 7/16	9⅛	3⁹
S12×35	10.2	12.0	12	0.428	7/16	1/4	5.08	5⅛	0.544	9/16	1 3/16	9⅝	3⁹
×31.8	9.31	12.0	12	0.350	3/8	3/16	5.00	5	0.544	9/16	1 3/16	9⅝	3⁹
S10×35	10.3	10.0	10	0.594	5/8	5/16	4.94	5	0.491	1/2	1⅛	7¾	2¾⁹
×25.4	7.45	10.0	10	0.311	5/16	3/16	4.66	4⅝	0.491	1/2	1⅛	7¾	2¾⁹
S8×23	6.76	8.00	8	0.441	7/16	1/4	4.17	4⅛	0.425	7/16	1	6	2¼⁹
×18.4	5.40	8.00	8	0.271	1/4	1/8	4.00	4	0.425	7/16	1	6	2¼⁹
S6×17.2	5.06	6.00	6	0.465	7/16	1/4	3.57	3⅝	0.359	3/8	13/16	4⅜	—
×12.5	3.66	6.00	6	0.232	1/4	1/8	3.33	3⅜	0.359	3/8	13/16	4⅜	—
S5×10	2.93	5.00	5	0.214	3/16	1/8	3.00	3	0.326	5/16	3/4	3½	—
S4×9.5	2.79	4.00	4	0.326	5/16	3/16	2.80	2¾	0.293	5/16	3/4	2½	—
×7.7	2.26	4.00	4	0.193	3/16	1/8	2.66	2⅝	0.293	5/16	3/4	2½	—
S3×7.5	2.20	3.00	3	0.349	3/8	3/16	2.51	2½	0.260	1/4	5/8	1¾	—
×5.7	1.66	3.00	3	0.170	3/16	1/8	2.33	2⅜	0.260	1/4	5/8	1¾	—

⁹ The actual size, combination, and orientation of fastener components should be compared with the geometry of the cross-section to ensure compatibility.
— Flange is too narrow to establish a workable gage.

Copyright © American Institute of Steel Construction, Inc. Reprinted with permission.
All rights reserved.

Structural Metal Shape Designations. (CONTINUED)

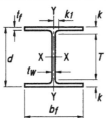

Table 1–4
HP Shapes
Dimensions

Shape	Area, A	Depth, d		Web			Flange				Distance			
				Thickness, t_w		$\frac{t_w}{2}$	Width, b_f		Thickness, t_f		k	k_1	T	Workable Gage
	in.²	in.		in.		in.	in.		in.		in.	in.	in.	in.
HP14×117[f]	34.4	14.2	14 1/4	0.805	13/16	7/16	14.9	14 7/8	0.805	13/16	1 1/2	1 1/16	11 1/4	5 1/2
×102[f]	30.0	14.0	14	0.705	11/16	3/8	14.8	14 3/4	0.705	11/16	1 3/8	1		
×89[f]	26.1	13.8	13 7/8	0.615	5/8	5/16	14.7	14 3/4	0.615	5/8	1 5/16	15/16	↓	↓
×73[c,f]	21.4	13.6	13 5/8	0.505	1/2	1/4	14.6	14 5/8	0.505	1/2	1 3/16	7/8		
HP12×84	24.6	12.3	12 1/4	0.685	11/16	3/8	12.3	12 1/4	0.685	11/16	1 3/8	1	9 1/2	5 1/2
×74[f]	21.8	12.1	12 1/8	0.605	5/8	5/16	12.2	12 1/4	0.610	5/8	1 5/16	15/16		
×63[f]	18.4	11.9	12	0.515	1/2	1/4	12.1	12 1/8	0.515	1/2	1 1/4	7/8	↓	↓
×53[f]	15.5	11.8	11 3/4	0.435	7/16	1/4	12.0	12	0.435	7/16	1 1/8	7/8		
HP10×57[f]	16.8	9.99	10	0.565	9/16	5/16	10.2	10 1/4	0.565	9/16	1 1/4	15/16	7 1/2	5 1/2
×42[f]	12.4	9.70	9 3/4	0.415	7/16	1/4	10.1	10 1/8	0.420	7/16	1 1/8	13/16	7 1/2	5 1/2
HP8×36[f]	10.6	8.02	8	0.445	7/16	1/4	8.16	8 1/8	0.445	7/16	1 1/8	7/8	5 3/4	5 1/2

[c] Shape is slender for compression with F_y = 50 ksi.
[f] Shape exceeds compact limit for flexure with F_y = 50 ksi.

Copyright © American Institute of Steel Construction, Inc. Reprinted with permission.
All rights reserved.

Structural Metal Shape Designations. (CONTINUED)

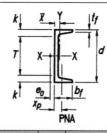

PNA

Table 1–5
C Shapes
Dimensions

Shape	Area, A	Depth, d		Web Thickness, t_w		$\frac{t_w}{2}$	Flange Width, b_f		Flange Thickness, t_f		k	T	Workable Gage	r_{ts}	h_o
	in.²	in.		in.		in.	in.		in.		in.	in.	in.	in.	in.
C15×50	14.7	15.0	15	0.716	11/16	3/8	3.72	3³/₄	0.650	5/8	1⁷/₁₆	12¹/₈	2¹/₄	1.17	14.4
×40	11.8	15.0	15	0.520	1/2	1/4	3.52	3¹/₂	0.650	5/8	1⁷/₁₆	12¹/₈	2	1.15	14.4
×33.9	10.0	15.0	15	0.400	3/8	3/16	3.40	3³/₈	0.650	5/8	1⁷/₁₆	12¹/₈	2	1.13	14.4
C12×30	8.81	12.0	12	0.510	1/2	1/4	3.17	3¹/₈	0.501	1/2	1¹/₈	9³/₄	1³/₄ᵍ	1.01	11.5
×25	7.34	12.0	12	0.387	3/8	3/16	3.05	3	0.501	1/2	1¹/₈	9³/₄	1³/₄ᵍ	1.00	11.5
×20.7	6.08	12.0	12	0.282	5/16	3/16	2.94	3	0.501	1/2	1¹/₈	9³/₄	1³/₄ᵍ	0.983	11.5
C10×30	8.81	10.0	10	0.673	11/16	3/8	3.03	3	0.436	7/16	1	8	1³/₄ᵍ	0.925	9.56
×25	7.34	10.0	10	0.526	1/2	1/4	2.89	2⁷/₈	0.436	7/16	1	8	1³/₄ᵍ	0.911	9.56
×20	5.87	10.0	10	0.379	3/8	3/16	2.74	2³/₄	0.436	7/16	1	8	1¹/₂ᵍ	0.894	9.56
×15.3	4.48	10.0	10	0.240	1/4	1/8	2.60	2⁵/₈	0.436	7/16	1	8	1¹/₂ᵍ	0.869	9.56
C9×20	5.87	9.00	9	0.448	7/16	1/4	2.65	2⁵/₈	0.413	7/16	1	7	1¹/₂ᵍ	0.848	8.59
×15	4.41	9.00	9	0.285	5/16	3/16	2.49	2¹/₂	0.413	7/16	1	7	1³/₈ᵍ	0.824	8.59
×13.4	3.94	9.00	9	0.233	1/4	1/8	2.43	2³/₈	0.413	7/16	1	7	1³/₈ᵍ	0.813	8.59
C8×18.7	5.51	8.00	8	0.487	1/2	1/4	2.53	2¹/₂	0.390	3/8	15/16	6¹/₄	1¹/₂ᵍ	0.800	7.61
×13.7	4.04	8.00	8	0.303	5/16	3/16	2.34	2³/₈	0.390	3/8	15/16	6¹/₄	1³/₈ᵍ	0.774	7.61
×11.5	3.37	8.00	8	0.220	1/4	1/8	2.26	2¹/₄	0.390	3/8	15/16	6¹/₄	1³/₈ᵍ	0.756	7.61
C7×14.7	4.33	7.00	7	0.419	7/16	1/4	2.30	2¹/₄	0.366	3/8	7/8	5¹/₄	1¹/₄ᵍ	0.738	6.63
×12.2	3.60	7.00	7	0.314	5/16	3/16	2.19	2¹/₄	0.366	3/8	7/8	5¹/₄	1¹/₄ᵍ	0.721	6.63
×9.8	2.87	7.00	7	0.210	3/16	1/8	2.09	2¹/₈	0.366	3/8	7/8	5¹/₄	1¹/₄ᵍ	0.698	6.63
C6×13	3.81	6.00	6	0.437	7/16	1/4	2.16	2¹/₈	0.343	5/16	13/16	4 /8	1³/₈ᵍ	0.689	5.66
×10.5	3.08	6.00	6	0.314	5/16	3/16	2.03	2	0.343	5/16	13/16	4³/₈	1¹/₈ᵍ	0.669	5.66
×8.2	2.39	6.00	6	0.200	3/16	1/8	1.92	1⁷/₈	0.343	5/16	13/16	4³/₈	1¹/₈ᵍ	0.643	5.66
C5×9	2.64	5.00	5	0.325	5/16	3/16	1.89	1⁷/₈	0.320	5/16	3/4	3¹/₂	1¹/₈ᵍ	0.617	4.68
×6.7	1.97	5.00	5	0.190	3/16	1/8	1.75	1³/₄	0.320	5/16	3/4	3¹/₂	—	0.584	4.68
C4×7.2	2.13	4.00	4	0.321	5/16	3/16	1.72	1³/₄	0.296	5/16	3/4	2¹/₂	1ᵍ	0.563	3.70
×5.4	1.58	4.00	4	0.184	3/16	1/8	1.58	1⁵/₈	0.296	5/16	3/4	2¹/₂	—	0.528	3.70
×4.5	1.38	4.00	4	0.125	1/8	1/16	1.58	1⁵/₈	0.296	5/16	3/4	2¹/₂	—	0.524	3.70
C3×6	1.76	3.00	3	0.356	3/8	3/16	1.60	1⁵/₈	0.273	1/4	11/16	1⁵/₈	—	0.519	2.73
×5	1.47	3.00	3	0.258	1/4	1/8	1.50	1¹/₂	0.273	1/4	11/16	1⁵/₈	—	0.495	2.73
×4.1	1.20	3.00	3	0.170	3/16	1/8	1.41	1³/₈	0.273	1/4	11/16	1⁵/₈	—	0.469	2.73
×3.5	1.09	3.00	3	0.132	1/8	1/16	1.37	1³/₈	0.273	1/4	11/16	1⁵/₈	—	0.455	2.73

ᵍ The actual size, combination, and orientation of fastener components should be compared with the geometry of the cross-section to ensure compatibility.
— Flange is too narrow to establish a workable gage.

Copyright © American Institute of Steel Construction, Inc. Reprinted with permission. All rights reserved.

Structural Metal Shape Designations. (CONTINUED)

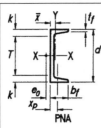

Table 1–6
MC Shapes
Dimensions

Shape	Area, A	Depth, d		Web Thickness, t_w		$\frac{t_w}{2}$	Flange Width, b_f		Average Thickness, t_f		Distance k	T	Workable Gage	r_{ts}	h_o
	in.²	in.		in.		in.	in.		in.		in.	in.	in.	in.	in.
MC18×58	17.1	18.0	18	0.700	11/16	3/8	4.20	4 1/4	0.625	5/8	1 7/16	15 1/8	2 1/2	1.35	17.4
×51.9	15.3	18.0	18	0.600	5/8	5/16	4.10	4 1/8	0.625	5/8	1 7/16	↓	↓	1.35	17.4
×45.8	13.5	18.0	18	0.500	1/2	1/4	4.00	4	0.625	5/8	1 7/16			1.34	17.4
×42.7	12.6	18.0	18	0.450	7/16	1/4	3.95	4	0.625	5/8	1 7/16	↓	↓	1.34	17.4
MC13×50	14.7	13.0	13	0.787	13/16	7/16	4.41	4 3/8	0.610	5/8	1 7/16	10 1/8	2 1/2	1.41	12.4
×40	11.8	13.0	13	0.560	9/16	5/16	4.19	4 1/8	0.610	5/8	1 7/16	↓		1.38	12.4
×35	10.3	13.0	13	0.447	7/16	1/4	4.07	4 1/8	0.610	5/8	1 7/16			1.35	12.4
×31.8	9.35	13.0	13	0.375	3/8	3/16	4.00	4	0.610	5/8	1 7/16	↓	↓	1.34	12.4
MC12×50	14.7	12.0	12	0.835	13/16	7/16	4.14	4 1/8	0.700	11/16	1 5/16	9 3/8	2 1/2	1.37	11.3
×45	13.2	12.0	12	0.710	11/16	3/8	4.01	4	0.700	11/16	1 5/16			1.35	11.3
×40	11.8	12.0	12	0.590	9/16	5/16	3.89	3 7/8	0.700	11/16	1 5/16	↓	↓	1.33	11.3
×35	10.3	12.0	12	0.465	7/16	1/4	3.77	3 3/4	0.700	11/16	1 5/16			1.30	11.3
×31	9.12	12.0	12	0.370	3/8	3/16	3.67	3 5/8	0.700	11/16	1 5/16	↓	2 1/4	1.28	11.3
MC12×10.6[c]	3.10	12.0	12	0.190	3/16	1/8	1.50	1 1/2	0.309	5/16	3/4	10 1/2	—	0.477	11.7
MC10×41.1	12.1	10.0	10	0.796	13/16	7/16	4.32	4 3/8	0.575	9/16	1 5/16	7 3/8	2 1/2[g]	1.44	9.43
×33.6	9.87	10.0	10	0.575	9/16	5/16	4.10	4 1/8	0.575	9/16	1 5/16	7 3/8	2 1/2[g]	1.40	9.43
×28.5	8.37	10.0	10	0.425	7/16	1/4	3.95	4	0.575	9/16	1 5/16	7 3/8	2 1/2[g]	1.36	9.43
MC10×25	7.35	10.0	10	0.380	3/8	3/16	3.41	3 3/8	0.575	9/16	1 5/16	7 3/8	2[g]	1.17	9.43
×22	6.45	10.0	10	0.290	5/16	3/16	3.32	3 3/8	0.575	9/16	1 5/16	7 3/8	2[g]	1.14	9.43
MC10×8.4[c]	2.46	10.0	10	0.170	3/16	1/8	1.50	1 1/2	0.280	1/4	3/4	8 1/2	—	0.486	9.72
×6.5[c]	1.95	10.0	10	0.152	1/8	1/16	1.17	1 1/8	0.202	3/16	9/16	8 7/8	—	0.364	9.80
MC9×25.4	7.47	9.00	9	0.450	7/16	1/4	3.50	3 1/2	0.550	9/16	1 1/4	6 1/2	2[g]	1.20	8.45
×23.9	7.02	9.00	9	0.400	3/8	3/16	3.45	3 1/2	0.550	9/16	1 1/4	6 1/2	2[g]	1.18	8.45
MC8×22.8	6.70	8.00	8	0.427	7/16	1/4	3.50	3 1/2	0.525	1/2	1 3/16	5 5/8	2[g]	1.20	7.48
×21.4	6.28	8.00	8	0.375	3/8	3/16	3.45	3 1/2	0.525	1/2	1 3/16	5 5/8	2[g]	1.18	7.48
MC8×20	5.88	8.00	8	0.400	3/8	3/16	3.03	3	0.500	1/2	1 1/8	5 3/4	2[g]	1.03	7.50
×18.7	5.50	8.00	8	0.353	3/8	3/16	2.98	3	0.500	1/2	1 1/8	5 3/4	2[g]	1.02	7.50
MC8×8.5	2.50	8.00	8	0.179	3/16	1/8	1.87	1 7/8	0.311	5/16	13/16	6 3/8	1 1/8[g]	0.624	7.69

[c] Shape is slender for compression with F_y = 36 ksi.
[g] The actual size, combination, and orientation of fastener components should be compared with the geometry of the cross-section to ensure compatibility.
— Flange is too narrow to establish a workable gage.

Copyright © American Institute of Steel Construction, Inc. Reprinted with permission.
All rights reserved.

Structural Metal Shape Designations. (CONTINUED)

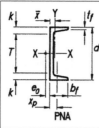

Table 1–6 (continued)
MC Shapes
Dimensions

Shape	Area, A	Depth, d		Web Thickness, t_w		$\frac{t_w}{2}$	Flange Width, b_f		Average Thickness, t_f		Distance k	T	Workable Gage	r_{ts}	h_o
	in.²	in.		in.		in.	in.		in.		in.	in.	in.	in.	in.
MC7×22.7	6.67	7.00	7	0.503	1/2	1/4	3.60	3 5/8	0.500	1/2	1 1/8	4 3/4	2ᵍ	1.23	6.50
×19.1	5.61	7.00	7	0.352	3/8	3/16	3.45	3 1/2	0.500	1/2	1 1/8	4 3/4	2ᵍ	1.18	6.50
MC6×18	5.29	6.00	6	0.379	3/8	3/16	3.50	3 1/2	0.475	1/2	1 1/16	3 7/8	2ᵍ	1.20	5.53
×15.3	4.49	6.00	6	0.340	5/16	3/16	3.50	3 1/2	0.385	3/8	7/8	4 1/4	2ᵍ	1.20	5.62
MC6×16.3	4.79	6.00	6	0.375	3/8	3/16	3.00	3	0.475	1/2	11/16	3 7/8	1 3/4ᵍ	1.03	5.53
×15.1	4.44	6.00	6	0.316	5/16	3/16	2.94	3	0.475	1/2	11/16	3 7/8	1 3/4ᵍ	1.01	5.53
MC6×12	3.53	6.00	6	0.310	5/16	3/16	2.50	2 1/2	0.375	3/8	7/8	4 1/4	1 1/2ᵍ	0.856	5.63
MC6×7	2.09	6.00	6	0.179	3/16	1/8	1.88	1 7/8	0.291	5/16	3/4	4 1/2	—	0.638	5.71
×6.5	1.95	6.00	6	0.155	1/8	1/16	1.85	1 7/8	0.291	5/16	3/4	4 1/2	—	0.630	5.71
MC4×13.8	4.03	4.00	4	0.500	1/2	1/4	2.50	2 1/2	0.500	1/2	1	2	—	0.852	3.50
MC3×7.1	2.11	3.00	3	0.312	5/16	3/16	1.94	2	0.351	3/8	13/16	1 3/8	—	0.657	2.65

ᵍ The actual size, combination, and orientation of fastener components should be compared with the geometry of the cross-section to ensure compatibility.
— Flange is too narrow to establish a workable gage.

Copyright © American Institute of Steel Construction, Inc. Reprinted with permission.
All rights reserved.

Structural Metal Shape Designations. (CONTINUED)

glossary of key terms

active animation An animation in which the observer (camera) as well as objects in the scene actively move around and through the scene.

additive color model The RGB color system in which the primary colors of red, green, and blue are added together to create white.

adjacent views Orthogonal views created immediately next to each other, aligned side by side to share a common dimension, and presented on a single plane.

agenda The list of topics for discussion/action at a team meeting.

algebraic constraints Constraint that define the value of a selected variable as the result of an algebraic expression containing other variables from the solid model.

allowance The difference between the maximum material limits of mating parts. It is the minimum clearance or maximum interference between parts.

alpha channel An optional layer of image data containing an additional 8 bits of grayscale data that can be used to control transparency affecting the entire image.

ambient light Indirect light in a scene that does not come directly from a light source, but arrives at a surface by bouncing around or reflecting off other surfaces in the scene.

analysis The study of the behavior of a physical system under certain imposed conditions.

anchor edge The same edge that can be easily and confidently located on multiple views and on a pictorial for an object.

anchor point The same point, usually a vertex, that can be easily and confidently located on multiple views and on a pictorial for an object.

anchor surface The same surface that can be easily and confidently located on multiple views and on a pictorial for an object.

angle of thread The angle between the side of a thread and a line perpendicular to the axis of the thread.

ANSI Y14.5 *(ASME Y14.5M-1994)* Industry standard document that outlines uniform practices for displaying and interpreting dimensions and related information on drawings and other forms of engineering documentation.

approval signatures The dated signatures or initials of the people responsible for certain aspects of a formal drawing, such as the people who did the drafting or the engineer responsible for the function of the part.

arc A curved entity that represents a portion of a circle.

architects Professionals who complete conceptual designs for civil engineering projects.

Architect's scale A device used to measure or draw lines in the English system of units with a base unit of inches and fractions of an inch.

arrowhead A small triangle at the end of dimension lines and leaders to indicate the direction and extent of a dimension.

as-built drawings The marked-up drawings from a civil engineering project that show any modifications implemented in the field during construction.

as-built plans Drawings that show exactly how buildings were constructed, especially when variations exist between the final building and the plans created during the design phase.

aspect A quantitative measure of the direction of a slope face.

assembly A collection of parts and/or subassemblies that have been put together to make a device or structure that performs a specific function.

assembly constraints Used to establish relationships between instances in the development of a flexible assembly model.

assembly dimensions Dimensions that show where parts must be placed relative to other parts when the device is being put together.

associative constraints *See* algebraic constraints.

associativity The situation whereby parts can be modified and the components referenced to the parts will be modified accordingly.

attribute Spatial information that describes the characteristics of spatial features.

auxiliary views Views on any projection plane other than a primary or principal projection plane.

axis The longitudinal centerline that passes through a screw.

axonometric drawing   A drawing in which all three dimensional axes on an object can be seen, with the scaling factor constant in each direction. Usually, one axis is shown as being vertical.

back light   A scene light, usually located behind objects in the scene, which is used to create a defining edge that visually separates foreground objects from the background.

balloons   Closed geometric shapes, usually circles, containing identification numbers and placed beside parts on a layout or assembly drawing to help identify those parts.

bar chart   A chart using bars of varying heights and widths to represent quantitative data.

base feature   The first feature created for a part, usually a protrusion.

base instance   The one fixed instance within an assembly.

baseline dimensioning   A method for specifying the location of features on a part whereby all the locations are relative to a common feature or edge.

basic dimension   A dimension that is theoretically exact. It is identified by a box around the dimension. It locates the perfect position of features from clearly identified datums.

bearing   The angle that a line makes with a North-South line as seen in a plan view.

benchmarks   Points established by the U.S. Geological Survey that can be used to accurately locate control points on a construction site.

bill of materials (BOM)   A drawing or table in a drawing that lists all of the parts needed to build a device by (at least) the part number, part name, type of material used, and number of times the part is used in the device.

bitmap textures   Texture mapping routines that are based on referencing external image files.

black box diagram   A diagram that shows the major inputs and outputs from a system.

blend   A solid formed by a smooth transition between two or more profiles.

blind extrusion   An extrusion made to a specified length in a selected direction.

blind hole   A hole that does not pass completely through a part.

blueprints   The name sometimes given to construction drawings based on historical blue-on-white drawings that were produced from ink drawings.

bolt   A threaded fastener that passes completely through parts and holds them together using a nut.

Boolean operations   In early versions of 3-D CAD software, commands used to combine solids.

border   A thick line that defines the perimeter of a drawing.

boring   The general process of making a hole in a part by plunging a rotating tool bit into a part, moving a rotating part into a stationary tool bit, or moving a part into a rotating tool bit.

bottom-up modeling   The process of creating individual parts and then creating an assembly from them.

boundary conditions   The constraints and loads added to the boundaries of a finite element model.

boundary representation (b-rep)   A method used to build solid models from their bounding surfaces.

bounding box   A square box used to sketch circles or ellipses.

brainstorming   The process of group creative thinking used to generate as many ideas as possible for consideration.

brainwriting   A process of group creative thinking where sketching is the primary mode of communication between team members.

brazing   A method for joining separate metal parts by heating the parts, flowing a molten metal (solder) between them, and allowing the unit to cool and harden.

brief   A small graphic using word content alone.

broach   A long, shaped cutting tool that moves along the length of a part when placed against it. It is used to create uniquely shaped holes and slots.

broaching   A process of creating uniquely shaped holes and slots using a long, shaped cutting tool that moves along the length of a part in a single stroke when placed against the part.

broken-out section   The section view produced when the cutting plane is partially imbedded into the object, requiring an irregular portion of the object to be removed before the hypothetically cut surface can be seen.

buffer   Measured in units of distance or time, a zone around a map feature. A buffer is useful for proximity analysis.

bump mapping   A technique used to create the illusion of rough or bumpy surface detail through surface normal perturbation.

business diagram   A diagram used in an organization to show organizational hierarchy, task planning or analysis, or relationships between different groups or sets of information.

butt joint   A joint between two parts wherein the parts are butted, or placed next to each other.

CAD   Computer-aided drawing. The use of computer hardware and software for the purpose of creating, modifying, and storing engineering drawings in an electronic format.

CAD designers   Designers who create 3-D computer models for analysis and detailing.

cabinet oblique drawing   An oblique drawing where one half the true length of the depth dimension is measured along the receding axes.

caliper   A handheld device used to measure objects with a fair degree of accuracy.

cap screw   A small threaded fastener that mates with a threaded hole.

casting   A method of creating a part by pouring or injecting molten material into the cavity of a mold, allowing it to harden, and then removing it from the mold.

cavalier oblique drawing   An oblique drawing where the true length of the depth dimension is measured along the receding axes.

center-of-mass (centroid)   The origin of the coordinate axes for which the first moments are zero.

centerline   A series of alternating long and short dashed lines used to identify an axis of rotational symmetry.

centermark   A small right-angle cross that is used to identify the end view of an axis of rotational symmetry.

Central Meridian   The line of longitude that defines the center and is often the x-origin of a projected coordinate system.

Central Parallel   The line of latitude that divides a map into north and south halves and is often the y-origin of a projected coordinate system.

chain dimensioning   A method for specifiying the location of features on a part whereby the location of each feature is successively specified relative to the location of the previous feature.

chamfers   Angled cut transitions between two intersecting surfaces.

charts   Charts, graphs, tables, and diagrams of ideas and quantitative data.

child feature   A feature that is dependent upon the existence of a previously created feature.

chief designer   The individual who oversees other members of the design team and manages the overall project.

circle   A closed curved figure where all points on it are equidistant from its center point.

Clarke Ellipsoid of 1866   A reference ellipsoid having a semimajor axis of approximately 6,378,206.4 meters and a flattening of 1/294.9786982. It is the basis for the North American Datum of 1927 (NAD27) and other datums.

clearance   A type of fit where space exists between two mating parts.

clearances   The minimum distances between two instances in an assembly.

clip   A geoprocessing command that extracts the features from a coverage that reside entirely within a boundary defined by features in another coverage.

clipping plane   A 3-D virtual camera technique that allows you to selectively exclude, and not view or render, unnecessary objects in a scene that are either too close or too far away.

CODEC   Video compression-decompression algorithm.

collision detection   A built-in software capability for calculating and graphically animating the results of collisions between multiple objects based on object properties of speed, mass, and gravity.

color mapping   Sometimes called diffuse mapping, color mapping replaces the main surface color of a model with an external image map or texture.

combining solids   The process of cutting, joining, or intersecting two objects to form a third object.

components   References of object geometry used in assembly models.

compositing   The technique and art of rendering in layers or passes, editing the image on each layer as needed, and compiling the edited layers or images into a single unified final image.

computer-aided design (CAD)   The process by which computers are used to model and analyze designed products.

computer-aided manufacturing (CAM)   The process by which parts are manufactured directly from 3-D computer models.

concept mapping   The creative process by which the central idea is placed in the middle of a page and related concepts radiate out from that central idea.

conceptual design   The initial idea for a design before analysis has been performed.

concurrent engineering   The process by which designers, analysts, and manufacturers work together from the start to design a product.

consensus   A process of decision making where an option is chosen that everyone supports.

constraint   A boundary condition applied to a finite element model to prevent it from moving through space.

constraints   Geometric relationships, dimensions, or equations that control the size, shape, and/or orientation of entities in a sketch or solid model.

constructive solid geometry (CSG)   A method used to build solid models from primitive shapes based on Boolean set theory.

construction drawings   Working drawings, often created by civil engineers, that are used to build large-scale, one-of-a-kind structures.

construction line A faint line used in sketching to align items and define shapes.

continuation blocks Header blocks used on the second and subsequent pages of multipage drawings.

contour dimensioning Placing each dimension in the view where the contour or shape of the feature shows up best.

contour interval The vertical distance between contours.

contour rule A drawing practice where each dimension should be placed in the view where the contour shape is best shown.

contours Lines or curves that represent the same elevation across the landscape.

control points Points at a construction site that are referenced to an origin by north, south, east, or west coordinates.

coordinate measuring machine A computer-based tool used to digitize object geometry for direct input to a 3-D CAD system.

corner views An isometric view of an object created from the perspective at a given corner of the object.

cosmetic features Features that modify the appearance of the surface but do not alter the size or shape of the object.

cover sheet The first page in a set of construction drawings showing a map of the location of the project and possibly an index.

crest The top surface or point joining the sides of a thread.

critical path The sequence of activities in a project that have the longest duration.

critical path method (CPM) A tool for determining the least amount of time in which a project can be completed.

cross-section The intersection between a cutting plane and a 3-D object.

curved surface Any nonflat surface on an object.

cut (noun) A feature created by the removal of solid volume from a model.

cut (verb) To remove the volume of interference between two objects from one of the objects.

cutaway diagram A diagram that allows the reader to see a slice of an object.

cutting-plane An imaginary plane that intersects with an object to form a cross section.

cutting plane A theoretical plane used to hypothetically cut and remove a portion of an object to reveal its interior details.

cutting plane line On an orthographic view of an object, the presentation of the edge view of a cutting plane used to hypothetically cut and remove a portion of that object for viewing.

cutting segment On a stepped cutting plane for an offset section view, that portion of the plane that hypothetically cuts and reveals the interior detail of a feature of interest.

data structure The organization of data within a specific computer system that allows the information to be stored and manipulated effectively.

database A collection of information for a computer and a method for interpretation of the information from which the original model can be re-created.

datum A theoretical plane or axis established by real features on an object for the purpose of defining the datum reference frame.

datum geometries Geometric entities such as points, axes, and planes that do not actually exist on real parts, but are used to help locate and define other features.

datum planes The planes used to define the locations of features and entities in the construction of a solid model.

datum reference frame A system of three mutually perpendicular planes used as the coordinate system for geometric dimensioning.

decimal degrees (DD) A measuring system in which values of latitude and longitude are expressed in decimal format rather than in degrees, minutes, and seconds, such as 87.5°.

deep drawing Creating a thin-shelled part by pressing sheet metal into a deep cavity mold.

default tolerances Usually appearing in the drawing header, the tolerances to be assumed for any dimension show on a part when that dimension does not specify any tolerances.

degrees, minutes, seconds (DMS) A measuring system for longitude and latitude values, such as 87° 30' 00", in which 60 seconds equals 1 minute and 60 minutes equals 1 degree.

density The mass per unit volume for a given material.

depiction An illustration describing and simplifying factual information on a real-world system.

depth of thread The distance between the crest and the root of a thread, measured normal to the axis.

depth-mapped shadows Also called shadow-mapped shadows, depth-mapped shadows use a precalculated depth map to determine the location, density, and edge sharpness of shadows.

descriptive geometry A two-dimensional graphical construction technique used for geometric analysis of three-dimensional objects.

design (noun)   An original manifestation of a device or method created for performing one or more useful functions.

design (verb)   The process of creating a design (noun).

design analysts   Individuals who analyze design concepts by computer methods to determine their structural, thermal, or vibration characteristics.

design documentation   The set of drawings and specifications that illustrate and thoroughly describe a designed product.

design process   The multistep, iterative process by which products are conceived and produced.

design table   A table or spreadsheet that lists all of the versions of a family model, the dimensions or features that may change, and the values in any of its versions.

design tree   *See* model tree.

detail designers   The individuals who create engineering drawings, complete with annotation, from 3-D computer models or from engineering sketches.

detail drawing   A formal drawing that shows the geometry, dimensions, tolerances, materials, and any processes needed to fabricate a part.

detail sections   Drawings included in a set of construction plans that show how the various components are assembled.

devil's advocate   The team member who challenges ideas to ensure that all options are considered by the group.

diagram   An illustration that explains information, represents a process, or shows how pieces are put together.

diametric drawing   An axonometric drawing in which the scaling factor is the same for two of the axes.

die   A special tool made specifically to deform raw or stock material into a desired outline of a part or feature in a single operation.

die casting   A method of casting where the mold is formed by cutting a cavity into steel or another hard material. *See* casting.

digital elevation model (DEM)   The representation of continuous elevation values over a topographic surface by a regular array of z-values referenced to a common datum. It is typically used to represent terrain relief.

dimension   A numerical value expressed in appropriate units of measure and used to define the size, location, geometric characteristic, or surface texture of a part or part feature.

dimension line   A thin, dark, solid line that terminates at each end with arrowheads. The value of a dimension typically is shown in the center of the dimension line.

dimension name   The unique alphanumeric designation of a variable dimension.

dimensional constraints   Measurements used to control the size or position of entities in a sketch.

direct dimensioning   Dimensioning between two key points to minimize tolerance accumulation.

directional light   A computer-generated light source designed to simulate the effect of light sources, such as the sun, that are so far away from objects in the scene that lighting and shadow patterns in the scene appear to be parallel.

displacement   A change in the location of points on an object after it has been subjected to external loads.

dissolve   A geoprocessing command that removes boundaries between adjacent polygons that have the same value for a specified attribute.

draft   The slight angling of the walls of a cast, forged, drawn, or stamped part to enable the part to be removed from the mold more easily.

drawing   A collection of images and other detailed graphical specifications intended to represent physical objects or processes for the purpose of accurately re-creating those objects or processes.

drill bit   A long, rotating cutting tool with a sharpened tip used to make holes.

drilling   A process of making a hole by plunging a rotating tool bit into a part.

drill press   A machine that holds, spins, and plunges a rotating tool bit into a part to make holes.

driven dimension   A variable connected to an algebraic constraint that can be modified only by user changes to the driving dimensions.

driving dimension   A variable used in an algebraic constraint to control the values of another (driven) dimension.

double-sided extrusion   A solid formed by the extrusion of a profile in both directions from its sketching plane.

EC Level   A number included in the title block of a drawing indicating that the part has undergone a revision.

edge tracking   A procedure by which successive edges on an object are simultaneously located on a pictorial image and on a multiview image of that object.

edge view (of a plane)   A view in which the given plane appears as a straight line.

EDM   Electric discharge machining; a process by which material is eroded from a part by passing an electric current between the part and an electrode (or a wire) through an electrolytic fluid.

electrical plan   A plan view showing the layout of electrical devices on a floor in a building.

elevation view In the construction of a perspective view, the object as viewed from the front, as if created by orthogonal projection.

elevation views Views of a structure that show changes in elevation (side or front views).

ellipse A closed curve figure where the sum of the distance between any point on the figure and its two foci is constant.

end mill A rotating cutting tool that, when placed in the spindle of a milling machine, can remove material in directions parallel or perpendicular to its rotation axis.

engineer (noun) A person who engages in the art of engineering.

engineer (verb) To plan and build a device that does not occur naturally within the environment.

Engineer's scale A device used to measure or draw lines in the English system of units with a base unit of inches and tenths of an inch.

engineering The profession in which knowledge of mathematical and natural sciences gained by study, experience, and practice is applied with judgment to develop and utilize economically the materials and forces of nature for the benefit of humanity.

engineering animation A dynamic virtual 3-D prototype of a mechanism or system that can be assembled (usually from preexisting or newly created 3-D CAD part models) and/or shown in operation over a period of time.

engineering change (EC) number A dated number that defines the degree to which the specifications of a part have been updated.

engineering design The process by which many competing factors of a product are weighed to select the best alternative in terms of cost, sustainability, and function.

engineering scale A device used to make measurements in much the same way a ruler is used.

explanation diagram An illustration explaining the way something works; a basic process; or the deconstruction of an object, a plan, or a drawing.

exploded assembly drawing A formal drawing, usually in pictorial form, that shows the orientation and sequence in which parts are put together to make a device.

exploded configuration A configuration of an assembly that shows instances separated from one another. An exploded configuration is used as the basis for an assembly drawing.

extension line A thin, dark, solid line extending from a point on an object, perpendicular to a dimension line used to indicate the extension of a surface or point to a location preferably outside the part outline.

external thread Threads that are formed on the outside of a cylindrical feature, such as on a bolt or stud.

extrude through all An extrusion that begins on the sketching plane and protrudes or cuts through all portions of the solid model that it encounters.

extrude to selected surface An extrusion where the protrusion or cut begins on the sketching plane and stops when it intersects a selected surface.

extrusion (in fabrication) A process for making long, solid shapes with a constant cross section by squeezing raw material under elevated temperatures and pressure through an orifice shaped with that cross section.

extrusion (in 3D modeling) A solid that is bounded by the surfaces swept out in space by a planar profile as it is pulled along a path perpendicular to the plane of the profile.

fabricate To make something from existing materials.

family model A collection of different versions of a part in a single model that can display any of the versions.

false easting A value applied to the origin of a coordinate system to modify the x-coordinate readings, usually to make all of the coordinate values positive.

false northing A value applied to the origin of a coordinate system to modify the y-coordinate readings, usually to make all of the coordinate values positive.

fastener A manufactured part whose primary function is to join two or more parts.

feature array A method for making additional features by placing copies of a master feature on the model at a specified equal spacing.

feature generalization The process of going from the specific to the general in analyzing data.

features Distinctive geometric shapes on solid parts; 3-D geometric entities that exist to serve some function.

feature-based solid modeling A solid modeling system that uses features to build models.

feature control frame The main alphabet of the language of geometric dimensioning and tolerancing. These boxes contain the geometric characteristic symbol, the geometric tolerances, and the relative datums.

feature pattern *See* feature array.

feature tree *See* model tree.

feature with size A cylindrical or spherical surface or a set of two opposed elements or opposed parallel surfaces associated with a size dimension. Typical features with size are holes, cylinders, spheres, and opposite sides of a rectangular block.

feature without size A planar surface or a feature where the normal vectors point in the same direction.

field A column in a table that stores the values for a single attribute.

fill light A light that softens and extends the illumination of the objects provided by the key light.

fillets   Smooth transitions of the internal edge created by two intersecting surfaces and tangent to both intersecting surfaces.

Finite Element Analysis   An advanced computer-based design analysis technique that involves subdividing an object into several small elements to determine stresses, displacements, pressure fields, thermal distributions, or electromagnetic fields.

first-angle projection   The process of creating a view of an object by imprinting its image, using orthogonal projection, on an opaque surface behind that object.

fishbone diagram   A diagram that shows the various subsystems in a device and the parts that make up each subsystem.

fixture   A mechanical device, such as a clamps or bracket, used for holding a workpiece in place while it is being modified.

flash   Bits of material that are left on a part from a casting or molding operation and found along the seams where the mold pieces separate to allow removal of the part.

floor plan   A plan view of a single floor in a building that shows the layout of the rooms.

flowchart   A quality improvement tools used to document, plan, or analyze a process or series of tasks.

foreshortened (line or plane)   Appearing shorter than its actual length in one of the primary views.

forging   A process of deforming metal with a common shape at room temperature into a new but similar shape by pressing it into a mold under elevated pressure.

form   The shape of the thread cross section when cut through the axis of the thread cylinder.

form feature   A recognizable area on a solid model that has a specific function.

forward kinematics   In a hierarchical link, total motion in which the motion of the parent is transferred to the motion of the child.

foundation plan   A plan view of the foundation of a building showing footings and other support structures.

foundation space   The rectilinear volume that represents the limits of the volume occupied by an object.

foundation space   The rectilinear volume that represents the limits of the volume occupied by an object.

frame rate   The rate of speed, usually in frames per second, in which individual images or frames are played when an animation is viewed.

frontal surface   A surface on an object being viewed that is parallel to the front viewing plane.

full section   The section view produced when a single cutting plane is used to hypothetically cut an object completely into two pieces.

function curve   A graphical method of displaying and controlling an object's transformations.

functional gage   An inspection tool built uniquely for the purpose of quickly checking a specific dimension or geometric condition on a part to determine whether or not it fall within tolerance limits.

fused deposition   A process where parts are gradually built up by bits of molten plastic that are deposited by a heated tip at selected locations and then solidified by cooling.

Gantt chart   A tool for scheduling a project timeline.

general sections   Sections through entire structures that show the layout of rooms but provide little detail.

geographic coordinate system   A spatial reference system using a grid network of parallels and meridians to locate spatial features on the earth's surface.

geographically referenced data   Information that is referenced to a specific geographic location, usually on the earth's surface.

geometric constraints   Definitions used to control the shape of a profile sketch through geometric relationships.

geometric dimensioning and tolerancing (GD&T)   A 3-D mathematical system that allows a designer to describe the form, orientation, and location of features on a part within precise tolerance zones.

geometric transformation   Transformations used to alter the position, size, or orientation of a part, camera, or light over a specified period of time.

georeferenced data   *See* geographically referenced data.

glass box   A visualization aid for understanding the locations and orientations of images of an object produced by third-angle projection on a drawing. The images of an object are projected, using orthogonal projection, on the sides of a hypothetical transparent box that is then unfolded into a single plane.

global positioning systems (GPS)   A system of geosynchronous, radio-emitting and receiving satellites used for determining positions on the earth.

graphical user interface (GUI)   The format of information on the visual display of a computer, giving its user control of the input, output, and editing of the information.

green engineering   The process by which environmental and life cycle considerations are examined from the outset in design.

grinding   A method of removing small amounts of material from a part using a rotation abrasive wheel, thus creating surfaces of very accurate planar or cylindrical geometries.

ground constraint   A constraint usually applied to a new sketch to fix the location of the sketch in space.

ground line (GL) In the construction of a perspective view, a line on the elevation view that represents the height of the ground.

GRS80 spheroid The satellite-based spheroid for the Geodetic Reference System 1980.

half section The section view produced when a single cutting plane is used to hypothetically cut an object up to a plane or axis of symmetry, leaving that portion beyond the plane or axis intact.

header A premade outline on which working drawings are created to ensure that all information required for fabrication and record keeping is entered.

heating and ventilation plan A plan view of the ventilation systems on a specific floor of a building, including ductwork and devices such as air conditioning units.

hidden lines The representation, using dashed lines, on a drawing of an object of the edges that cannot be seen because the object is opaque.

hierarchy The parent-child relationships between instances in an assembly.

hierarchical link A series of user-defined or linked objects that have a parent-child-grandchild relationship.

history tree *See* model tree.

holes A cut feature added to a model that will often receive a fastener for system assembly.

horizon line (HL) In the construction of a perspective view, the line that represent the horizon, which is the separation between the earth and the sky at a long distance. The left and right vanishing points are located on the HL. The PP and the HL are usually parallel to each other.

horizontal modeling A strategy for creating solid models that reduces parent-child relationships within the feature tree.

horizontal surface A surface on an object being viewed that is parallel to the top viewing plane.

identity A geometric integration of spatial datasets that preserves only the geographic features from the first input layer; the second layer merely adds more information to the dataset.

image A collection of printed, displayed, or imagined patterns intended to represent real objects, data, or processes.

inclined surface A flat surface on an object being viewed that is perpendicular to one primary view and angled with respect to the other two views.

index A list of all sheets of drawings contained in a set of construction plans.

industrial designers The individuals who use their creative abilities to develop conceptual designs of potential products.

infographic A shortened form of *informational graphic* or *information graphic*.

information graphics Often referred to as *infographic*, visual explanations.

injection molding A process for creating a plastic part by injecting molten plastic into a mold under pressure, allowing the material to solidify, and removing the part from the mold.

instances Copies of components that are included within an assembly model.

instructional diagram A diagram showing how a specific action within an object occurs.

instruments In engineering drawing, mechanical devices used to aid in creating accurate and precise images.

interchangeable manufacturing A process by which parts are made at different locations and brought together for assembly. For many industries, this process opens the door for third-party companies to produce replacement parts or custom parts.

interference A fit where two mating parts have intersecting nominal volumes, requiring the deformation of the parts . For example, the diameter of the shaft is larger than the diameter of the hole. When assembled, the intent is that the shaft will not spin in the hole.

interference The amount of overlap between two instances in an assembly.

internal thread Threads that are formed on the inside of a hole.

international sheet sizes The internationally accepted paper dimensions used when drawings are created or printed to their full intended size.

intersect To create a new object that consists of the volume of interference between two objects.

intersection A geometric integration of spatial datasets that preserves features or portions of features that fall within areas common to all input datasets.

inverse kinematics A bidirectional set of constraints that allows motion of a set of linked objects by moving the very end of the hierarchically linked chain and having the rest of the links move in response.

investment casting A method of casting where the mold is formed by successive dipping of a master form into progressively coarser slurries, allowing each layer to harden between each dipping. *See* casting.

isometric axes A set of three coordinate axes that are portrayed on the paper at 120 degrees relative to one another.

isometric dot paper Paper used for sketching purposes that includes dots located along lines that meet at 120 degrees.

isometric drawing   An axonometric drawing in which the scaling factor is the same for all three axes.

isometric grid paper Paper used for sketching purposes that includes grid lines at 120 degrees relative to one another.

isometric lines   Lines on an isometric drawing that are parallel or perpendicular to the front, top, or profile viewing planes.

isometric pictorial A sketch of an object that shows its three dimensions where isometric axes were used as the basis for defining the edges of the object.

item number   A number used to identify a part on a layout or assembly drawing.

join   To absorb the volume of interference between two objects to form a third object.

key   A small removable part similar to a wedge that provides a positive means of transferring torque between a shaft and a hub.

key light   A light that creates an object's main illumination, defines the dominant angle of the lighting, and is responsible for major highlights on objects in a scene.

keyframe   A specific frame located at a specified time within an animation where an object's location, orientation, and scale are defined perfectly.

keyseat   A rectangular groove cut in a shaft to position a key.

keyway   A rectangular groove cut in a hub to position a key.

landscape   The drawing orientation in which the horizontal size is larger than the vertical size.

lap joint   A joint between two parts wherein the parts are overlapped.

laser scanning (three-dimensional)   A process where cameras and lasers are used to digitize an object based on the principle of triangulation.

lathe   A machine used to make axially symmetric parts or features using a material removal process known as turning.

latitude   An imaginary line around the Earth's surface in which all of the points on the line are equidistant from the Equator.

layout drawing   A formal drawing that shows a device in its assembled state with all of its parts identified.

lead   The distance a screw thread advances axially in one full turn.

leader   A thin, dark, solid line terminating with an arrowhead at one end and a dimension, note, or symbol at the other end.

left-handed system Any 3-D coordinate system that is defined by the left-hand rule.

level of detail   The number of polygon mesh triangles used to define the surface shape of a 3-D model. For rendering speed, as a general case, objects close to the camera in a scene require a higher number of polygons to more accurately define their surfaces while more distant objects can be effectively rendered with fewer polygons.

life cycle   The amount of time a product will be used before it is no longer effective.

line   A spatial feature that has location and length but no area and is represented by a series of nodes, points, and arcs.

line chart   A graph showing the relationship between two sets of data, where line segments are used to link the data to show trends in their changes.

list   A boxed series of components, definitions, tips, etc.

location   A dimension associated with the position of a feature on a part.

location grid   An imaginary alphanumeric grid, similar to that of a street map, on a drawing that is used to specify area locations on the drawing.

longitude   An imaginary north-south line on the Earth's surface that extends from the North Pole to the South Pole.

machine screw   A threaded fastener wherein the threads are cut along the entire length of the cylindrical shaft. Machine screws can mate with a threaded hole or nut.

major diameter   The largest diameter on an internal or external thread.

main assembly   A completed device usually composed of multiple smaller parts and/or subassemblies.

main title block   A bordered area of a drawing (and part of the drawing header) that contains important information about the identification, fabrication, history, and ownership of the item shown on the drawing.

manufacturing drawings   Working drawings, often created by mechanical engineers, that are used to mass-produce products for consumers.

map   A diagram of the location of events with geography.

map projection   A systematic arrangement of parallels and meridians on a plane surface representing the geographic coordinate system.

mapping coordinates   Also called UVW coordinates, mapping coordinates are special coordinate systems designed to correctly place and control the shape of external and procedurally generated images on the surfaces of 3-D models.

mass   A property of an object's ability to resist a change in acceleration.

mass properties analysis A computer-generated document that gives the mechanical properties of a 3-D solid model.

master feature A feature or collection of features that is to be copied for placement at other locations in a model.

master model In a collection of similar parts, the model that includes all of the features that may appear in any of the other parts.

matt object An object with a combined material and alpha channel map.

maximum material condition The condition in which a feature of size contains the maximum amount of material within the stated limits of size.

measuring line (ML) In the construction of a perspective view, a vertical line used in conjunction with the elevation view to locate vertical points on the perspective drawing.

measuring wall In the construction of a perspective view, a line that extends from the object to the vanishing point to help establish the location of horizontal points on the drawing.

mechanical dissection The process of taking apart a device to determine the function of each part.

mechanical stress Developed force applied per unit area that tries to deform an object.

mental rotations The ability to mentally turn an object in space.

meridian A line of longitude through the North and South Poles that measure either E or W in a geographic coordinate system.

mesh The series of elements and nodal points on a finite element model.

Metric scale A device used to measure or draw lines in the metric system of units with drawings scales reported as ratios.

metrology The practice of measuring parts.

milling A process of removing material from a part using a rotating tool bit that can remove material in directions parallel or perpendicular to the tool bit's rotation axis.

milling machine A machine used to make parts through a material removal process known as milling.

minor diameter The smallest diameter on an internal or external thread.

mirrored feature A feature that is created as a mirror image of a master feature.

model A mathematical representation of an object or a device from which information about its function, appearance, or physical properties can be extracted.

model builders Engineers who make physical mock-ups of designs using modern rapid prototyping and CAM equipment.

model tree A list of all of the features of a solid model in the order in which they were created, providing a "history" of the sequence of feature creation.

mold A supported cavity shaped like a desired part into which molten material is poured or injected.

moment-of-inertia The measure of an object's ability to resist rotational acceleration about an axis.

morphological chart A chart used to generate ideas about the desirable qualities of a product and all of the possible options for achieving them.

motion blur The amount of movement of a high-speed object recorded as it moves through a single frame.

motion path Spline curves that serve as a trajectory for the motion of objects in animation.

multiple thread A thread made up of two or more continuous ridges side by side.

multiple views The presentation of an object using more than one image on the same drawing, each image representing a different orientation of the object.

multiview Refers to a drawing that contains more than one image of an object and whose adjacent images are generated from orthogonal viewing planes.

node A point at the beginning and end of a line feature or a point that defines a polygon feature.

normal surface A surface on an object being viewed that is parallel to one of the primary viewing planes.

note taker The person who records the actions discussed and taken at team meetings and then prepares the formal written notes for the meeting.

notes Additional information or instructions placed on a drawing that are not contained on the dimensions, tolerances, or header.

nut The threaded mate to a bolt used to hold two or more pieces of material together.

oblate ellipsoid An ellipsoid created by rotating an ellipse around its minor axis.

oblique axes A set of three coordinate axes that are portrayed on the paper as two perpendicular lines, with the third axis meeting them at an angle, typically 45 degrees.

oblique pictorial A sketch of an object that shows one face in the plane of the paper and the third dimension receding off at an angle relative to the face.

oblique surface A flat surface on an object being viewed that is neither parallel nor perpendicular to any of the primary views.

offset section The section view produced by a stepped cutting plane that is used to hypothetically cut an object completely into two pieces. Different portions of the plane are used to reveal the interior details of different features of interest.

one-off A one-of-a-kind engineering project for which no physical prototypes are created.

optimization   Modification of shapes, sizes, and other variables to achieve the best performance based on predefined criteria.

organizational chart   A chart representing the relationships of entities of an organization in terms of responsibility or authority.

orthogonal projection   The process by which the image of an object is created on a viewing plane by rays from the object that are perpendicular to that plane.

outline assembly drawing   See layout drawing.

parallel   An imaginary line parallel to the equator that corresponds to a measurement of latitude either N or S in a geographic coordinate system.

parameters   The attributes of features, such as dimensions, that can be modified.

parametric solid modeling   A solid modeling system that allows the user to vary the dimensions and other parameters of the model.

parametric techniques   Modeling techniques where all driven dimensions in algebraic expressions must be known for the value of the dependent variables to be calculated.

parent feature   A feature used in the creation of another feature, which is called its child feature.

part   An object expected to be delivered from a fabricator as a single unit with only its external dimensions and functional requirements specified.

part name   A very short descriptive title given to a part, subassembly, or device.

part number   Within a company, a string of alphanumeric characters used to identify a part, a subassembly, an assembly, or a device.

particle system   Specialized software modules used to generate, control, and animate very large numbers of small objects involved in complex events.

parts list   See bill of materials.

path   The specified curve on which a profile is placed to create a swept solid.

passive animation   An animation in which the observer remains still while the action occurs around him or her.

patents   A formal way to protect intellectual property rights for a new product.

pattern   A master part from which molds can be made for casting final parts.

perspective drawing   A drawing in which all three-dimensional axes on an object can be seen, with the scaling factor linearly increasing or decreasing in each direction. Usually one axis is shown as being vertical. This type of drawing generally offers the most realistic presentation of an object.

pictorial   A drawing that shows the 3-D aspects and features of an object.

picture plane (PP)   In the construction of a perspective view, the viewing plane through which the object is seen. The PP appears as a line (edge view of the viewing plane) in the plan view.

pie chart   A circular chart that is divided into wedges like a pie, representing a piece of the whole.

pin   A cylindrical (or slightly tapered) fastener typically used to maintain a desired position or orientation between parts.

pitch   The distance from one point on a thread to the corresponding point on the adjacent thread as measured parallel to its axis.

pitch diameter   The diameter of an imaginary cylinder that is halfway between the major and minor diameters of the screw thread.

pivot point   An independent, movable coordinate system on an object that can be used for location, orientation, and scale transformations.

pixel   The contraction for "picture element"; the smallest unit of information within a grid or raster data set.

plan and profile drawings   Construction drawings typically used for roads or other linear entities that show the road from above as well as from the side, with the profile view usually drawn with an exaggerated vertical scale.

plan view   In the construction of a perspective view, the object as viewed from the top, as if created by orthogonal projection.

plan views   Drawings created from a viewpoint above the structure (top view).

planar coordinate system   A 2-D measurement system that locates features on a plane based on their distance from an origin (0,0) along two perpendicular axes.

point   A spatial feature that has only location, has neither length nor area, and is represented by a pair of xy coordinates.

point light   A computer-generated light source, also called an omni light, that emits light rays and casts shadows uniformly in all directions. Also called an omnidirectional light.

point tracking   A procedure by which successive vertices on an object are simultaneously located on a pictorial image and a multiview image of that object.

polygon   A spatial feature that has location, area, and perimeter and is represented by a series of nodes, points, and arcs that must form a closed boundary.

portrait   The drawing orientation in which the vertical size is larger than the horizontal size.

preferred configuration   The drawing presentation of an object using its top, front, and right-side views.

primary modeling planes   The planes representing the XY-, XZ-, and YZ-planes in a Cartesian coordinate system.

primitives   The set of regular shapes, such as boxes, spheres, or cylinders that are used to build solid models with constructive solid geometry methods (CSG).

principal viewing planes   The planes in space on which the top, bottom, front, back, and right and left side views are projected.

problem identification   The first stage in the design process where the need for a product or a product modification is clearly defined.

procedural textures   Texture mapping routines based on algorithms written into the rendering software that can generate a specialized colored pattern such as wood, water, a checker pattern, a tile pattern, stucco, and many others without reference to external image files.

process check   A method for resolving differences and making adjustments in team performance.

process diagram   An illustration that explains how system elements work and how interactions occur.

professional engineer (PE)   An individual who has received an engineering degree, who has worked under the supervision of a PE for a number of years, and who has passed two examinations certifying knowledge of engineering practice.

profile   A planar sketch that is used to create a solid.

profile surface   A surface on an object being viewed that is parallel to a side viewing plane.

profile views   Views of a structure that show horizontal surfaces in edge view (side or front views).

project   In engineering, a collection of tasks that must be performed to create, operate, or retire a system or device.

projection ray   A line perpendicular to the projection plane. It transfers the 2-D shape from the object to an adjacent view. Projection rays are drawn lightly or are not shown at all on a finished drawing.

prototype   The initial creation of a product for testing and analysis before it is mass-produced.

protrusion   A feature created by the addition of solid volume to a model.

qualitative data   Information collected using words and ideas.

quantitative data   Numeric information.

quantity per machine (Q/M)   The number of times a part is required to build its next highest assembly.

radius-of-gyration   The distance from an axis where all of the mass can be concentrated and still produce the same moment-of-inertia.

rapid prototyping   Various methods for creating a part quickly by selective hardening of a powder or liquid raw material at room temperature.

raster data model   A representation of the geographic location as a surface divided into a regular grid of cells or pixels.

raytraced shadows   Shadows calculated by a process called raytracing, which traces the path that a ray of light would take from the light source to illuminate or shade each point on an object.

raytracing   A method of rendering that builds an image by tracing rays from the observer, bouncing them off the surfaces of objects in the scene, and tracing them back to the light sources that illuminate the scene.

reaming   A process for creating a hole with a very accurate final diameter using an accurately made cylindrical cutting tool similar to a drill bit to remove final bits of material after a smaller initial hole is created.

rebars   Steel bars added to concrete for reinforcement or for temperature control.

receding dimension   The portion of the object that appears to go back from the plane of the paper in an oblique pictorial.

record   A set of related data fields, often a row in a database, containing the attribute values for a single feature.

reference dimensions   Unneeded dimensions shown for the convenience of the reader used to show overall dimensions that could be extracted from other dimensions on the part or from other drawings.

reference line   Edges of the glass box or the intersection of the perpendicular planes. The reference line is drawn only when needed to aid in constructing additional views. The reference line should be labeled in constructing auxiliary views to show its association between the planes it is representing; for example, H/F for the hinged line between the frontal and horizontal planes. A reference line is also referred to as a fold line or a hinged line.

reflection   The process of obtaining a mirror image of an object from a plane of reflection.

reflection mapping   Mapping that allows the use of grayscale values in an image file to create the illusion of a reflection on the surface of a part. White creates reflective highlights, while black is transparent to the underlying color of the surface.

regeneration   The process of updating the profile or part to show its new shape after constraints are added or changed.

related views   Views adjacent to the same view that share a common dimension that must be transferred in creating auxiliary views.

removed section   The section view produced when a cutting plane is used to hypothetically remove an infinitesimally thin slice of an object for viewing.

rendering   The process where a software program uses all of the 3-D geometric object and lighting data to calculate and display a finished image of a 3-D scene in a 2-D viewport.

retaining rings   Precision-engineered fasteners that provide removable shoulders for positioning or limiting movement in an assembly.

reverse engineering   A systematic methodology for analyzing the design of an existing device.

revolved section   The section view produced when a cutting plane is used to hypothetically create an infinitesimally thin slice, which is rotated 90 degrees for viewing, on an object.

revolved solid   A solid formed when a profile curve is rotated about an axis.

ribs   Constant thickness protrusions that extend from the surface of a part and are used to strengthen or stiffen the part.

right-hand rule   Used to define a 3-D coordinate system whereby by pointing the fingers of the right hand down the x-axis and curling them in the direction of the y-axis, the thumb will point down the z-axis.

right-handed system   Any 3-D coordinate system that is defined by the right-hand-rule.

rivet   A cylindrical pin with heads at both ends, one head being formed during the assembly process, forming a permanent fastener often used to hold sheet metal together.

rolling   A process for creating long bars with flat, round, or rectangular cross sections by squeezing solid raw material between large rollers. This can be done when the material is in a hot, soft state (hot rolling) or when the material is near room temperature (cold rolling).

root   The bottom surface or point of a screw thread.

rounds   Smooth radius transitions of external edges created by two intersecting surfaces and tangent to both intersecting surfaces.

sand casting   A casting process where the mold is made of sand and binder material hardened around a master pattern that is subsequently removed to form the cavity. *See* casting.

sawing   A cutting process that uses a multitoothed blade that moves rapidly across and then through the part.

scatter plot   A graph using a pattern of dots showing the relationship between two sets of data.

schedule of materials   A list of the materials, such as doors and windows, necessary for a construction project.

schematic diagram   A diagram explaining how components work together, what the measurements are, how components are set up, or how pieces are connected.

screw thread   A helix or conical spiral formed on the external surface of a shaft or on the internal surface of a cylindrical hole.

scripting   A programming capability that allows a user to access and write code at or near the source code level of the software.

secondary title block   An additional bordered area of a drawing (and part of the drawing header) that contains important information about the identification, fabrication, and history of the item shown on the drawing.

section lines   Shading used to indicate newly formed or cut surfaces that result when an object is hypothetically cut.

section view   A general term for any view that presents an object that has been hypothetically cut to reveal the interior details of its features, with the cut surfaces perpendicular to the viewing direction and filled with section lines for improved presentation.

sectioned assembly drawing   A formal drawing, usually in pictorial form, that shows the device in its assembled form but with sections removed from obscuring parts to reveal formerly hidden parts.

selective laser sintering   A process where a high-powered laser is used to selectively melt together the particles on a bed of powdered metal to form the shape of a desired part.

self-tapping screw   A fastener that creates its own mating thread.

sequence diagram   A group of diagrams that includes process diagrams, timelines, and step-by-step diagrams.

set of construction plans   A collection of drawings, not necessarily all of them plan views, needed to construct a building or infrastructure project.

set screw   A small screw used to prevent parts from moving due to vibration or rotation, such as to hold a hub on a shaft.

shading   Marks added to surfaces and features of a sketch to highlight 3-D effects.

shading algorithms   Algorithms designed to deal with the diffuse and specular light transmission on the surface of an object.

shelling   Removing most of the interior volume of a solid model, leaving a relatively thin wall of material that closely conforms to the outer surfaces of the original model.

sidebar   Small infographics used within a body of text that are subdivided into briefs, lists, and bio profiles.

single thread   A thread that is formed as one continuous ridge.

sintering   A process where a part is formed by placing powdered metal into a mold and then applying heat and pressure to fuse the powder into a single solid shape.

site plan   A plan view showing the construction site for an infrastructure project.

site survey   Data regarding the existing topography and structures gathered during the preliminary design stages by trained surveying crews.

six standard views (or six principal views)   The drawing presentation of an object using the views produced by the glass box (i.e., the top, front, bottom, rear, left-side, and right-side views).

size   The general term for the size of a feature, such as a hole, cylinder, or set of opposed parallel surfaces.

sketches   Collections of 2-D entities.

sketching editor   A software tool used to create and edit sketches.

sketching plane   A plane where 2-D sketches and profiles can be created.

slope   The rate of change of elevation (rise) over a specified distance (run). Measured in percent or degrees.

solid model   A mathematical representation of a physical object that includes the surfaces and the interior material, usually including a computer-based simulation that produces a visual display of an object as if it existed in three dimensions.

solid modeling   Three-dimensional modeling of parts and assemblies originally developed for mechanical engineering use but presently used in all engineering disciplines.

spatial data   A formalized schema for representing data that has both geographic location and descriptive information.

spatial orientation   The ability of a person to mentally determine his own location and orientation within a given environment.

spatial perception   The ability to identify horizontal and vertical directions.

spatial relations   The ability to visualize the relationship between two objects in space, i.e., overlapping or nonoverlapping.

spatial visualization   The ability to mentally transform (rotate, translate, or mirror) or to mentally alter (twist, fold, or invert) 2-D figures and/or 3-D objects.

specifications (specs)   The written instructions that accompany a set of construction plans used to build an infrastructure project.

spheroid   *See* oblate ellipsoid.

spindle   That part of a production cutting machine that spins rapidly, usually holding a cutting tool or a workpiece.

splines   Polynomial curves that pass through multiple data points.

split line   The location where a mold can be disassembled for removal of a part once the molten raw material inside has solidified.

spotlight   A computer-generated light that simulates light being emitted from a point in space through a cone or beam, with the angle and direction of light controlled by the user.

spring pin   A hollow pin that is manufactured by cold-forming strip metal in a progressive roll-forming operation. Spring pins are slightly larger in diameter than the hole into which they are inserted and must be radially compressed for assembly.

sprue   Bits of material that are left on the part from a casting or molding operation and found at the ports where the molten material is injected into the mold or at the ports where air is allowed to escape.

stage   That part of a machine that secures and slowly moves a cutting tool or workpiece in one or more directions.

stamping   A process for cutting and shaping sheet metal by shearing and bending it inside forms with closely fitting cutouts and protrusions.

standard commercial shape   A common shape for raw material as would be delivered from a material manufacturer.

State Plane Coordinate System   The planar coordinate system developed in the 1930s for each state to permanently record the locations of the original land survey monuments in the United States.

station point (SP)   In the construction of a perspective view, the theoretical location of the observer who looks at the object through the picture plane.

statistical tolerancing   A way to assign tolerances based on sound statistical practices rather than conventional tolerancing practices.

step segment   On a stepped cutting plane for an offset section view, that portion of the plane that connects the cutting segments and is usually perpendicular to them but does not intersect any interior features.

step-by-step diagram   An illustration that visually explains a complex process; it is a type of a sequence diagram.

stereolithography   A process for creating solid parts from a liquid resin by selectively focusing heat or ultraviolet light into a pool of the resin, causing it to harden and cure in the selected areas.

storyboard   A sequential set of keyframe sketches or drawings, including brief descriptions, indications of object and camera movement, lighting, proposed frame numbers, and timelines sufficient to produce a complete animation project.

stud   A fastener that is a steel rod with threads at both ends.

subassembly   A logical grouping of assembly instances that is treated as a single entity within the overall assembly model.

subassemblies   Collections of parts that have been put together for the purpose of installing the collections as single units into larger assemblies.

successive cuts   A method of forming an object with a complex shape by starting with a basic shape and removing parts of it through subtraction of other basic shapes.

suppressed   Refers to the option for not displaying a selected feature.

surface area   The total area of the surfaces that bound an object.

surface model   A CAD-generated model created to show a part as a collection of intersecting surfaces that bound a solid.

surface modeling   The technique of creating a 3-D computer model to show a part or an object as a collection of intersecting surfaces that bound the part's solid shape.

surface normal   A vector that is perpendicular to each polygon contained in a polygon mesh model.

surface tracking   A procedure by which successive surfaces on an object are simultaneously located on a pictorial image and a multiview image of that object.

sustainable design   A paradigm for making design decisions based on environmental considerations and life cycle analysis.

swept feature   A solid that is bound by the surfaces swept out in space as a profile is pulled along a path.

symmetry   The characteristic of an object in which one half of the object is a mirror image of the other half.

system   A collection of parts, assemblies, structures, and processes that work together to perform one or more prescribed functions.

table   Data organized in columns and rows.

tangent edge   The intersection line between two surfaces that are tangent to each other.

tap   The machine tool used to form an interior thread. Tapping is the process of making an internal thread.

tap drill   A drill used to make a hole in material before the internal threads are cut.

tapped hole   A hole that has screw threads inside it.

task credit matrix   A table that lists all team members and their efforts on project tasks.

team contract   The rules under which a team agrees to operate (also known as a code of conduct, an agreement to cooperate, or rules of engagement).

team leader   The person who calls the meetings, sets the agenda, and maintains the focus of team meetings.

team roles   The roles that team members fill to ensure maximum effectiveness for a team.

technical diagram   A diagram depicting a technical illustration's measurements, movement, dissection, or relationship of parts.

telephoto   As seen through a camera lens with a focal length longer than 80 degrees, creating a narrow field of view and resulting in a flattened perspective.

texture mapping   The technique of adding variation and detail to a surface that goes beyond the level of detail modeled in the geometry of an object.

thematic layer   Features of one type that are generally placed together in a single georeferenced data layer.

thematic layer overlay   The process of combining spatial information from two thematic layers.

third-angle projection   The process of creating a view of an object by imprinting its image, using orthogonal projection, on translucent surface in front of that object.

thread note   Information on a drawing that clearly and completely identifies a thread.

thread series   The number of threads per inch on a standard thread.

3-D coordinate system A set of three mutually perpendicular axes used to define 3-D space.

3-D printing   A process for creating solid objects from a powder material by spraying a controlled stream of a binding fluid into a bed of that powder, thus fusing the powder in the selected areas.

three-axis mill   A milling machine whose spindle, which holds the rotating cutting tool, can be oriented along any one of three Cartesian axes.

three-dimensional (3-D) modeling   Mathematical modeling where the appearance, volumetric, and inertial properties of parts, assemblies, or structures are created with the assistance of computers and display devices.

through hole   A hole that extends all the way through a part.

tick mark A short dash used in sketching to locate points on the paper.

timekeeper   The person who keeps track of the meeting agenda, keeping the team on track to complete all necessary items within the alotted time frame.

timeline   A specific type of sequence diagram used to highlight significant moments in history.

title block   Usually the main title block, which is a bordered area of the drawing (and part of the drawing header) that contains important information about the identification, fabrication, history, and ownership of the item shown on the drawing.

tolerance   The total amount a specific dimension is permitted to vary. It is the difference between the upper and lower limits of the dimension.

tool bit   A fixed or moving replaceable cutting implement with one or more sharpened edges used to remove material from a part.

tool runout   The distance a tool may go beyond the required full thread length.

tooling   Tools and fixtures used to hold, align, create, or transport a part during its production.

top-down modeling   The process of establishing the assembly and hierarchy before individual components are created.

trail   Dashed lines on an assembly drawing that show how various parts or subassemblies are inserted to create a larger assembly.

trajectory   *See* path.

transparency/opacity mapping   A technique used to create areas of differing transparency on a surface or an object.

trimetric drawing   An axonometric drawing in which the scaling factor is different for all three axes.

true shape (of a plane)   The actual shape and size of a plane surface as seen in a view that is parallel to the surface in question.

two-dimensional (2-D) drawing   Mathematical modeling or drawing where the appearance of parts, assemblies, or structures are represented by a collection of two-dimensional geometric shapes.

tumbling   A process for removing sharp external edges and extraneous bits of material from a part by surrounding it in a pool of fine abrasive pellets and then shaking the combination.

turning   A process for making axially symmetric parts or features by rotating the part on a spindle and applying a cutting to the part.

undercut feature   A concave feature in which the removed material expands outward anywhere along its depth.

union   A topological overlay of two or more polygon spatial datasets that preserves the features that fall within the spatial extent of either input dataset; that is, all features from both datasets are retained and extracted into a new polygon dataset.

Universal Transverse Mercator (UTM)   The planar coordinate system that divides the earth's surface between 84° N and 80° S into 60 zones, each 6° longitude wide.

unsuppressed   Refers to the option for displaying a selected feature.

US sheet sizes   The accepted paper dimensions used in the United States when drawings are created or printed to their intended size.

vanishing point (VP)   In the construction of a perspective view, the point on the horizon where all parallel lines in a single direction converge.

variational techniques   Modeling techniques in which algebraic expressions or equations that express relationships between a number of variables and constants, any one of which can be calculated when all of the others are known.

vector data model   A data model that uses nodes and their associated geographic coordinates to construct and define spatial features.

Venn diagram   A type of business diagram that shows the mathematical or logical relationships and overlapping connections between different groups or sets of information.

vertex   A point that is used to define the endpoint of an entity such as a line segment or the intersection of two geometric entities.

video compression   One of a number of algorithms designed to reduce the size and storage requirements of video content.

viewing direction   The direction indicated by arrows on the cutting plane line from the eye to the object of interest that corresponds to the tail and point of the arrow, respectively.

viewing plane   A hypothetical plane between an object and its viewer onto which the image of the object, as seen by the viewer, is imprinted.

visual storytelling diagram   An illustration that displays empirical data or clarification of ideas.

visual thinking   A method for creative thinking, usually through sketching, where visual feedback assists in the development of creative ideas.

visualization   The ability to create and manipulate mental images of devices or processes.

volume   The quantity of space enclosed within an object's boundary surfaces.

volume of interference   The volume that is common between two overlapping objects.

wall sections   Sectional views of walls from foundation to roof for a construction project.

washer   A flat disk with a center hole to allow a fastener to pass through it.

webs   Small, thin protrusions that connect two or more thicker regions on a part.

weighted decision table   A matrix used to weigh design options to determine the best possible design characteristics.

welding   A method for joining two or more separate parts by applying heat to the edges where they meet and melting the edges together along with a filler of essentially the same material composition as the parts.

wide-angle   As seen through a camera lens with a focal length shorter than 30 degrees, creating a wide field of view and resulting in a distorted and exaggerated perspective.

wire drawing   The process of reducing the diameter of a solid wire by pulling it through a nozzle with a reducing aperture.

wireframe models   CAD models created using lines, arcs, and other 2-D entities to represent the edges of the part; surfaces or solid volumes are not defined.

working drawings   A collection of all drawings needed to fabricate and put together a device or structure.

workpiece   A common name for a part while it is still in the fabrication process, that is, before it is a finished part.

z-buffer rendering   A scene-rendering technique that uses visible-surface determination in which each pixel records (in addition to color) its distance from the camera, its angle, light source orientation, and other information defining the visible structure of the scene.

z-value   The value for a given surface location that represents an attribute other than position. In an elevation or terrain model, the z-value represents elevation.

index